Applied Analytics Using SAS® Enterprise Miner™

Course Notes

D1444964

Copyright © 2011, SAS Institute Inc., Cary, North Carolina, USA. ALL RIGHTS RESERVED.

Applied Analytics Using SAS® Enterprise Miner™ Course Notes was developed by Peter Christie, Jim Georges, Jeff Thompson, and Chip Wells. Additional contributions were made by Tom Bohannon, Mike Hardin, Dan Kelly, Bob Lucas, and Sue Walsh. Editing and production support was provided by the Curriculum Development and Support Department.

SAS and all other SAS Institute Inc. product or service names are registered trademarks or trademarks of SAS Institute Inc. in the USA and other countries. ® indicates USA registration. Other brand and product names are trademarks of their respective companies.

Applied Analytics Using SAS® Enterprise Miner™ Course Notes

Copyright © 2011 SAS Institute Inc. Cary, NC, USA. All rights reserved. Printed in the United States of America. No part of this publication may be reproduced, stored in a retrieval system, or transmitted, in any form or by any means, electronic, mechanical, photocopying, or otherwise, without the prior written permission of the publisher, SAS Institute Inc.

Book code E2056, course code LWAAEM71/AAEM71, prepared date 18Oct2011.   LWAAEM71_001

ISBN 978-1-61290-139-8

Copyright © 2011, SAS Institute Inc., Cary, North Carolina, USA. ALL RIGHTS RESERVED.

Table of Contents

Copyright © 2011, SAS Institute Inc., Cary, North Carolina, USA. ALL RIGHTS RESERVED.

Copyright © 2011, SAS Institute Inc., Cary, North Carolina, USA. ALL RIGHTS RESERVED.

Copyright © 2011, SAS Institute Inc., Cary, North Carolina, USA. ALL RIGHTS RESERVED.

Copyright © 2011, SAS Institute Inc., Cary, North Carolina, USA. ALL RIGHTS RESERVED.

Copyright © 2011, SAS Institute Inc., Cary, North Carolina, USA. ALL RIGHTS RESERVED.

Copyright © 2011, SAS Institute Inc., Cary, North Carolina, USA. ALL RIGHTS RESERVED.

Copyright © 2011, SAS Institute Inc., Cary, North Carolina, USA. ALL RIGHTS RESERVED.

Course Description

This course covers the skills required to assemble analysis flow diagrams using the rich tool set of SAS Enterprise Miner for both pattern discovery (segmentation, association, and sequence analyses) and predictive modeling (decision tree, regression, and neural network models).

To learn more...

For information on other courses in the curriculum, contact the SAS Education Division at 1-800-333-7660, or send e-mail to training@sas.com. You can also find this information on the Web at support.sas.com/training/ as well as in the Training Course Catalog.

For a list of other SAS books that relate to the topics covered in this Course Notes, USA customers can contact our SAS Publishing Department at 1-800-727-3228 or send e-mail to sasbook@sas.com. Customers outside the USA, please contact your local SAS office.

Also, see the Publications Catalog on the Web at support.sas.com/pubs for a complete list of books and a convenient order form.

Copyright © 2011, SAS Institute Inc., Cary, North Carolina, USA. ALL RIGHTS RESERVED.

Prerequisites

Before attending this course, you should be acquainted with Microsoft Windows and Windows-based software. In addition, you should have at least an introductory-level familiarity with basic statistics and regression modeling. Previous SAS software experience is helpful but not required.

Copyright © 2011, SAS Institute Inc., Cary, North Carolina, USA. ALL RIGHTS RESERVED.

Copyright © 2011, SAS Institute Inc., Cary, North Carolina, USA. ALL RIGHTS RESERVED.

Chapter 1   Introduction

Copyright © 2011, SAS Institute Inc., Cary, North Carolina, USA. ALL RIGHTS RESERVED.

Copyright © 2011, SAS Institute Inc., Cary, North Carolina, USA. ALL RIGHTS RESERVED.

1.1 Introduction to SAS Enterprise Miner

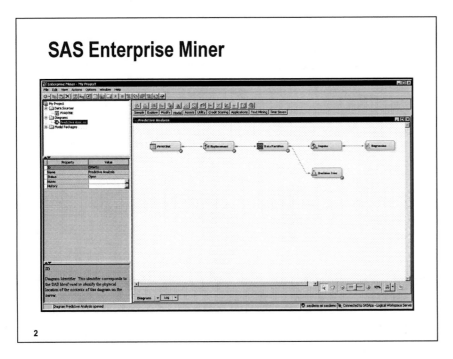

The SAS Enterprise Miner interface simplifies many common tasks associated with applied analysis. It offers secure analysis management and provides a wide variety of tools with a consistent graphical interface. You can customize it by incorporating your choice of analysis methods and tools.

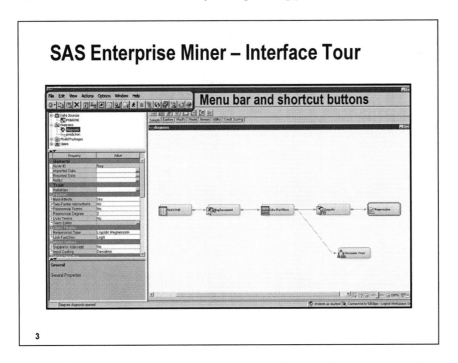

The interface window is divided into several functional components. The *menu bar* and corresponding *shortcut buttons* perform the usual windows tasks, in addition to starting, stopping, and reviewing analyses.

Copyright © 2011, SAS Institute Inc., Cary, North Carolina, USA. ALL RIGHTS RESERVED.

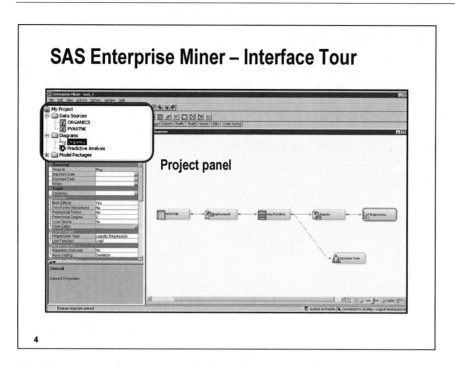

The *Project panel* manages and views data sources, diagrams, results, and project users.

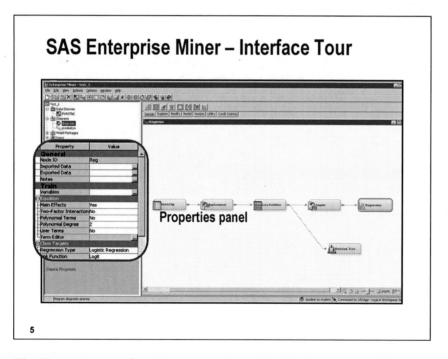

The *Properties panel* enables you to view and edit the settings of data sources, diagrams, nodes, results, and users.

Copyright © 2011, SAS Institute Inc., Cary, North Carolina, USA. ALL RIGHTS RESERVED.

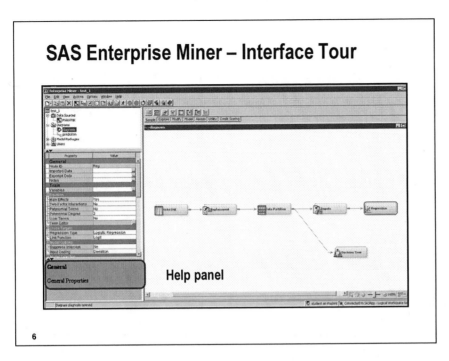

The *Help panel* displays a short description of the property that you select in the Properties panel. Extended help can be found in the Help Topics selection from the Help main menu.

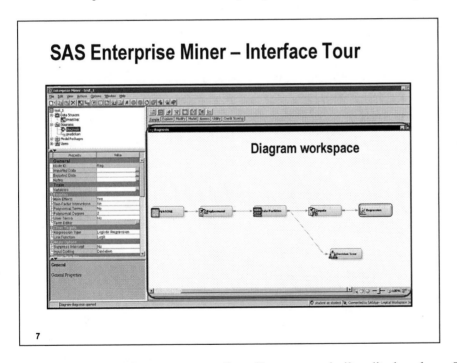

In the *diagram workspace*, process flow diagrams are built, edited, and run. The workspace is where you graphically sequence the tools that you use to analyze your data and generate reports.

Copyright © 2011, SAS Institute Inc., Cary, North Carolina, USA. ALL RIGHTS RESERVED.

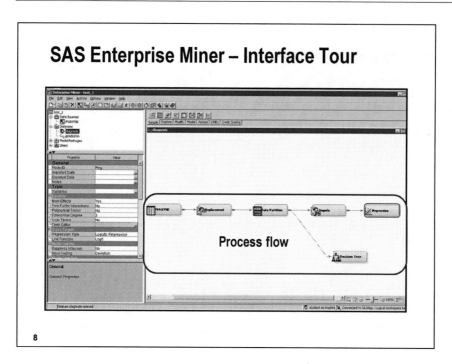

The diagram workspace contains one or more process flows. A *process flow* starts with a data source and sequentially applies SAS Enterprise Miner tools to complete your analytic objective.

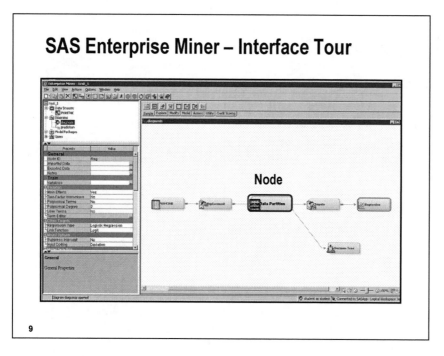

A process flow contains several nodes. *Nodes* are SAS Enterprise Miner tools connected by arrows to show the direction of information flow in an analysis.

Copyright © 2011, SAS Institute Inc., Cary, North Carolina, USA. ALL RIGHTS RESERVED.

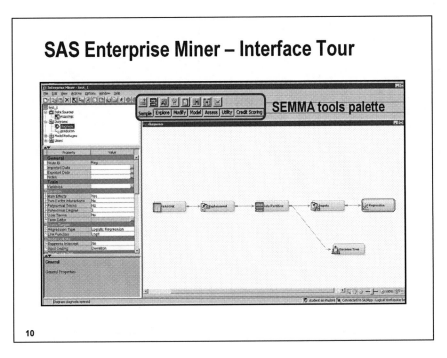

The SAS Enterprise Miner tools available to your analysis are contained in the *tools palette*. The tools palette is arranged according to a process for data mining, SEMMA.

SEMMA is an acronym for the following:

Sample You sample the data by creating one or more data tables. The samples should be large enough to contain the significant information, but small enough to process.

Explore You explore the data by searching for anticipated relationships, unanticipated trends, and anomalies in order to gain understanding and ideas.

Modify You modify the data by creating, selecting, and transforming the variables to focus the model selection process.

Model You model the data by using the analytical tools to search for a combination of the data that reliably predicts a desired outcome.

Assess You assess competing predictive models (build charts to evaluate the usefulness and reliability of the findings from the data mining process).

Additional tools are available under the Utility group and, if licensed, the Credit Scoring group. Other specialized group tools, for example Text Mining and Time Series, are also available if licensed.

Copyright © 2011, SAS Institute Inc., Cary, North Carolina, USA. ALL RIGHTS RESERVED.

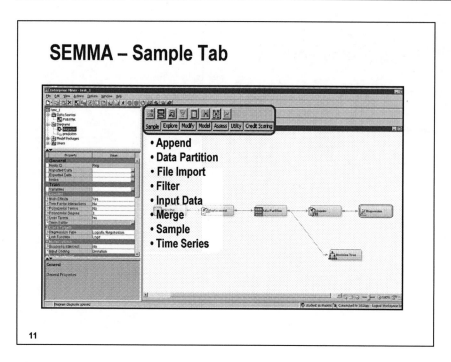

SEMMA – Sample Tab

- Append
- Data Partition
- File Import
- Filter
- Input Data
- Merge
- Sample
- Time Series

11

The tools in each Tool tab are arranged alphabetically.

The **Append** tool is used to append data sets that are exported by two different paths in a single process flow diagram. The Append node can also append train, validation, and test data sets into a new training data set.

The **Data Partition** tool enables you to partition data sets into training, test, and validation data sets. The *training data set* is used for preliminary model fitting. The *validation data set* is used to monitor and tune the model during estimation and is also used for model assessment. The *test data set* is an additional holdout data set that you can use for model assessment. This tool uses simple random sampling, stratified random sampling, or cluster sampling to create partitioned data sets.

The **File Import** tool enables you to convert selected external flat files, spreadsheets, and database tables into a format that SAS Enterprise Miner recognizes as a data source.

The **Filter** tool creates and applies filters to your training data set, and optionally, to the validation and test data sets. You can use filters to exclude certain observations, such as extreme outliers and errant data that you do not want to include in your mining analysis.

The **Input Data** tool represents the data source that you choose for your mining analysis and provides details (metadata) about the variables in the data source that you want to use.

The **Merge** tool enables you to merge observations from two or more data sets into a single observation in a new data set. The Merge tool supports both one-to-one and match merging.

The **Sample** tool enables you to take simple random samples, n^{th} observation samples, stratified random samples, first-n samples, and cluster samples of data sets. For any type of sampling, you can specify either a number of observations or a percentage of the population to select for the sample. If you are working with rare events, the Sample tool can be configured for oversampling or stratified sampling.

Sampling is recommended for extremely large databases because it can significantly decrease model training time. If the sample is sufficiently representative, relationships found in the sample can be expected to generalize to the complete data set. The Sample tool writes the sampled observations to an output data set and saves the seed values that are used to generate the random numbers for the samples so that you can replicate the samples.

Copyright © 2011, SAS Institute Inc., Cary, North Carolina, USA. ALL RIGHTS RESERVED.

The **Time Series** tool converts transactional data to time series data. *Transactional data* is time-stamped data that is collected over time at no particular frequency. By contrast, *time series data* is time-stamped data that is summarized over time at a specific frequency. You might have many suppliers and many customers, as well as transaction data that is associated with both. The size of each set of transactions can be very large, which makes many traditional data mining tasks difficult. By condensing the information into a time series, you can discover trends and seasonal variations in customer and supplier habits that might not be visible in transactional data.

Copyright © 2011, SAS Institute Inc., Cary, North Carolina, USA. ALL RIGHTS RESERVED.

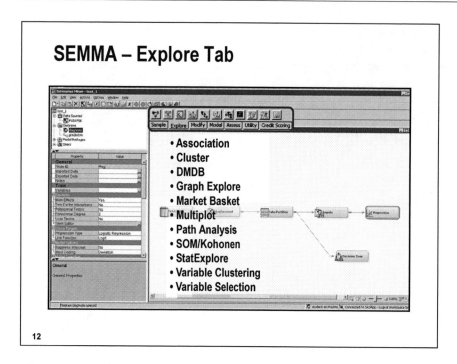

The **Association** tool enables you to perform association discovery to identify items that tend to occur together within the data. For example, if a customer buys a loaf of bread, how likely is the customer to also buy a gallon of milk? This type of discovery is also known as *market basket analysis*. The tool also enables you to perform sequence discovery if a timestamp variable (a sequence variable) is present in the data set. This enables you to take into account the ordering of the relationships among items.

The **Cluster** tool enables you to segment your data; that is, it enables you to identify data observations that are similar in some way. Observations that are similar tend to be in the same cluster, and observations that are different tend to be in different clusters. The cluster identifier for each observation can be passed to subsequent tools in the diagram.

The **DMDB** tool creates a data mining database that provides summary statistics and factor-level information for class and interval variables in the imported data set.

The **Graph Explore** tool is an advanced visualization tool that enables you to explore large volumes of data graphically to uncover patterns and trends and to reveal extreme values in the database. The tool creates a run-time sample of the input data source. You use the Graph Explore node to interactively explore and analyze your data using graphs. Your exploratory graphs are persisted when the Graph Explore Results window is closed. When you reopen the Graph Explore Results window, the persisted graphs are re-created.

The experimental **Market Basket** tool performs association rule mining over transaction data in conjunction with item taxonomy. Transaction data contains sales transaction records with details about items bought by customers. Market basket analysis uses the information from the transaction data to give you insight about which products tend to be purchased together.

The **MultiPlot** tool is a visualization tool that enables you to explore large volumes of data graphically. The MultiPlot tool automatically creates bar charts and scatter plots for the input and target. The code created by this tool can be used to create graphs in a batch environment.

The **Path Analysis** tool enables you to analyze Web log data to determine the paths that visitors take as they navigate through a Web site. You can also use the tool to perform sequence analysis.

Copyright © 2011, SAS Institute Inc., Cary, North Carolina, USA. ALL RIGHTS RESERVED.

The **SOM/Kohonen** tool performs unsupervised learning by using Kohonen vector quantization (VQ), Kohonen self-organizing maps (SOMs), or batch SOMs with Nadaraya-Watson or local-linear smoothing. Kohonen VQ is a clustering method, whereas SOMs are primarily dimension-reduction methods. For cluster analysis, the Clustering tool is recommended instead of Kohonen VQ or SOMs.

The **StatExplore** tool is a multipurpose tool used to examine variable distributions and statistics in your data sets. The tool generates summarization statistics. You can use the StatExplore tool to do the following:

- select variables for analysis, for profiling clusters, and for predictive models
- compute standard univariate distribution statistics
- compute standard bivariate statistics by class target and class segment
- compute correlation statistics for interval variables by interval input and target

The **Variable Clustering** tool is useful for data reduction, such as choosing the best variables or cluster components for analysis. Variable clustering removes collinearity, decreases variable redundancy, and helps to reveal the underlying structure of the input variables in a data set.

The **Variable Selection** tool enables you to evaluate the importance of input variables in predicting or classifying the target variable. To select the important inputs, the tool uses either an R-squared or a Chi-squared selection criterion. The R-squared criterion enables you to remove variables in hierarchies, remove variables that have large percentages of missing values, and remove class variables that are based on the number of unique values. The variables that are not related to the target are set to a status of *rejected*. Although rejected variables are passed to subsequent tools in the process flow diagram, these variables are not used as model inputs by more detailed modeling tools, such as the Neural Network and Decision Tree tools. You can reassign the input model status to rejected variables.

Copyright © 2011, SAS Institute Inc., Cary, North Carolina, USA. ALL RIGHTS RESERVED.

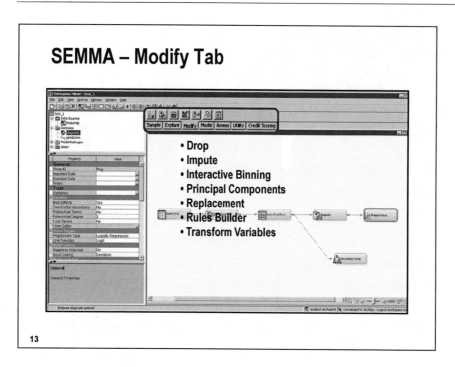

The **Drop** tool is used to remove variables from scored data sets. You can remove all variables with the role type that you specify, or you can manually specify individual variables to drop. For example, you could remove all hidden, rejected, and residual variables from your exported data set, or you could remove only a few variables that you identify yourself.

The **Impute** tool enables you to replace values for observations that have missing values. You can replace missing values for interval variables with the mean, median, midrange, mid-minimum spacing, or distribution-based replacement, or you can use a replacement M-estimator such as Tukey's biweight, Huber's, or Andrew's Wave. You can also estimate the replacement values for each interval input by using a tree-based imputation method. Missing values for class variables can be replaced with the most frequently occurring value, distribution-based replacement, tree-based imputation, or a constant.

The **Interactive Binning** tool is an interactive grouping tool that you use to model nonlinear functions of multiple modes of continuous distributions. The Interactive tool computes initial bins by quantiles. Then you can interactively split and combine the initial bins. You use the Interactive Binning node to create bins or buckets or classes of all input variables, which include both class and interval input variables. You can create bins in order to reduce the number of unique levels as well as attempt to improve the predictive power of each input.

The **Principal Components** tool calculates eigenvalues and eigenvectors from the uncorrected covariance matrix, corrected covariance matrix, or the correlation matrix of input variables. Principal components are calculated from the eigenvectors and are usually treated as the new set of input variables for successor modeling tools. A principal components analysis is useful for data interpretation and data dimension reduction.

The **Replacement** tool enables you to reassign and consolidate levels of categorical inputs. This can improve the performance of predictive models.

The **Rules Builder** tool opens the Rules Builder window so that you can create ad hoc sets of rules with user-definable outcomes. You can interactively define the values of the outcome variable and the paths to the outcome. This is useful in ad hoc rule creation such as applying logic for posterior probabilities and scorecard values.

Copyright © 2011, SAS Institute Inc., Cary, North Carolina, USA. ALL RIGHTS RESERVED.

The **Transform Variables** tool enables you to create new variables that are transformations of existing variables in your data. Transformations are useful when you want to improve the fit of a model to the data. For example, transformations can be used to stabilize variances, remove nonlinearity, improve additivity, and correct nonnormality in variables. The Transform Variables tool supports various transformation methods. The available methods depend on the type and the role of a variable.

Copyright © 2011, SAS Institute Inc., Cary, North Carolina, USA. ALL RIGHTS RESERVED.

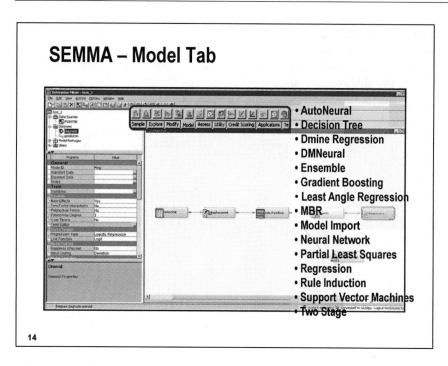

SEMMA – Model Tab

- AutoNeural
- Decision Tree
- Dmine Regression
- DMNeural
- Ensemble
- Gradient Boosting
- Least Angle Regression
- MBR
- Model Import
- Neural Network
- Partial Least Squares
- Regression
- Rule Induction
- Support Vector Machines
- Two Stage

14

The **AutoNeural** tool can be used to automatically configure a neural network. It conducts limited searches for a better network configuration.

The **Decision Tree** tool enables you to perform multiway splitting of your database based on nominal, ordinal, and continuous variables. The tool supports both automatic and interactive training. When you run the Decision Tree tool in automatic mode, it automatically ranks the input variables based on the strength of their contributions to the tree. This ranking can be used to select variables for use in subsequent modeling. In addition, dummy variables can be generated for use in subsequent modeling. You can override any automatic step with the option to define a splitting rule and prune explicit tools or subtrees. Interactive training enables you to explore and evaluate a large set of trees as you develop them.

The **Dmine Regression** tool performs a regression analysis on data sets that have a binary or interval level target variable. The Dmine Regression tool computes a forward stepwise least squares regression. In each step, an independent variable is selected that contributes maximally to the model R-square value. The tool can compute all two-way interactions of classification variables, and it can also use AOV16 variables to identify nonlinear relationships between interval variables and the target variable. In addition, the tool can use group variables to reduce the number of levels of classification variables.

 If you want to create a regression model on data that contains a nominal or ordinal target, then you would use the Regression tool.

The **DMNeural** tool is another modeling tool that you can use to fit a nonlinear model. The nonlinear model uses transformed principal components as inputs to predict a binary or an interval target variable.

Copyright © 2011, SAS Institute Inc., Cary, North Carolina, USA. ALL RIGHTS RESERVED.

The **Ensemble** tool creates new models by combining the posterior probabilities (for class targets) or the predicted values (for interval targets) from multiple predecessor models. The new model is then used to score new data. One common ensemble approach is to use multiple modeling methods, such as a neural network and a decision tree, to obtain separate models from the same training data set. The component models from the two complementary modeling methods are integrated by the Ensemble tool to form the final model solution. It is important to note that the ensemble model can only be more accurate than the individual models if the individual models disagree with one another. You should always compare the model performance of the ensemble model with the individual models. You can compare models using the Model Comparison tool.

The **Gradient Boosting** tool uses a partitioning algorithm described in "A Gradient Boosting Machine," and "Stochastic Gradient Boosting" by Jerome Friedman. A *partitioning algorithm* searches for an optimal partition of the data defined in terms of the values of a single variable. The optimality criterion depends on how another variable, the target, is distributed into the partition segments. When the target values are more similar within the segments, the worth of the partition is greater. Most partitioning algorithms further partition each segment in a process called *recursive partitioning*. The partitions are then combined to create a predictive model. The model is evaluated by goodness-of-fit statistics defined in terms of the target variable. These statistics are different than the measure of worth of an individual partition. A good model might result from many mediocre partitions.

The **Least Angle Regressions (LARS)** tool can be used for both input variable selection and model fitting. When used for variable selection, the LAR algorithm chooses input variables in a continuous fashion that is similar to Forward selection. The basis of variable selection is the magnitude of the candidate inputs' estimated coefficients as they grow from zero to the least squares' estimate. Either a LARS or LASSO algorithm can be used for model fitting. See Efron et al. (2004) and Hastie, Tibshirani, and Friedman (2001) for further details.

The **Memory-Based Reasoning (MBR)** tool is a modeling tool that uses a k-nearest neighbor algorithm to categorize or predict observations. The k-nearest neighbor algorithm takes a data set and a probe, where each observation in the data set consists of a set of variables and the probe has one value for each variable. The distance between an observation and the probe is calculated. The k observations that have the smallest distances to the probe are the k-nearest neighbors to that probe. In SAS Enterprise Miner, the k-nearest neighbors are determined by the Euclidean distance between an observation and the probe. Based on the target values of the k-nearest neighbors, each of the k-nearest neighbors votes on the target value for a probe. The votes are the posterior probabilities for the class target variable.

The **Model Import** tool imports and assesses a model that was not created by one of the SAS Enterprise Miner modeling nodes. You can then use the Assessment node to compare the user-defined model(s) with a model(s) that you developed with a SAS Enterprise Miner modeling node. This process is called *integrated assessment*.

The **Neural Network** tool enables you to construct, train, and validate multilayer feed-forward neural networks. In general, each input is fully connected to the first hidden layer, each hidden layer is fully connected to the next hidden layer, and the last hidden layer is fully connected to the output. The Neural Network tool supports many variations of this general form.

The **Partial Least Squares** tool models continuous and binary targets based on the SAS/STAT PLS procedure. The Partial Least Squares node produces DATA step score code and standard predictive model assessment results.

Copyright © 2011, SAS Institute Inc., Cary, North Carolina, USA. ALL RIGHTS RESERVED.

The **Regression** tool enables you to fit both linear and logistic regression models to your data. You can use continuous, ordinal, and binary target variables. You can use both continuous and discrete variables as inputs. The tool supports the stepwise, forward, and backward selection methods. The interface enables you to create higher-order modeling terms such as polynomial terms and interactions.

The **Rule Induction** tool enables you to improve the classification of rare events in your modeling data. The Rule Induction tool creates a Rule Induction model that uses split techniques to remove the largest pure split tool from the data. Rule induction also creates binary models for each level of a target variable and ranks the levels from the rarest event to the most common.

The **Support Vector Machine (SVM)** tool is experimental in Enterprise Miner 7.1, which means the node may be subject to change. A support vector machine (SVM) is a supervised machine learning method that is used to perform classification and regression analysis. The standard SVM problem solves binary classification problems that produce non-probability output (only sign +1/-1) by constructing a set of hyperplanes that maximize the margin between two classes. Most of problems in a finite dimensional space are not linearly separable. In this case, the original space needs to be mapped into a much higher dimensional space or an infinite dimensional space, which makes the separation easier. SVM uses a kernel function to define the larger dimensional space.

The **TwoStage** tool enables you to model a class target and an interval target. The interval target variable is usually the value that is associated with a level of the class target. For example, the binary variable **PURCHASE** is a class target that has two levels, **Yes** and **No**, and the interval variable **AMOUNT** can be the value target that represents the amount of money that a customer spends on the purchase.

Copyright © 2011, SAS Institute Inc., Cary, North Carolina, USA. ALL RIGHTS RESERVED.

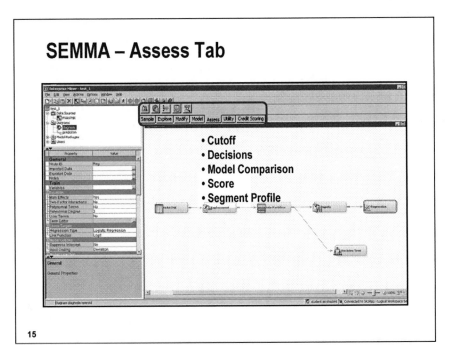

The Cutoff tool provides tabular and graphical information to assist users in determining appropriate probability cutoff point(s) for decision making with binary target models. The establishment of a cutoff decision point entails the risk of generating false positives and false negatives, but an appropriate use of the Cutoff node can help minimize those risks.

The **Decisions** tool enables you to define target profiles for a target that produces optimal decisions. The decisions are made using a user-specified decision matrix and output from a subsequent modeling procedure.

The **Model Comparison** tool provides a common framework for comparing models and predictions from any of the modeling tools. The comparison is based on the expected and actual profits or losses that would result from implementing the model. The tool produces several charts that help to describe the usefulness of the model, such as lift charts and profit/loss charts.

The **Score** tool enables you to manage, edit, export, and execute scoring code that is generated from a trained model. Scoring is the generation of predicted values for a data set that might not contain a target variable. The Score tool generates and manages scoring formulas in the form of a single SAS DATA step, which can be used in most SAS environments even without the presence of SAS Enterprise Miner. The Score tool can also generate C score code and Java score code.

The **Segment Profile** tool enables you to examine segmented or clustered data and identify factors that differentiate data segments from the population. The tool generates various reports that aid in exploring and comparing the distribution of these factors within the segments and population.

Copyright © 2011, SAS Institute Inc., Cary, North Carolina, USA. ALL RIGHTS RESERVED.

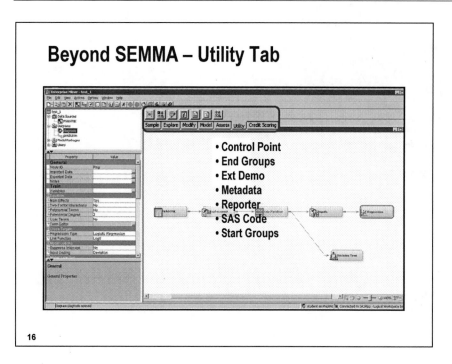

The **Control Point** tool enables you to establish a control point to reduce the number of connections that are made in process flow diagrams. For example, suppose that three Input Data Source tools are to be connected to three modeling tools. If no Control Point tool is used, then nine connections are required to connect all of the Input Data Source tools to all of the modeling tools. However, if a Control Point tool is used, only six connections are required.

The **End Groups** tool is used only in conjunction with the Start Groups tool. The End Groups node acts as a boundary marker that defines the end-of-group processing operations in a process flow diagram. Group processing operations are performed on the portion of the process flow diagram that exists between the Start Groups node and the End Groups node.

The **Ext Demo** tool is designed to illustrate the various property types that can be implemented in Enterprise Miner extension nodes. The properties of an Enterprise Miner node enable users to pass arguments to the node's underlying SAS program. By choosing an appropriate property type, an extension node developer can control how information about the node's arguments are presented to the user and place restrictions on the values of the arguments. The Ext Demo node's results also provide examples of the various types of graphs that can be generated by an extension node using the %EM_REPORT macro.

The **Metadata** tool enables you to modify the columns metadata information at some point in your process flow diagram. You can modify attributes such as roles, measurement levels, and order.

The **Reporter** tool uses SAS Output Delivery System (ODS) capability to create a single PDF or RTF file that contains information about the open process flow diagram. The PDF or RTF documents can be viewed and saved directly and are included in SAS Enterprise Miner report package files.

Copyright © 2011, SAS Institute Inc., Cary, North Carolina, USA. ALL RIGHTS RESERVED.

The **SAS Code** tool enables you to incorporate new or existing SAS code into process flow diagrams. The ability to write SAS code enables you to include additional SAS procedures into your data mining analysis. You can also use a SAS DATA step to create customized scoring code, to conditionally process data, and to concatenate or merge existing data sets. The tool provides a macro facility to dynamically reference data sets used for training, validation, testing, or scoring variables, such as input, target, and predict variables. After you run the SAS Code tool, the results and the data sets can then be exported for use by subsequent tools in the diagram.

The **Start Groups** tool is useful when your data can be segmented or grouped, and you want to process the grouped data in different ways. The Start Groups node uses BY-group processing as a method to process observations from one or more data sources that are grouped or ordered by values of one or more common variables. BY variables identify the variable or variables by which the data source is indexed, and BY statements process data and order output according to the BY-group values.

Copyright © 2011, SAS Institute Inc., Cary, North Carolina, USA. ALL RIGHTS RESERVED.

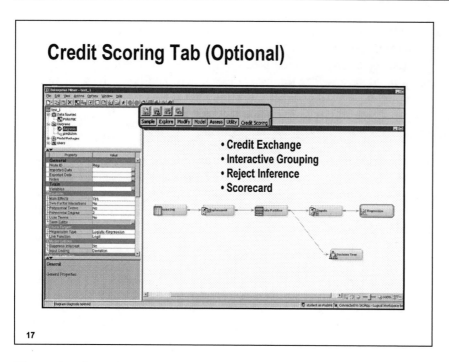

Credit Scoring Tab (Optional)

- Credit Exchange
- Interactive Grouping
- Reject Inference
- Scorecard

17

The optional Credit Scoring tab provides functionality related to credit scoring.

 Credit Scoring for the SAS Enterprise Miner solution is not included with the base version of SAS Enterprise Miner. If your site did not license Credit Scoring for SAS Enterprise Miner, the Credit Scoring tab and its associated tools do not appear in your SAS Enterprise Miner software.

The **Credit Exchange** tool enables you to exchange the data that is created in SAS Enterprise Miner with the SAS Credit Risk Management solution.

The **Interactive Grouping** tool creates groupings, or classes, of all input variables. (This includes both class and interval input variables.) You can create groupings in order to reduce the number of unique levels as well as attempt to improve the predictive power of each input. Along with creating group levels for each input, the Interactive Grouping tool creates Weight of Evidence (WOE) values.

The **Reject Inference** tool uses the model that was built using the accepted applications to score the rejected applications in the retained data. The observations in the rejected data set are classified as inferred "goods" and inferred "bads." The inferred observations are added to the **Accepts** data set that contains the actual "good" and "bad" records, forming an augmented data set. This augmented data set then serves as the input data set of a second credit-scoring modeling run. During the second modeling run, attribute classification is readjusted and the regression coefficients are recalculated to compensate for the data set augmentation.

The **Scorecard** tool enables you to rescale the logit scores of binary prediction models to fall within a specified range.

Copyright © 2011, SAS Institute Inc., Cary, North Carolina, USA. ALL RIGHTS RESERVED.

1.01 Poll

Tools under the Sample tab change the number of columns of the data, whereas tools under the Modify tab change the number of rows.

○ True
○ False

19

The Analytic Workflow

Analytic workflow

- Define analytic objective
- Select cases
- Extract input data
- Validate input data
- Repair input data
- Transform input data
- Apply analysis
- Generate deployment methods
- Integrate deployment
- Gather results
- Assess observed results
- Refine analytic objective

21

The *analytic workflow* is the sequence of steps required to fulfill an applied analytic objective. The tools and capabilities of SAS Enterprise Miner occupy the central steps of this workflow. Before using SAS Enterprise Miner, you must carefully define your analytic objective, select analysis cases, and extract, validate, and possibly repair analysis data. SAS Enterprise Miner then enables you to further transform your data, apply the analysis of interest, and generate deployment methods. The analytic workflow then continues outside the competencies of SAS Enterprise Miner. Deployment methods must be integrated into production systems, and results from this integration must be captured, assessed, and used to refine the next iteration of analysis.

Copyright © 2011, SAS Institute Inc., Cary, North Carolina, USA. ALL RIGHTS RESERVED.

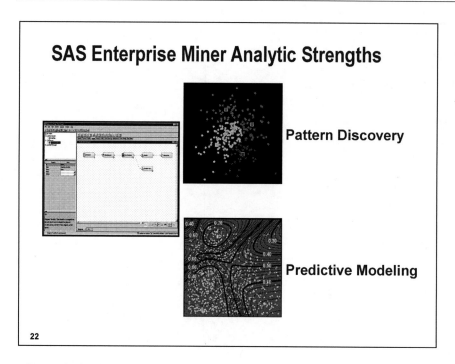

The analytic strengths of SAS Enterprise Miner lie in the realm traditionally known as *data mining*. There are a great number of analytic methods identified with data mining, but they usually fall into two broad categories: *pattern discovery* and *predictive modeling* (Hand 2005). SAS Enterprise Miner provides a variety of pattern discovery and predictive modeling tools.

Chapters 2 through 7 demonstrate SAS Enterprise Miner's predictive modeling capabilities. In those chapters, you use a rich collection of modeling tools to create, evaluate, and improve predictions from prepared data. Special topics in predictive modeling are featured in Chapter 9.

Chapter 8 introduces some of SAS Enterprise Miner's pattern discovery tools. In this chapter, you see how to use SAS Enterprise Miner to graphically evaluate and transform prepared data. You use SAS Enterprise Miner's tools to cluster and segment an analysis population. You can also choose to try SAS Enterprise Miner's market basket analysis and sequence analysis capabilities.

Copyright © 2011, SAS Institute Inc., Cary, North Carolina, USA. ALL RIGHTS RESERVED.

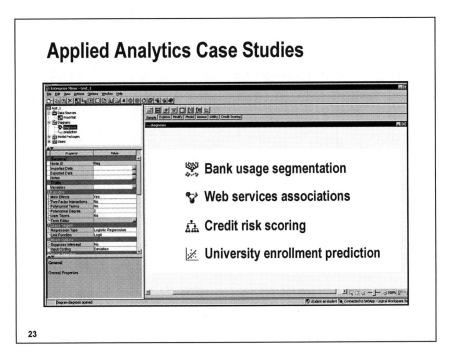

Appendix A further illustrates SAS Enterprise Miner's analytic capabilities with case studies drawn from real-world business applications.

- A consumer bank sought to segment its customers based on historic usage patterns. Segmentation was to be used for improving contact strategies in the Marketing Department.

- A radio station developed a Web site to provide such services to its audience as podcasts, news streams, music streams, archives, and live Web music performances. The station tracked usage of these services by URL. Analysts at the station wanted to see whether any unusual patterns existed in the combinations of services selected.

- A bank sought to use performance on an in-house subprime credit product to create an updated risk model. The risk model was to be combined with other factors to make future credit decisions.

- The administration of a large private university requested that the Office of Enrollment Management and the Office of Institutional Research work together to identify prospective students who would most likely enroll as freshmen.

Copyright © 2011, SAS Institute Inc., Cary, North Carolina, USA. ALL RIGHTS RESERVED.

1.2 Solutions

Solutions to Student Activities (Polls/Quizzes)

1.01 Poll – Correct Answer

Tools under the Sample tab change the number of columns of the data, whereas tools under the Modify tab change the number of rows.

○ True
⊙ False

20

Copyright © 2011, SAS Institute Inc., Cary, North Carolina, USA. ALL RIGHTS RESERVED.

Chapter 2 Accessing and Assaying Prepared Data

Copyright © 2011, SAS Institute Inc., Cary, North Carolina, USA. ALL RIGHTS RESERVED.

Copyright © 2011, SAS Institute Inc., Cary, North Carolina, USA. ALL RIGHTS RESERVED.

2.1 Introduction

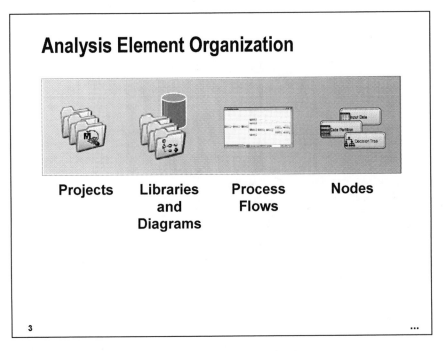

Analysis Element Organization

Projects   Libraries and Diagrams   Process Flows   Nodes

3   ...

Analyses in SAS Enterprise Miner start by defining a project. A *project* is a container for a set of related analyses. After a project is defined, you define libraries and diagrams. A *library* is a collection of data sources accessible by the SAS Foundation Server. A *diagram* holds analyses for one or more data sources. Process flows are the specific steps you use in your analysis of a data source. Each step in a process flow is indicated by a node. The *nodes* represent the SAS Enterprise Miner tools that are available to the user.

✎   A core set of tools is available to all SAS Enterprise Miner users. Additional tools can be added by licensing additional SAS products or by creating SAS Enterprise Miner extensions.

Before you can create a process flow, you need to define the following items:

- a SAS Enterprise Miner project to contain the data sources, diagrams, and model packages
- one or more SAS libraries inside your project, linking SAS Enterprise Miner to analysis data
- a diagram workspace to display the steps of your analysis

A SAS administrator can define these for you in advance of using SAS Enterprise Miner or you can define them yourself.

✎   The demonstrations show you how to create the items in the list above.

Copyright © 2011, SAS Institute Inc., Cary, North Carolina, USA. ALL RIGHTS RESERVED.

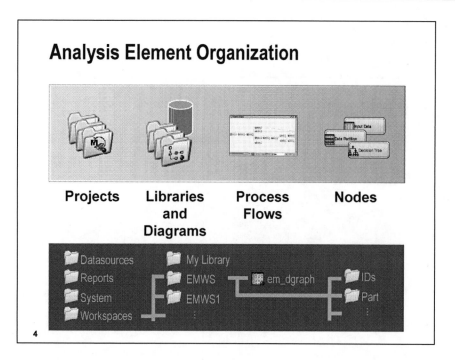

Behind the scenes (on the SAS Foundation Server where the project resides), the organization is more complicated. Fortunately, the SAS Enterprise Miner client shields you from this complexity.

At the top of the hierarchy is the SAS Enterprise Miner project, corresponding to a directory on (or accessible by) the SAS Foundation. When a project is defined, four subdirectories are automatically created within the project directory: Datasources, Reports, System, and Workspaces. The SAS Enterprise Miner client via the SAS Foundation handles the writing, reading, and maintenance of these directories.

 In both the personal workstation and SAS Enterprise Miner client configurations, all references to computing resources such as LIBNAME statements and access to SAS Foundation technologies must be made from the selected SAS Foundation Server's perspective. This is important because data and directories that are visible to the client machine might not be visible to the server.

Projects are defined to contain diagrams, the next level of the SAS Enterprise Miner organizational hierarchy. Diagrams usually pertain to a single analysis theme or project. When a diagram is defined, a new subdirectory is created in the Workspaces directory of the corresponding project. Each diagram is independent, and no information can be passed from one diagram to another.

Libraries are defined using a LIBNAME statement. You can create a library using the SAS Enterprise Miner Library Wizard, using SAS Management Console, or by using the Start-Up Code window when you define a project. Any data source compatible with a LIBNAME statement can provide data for SAS Enterprise Miner.

Specific analyses in SAS Enterprise Miner occur in process flows. A *process flow* is a sequence of tasks or nodes connected by arrows in the user interface, and it defines the order of analysis. The organization of a process flow is contained in a file, EM_DGRAPH, which is stored in the diagram directory. Each node in the diagram corresponds to a separate subdirectory in the diagram directory. Information in one process flow can be sent to another by connecting the two process flows.

Copyright © 2011, SAS Institute Inc., Cary, North Carolina, USA. ALL RIGHTS RESERVED.

2.2 Creating a SAS Enterprise Miner Project, Library, and Diagram

Your first task when you start an analysis is creating a SAS Enterprise Miner project, data library, and diagram. Often these are set up by a SAS administrator (or reused from a previous analysis), but knowing how to set up these items yourself is fundamental to learning about SAS Enterprise Miner.

Before attempting the processes described in the following demonstrations, you need to log on to your computer, and start and log on to the SAS Enterprise Miner client program.

Copyright © 2011, SAS Institute Inc., Cary, North Carolina, USA. ALL RIGHTS RESERVED.

Creating a SAS Enterprise Miner Project

A SAS Enterprise Miner project contains materials related to a particular analysis task. These materials include analysis process flows, intermediate analysis data sets, and analysis results.

To define a project, you must specify a project name and the location of the project on the SAS Foundation Server. Follow the steps below to create a new SAS Enterprise Miner project.

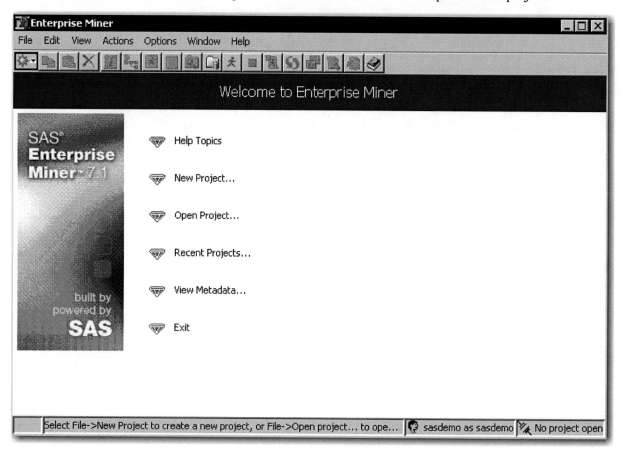

Copyright © 2011, SAS Institute Inc., Cary, North Carolina, USA. ALL RIGHTS RESERVED.

1. Select **File** ⇨ **New** ⇨ **Project** from the main menu. The Create New Project wizard opens at Step 1.

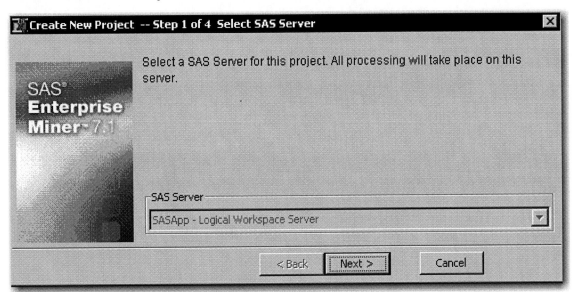

In this configuration of SAS Enterprise Miner, the only server available for processing is the host server listed above.

2. Select **Next**.

3. Step 2 of the Create New Project wizard is used to specify the following information:
   - the name of the project you are creating
   - the location of the project

   Type a project name, for example, **My Project**, in the **Name** field.

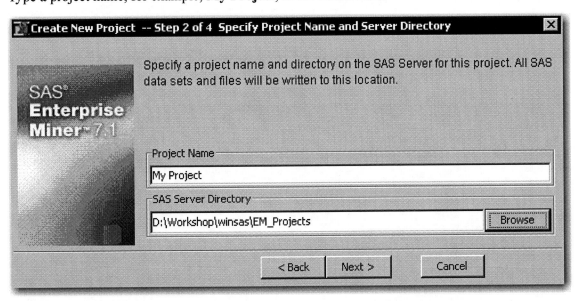

The path specified by the **SAS Server Directory** field is the physical location where the project folder will be created.

4. Select **Next**.

Copyright © 2011, SAS Institute Inc., Cary, North Carolina, USA. ALL RIGHTS RESERVED.

✐   If you have an existing project directory with the same name and location as specified, this project will be added to the list of available projects in SAS Enterprise Miner. This technique can be used to import a project created by another installation of SAS Enterprise Miner.

5. Select a location for the project's metadata.

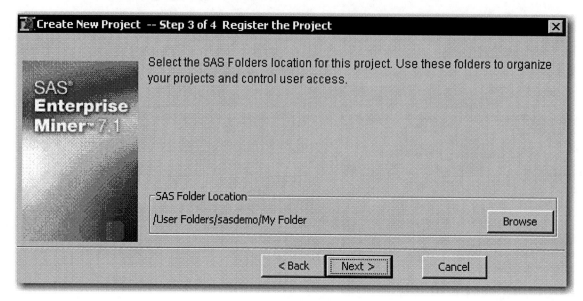

✐   The SAS folder, My Folder, is where the metadata associated with the project is stored. This folder can be accessed and modified using SAS Management Console.

6. Select **Next**.

Information about your project is summarized in Step 4.

7. To finish defining the project, select **Finish**.

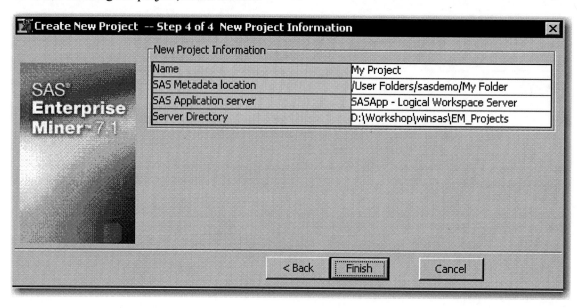

Copyright © 2011, SAS Institute Inc., Cary, North Carolina, USA. ALL RIGHTS RESERVED.

The SAS Enterprise Miner client application opens the project that you created.

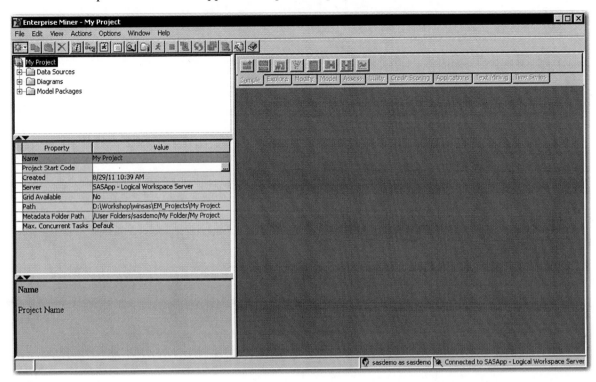

Copyright © 2011, SAS Institute Inc., Cary, North Carolina, USA. ALL RIGHTS RESERVED.

Creating a SAS Library

A SAS library connects SAS Enterprise Miner with the raw data sources, which are the basis of your analysis. A library can link to a directory on the SAS Foundation server, a relational database, or even an Excel workbook.

To define a library, you need to know the name and location of the data structure that you want to link with SAS Enterprise Miner, in addition to any associated options, such as user names and passwords.

Follow the steps below to create a new SAS library.

1. Select **File** ⇨ **New** ⇨ **Library** from the main menu. The Library Wizard – Step 1 of 3 Select Action window appears.

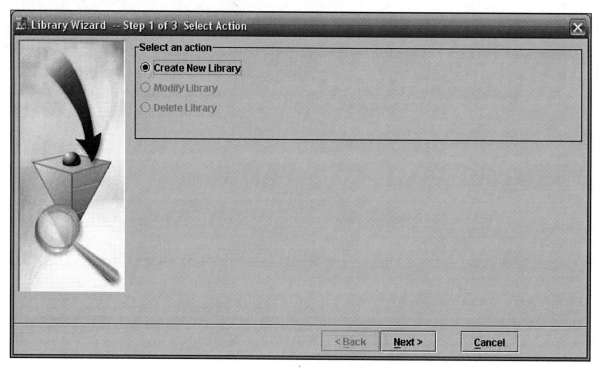

2. Select **Next**. The Library Wizard is updated to show Step 2 of 3 Create or Modify.

Copyright © 2011, SAS Institute Inc., Cary, North Carolina, USA. ALL RIGHTS RESERVED.

3. Type **AAEM** in the **Name** field. Type the path **D:\Workshop\winsas\aaem** in the **Path** field.

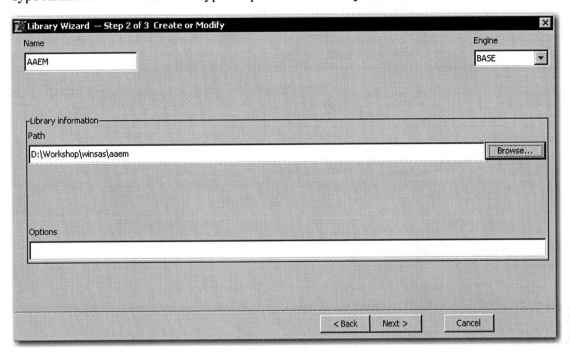

🖉   If your data is located in a different directory, specify that directory in the **Path** field.

4. Select **Next**. The Library Wizard window is updated to show Step 3 of 3 Confirm Action.

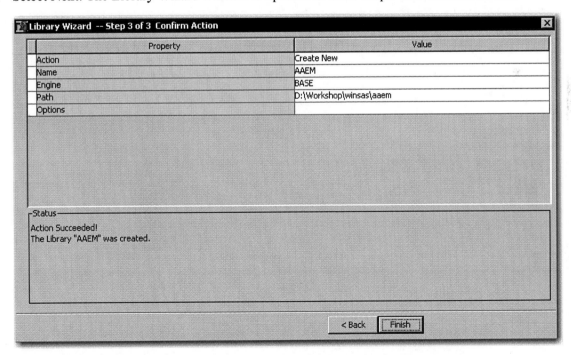

The Confirm Action window shows the name, type, and path of the created SAS library.

5. Select **Finish**.

All data available in the SAS library can now be used by SAS Enterprise Miner.

Copyright © 2011, SAS Institute Inc., Cary, North Carolina, USA. ALL RIGHTS RESERVED.

Creating a SAS Enterprise Miner Diagram

A SAS Enterprise Miner diagram workspace contains and displays the steps involved in your analysis. To define a diagram, you only need to specify its name.

Follow the steps below to create a new SAS Enterprise Miner diagram workspace.

1. Select **File** ⇨ **New** ⇨ **Diagram** from the main menu.

2. Type the name **Predictive Analysis** in the **Diagram Name** field and select **OK**.

    SAS Enterprise Miner creates an analysis workspace window labeled Predictive Analysis

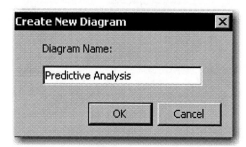

You will use the Predictive Analysis window to create process flow diagrams.

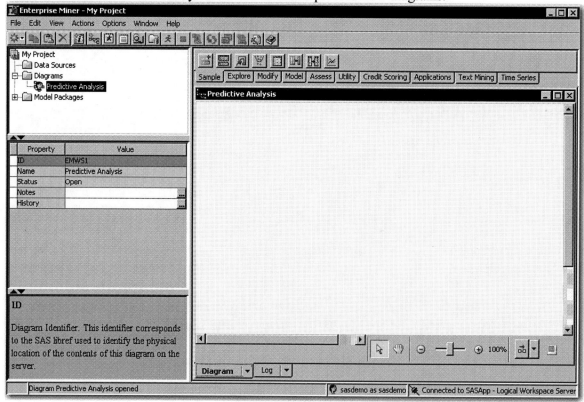

Copyright © 2011, SAS Institute Inc., Cary, North Carolina, USA. ALL RIGHTS RESERVED.

 **Exercises**

1. **Creating a Project, Defining a Library, and Creating an Analysis Diagram**

    a. Use the steps in the "Creating a SAS Enterprise Miner Project" demonstration to create a project for your SAS Enterprise Miner analyses on your computer.

    b. Use the steps in the "Creating a SAS Library" demonstration to define a SAS library to access the course data from your project.

    ✎ Your instructor will provide the path to the data if it is different than the path that is specified in these course notes.

    c. Use the steps in the "Creating a SAS Enterprise Miner Diagram" demonstration to create an analysis diagram in your project.

Copyright © 2011, SAS Institute Inc., Cary, North Carolina, USA. ALL RIGHTS RESERVED.

2.3 Defining a Data Source

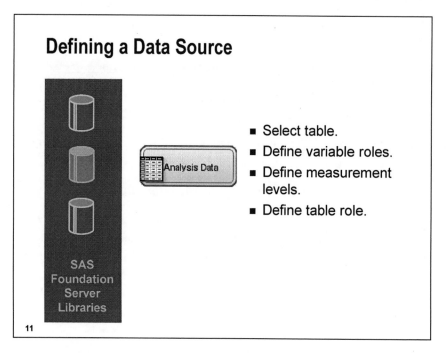

After you define a new project and diagram, your next analysis task in SAS Enterprise Miner is usually to create an analysis data source. A *data source* is a link between an existing SAS table and SAS Enterprise Miner. To define a data source, you need to select the analysis table and define metadata appropriate to your analysis task.

The selected table must be visible to the SAS Foundation Server via a predefined SAS library. Any table found in a SAS library can be used, including those stored in formats external to SAS, such as tables from a relational database. (To define a SAS library to such tables might require SAS/ACCESS product licenses.)

The metadata definition serves three primary purposes for a selected data set. It informs SAS Enterprise Miner of the following:

- the analysis role of each variable
- the measurement level of each variable
- the analysis role of the data set

The analysis role of each variable tells SAS Enterprise Miner the purpose of the variable in the current analysis. The measurement level of each variable distinguishes continuous numeric variables from categorical variables. The analysis role of the data set tells SAS Enterprise Miner how to use the selected data set in the analysis. All of this information must be defined in the context of the analysis at hand.

Other (optional) metadata definitions are specific to certain types of analyses. These are discussed in the context of these analyses.

✏ Any data source that is defined for use in SAS Enterprise Miner should be largely ready for analysis. Usually, most of the data preparation work is completed before a data source is defined. It is possible (and useful for documentation purposes) to write the completed data preparation process in a SAS Code node embedded in SAS Enterprise Miner. Those details are outside the scope of this discussion.

Copyright © 2011, SAS Institute Inc., Cary, North Carolina, USA. ALL RIGHTS RESERVED.

2.01 Multiple Choice Poll

A data source in SAS Enterprise Miner differs from a raw data file because a data source has additional metadata attached. This metadata includes which of the following?

a. the variable roles

b. the variable measurement levels

c. the data table role

d. all of the above

13

Copyright © 2011, SAS Institute Inc., Cary, North Carolina, USA. ALL RIGHTS RESERVED.

Charity Direct Mail Demonstration

Analysis goal:

A veterans' organization seeks continued contributions from lapsing donors. Use lapsing-donor responses from an earlier campaign to predict future lapsing-donor responses.

15   ...

To demonstrate defining a data source, and later, using SAS Enterprise Miner's predictive modeling tools, consider the following specific analysis example:

A national veterans' organization seeks to better target its solicitations for donation. By only soliciting the most likely donors, less money will be spent on solicitation efforts and more money will be available for charitable concerns. Solicitations involve sending a small gift to an individual and include a request for a donation. Gifts to donors include mailing labels and greeting cards.

The organization has more than 3.5 million individuals in its mailing database. These individuals are classified by their response behaviors to previous solicitation efforts. Of particular interest is the class of individuals identified as *lapsing donors*. These individuals made their most recent donation between 12 and 24 months ago. The organization seeks to rank its lapsing donors based on their responses to a greeting card mailing sent in June of 1997. (The charity calls this the 97NK Campaign.) With this ranking, a decision can be made to either solicit or ignore a lapsing individual in the June 1998 campaign.

Copyright © 2011, SAS Institute Inc., Cary, North Carolina, USA. ALL RIGHTS RESERVED.

Charity Direct Mail Demonstration

Analysis goal:

A veterans' organization seeks continued contributions from lapsing donors. Use lapsing-donor responses from an earlier campaign to predict future lapsing-donor responses.

Analysis data:
- **Extracted from previous year's campaign**
- **Sample balances response/non-response rate**
- **Actual response rate approximately 5%**

16

The source of this data is the Association for Computing Machinery's (ACM) 1998 KDD-Cup competition. The data set and other details of the competition are publicly available at the UCI KDD Archive at **kdd.ics.uci.edu**.

For model development, the data were sampled to balance the response and non-response rates. (The reason and consequences of this action are discussed in later chapters.) In the original campaign, the response rate was approximately 5%.

The following demonstrations show how to access the 97NK campaign data in SAS Enterprise Miner. The process is divided into three parts:

- specifying the source data
- setting the columns metadata
- finalizing the data source specification

Copyright © 2011, SAS Institute Inc., Cary, North Carolina, USA. ALL RIGHTS RESERVED.

Defining a Data Source

Specifying Source Data

A data source links SAS Enterprise Miner to an existing analysis table. To specify a data source, you need to define a SAS library and know the name of the table that you will link to SAS Enterprise Miner.

Follow these steps to specify a data source.

1. Select **File** ➪ **New** ➪ **Data Source** from the main menu. The Data Source Wizard – Step 1 of 8 Metadata Source window appears.

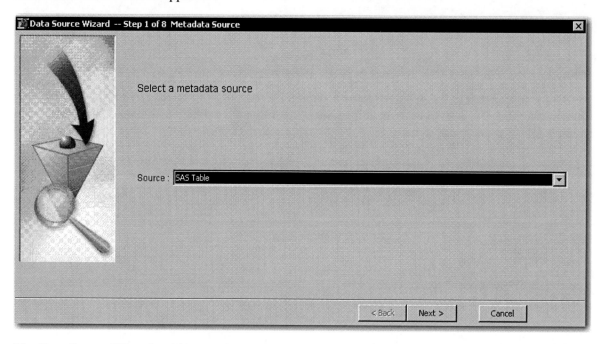

The Data Source Wizard guides you through creating a SAS Enterprise Miner data source. Step 1 tells SAS Enterprise Miner where to look for initial metadata values. The default and typical choice is the SAS table that you link to in the next step.

Copyright © 2011, SAS Institute Inc., Cary, North Carolina, USA. ALL RIGHTS RESERVED.

2. Select **Next** to use a SAS table (the common choice) as the source for the metadata.

    The Data Source Wizard continues to Step 2 Select a SAS Table.

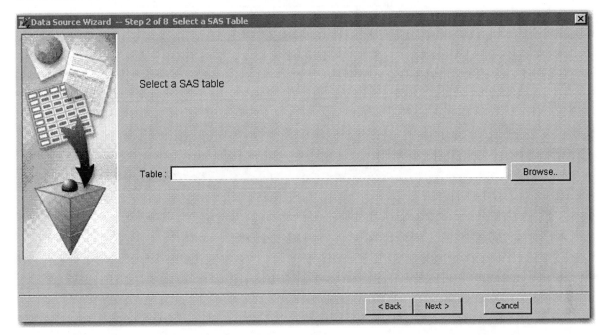

    In this step, select the SAS table that you want to make available to SAS Enterprise Miner. You can either type the library name and SAS table name as ***libname.tablename*** or select the SAS table from a list.

3. Select **Browse** to choose a SAS table from the libraries that are visible to the SAS Foundation Server. The Select a SAS Table window appears.

4. One of the libraries listed is named AAEM, which is the library name defined in the Library Wizard. Double-click **Aaem**, which is the library name defined in the Library Wizard. The panel on the right is shows the contents of the library.

5. Select the **Pva97nk** SAS table.

Copyright © 2011, SAS Institute Inc., Cary, North Carolina, USA. ALL RIGHTS RESERVED.

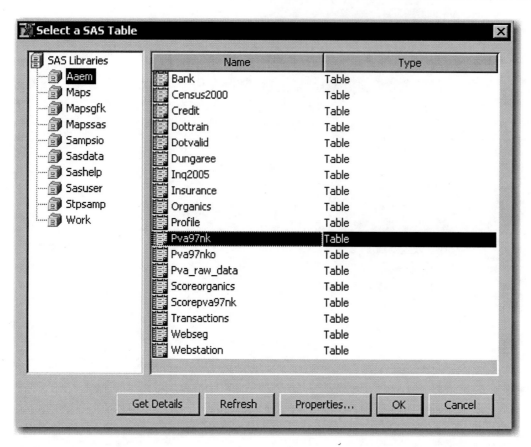

6. Select **OK**. The Select a SAS Table window closes and the selected table appears in the **Table** field.

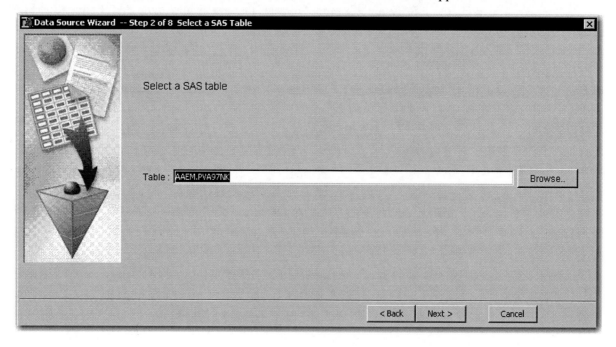

Copyright © 2011, SAS Institute Inc., Cary, North Carolina, USA. ALL RIGHTS RESERVED.

7. Select **Next**. The Data Source Wizard proceeds to Step 3 Table Information.

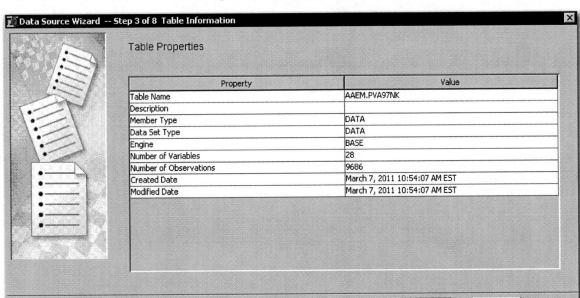

This step of the Data Source Wizard provides basic information about the selected table.

📎 The SAS table **PVA97NK** is used in this chapter and subsequent chapters to demonstrate the predictive modeling tools of SAS Enterprise Miner. The table contains 9,686 cases and 28 variables.

Defining Column Metadata

With a data set specified, your next task is to set the column metadata. To do this, you need to know the modeling role and proper measurement level of each variable in the source data set.

Follow these steps to define the column metadata.

1. Select **Next**. The Data Source Wizard proceeds to Step 4 Metadata Advisor Options.

Copyright © 2011, SAS Institute Inc., Cary, North Carolina, USA. ALL RIGHTS RESERVED.

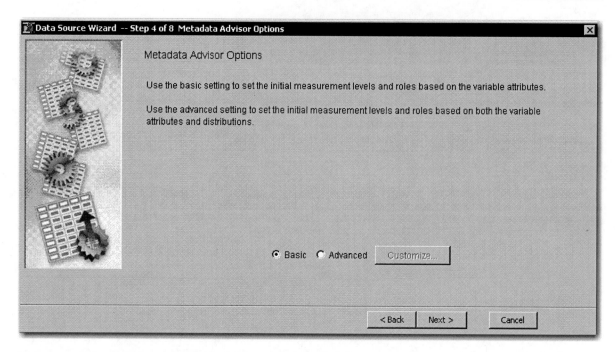

This step of the Data Source Wizard starts the metadata definition process. SAS Enterprise Miner assigns initial values to the metadata based on characteristics of the selected SAS table. The Basic setting assigns initial values to the metadata based on variable attributes such as the variable name, data type, and assigned SAS format. The Advanced setting assigns initial values to the metadata in the same way as the Basic setting, but it also assesses the distribution of each variable to better determine the appropriate measurement level.

2. Select **Next** to use the Basic setting.

Copyright © 2011, SAS Institute Inc., Cary, North Carolina, USA. ALL RIGHTS RESERVED.

The Data Source Wizard proceeds to Step 5 Column Metadata. Select the box next to **Label**.

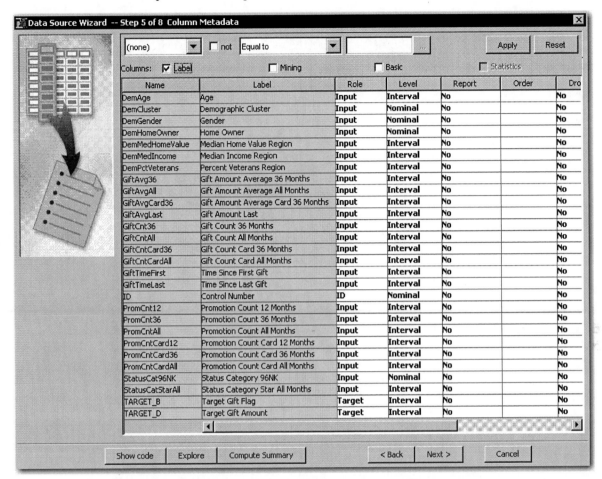

The Data Source Wizard displays its best guess for the metadata assignments. This guess is based on the name and data type of each variable. The correct values for model role and measurement level are found in the **PVA97NK** metadata table on the next page.

A comparison of the currently assigned metadata to that in the **PVA97NK** metadata table shows several discrepancies. While the assigned modeling roles are mostly correct, the assigned measurement levels for several variables are in error.

It is possible to improve the default metadata assignments by using the Advanced option in the Metadata Advisor.

3. Select **Back** in the Data Source Wizard. This returns you to Step 4 Metadata Advisor Options.

4. Select the **Advanced** option.

Copyright © 2011, SAS Institute Inc., Cary, North Carolina, USA. ALL RIGHTS RESERVED.

PVA97NK Metadata Table

Name	Model Role	Measurement Level	Description
DemAge	Input	Interval	Age
DemCluster	Input	Nominal	Demographic Cluster
DemGender	Input	Nominal	Gender
DemHomeOwner	Input	Binary	Home Owner
DemMedHomeValue	Input	Interval	Median Home Value Region
DemMedIncome	Input	Interval	Median Income Region
DemPctVeterans	Input	Interval	Percent Veterans Region
GiftAvg36	Input	Interval	Gift Amount Average 36 Months
GiftAvgAll	Input	Interval	Gift Amount Average All Months
GiftAvgCard36	Input	Interval	Gift Amount Average Card 36 Months
GiftAvgLast	Input	Interval	Gift Amount Last
GiftCnt36	Input	Interval	Gift Count 36 Months
GiftCntAll	Input	Interval	Gift Count All Months
GiftCntCard36	Input	Interval	Gift Count Card 36 Months
GiftCntCardAll	Input	Interval	Gift Count Card All Months
GiftTimeFirst	Input	Interval	Time Since First Gift
GiftTimeLast	Input	Interval	Time Since Last Gift
ID	ID	Nominal	Control Number
PromCnt12	Input	Interval	Promotion Count 12 Months
PromCnt36	Input	Interval	Promotion Count 36 Months
PromCntAll	Input	Interval	Promotion Count All Months
PromCntCard12	Input	Interval	Promotion Count Card 12 Months
PromCntCard36	Input	Interval	Promotion Count Card 36 Months
PromCntCardAll	Input	Interval	Promotion Count Card All Months
StatusCat96NK	Input	Nominal	Status Category 96NK
StatusCatStarAll	Input	Binary	Status Category Star All Months
TARGET_B	Target	Binary	Target Gift Flag
TARGET_D	Rejected	Interval	Target Gift Amount

Copyright © 2011, SAS Institute Inc., Cary, North Carolina, USA. ALL RIGHTS RESERVED.

5. Select **Next** to use the Advanced setting. The Data Source Wizard again proceeds to Step 5 Column Metadata.

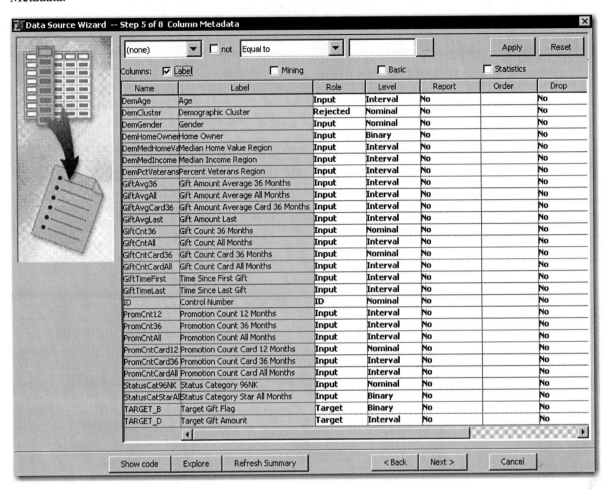

While many of the default metadata settings are correct, there are several items that need to be changed. For example, the **DemCluster** variable is rejected (for having too many distinct values), and several numeric inputs have their measurement level set to Nominal instead of Interval (for having too few distinct values).

To avoid the time-consuming task of making metadata adjustments, go back to the previous Data Source Wizard step and customize the Metadata Advisor.

6. Select **Back**. You return to the Metadata Advisor Options window.

Copyright © 2011, SAS Institute Inc., Cary, North Carolina, USA. ALL RIGHTS RESERVED.

7.   Select **Customize**. The Advanced Advisor Options dialog box appears.

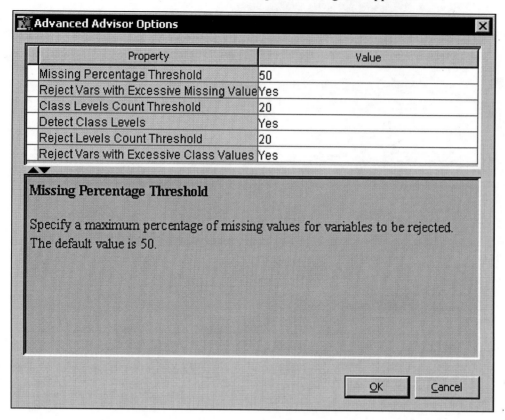

Using the default Advanced options, the Metadata Advisor can do the following:

- reject variables with an excessive number of missing values (default=50%)

- detect the number class levels of **_numeric_** variables and assign a role of Nominal to those with class counts below the selected threshold (default=20)

- detect the number class levels of **_character_** variables and assign a role of Rejected to those with class counts above the selected threshold (default=20)

In the **PVA97NK** table, there are several numeric variables with fewer than 20 distinct values that should **_not_** be treated as nominal. Similarly, there is one class variable with more than 20 levels that should **_not_** be rejected.

To avoid changing many metadata values in the next step of the Data Source Wizard, you should alter these defaults.

Copyright © 2011, SAS Institute Inc., Cary, North Carolina, USA. ALL RIGHTS RESERVED.

8. Type **2** as the Class Levels Count Threshold value so that only binary numeric variables are treated as categorical variables.

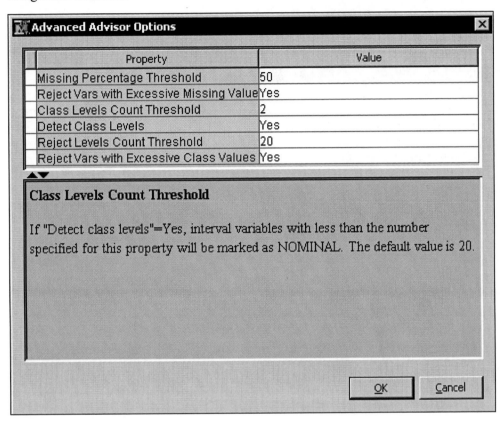

Copyright © 2011, SAS Institute Inc., Cary, North Carolina, USA. ALL RIGHTS RESERVED.

9. Type **100** as the Reject Levels Count Threshold value so that only character variables with more than 100 distinct values are rejected.

Be sure to press ENTER after you type the number **100**. Otherwise, the value might not be registered in the field.

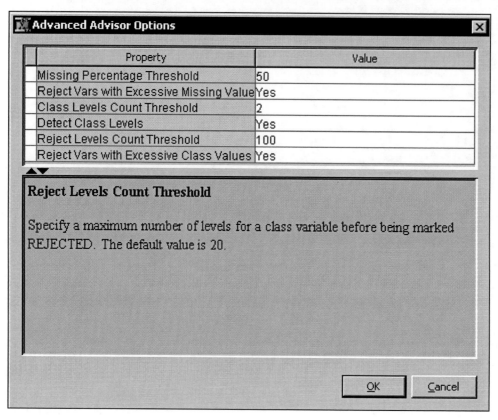

10. Select **OK** to close the Advanced Advisor Options dialog box.

Copyright © 2011, SAS Institute Inc., Cary, North Carolina, USA. ALL RIGHTS RESERVED.

11. Select **Next** to proceed to Step 5 of the Data Source Wizard.

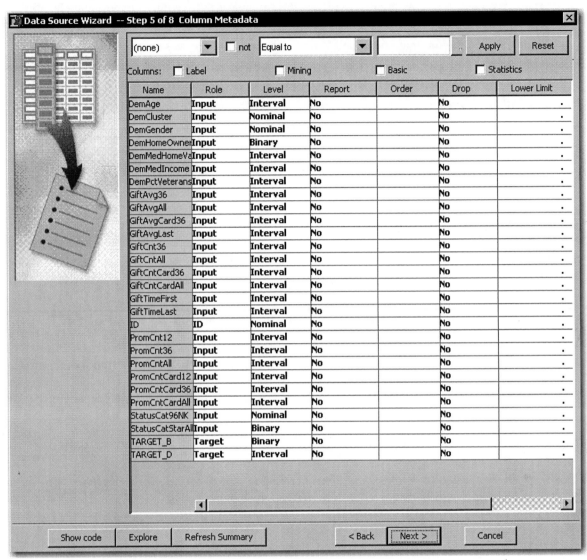

A comparison of the Column Metadata table to the table at the beginning of the demonstration shows that most of the metadata is correctly defined. SAS Enterprise Miner correctly inferred the model roles for the non-input variables by their names. The measurement levels are correctly defined by using the Advanced Metadata Advisor.

The analysis of the **PVA97NK** data in this course focuses on the **TARGET_B** variable, so the **TARGET_D** variable should be rejected.

12. Select **Role** ⇨ **Rejected** for **TARGET_D**.

Copyright © 2011, SAS Institute Inc., Cary, North Carolina, USA. ALL RIGHTS RESERVED.

In summary, Step 5 Column Metadata is usually the most time-consuming of the Data Source Wizard steps. You can use the following tips to reduce the amount of time required to define metadata for SAS Enterprise Miner predictive modeling data sets:

- Include only variables that you intend to use in the modeling process in your raw data source.

- For variables that are not inputs, use variable names that start with the intended role. For example, an ID variable should start with **ID** and a target variable should start with **Target**.

- Inputs that are to have a nominal measurement level should have a *character* data type.

- Inputs that are to be interval must have a *numeric* data type.

- Customize the Metadata Advisor to have a Class Level Count set equal to **2** and a Reject Levels Count set equal to a number greater than the maximum cardinality (level count) of your nominal inputs.

Finalizing the Data Source Specification

Follow these steps to complete the data source specification process.

1. Select **Next** to proceed to Decision Configuration.

    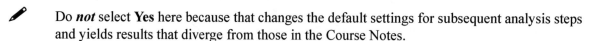   The Data Source Wizard gained an extra step due to the presence of a categorical (binary, ordinal, or nominal) target variable.

When you define a predictive modeling data set, it is important to properly configure decision processing. In fact, obtaining meaningful models often requires using these options. The **PVA97NK** table was structured so that reasonable models are produced *without* specifying decision processing. However, this might not be the case for data sources that you will encounter outside this course. Because you need to understand how to set these options, a detailed discussion of decision processing is provided in Chapter 6, "Model Assessment."

    Do *not* select **Yes** here because that changes the default settings for subsequent analysis steps and yields results that diverge from those in the Course Notes.

Copyright © 2011, SAS Institute Inc., Cary, North Carolina, USA. ALL RIGHTS RESERVED.

2. Select **Next** to proceed to Create Sample. No sample data set is created, so leave this step set to the default **No.**

3. Select **Next** and you reach the second to the last step of the Data Source Wizard.

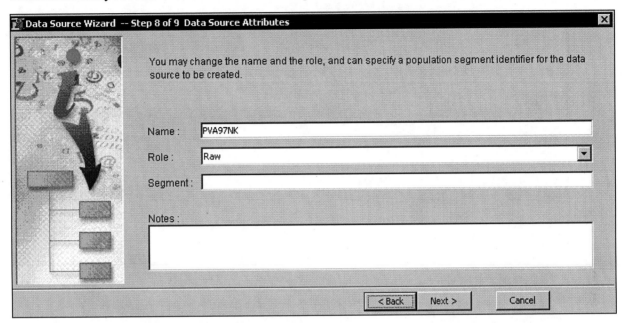

This step enables you to set a role for the data source and add descriptive comments about the data source definition. For the upcoming analysis, a table role of Raw is acceptable.

4. Select **Next**. The final step in the Data Source Wizard provides summary details about the data table that you created. Select **Finish**.

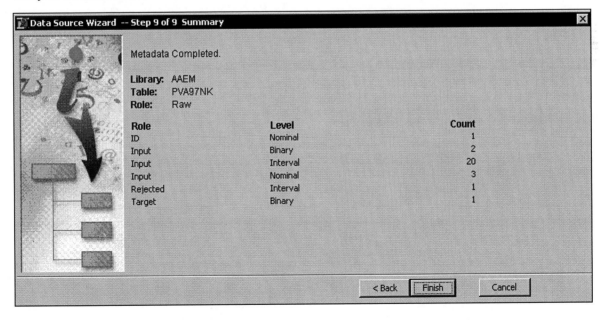

Copyright © 2011, SAS Institute Inc., Cary, North Carolina, USA. ALL RIGHTS RESERVED.

The **PVA97NK** data source is added to the Data Sources entry in the Project panel.

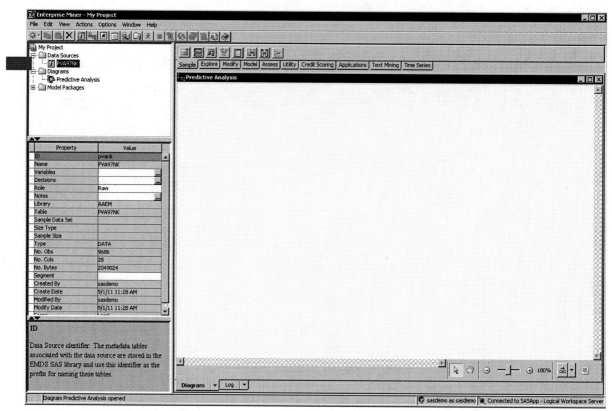

5. Select the **PVA97NK** data source to obtain table properties in the SAS Enterprise Miner Properties panel.

Copyright © 2011, SAS Institute Inc., Cary, North Carolina, USA. ALL RIGHTS RESERVED.

 **Exercises**

2. Creating a SAS Enterprise Miner Data Source

Use the steps in the "Defining a Data Source" demonstration to create a SAS Enterprise Miner data source from the **PVA97NK** data.

Copyright © 2011, SAS Institute Inc., Cary, North Carolina, USA. ALL RIGHTS RESERVED.

2.4   Exploring a Data Source

As stated in Chapter 1 and noted in Section 2.3, the task of data assembly largely occurs outside of SAS Enterprise Miner. However, it is quite worthwhile to explore and validate your data's content. By assaying the prepared data, you substantially reduce the chances of erroneous results in your analysis, and you can gain insights graphically into associations between variables.

In this exploration, you should look for sampling errors, unexpected or unusual data values, and interesting variable associations.

The next demonstrations illustrate SAS Enterprise Miner tools that are useful for data validation.

Copyright © 2011, SAS Institute Inc., Cary, North Carolina, USA. ALL RIGHTS RESERVED.

 **Exploring Source Data**

SAS Enterprise Miner can construct interactive plots to help you explore your data. This demonstration shows the basic features of the Explore window, including the following:

- opening the Explore window
- changing the Explore window sample size
- creating a histogram for a single variable
- changing graph properties for a histogram
- changing chart axes
- adding a missing bin to a histogram
- adding plots to the Explore window
- exploring variable associations

Accessing the Explore Window

There are several ways to access the Explore window. Use these steps to access the Explore window through the Project panel.

1. Open the Data Sources folder in the Project panel and right-click the data source of interest. The Data Source Option menu appears.

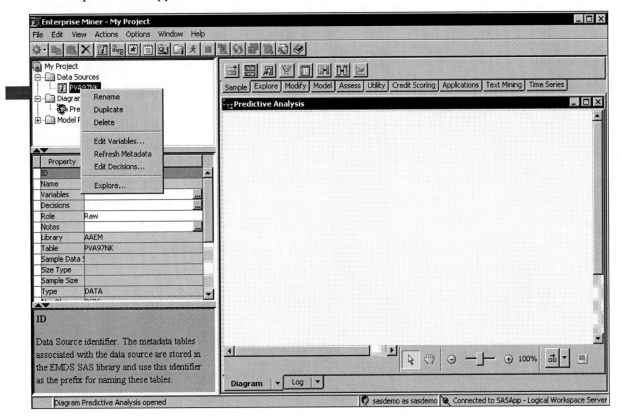

Copyright © 2011, SAS Institute Inc., Cary, North Carolina, USA. ALL RIGHTS RESERVED.

2. Select **Explore** from the Data Source Option menu.

By default, a maximum of 2000 observations are transferred from the SAS Foundation Server to the SAS Enterprise Miner client. This represents about one-fifth of the **PVA97NK** table.

The Explore - AAEM.PVA97NK window appears.

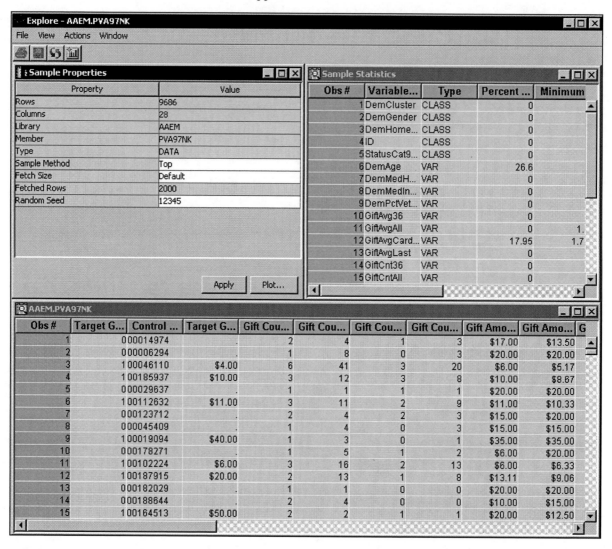

The Explore window features a 2000-observation sample from the **PVA97NK** data source. Sample properties and statistics are shown in the top half of the window and a data table is shown in the bottom half.

Copyright © 2011, SAS Institute Inc., Cary, North Carolina, USA. ALL RIGHTS RESERVED.

Changing the Explore Sample Size

The Sample Method property indicates that the sample is drawn from the *top* (first 2000 rows) of the data set. Use these steps to change the sampling properties in the Explore window.

🖊 Although selecting a sample through this method is quick to execute, fetching the top rows of a table might not produce a representative sample of the table.

1. Left-click the **Sample Method** value field. The Option menu lists two choices: Top (the current setting) and Random.

2. Select **Random** from the Option menu.

3. Select **Actions** ⇨ **Apply Sample Properties** from the Explore window menu. A new, random sample of 2000 observations is made. This 2000-row sample now has distributional properties that are similar to the original 9686 observation table. This gives you an idea about the general characteristics of the variables. If your goal is to examine the data for potential problems, it is wise to examine the entire data set.

🖊 SAS Enterprise Miner enables you to increase the sample transferred to the client (up to a maximum of 30,000 observations). See the SAS Enterprise Miner Help file to learn how to increase this maximum value.

4. Select the **Fetch Size** property and select **Max** from the Option menu.

5. Select **Actions** ⇨ **Apply Sample Properties**. Because there are fewer than 30,000 observations, the entire **PVA97NK** table is transferred to the SAS Enterprise Miner client machine, as indicated by the **Fetched Rows** field.

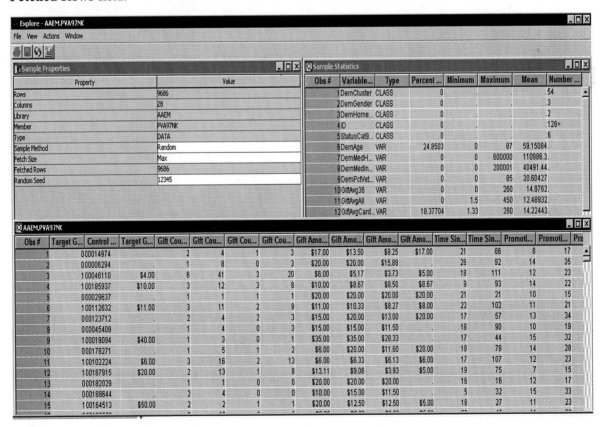

Copyright © 2011, SAS Institute Inc., Cary, North Carolina, USA. ALL RIGHTS RESERVED.

Creating a Histogram for a Single Variable

While you can use the Explore window to browse a data set, its primary purpose is to create statistical analysis plots. Use these steps to create a histogram in the Explore window.

1. Select **Actions** ⇨ **Plot** from the Explore window menu. The Chart wizard appears, and it is at the Select a Chart Type step.

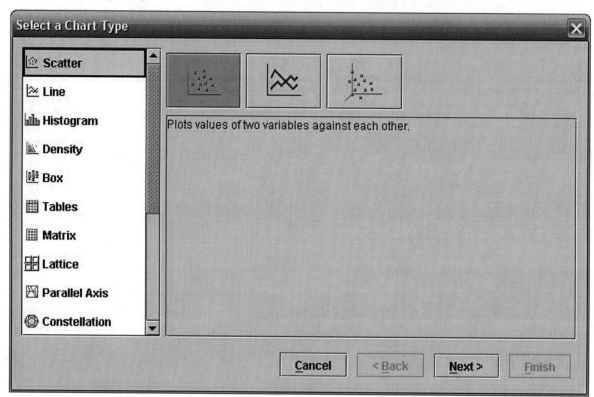

The Chart wizard enables the construction of a multitude of analysis charts. This demonstration focuses on histograms.

Copyright © 2011, SAS Institute Inc., Cary, North Carolina, USA. ALL RIGHTS RESERVED.

2. Select **Histogram**.

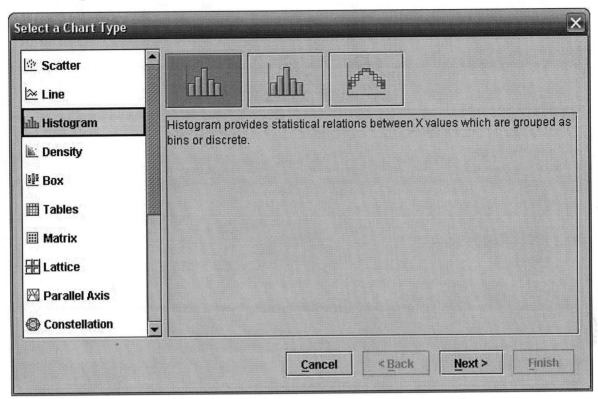

Histograms are useful for exploring the distribution of values in a variable.

Copyright © 2011, SAS Institute Inc., Cary, North Carolina, USA. ALL RIGHTS RESERVED.

3.   Select **Next**. The Chart wizard proceeds to the next step, Select Chart Roles.

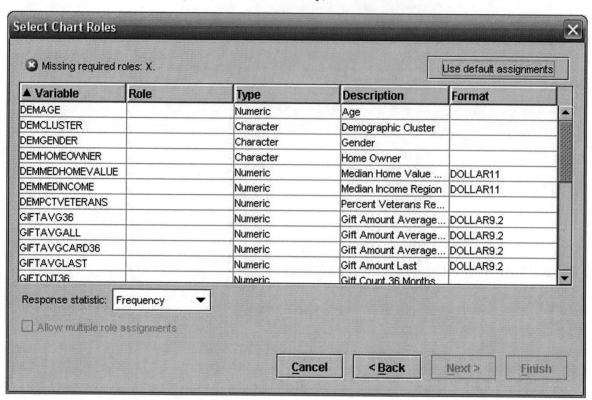

To draw a histogram, one variable must be selected to have the role X.

Copyright © 2011, SAS Institute Inc., Cary, North Carolina, USA. ALL RIGHTS RESERVED.

4. Select **Role** ⇨ **X** for the **DEMAGE** variable.

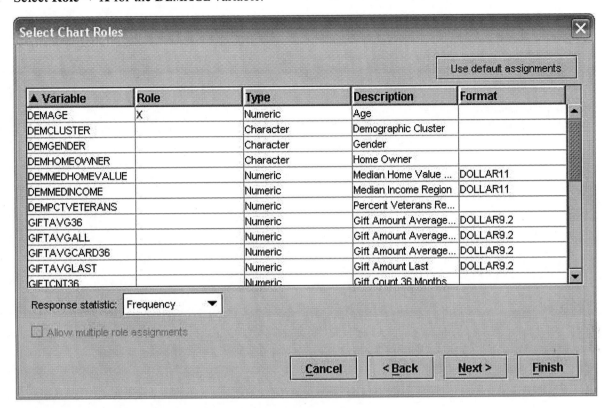

The Chart wizard is ready to make a histogram of the **DEMAGE** variable.

Copyright © 2011, SAS Institute Inc., Cary, North Carolina, USA. ALL RIGHTS RESERVED.

5. Select **Finish**. The Explore window is filled with a histogram of the **DEMAGE** variable.

> Variable descriptions, rather than variable names, are used to label the axes of plots in the Explore window.

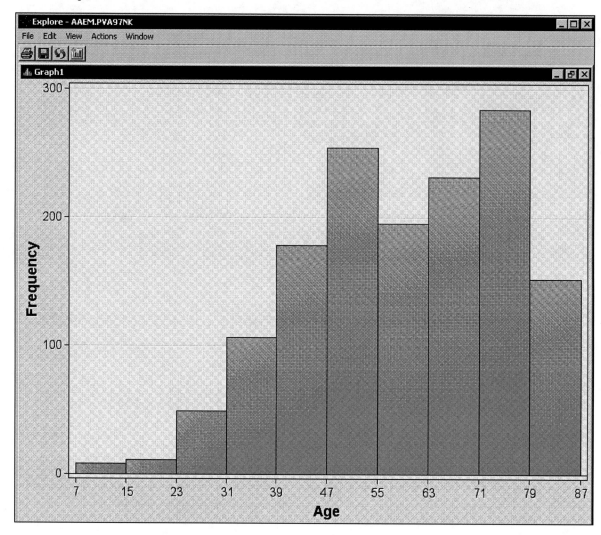

Axes in Explore window plots are chosen to range from the minimum to the maximum values of the plotted variable. Here you can see that **Age** has a minimum value of 0 and a maximum value of 87. The mode occurs in the ninth bin, which ranges between about 70 and 78. **Frequency** tells you that there are about 1400 observations in this range.

Copyright © 2011, SAS Institute Inc., Cary, North Carolina, USA. ALL RIGHTS RESERVED.

Changing the Graph Properties for a Histogram

By default, a histogram in SAS Enterprise Miner has 10 bins and is scaled to show the entire range of data. Use these steps to change the number of bins in a histogram and change the range of the axes.

While the default bin size is sufficient to show the general shape of a variable's distribution, it is sometimes useful to increase the number of bins to improve the histogram's resolution.

1. Right-click in the data area of the **Age** histogram and select **Graph Properties** from the Option menu. The Properties - Histogram window appears.

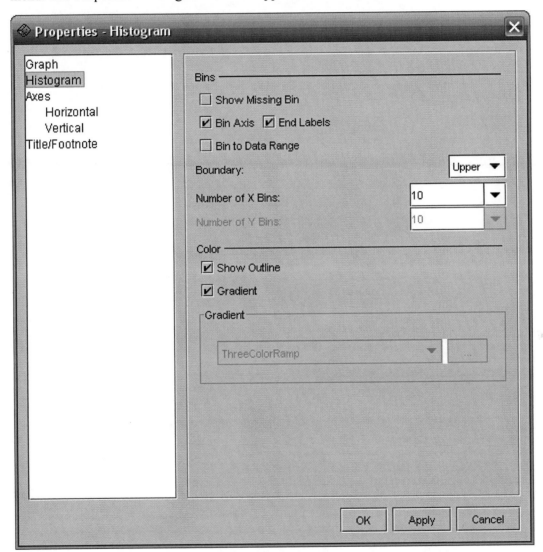

This window enables you to change the appearance of your charts. For histograms, the most important appearance property (at least in a statistical sense) is the number of bins.

Copyright © 2011, SAS Institute Inc., Cary, North Carolina, USA. ALL RIGHTS RESERVED.

2. Type **87** in the **Number of X Bins** field.

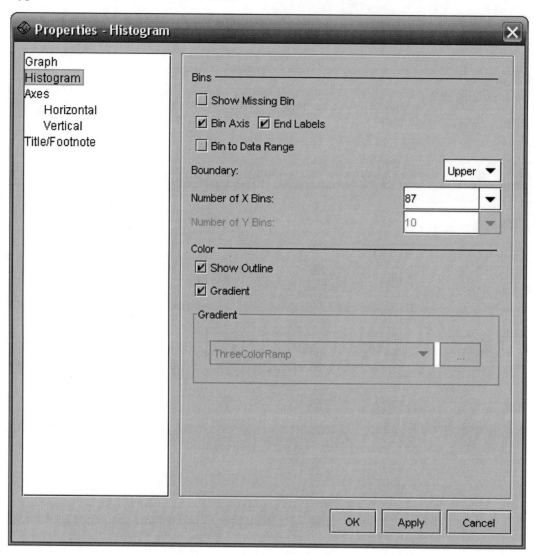

Because **Age** is integer-valued and the original distribution plot had a maximum of 87, there will be one bin per possible **Age** value.

Copyright © 2011, SAS Institute Inc., Cary, North Carolina, USA. ALL RIGHTS RESERVED.

3. Select **OK**. The Explore window reappears and shows many more bins in the **Age** histogram.

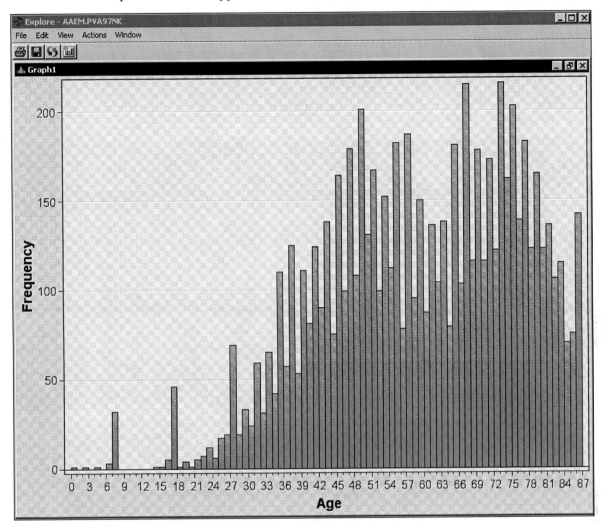

With the increase in resolution, unusual features become apparent in the **Age** variable. For example, there are unexpected spikes in the histogram at 10-year intervals, starting at **Age**=7. Also, you must question the veracity of ages below 18 for donors to the charity.

Copyright © 2011, SAS Institute Inc., Cary, North Carolina, USA. ALL RIGHTS RESERVED.

Changing Chart Axes

A very useful feature of the Explore window is the ability to zoom in on data of interest. Use the following steps to change chart axes in the Explore window.

1. Position your cursor under the histogram until the cursor appears as a magnifying glass.

2. Click with your mouse and drag the cursor to the right to magnify the horizontal axis of the histogram.

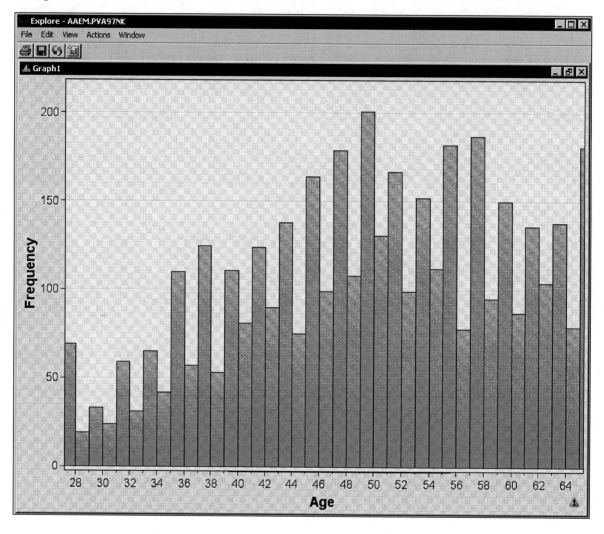

Copyright © 2011, SAS Institute Inc., Cary, North Carolina, USA. ALL RIGHTS RESERVED.

3. Position your cursor below the histogram but above the **Age** axis label. A horizontal scroll bar appears.

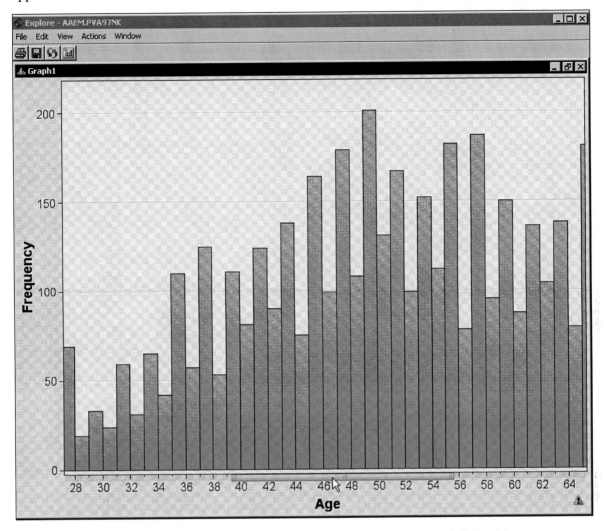

4. Click and drag the scroll bar to the left to translate the horizontal axis to the left. Position your cursor to the left of the histogram to make a similar adjustment to the vertical axis of the histogram.

Copyright © 2011, SAS Institute Inc., Cary, North Carolina, USA. ALL RIGHTS RESERVED.

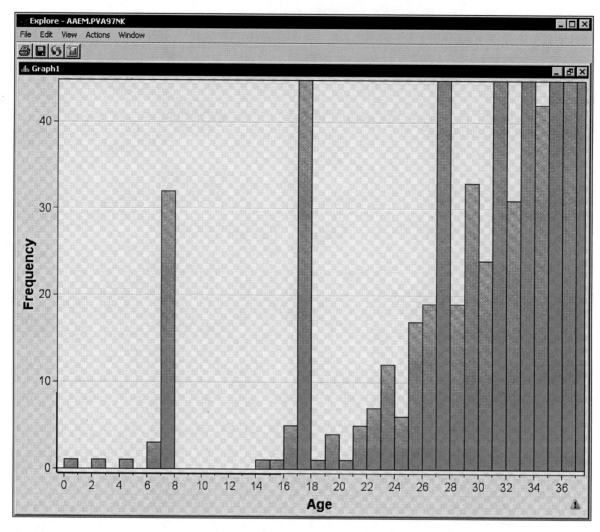

At this resolution, you can see that there are approximately 40 observations with **Age** less than 8. A review of the data preparation process might help you determine whether these values are valid.

5. Select ⚠ (the yellow triangle) in the lower right corner of the Explore window to reset the axes to their original ranges.

Copyright © 2011, SAS Institute Inc., Cary, North Carolina, USA. ALL RIGHTS RESERVED.

Adding a "Missing" Bin to a Histogram

Not all observations appear in the histogram for **Age**. There are many observations with missing values for this variable. Follow these steps to add a missing value bin to the **Age** histogram:

1. Right-click on the graph and select **Graph Properties** from the Option menu.

2. Select the **Show Missing Bin** option.

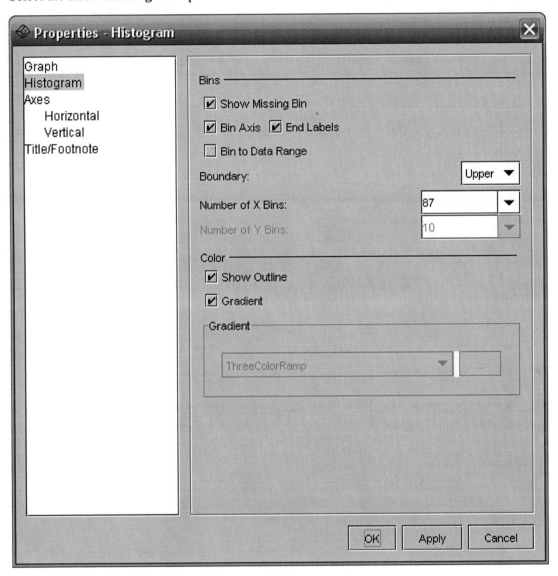

Copyright © 2011, SAS Institute Inc., Cary, North Carolina, USA. ALL RIGHTS RESERVED.

3. Select **OK**. The **Age** histogram is modified to show a missing value bin.

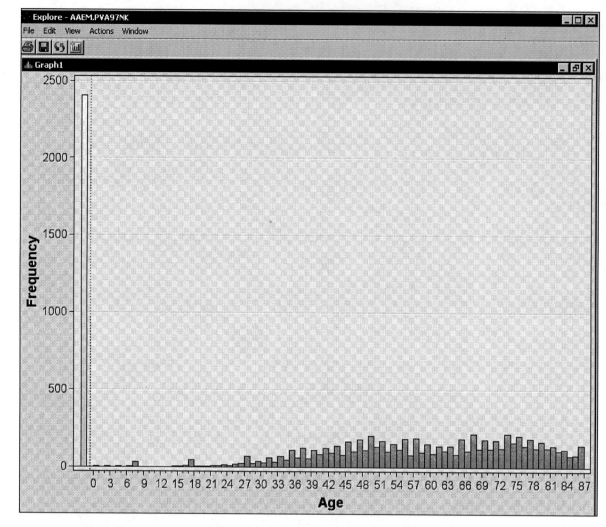

With the missing value bin added, it is easy to see that nearly a quarter of the observations are missing an **Age** value.

Copyright © 2011, SAS Institute Inc., Cary, North Carolina, USA. ALL RIGHTS RESERVED.

Adding Plots to the Explore Window

You can add other plots to the Explore window. Follow these steps to add a pie chart of the target variable.

1. Select **Actions** ⇨ **Plot** from the Explore window menu. The Chart wizard opens to the Select a Chart Type step.

2. Scroll down in the chart list and select **Pie**.

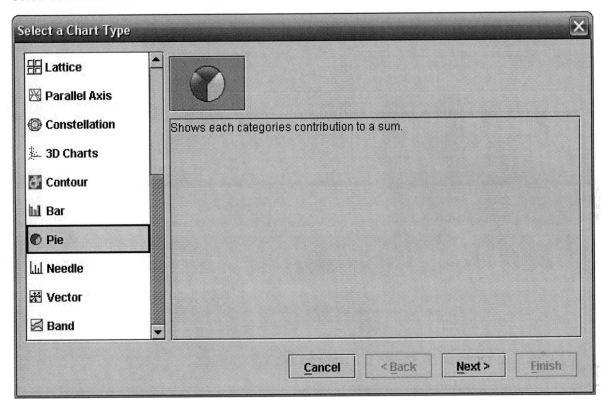

Copyright © 2011, SAS Institute Inc., Cary, North Carolina, USA. ALL RIGHTS RESERVED.

3.   Select **Next**. The Chart wizard continues to the Select Chart Roles step.

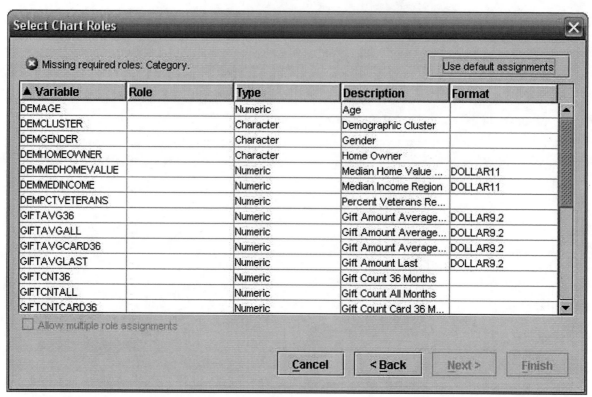

The message at the top of the Select Chart Roles window states that a variable must be assigned the Category role.

Copyright © 2011, SAS Institute Inc., Cary, North Carolina, USA. ALL RIGHTS RESERVED.

4. Scroll through the variable list and select **Role** ⇨ **Category** for the **TARGET_B** variable.

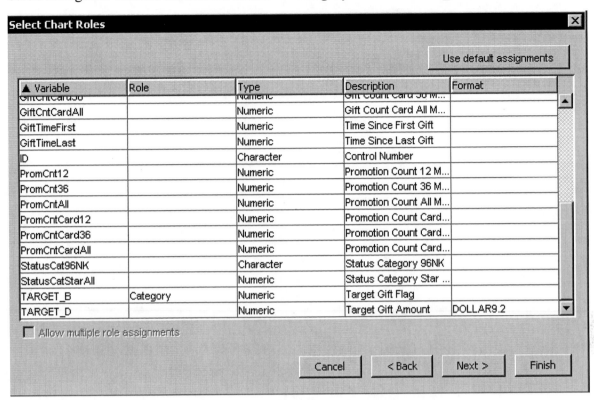

Copyright © 2011, SAS Institute Inc., Cary, North Carolina, USA. ALL RIGHTS RESERVED.

5. Select **Finish** to create the pie chart for **TARGET_B**.

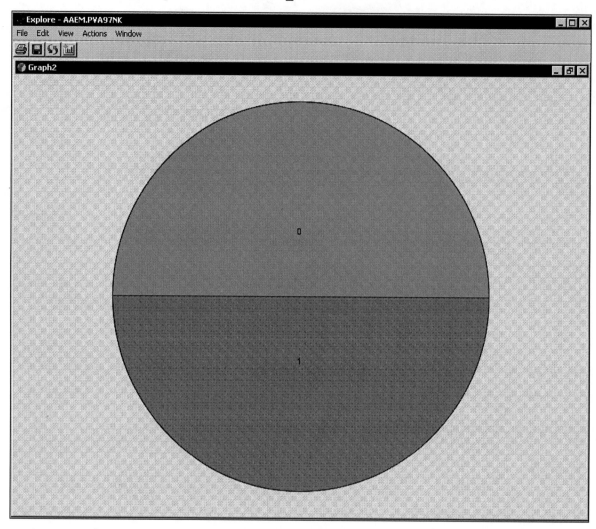

The chart shows an equal number of cases for **TARGET_B**=0 (top) and **TARGET_B**=1 (bottom).

Copyright © 2011, SAS Institute Inc., Cary, North Carolina, USA. ALL RIGHTS RESERVED.

6. Select **Window** ⇨ **Tile** to simultaneously view all sub-windows of the Explore window.

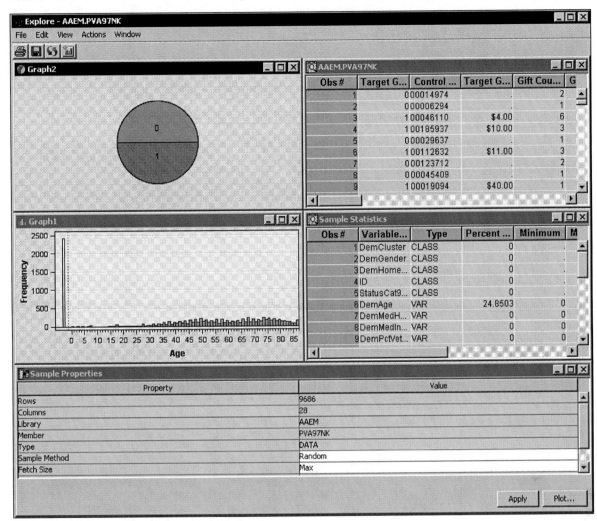

Copyright © 2011, SAS Institute Inc., Cary, North Carolina, USA. ALL RIGHTS RESERVED.

Exploring Variable Associations

All elements of the Explore window are connected. By selecting a bar in one histogram, for example, corresponding observations in the data table and other plots are also selected. Follow these steps to use this feature to explore variable associations.

1. Double-click the title bar of the **Age** histogram so that the histogram fills the Explore window.

2. Click and drag a rectangle in the **Age** histogram to select cases with **Age** in excess of 70 years.

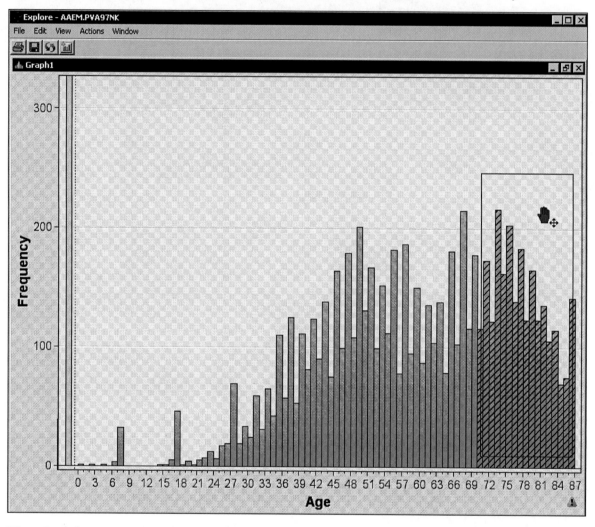

The selected cases are cross-hatched. (The vertical axis is rescaled to show the selection better.)

Copyright © 2011, SAS Institute Inc., Cary, North Carolina, USA. ALL RIGHTS RESERVED.

3. Double-click the **Age** histogram title bar. The tile display is restored.

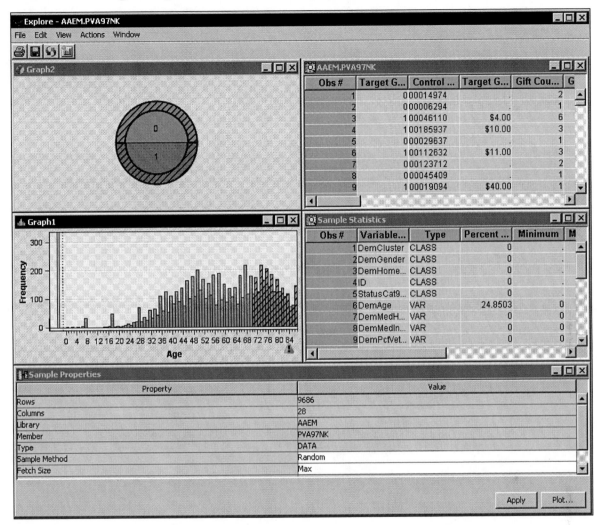

Notice that part of the **TARGET_B** pie chart is selected. This selection shows the relative proportion of observations with **Age** greater than 70 that do and do not donate. Because the arc on the **TARGET_B**=1 segment is slightly thicker, it appears that there is a slightly higher number of donors than non-donors in this **Age** selection.

Copyright © 2011, SAS Institute Inc., Cary, North Carolina, USA. ALL RIGHTS RESERVED.

4. Double-click the **TARGET_B** pie chart title bar to confirm this observation.

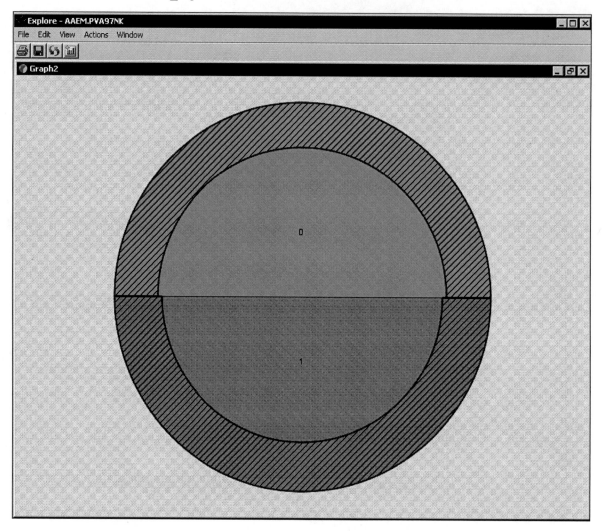

5. Close the Explore window to return to the SAS Enterprise Miner client interface screen.

Copyright © 2011, SAS Institute Inc., Cary, North Carolina, USA. ALL RIGHTS RESERVED.

Changing the Explore Window Sampling Defaults

Follow these steps to change the preference settings of SAS Enterprise Miner to use a random sample or all of the data source data in the Explore window:

1.   Select **Options** ⇨ **Preferences** from the main menu. The Preferences window appears.

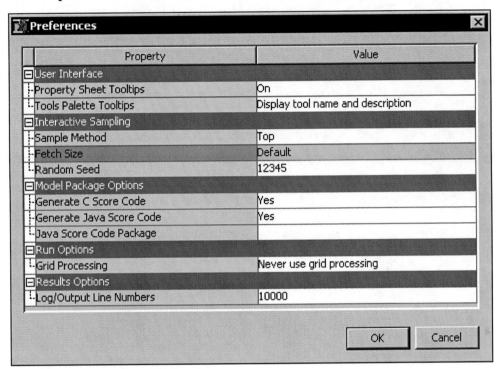

2.   Select **Sample Method** ⇨ **Random**.

The random sampling method improves on the default method (at the top of the data set) by guaranteeing that the Explore window data is representative of the original data source. The only negative aspect is an increase in processing time for extremely large data sources.

Copyright © 2011, SAS Institute Inc., Cary, North Carolina, USA. ALL RIGHTS RESERVED.

3. Select **Fetch Size** ➪ **Max**.

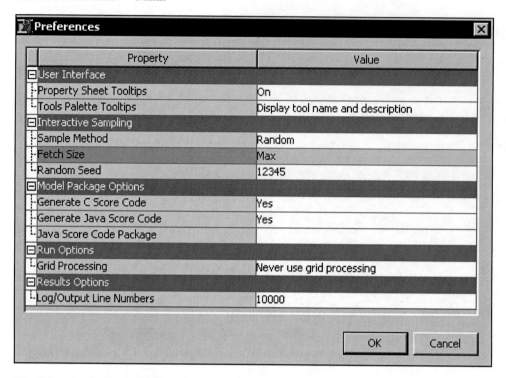

The Max fetch size enables a larger sample of data to be extracted for use in the Explore window.

If you use these settings, the Explore window uses the entire data set or a random sample of up to 30,000 observations (whichever is smaller).

Copyright © 2011, SAS Institute Inc., Cary, North Carolina, USA. ALL RIGHTS RESERVED.

 **Exercises**

3. **Using the Explore Window to Study Variable Distribution**

    Use the Explore window to study the distribution of the variable **Median Income Region**
    (**DemMedIncome**). Answer the following questions:

    a. What is unusual about the distribution of this variable? ___N_____

    _____

    b. What could cause this anomaly to occur? _____

    _____

    c. What do you think should be done to rectify the situation? _____

    _____

    — It looks like they used 0 if
    data was missing
    — Convert zeros for missing

Copyright © 2011, SAS Institute Inc., Cary, North Carolina, USA. ALL RIGHTS RESERVED.

Modifying and Correcting Source Data

In the previous exercise, the **DemMedIncome** variable was seen to have an unusual spike at 0. This phenomenon often occurs in data extracted from a relational database table where 0 or another number is used as a substitute for the value `missing` or `unknown`. Clearly, having zero income is considerably different from having an unknown income. If you properly use the **income** variable in a predictive model, this discrepancy can be addressed.

This demonstration shows you how to replace a placeholder value for missing with a true missing value indicator. In this way, SAS Enterprise Miner tools can correctly respond to the true, but unknown, value. SAS Enterprise Miner includes several tools that you can use to modify the source data for your analysis. The following demonstrations show how to use the Replacement node to modify incorrect or improper values for a variable:

Process Flow Setup

Use the following steps to set up the process flow that will modify the **DemMedIncome** variable.

1. Drag the **PVA97NK** data source to the Predictive Analysis workspace window.

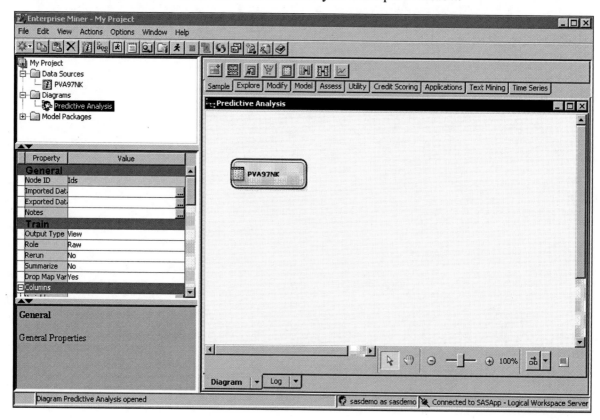

Copyright © 2011, SAS Institute Inc., Cary, North Carolina, USA. ALL RIGHTS RESERVED.

2. Select the **Modify** tab to access the Modify tool group.

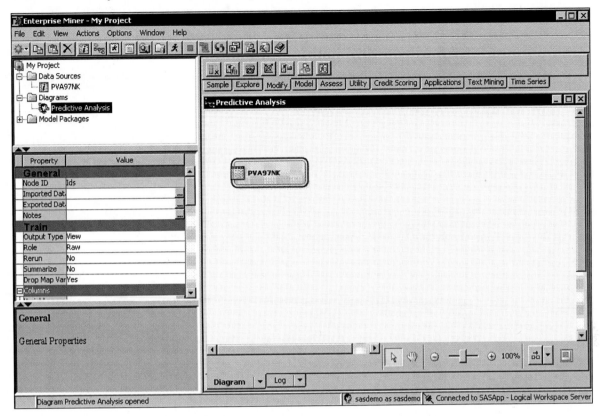

Copyright © 2011, SAS Institute Inc., Cary, North Carolina, USA. ALL RIGHTS RESERVED.

3. Drag the **Replacement** tool (third from the right) from the tools palette into the Predictive Analysis workspace window.

4. Connect the **PVA97NK** data to the Replacement node by clicking near the right side of the **PVA97NK** node and dragging an arrow to the left side of the Replacement node.

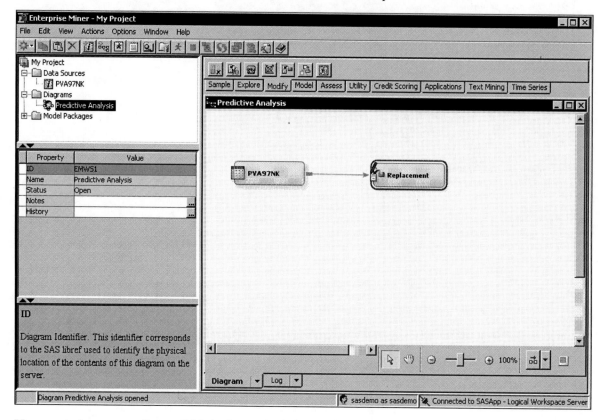

You created a process flow, which is the method that SAS Enterprise Miner uses to carry out analyses. The process flow, at this point, reads the raw **PVA97NK** data and replaces the unwanted values of the observations. You must, however, specify which variables have unwanted values and what the correct values are. To do this, you must change the settings of the Replacement node.

Changing the Replacement Node Properties

Use the following steps to modify the default settings of the Replacement node.

1. Select the **Replacement** node and examine the Properties panel.

   The Properties panel displays the analysis methods used by the node when it is run. By default, the node replaces all interval variables whose values are more than three standard deviations from the variable mean.

   🖉   You can control the number of standard deviations by selecting the **Cutoff Values** property.

   In this demonstration, you want to replace the value for **DemMedIncome** only when it equals zero. Thus, you need to change the default setting.

Copyright © 2011, SAS Institute Inc., Cary, North Carolina, USA. ALL RIGHTS RESERVED.

2. Select the **Default Limits Method** property and select **None** from the Options menu.

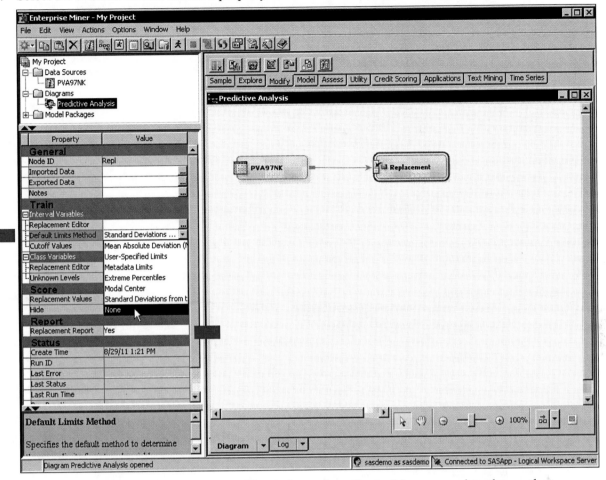

You want to replace improper values with missing values. To do this, you need to change the Replacement Value property.

Copyright © 2011, SAS Institute Inc., Cary, North Carolina, USA. ALL RIGHTS RESERVED.

3. Select the **Replacement Value** property and select **Missing** from the Options menu.

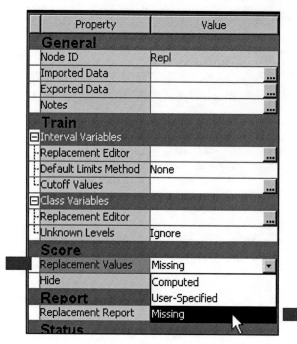

You are now ready to specify the variables that you want to replace.

4. Select 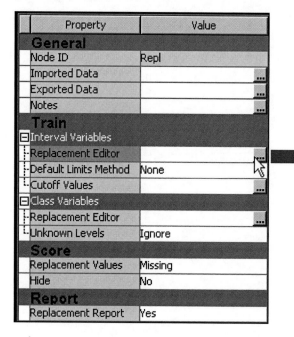 (Interval Variables: Replacement Editor ellipsis) from the Replacement node properties panel.

✎   Be careful to open the Replacement Editor for interval variables, ***not*** for class variables.

Copyright © 2011, SAS Institute Inc., Cary, North Carolina, USA. ALL RIGHTS RESERVED.

The Interactive Replacement Interval Filter window appears.

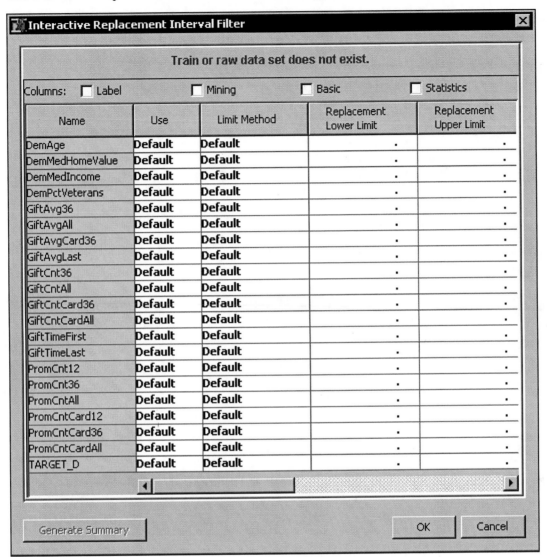

Name	Use	Limit Method	Replacement Lower Limit	Replacement Upper Limit
DemAge	Default	Default	.	.
DemMedHomeValue	Default	Default	.	.
DemMedIncome	Default	Default	.	.
DemPctVeterans	Default	Default	.	.
GiftAvg36	Default	Default	.	.
GiftAvgAll	Default	Default	.	.
GiftAvgCard36	Default	Default	.	.
GiftAvgLast	Default	Default	.	.
GiftCnt36	Default	Default	.	.
GiftCntAll	Default	Default	.	.
GiftCntCard36	Default	Default	.	.
GiftCntCardAll	Default	Default	.	.
GiftTimeFirst	Default	Default	.	.
GiftTimeLast	Default	Default	.	.
PromCnt12	Default	Default	.	.
PromCnt36	Default	Default	.	.
PromCntAll	Default	Default	.	.
PromCntCard12	Default	Default	.	.
PromCntCard36	Default	Default	.	.
PromCntCardAll	Default	Default	.	.
TARGET_D	Default	Default	.	.

Interactive Replacement Interval Filter

Train or raw data set does not exist.

Columns: □ Label   □ Mining   □ Basic   □ Statistics

Generate Summary   OK   Cancel

Copyright © 2011, SAS Institute Inc., Cary, North Carolina, USA. ALL RIGHTS RESERVED.

5. Select **User Specified** as the Limit Method value for **DemMedIncome**.

Name	Use	Limit Method	Replacement Lower Limit	Replacement Upper Limit
DemAge	Default	Default	.	
DemMedHomeValue	Default	Default	.	
DemMedIncome	Default	Default ▾	.	
DemPctVeterans	Default	Default	.	
GiftAvg36	Default	Extreme Percentiles	.	
GiftAvgAll	Default	Mean Absolute Deviati	.	
GiftAvgCard36	Default	Metadata Limits	.	
GiftAvgLast	Default	Modal Center	.	
GiftCnt36	Default	None	.	
GiftCntAll	Default	Standard Deviation	.	
GiftCntCard36	Default	User Specified	.	
GiftCntCardAll	Default	Default	.	
GiftTimeFirst	Default	Default	.	
GiftTimeLast	Default	Default	.	

Interactive Replacement Interval Filter

Train or raw data set does not exist.

Columns: ☐ Label   ☐ Mining   ☑ Basic

Copyright © 2011, SAS Institute Inc., Cary, North Carolina, USA. ALL RIGHTS RESERVED.

6. Type **1** as the Lower Limit value for **DemMedIncome**.

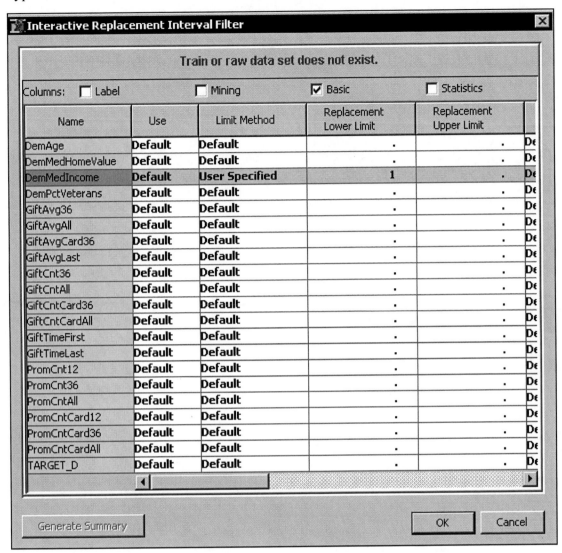

If you use this specification, any **DemMedIncome** values that fall below the lower limit of 1 are set to missing. All other values of this variable do not change.

7. Select **OK** to close the Interactive Replacement Interval Filter window.

Copyright © 2011, SAS Institute Inc., Cary, North Carolina, USA. ALL RIGHTS RESERVED.

Running the Analysis and Viewing the Results

Use these steps to run the process flow that you created.

1. Right-click on the **Replacement** node and select **Run** from the Option menu. A Confirmation window appears and requests that you verify the run action.

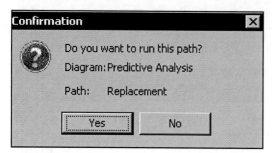

2. Select **Yes** to close the Confirmation window. A small animation in the lower right corner of each node indicates analysis activity in the node.

    The Run Status window opens when the process flow run is complete.

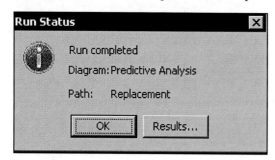

3. Select **Results** to review the analysis outcome. The Results - Node: Replacement Diagram: Predictive Analysis window appears.

Copyright © 2011, SAS Institute Inc., Cary, North Carolina, USA. ALL RIGHTS RESERVED.

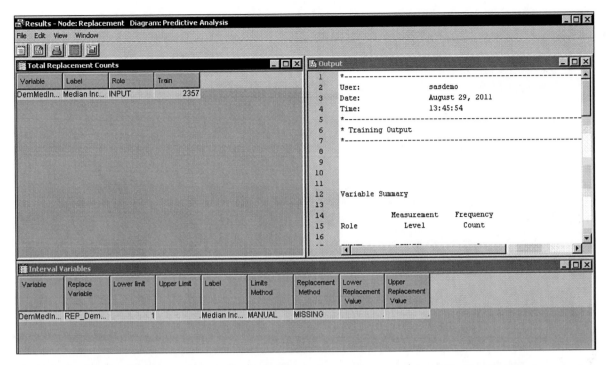

The Replacement Counts window shows that 2357 observations were modified by the Replacement node. The Interval Variables window summarizes the replacement that was conducted. The Output window provides more or less the same information as the Total Replacement Counts window and the Interval Variables window (but it is presented as a static text file).

4. Close the Results window.

Examining Exported Data

In a SAS Enterprise Miner process flow diagram, each node takes in data, analyzes it, creates a result, and exports a possibly modified version of the imported data. While the report gives the analysis results in abstract, it is good practice to see the actual effects of an analysis step on the exported data. This enables you to validate your expectations at each step of the analysis.

Use these steps to examine the data exported from the Replacement node.

1. Select the **Replacement** node in your process flow diagram.

2. Select **Exported Data** ⇨ .

Copyright © 2011, SAS Institute Inc., Cary, North Carolina, USA. ALL RIGHTS RESERVED.

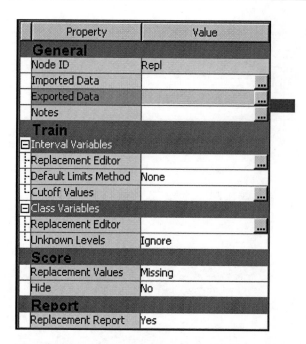

The Exported Data - Replacement window appears.

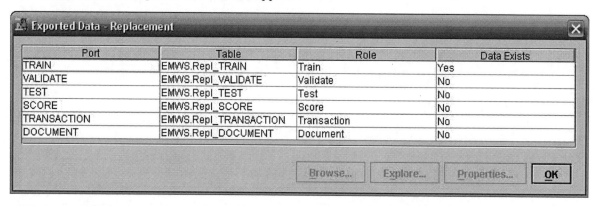

This window lists the types of data sets that can be exported from a SAS Enterprise Miner process flow node. As indicated, only a Train data set exists at this stage of the analysis.

3. Select the **TRAIN** table from the Exported Data - Replacement window.

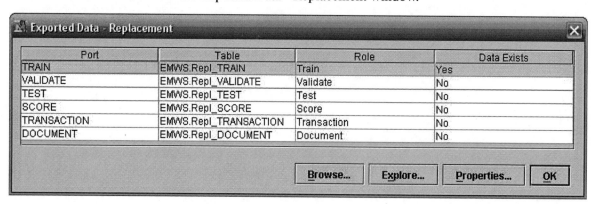

4. Select **Explore** to access the Explore window again.

Copyright © 2011, SAS Institute Inc., Cary, North Carolina, USA. ALL RIGHTS RESERVED.

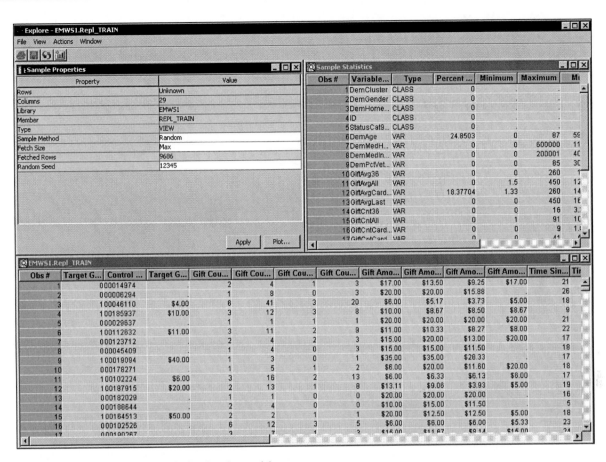

5. Scroll completely to the right in the data table.

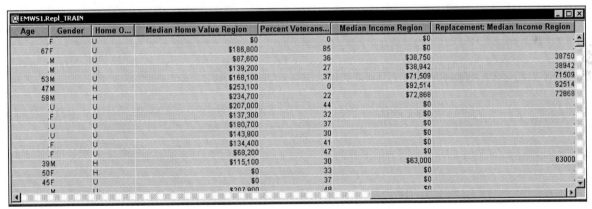

A new column is added to the analysis data: **Replacement: DemMedIncome**. Notice that the values of this variable match the **Median Income Region** variable, except when the original variables value equals zero. The replaced zero value is represented by a period, which indicates a missing value.

6. Close the Explore and Exported Data windows to complete this part of the analysis.

Copyright © 2011, SAS Institute Inc., Cary, North Carolina, USA. ALL RIGHTS RESERVED.

2.5 Chapter Summary

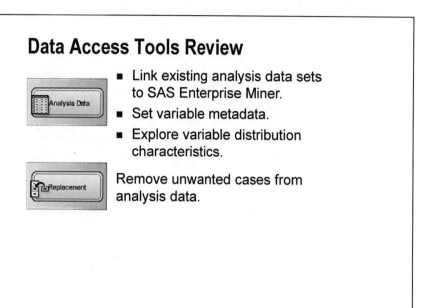

Analyses in SAS Enterprise Miner are organized hierarchically into projects, data libraries, diagrams, process flows, and analysis nodes. This chapter demonstrated the basics of creating each of these elements.

Most process flows begin with a data source node. To access a data source, you must define a SAS library. After a library is defined, a data source is created by linking a SAS table and associated metadata to SAS Enterprise Miner. After a data source is defined, you can assay the underlying cases using SAS Enterprise Miner Explore tools. Care should be taken to ensure that the sample of the data source that you explore is representative of the original data source.

You can use the Replacement node to modify variables that were incorrectly prepared. After all necessary modifications, the data is ready for subsequent analysis.

Copyright © 2011, SAS Institute Inc., Cary, North Carolina, USA. ALL RIGHTS RESERVED.

2.6 Solutions

Solutions to Exercises

1. **Creating a Project, Defining a Library, and Creating an Analysis Diagram**

    Complete the steps in the three demonstrations in Section 2.2.

2. **Creating a SAS Enterprise Miner Data Source**

    Complete the steps in the demonstration in Section 2.3.

3. **Using the Explore Window to Study Variable Distribution**

    a. What is unusual about the distribution of this variable?

        1) Right-click the **PVA97NK** data source in the Project panel. Select **Edit Variables**. Select **DemMedIncome** ⇨ **Explore**.

        2) Change the number of bins in the histogram for **DemMedIncome** to a large value, such as 100.

        There is a large spike in the histogram for income values close to zero.

    b. What could cause this anomaly to occur?

        People might not self-report income. A value of zero might be recorded for someone who does not report income.

    c. What do you think should be done to rectify the situation?

        Replace the zero income values with missing.

Copyright © 2011, SAS Institute Inc., Cary, North Carolina, USA. ALL RIGHTS RESERVED.

Solutions to Student Activities (Polls/Quizzes)

2.01 Multiple Choice Poll – Correct Answer

A data source in SAS Enterprise Miner differs from a raw data file because a data source has additional metadata attached. This metadata includes which of the following?

a. the variable roles
b. the variable measurement levels
c. the data table role
d. all of the above

14

Copyright © 2011, SAS Institute Inc., Cary, North Carolina, USA. ALL RIGHTS RESERVED.

Chapter 3   Introduction to Predictive Modeling: Decision Trees

Copyright © 2011, SAS Institute Inc., Cary, North Carolina, USA. ALL RIGHTS RESERVED.

Copyright © 2011, SAS Institute Inc., Cary, North Carolina, USA. ALL RIGHTS RESERVED.

3.1 Introduction

Predictive Modeling

The Essence of Data Mining

"Most of the big payoff [in data mining] has been in predictive modeling."

– Herb Edelstein

3

Predictive modeling has a long history of success in the field of data mining. Models are built from historical event records and are used to predict future occurrences of these events. The methods have great potential for monetary gain. Herb Edelstein states in a 1997 interview (Beck 1997):

> "I also want to stress that data mining is successfully applied to a wide range of problems. The beer-and-diapers type of problem is known as association discovery or market basket analysis, that is, describing something that has happened in existing data. This should be differentiated from predictive techniques. *Most of the big payoff stuff has been in predictive modeling.*"

Predicting the future has obvious financial benefit, but, for several reasons, the ability of predictive models to do so should not be overstated.

First, the models depend on a property known statistically as *stationarity*, meaning that its statistical properties do not change over time. Unfortunately, many processes that generate events of interest are not stationary enough to enable meaningful predictions.

Second, predictive models are often directed at predicting events that occur rarely, and in the aggregate, often look somewhat random. Even the best predictive model can only extract rough trends from these inherently *noisy* processes.

Copyright © 2011, SAS Institute Inc., Cary, North Carolina, USA. ALL RIGHTS RESERVED.

Predictive Modeling Applications

 Database marketing

 Financial risk management

 Fraud detection

 Process monitoring

 Pattern detection

4

Applications of predictive modeling are only limited by your imagination. However, the models created by SAS Enterprise Miner typically apply to one of the following categories.

- Database marketing applications include offer response, up-sell, cross-sell, and attrition models.

- Financial risk management models attempt to predict monetary events such as credit default, loan prepayment, and insurance claim.

- Fraud detection methods attempt to detect or impede illegal activity involving financial transactions.

- Process monitoring applications detect deviations from the norm in manufacturing, financial, and security processes.

- Pattern detection models are used in applications ranging from handwriting analysis to medical diagnostics.

Copyright © 2011, SAS Institute Inc., Cary, North Carolina, USA. ALL RIGHTS RESERVED.

Predictive Modeling Training Data

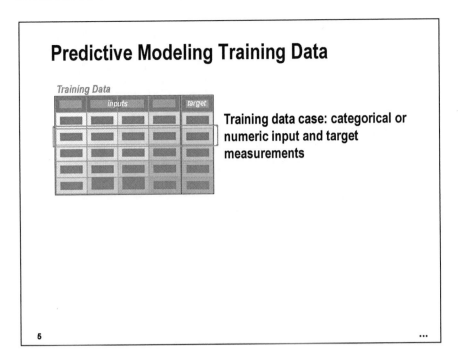

Training data case: categorical or numeric input and target measurements

To begin using SAS Enterprise Miner for predictive modeling, you should be familiar with standard terminology.

Predictive modeling (also known as *supervised prediction* or *supervised learning*) starts with a *training data set*. The observations in a training data set are known as *training cases* (also known as *examples*, *instances*, or *records*). The variables are called *inputs* (also known as *predictors*, *features*, *explanatory variables*, or *independent variables*) and *targets* (also known as a *response*, *outcome*, or *dependent variable*). For a given case, the inputs reflect your state of knowledge before measuring the target.

The measurement scale of the inputs and the target can be varied. The inputs and the target can be numeric variables, such as **income**. They can be nominal variables, such as **occupation**. They are often binary variables, such as a positive or negative response concerning home ownership.

Copyright © 2011, SAS Institute Inc., Cary, North Carolina, USA. ALL RIGHTS RESERVED.

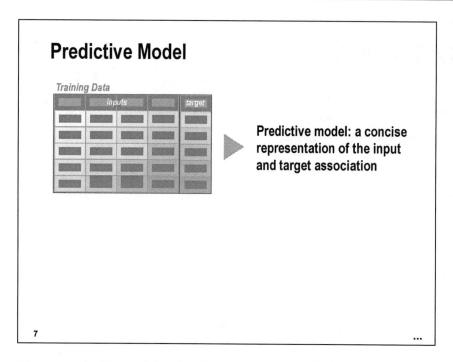

The purpose of the training data is to generate a predictive model. The *predictive model* is a concise representation of the association between the inputs and the target variables.

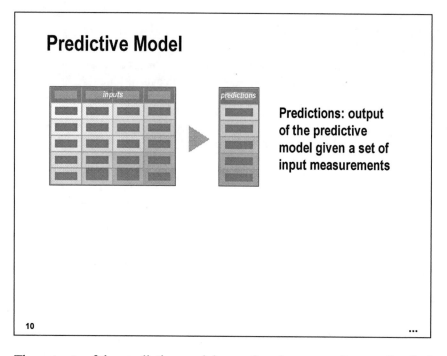

The outputs of the predictive model are referred to as *predictions*. Predictions represent your best guess for the target given a set of input measurements. The predictions are based on the associations **learned** from the training data by the predictive model.

Copyright © 2011, SAS Institute Inc., Cary, North Carolina, USA. ALL RIGHTS RESERVED.

Modeling Essentials

▶ **Predict new cases.**

▶ **Select useful inputs.**

▶ **Optimize complexity.**

12   ...

Predictive models are widely used and are available in many varieties. Any model, however, must perform three essential tasks:

- provide a rule to transform a measurement into a prediction
- have a means of choosing useful inputs from a potentially vast number of candidates
- be able to adjust its complexity to compensate for noisy training data

The following slides illustrate the general principles involved in each of these essentials. Later sections of the course detail the approach used by specific modeling tools.

Modeling Essentials

▶ **Predict new cases.**

▶ Select useful inputs.

▶ Optimize complexity.

13   ...

The process of predicting new cases is examined first.

Copyright © 2011, SAS Institute Inc., Cary, North Carolina, USA. ALL RIGHTS RESERVED.

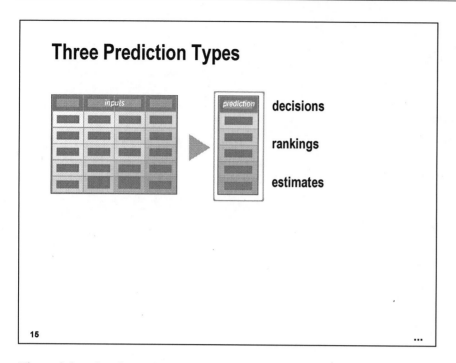

The training data is used to construct a model (rule) that relates the input variables to the original target variable. The predictions can be categorized into three distinct types:

- decisions
- rankings
- estimates

Copyright © 2011, SAS Institute Inc., Cary, North Carolina, USA. ALL RIGHTS RESERVED.

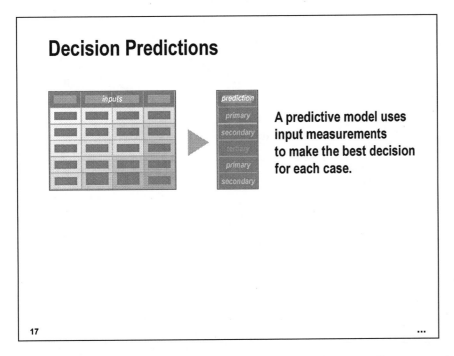

Decision Predictions

A predictive model uses input measurements to make the best decision for each case.

17

The simplest type of prediction is the *decision*. Decisions usually are associated with some type of action (such as classifying a case as a donor or a non-donor). For this reason, decisions are also known as *classifications*. Decision prediction examples include handwriting recognition, fraud detection, and direct mail solicitation.

Decision predictions usually relate to a categorical target variable. For this reason, they are identified as primary, secondary, and tertiary in correspondence with the levels of the target.

 By default, model assessment in SAS Enterprise Miner assumes decision predictions when the target variable has a categorical measurement level (binary, nominal, or ordinal).

Copyright © 2011, SAS Institute Inc., Cary, North Carolina, USA. ALL RIGHTS RESERVED.

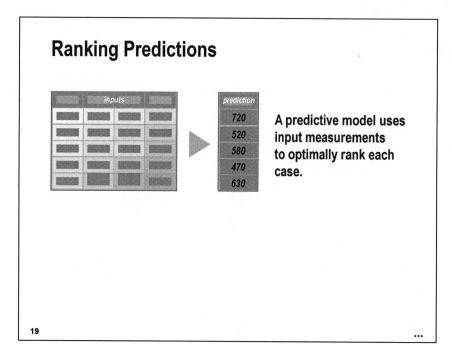

Ranking predictions order cases based on the input variables' relationships with the target variable. Using the training data, the prediction model attempts to rank **high value** cases higher than **low value** cases. It is assumed that a similar pattern exists in the scoring data so that **high value** cases have high scores. The actual, produced scores are inconsequential; only the relative order is important. The most common example of a ranking prediction is a credit score.

     Ranking predictions can be transformed into decision predictions by taking the primary decision for cases above a certain threshold while making secondary and tertiary decisions for cases below the correspondingly lower thresholds. In credit scoring, cases with a credit score above 700 can be called good risks; those with a score between 600 and 700 can be intermediate risks; and those below 600 can be considered poor risks.

Copyright © 2011, SAS Institute Inc., Cary, North Carolina, USA. ALL RIGHTS RESERVED.

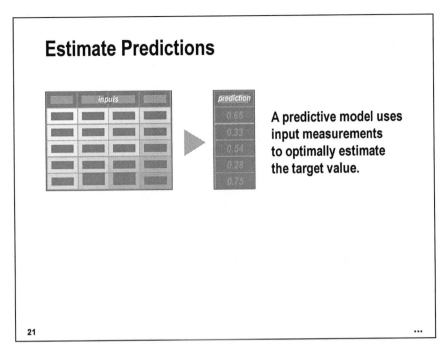

Estimate Predictions

A predictive model uses input measurements to optimally estimate the target value.

21

Estimate predictions approximate the expected value of the target, conditioned on the input values. For cases with numeric targets, this number can be thought of as the average value of the target for all cases having the observed input measurements. For cases with categorical targets, this number might equal the probability of a particular target outcome.

Prediction estimates are most commonly used when their values are integrated into a mathematical expression. An example is two-stage modeling, where the probability of an event is combined with an estimate of profit or loss to form an estimate of unconditional expected profit or loss. Prediction estimates are also useful when you are not certain of the ultimate application of the model.

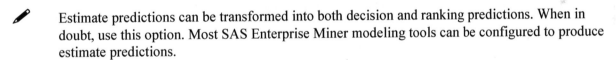 Estimate predictions can be transformed into both decision and ranking predictions. When in doubt, use this option. Most SAS Enterprise Miner modeling tools can be configured to produce estimate predictions.

Copyright © 2011, SAS Institute Inc., Cary, North Carolina, USA. ALL RIGHTS RESERVED.

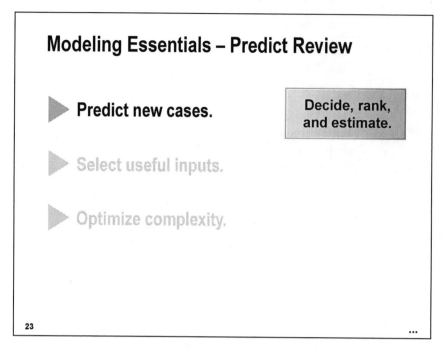

To summarize the first model essential, when a model predicts a new case, the model generates a decision, a rank, or an estimate.

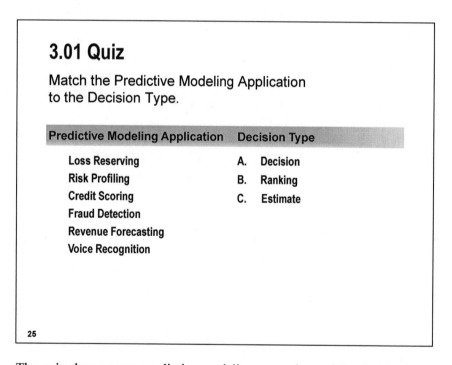

The quiz shows some predictive modeling examples and the decision types.

Copyright © 2011, SAS Institute Inc., Cary, North Carolina, USA. ALL RIGHTS RESERVED.

Modeling Essentials

▶ Predict new cases.

▶ **Select useful inputs.**

▶ Optimize complexity.

27   ...

Consider the task of selecting useful inputs.

Copyright © 2011, SAS Institute Inc., Cary, North Carolina, USA. ALL RIGHTS RESERVED.

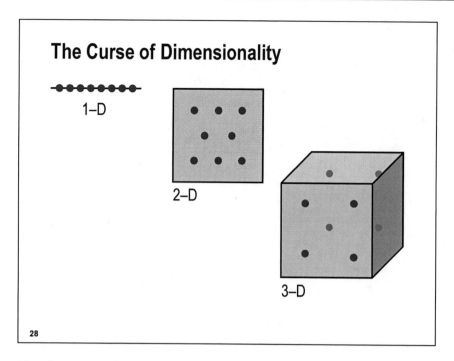

The *dimension* of a problem refers to the number of input variables (more accurately, *degrees of freedom*) that are available for creating a prediction. Data mining problems are often massive in dimension.

The *curse of dimensionality* refers to the exponential increase in data required to densely populate space as the dimension increases. For example, the eight points fill the one-dimensional space but become more separated as the dimension increases. In a 100-dimensional space, they would be similar to distant galaxies.

The curse of dimensionality limits your practical ability to fit a flexible model to noisy data (real data) when there are a large number of input variables. A densely populated input space is required to fit highly complex models. When you assess how much data is available for data mining, you must consider the dimension of the problem.

3.02 Quiz

How many inputs are in your modeling data?
Mark your selection in the polling area.

Copyright © 2011, SAS Institute Inc., Cary, North Carolina, USA. ALL RIGHTS RESERVED.

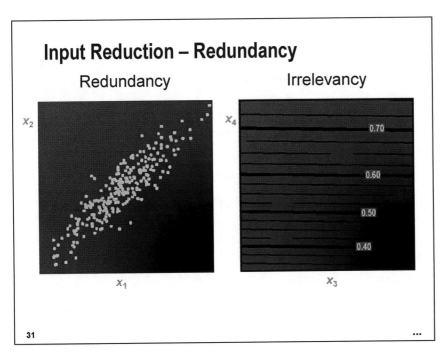

Input selection, that is, reducing the number of inputs, is the obvious way to thwart the curse of dimensionality. Unfortunately, reducing the dimension is also an easy way to disregard important information.

The two principal reasons for eliminating a variable are redundancy and irrelevancy.

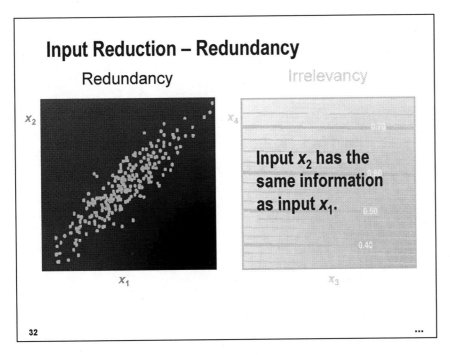

A *redundant* input does not give any new information that was not already explained by other inputs. In the example above, knowing the value of input x_1 gives you a good idea of the value of x_2.

For decision tree models, the modeling algorithm makes input redundancy a relatively minor issue. For other modeling tools, input redundancy requires more elaborate methods to mitigate the problem.

Copyright © 2011, SAS Institute Inc., Cary, North Carolina, USA. ALL RIGHTS RESERVED.

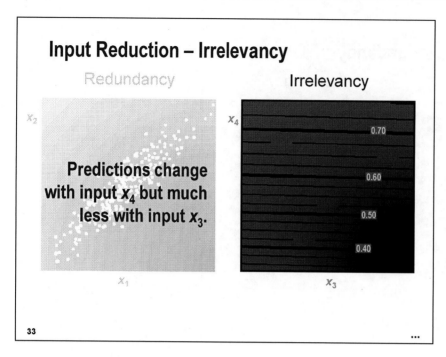

An *irrelevant* input does not provide information about the target. In the example above, predictions change with input x_4, but not with input x_3.

For decision tree models, the modeling algorithm automatically ignores irrelevant inputs. Other modeling methods must be modified or rely on additional tools to properly deal with irrelevant inputs.

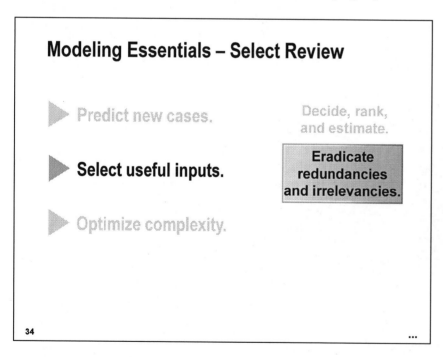

To thwart the curse of dimensionality, a model must select useful inputs. You can do this by eradicating redundant and irrelevant inputs (or more positively, by selecting an independent set of inputs that are correlated with the target).

Copyright © 2011, SAS Institute Inc., Cary, North Carolina, USA. ALL RIGHTS RESERVED.

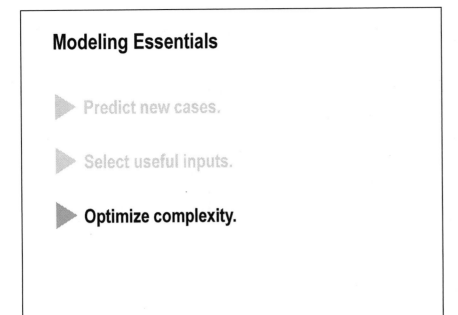

Modeling Essentials

▷ Predict new cases.

▷ Select useful inputs.

▶ **Optimize complexity.**

36

Finally, consider the task of optimizing model complexity.

Copyright © 2011, SAS Institute Inc., Cary, North Carolina, USA. ALL RIGHTS RESERVED.

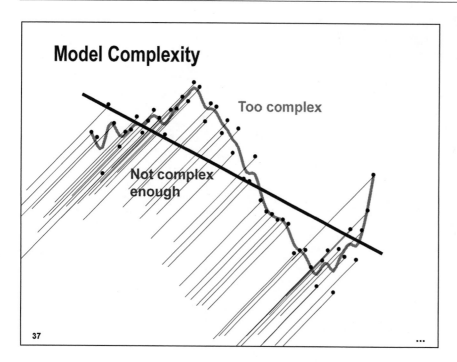

Fitting a model to data requires searching through the space of possible models. Constructing a model with good generalization requires choosing the right complexity.

Selecting model complexity involves a trade-off between bias and variance. An insufficiently complex model might not be flexible enough, which can lead to *underfitting*, that is, systematically missing the signal (high bias).

A naïve modeler might assume that the most complex model should always outperform the others, but this is not the case. An overly complex model might be too flexible, which can lead to *overfitting*, that is, accommodating nuances of the random noise in the particular sample (high variance). A model with the right amount of flexibility gives the best generalization.

Copyright © 2011, SAS Institute Inc., Cary, North Carolina, USA. ALL RIGHTS RESERVED.

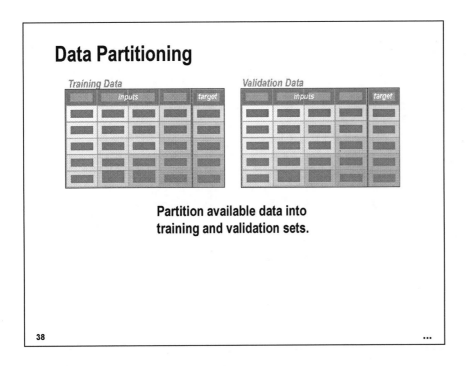

A quote from the popular introductory data analysis textbook *Data Analysis and Regression* by Mosteller and Tukey (1977) captures the difficulty of properly estimating model complexity.

> "Testing the procedure on the data that gave it birth is almost certain to overestimate performance, for the optimizing process that chose it from among many possible procedures will have made the greatest use of any and all idiosyncrasies of those particular data...."

In predictive modeling, the standard strategy for honest assessment of model performance is *data splitting*. A portion is used for fitting the model, that is, the training data set. The remaining data is separated for empirical validation.

The *validation data set* is used for monitoring and tuning the model to improve its generalization. The tuning process usually involves selecting among models of different types and complexities. The tuning process optimizes the selected model on the validation data.

 Because the validation data is used to select from a set of related models, reported performance will, on the average, be overstated. Consequently, a further holdout sample is needed for a final, unbiased assessment. The *test data set* has only one use, that is, to give a final honest estimate of generalization. Consequently, cases in the test set must be treated in the same way that new data would be treated. The cases cannot be involved in any way in the determination of the fitted prediction model. In practice, many analysts see no need for a final honest assessment of generalization. An optimal model is chosen using the validation data, and the model assessment measured on the validation data is reported as an upper bound on the performance expected when the model is deployed.

With small or moderate data sets, data splitting is inefficient; the reduced sample size can severely degrade the fit of the model. Computer-intensive methods, such as the *cross validation* and *bootstrap* methods, were developed so that all the data can be used for both fitting and honest assessment. However, data mining usually has the luxury of massive data sets.

Copyright © 2011, SAS Institute Inc., Cary, North Carolina, USA. ALL RIGHTS RESERVED.

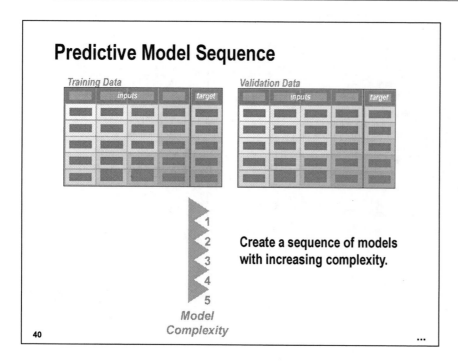

In SAS Enterprise Miner, the strategy for choosing model complexity is to build a sequence of similar models using the training component only. The models are usually ordered with increasing complexity.

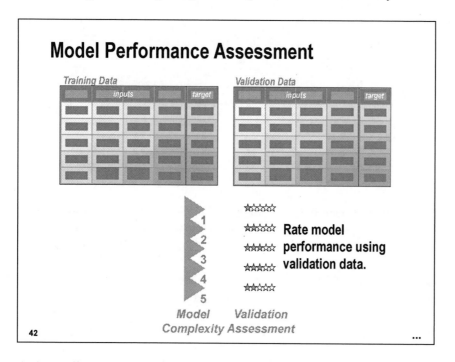

As Mosteller and Tukey caution in the earlier quotation, using performance on the training data set usually leads to selecting a model that is too complex. (The classic example is selecting linear regression models based on R square.) To avoid this problem, SAS Enterprise Miner selects the model from the sequence based on validation data performance.

Copyright © 2011, SAS Institute Inc., Cary, North Carolina, USA. ALL RIGHTS RESERVED.

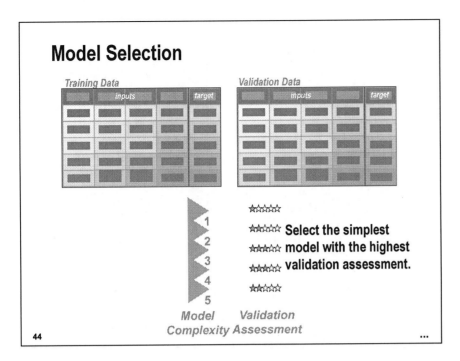

In keeping with Ockham's razor, the best model is the simplest model with the highest validation performance.

Copyright © 2011, SAS Institute Inc., Cary, North Carolina, USA. ALL RIGHTS RESERVED.

Modeling Essentials – Optimize Review

Predict new cases.

Select useful inputs.

Optimize complexity.

Decide, rank, and estimate.

Eradicate redundancies and irrelevancies.

Tune models with validation data.

46

...

To avoid overfitting (and underfitting) a predictive model, you should calibrate its performance with an independent validation sample. You can perform the calibration by partitioning the data into training and validation samples.

In Chapter 2, you assigned roles and measurement levels to the **PVA97NK** data set and created an analysis diagram and a simple process flow. In the following demonstration, you partition the raw data into training and validation components. This sets the stage for using the Decision Tree tool to generate a predictive model.

Copyright © 2011, SAS Institute Inc., Cary, North Carolina, USA. ALL RIGHTS RESERVED.

Creating Training and Validation Data

A critical step in prediction is choosing among competing models. Given a set of training data, you can easily generate models that very accurately predict a target value from a set of input values. Unfortunately, these predictions might be accurate only for the training data itself. Attempts to generalize the predictions from the training data to an independent, but similarly distributed, sample can result in substantial accuracy reductions.

To avoid this pitfall, SAS Enterprise Miner is designed to use a *validation data set* as a means of independently gauging model performance. Typically, the validation data set is created by partitioning the raw analysis data. Cases selected for training are used to build the model, and cases selected for validation are used to tune and compare models.

  SAS Enterprise Miner also enables the creation of a third partition, named the *test data set*. The test data set is meant for obtaining unbiased estimates of model performance from a single selected model.

This demonstration assumes that you completed the demonstrations in Chapter 2.

Copyright © 2011, SAS Institute Inc., Cary, North Carolina, USA. ALL RIGHTS RESERVED.

Your SAS Enterprise Miner workspace should appear as shown below:

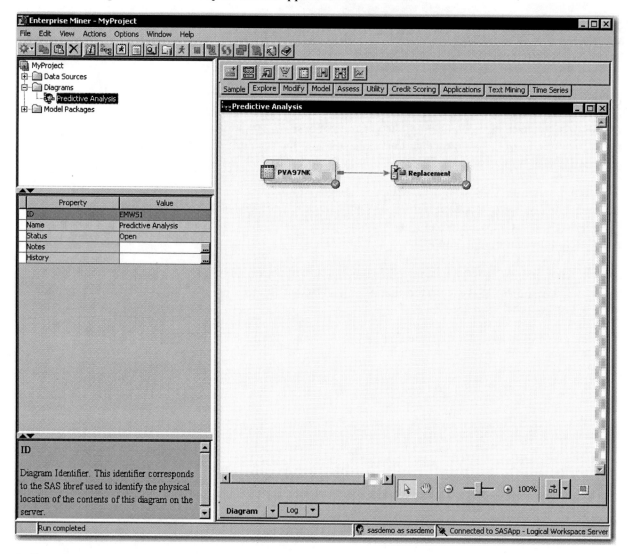

Follow these steps to partition the raw data into training and validation sets:

1. Select the **Sample** tool tab. The Data Partition tool is the second from the left.

2. Drag a **Data Partition** tool into the diagram workspace, next to the Replacement node.

3. Connect the **Replacement** node to the **Data Partition** node.

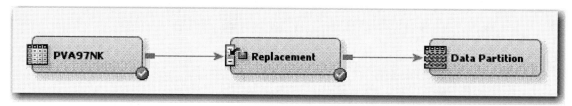

Copyright © 2011, SAS Institute Inc., Cary, North Carolina, USA. ALL RIGHTS RESERVED.

4. Select the **Data Partition** node and examine its Properties panel.

Property	Value	
General		
Node ID	Part	
Imported Data		[...]
Exported Data		[...]
Notes		[...]
Train		
Variables		[...]
Output Type	Data	
Partitioning Method	Default	
Random Seed	12345	
⊟ Data Set Allocations		
Training	40.0	
Validation	30.0	
Test	30.0	
Report		
Interval Targets	Yes	
Class Targets	Yes	

Use the Properties panel to select the fraction of data devoted to the Training, Validation, and Test partitions. By default, less than half the available data is used for generating the predictive models.

> ✎ There is a trade-off in various partitioning strategies. More data devoted to training results in more stable predictive models, but less stable model assessments (and vice versa). Also, the Test partition is used only for calculating fit statistics after the modeling and model selection is complete. Many analysts regard this as wasteful of data.
>
> A typical partitioning compromise foregoes a Test partition and places an equal number of cases in Training and Validation.

5. Type **50** as the Training value in the Data Partition node.

6. Type **50** as the Validation value in the Data Partition node.

7. Type **0** as the Test value in the Data Partition node.

⊟ Data Set Allocations	
Training	50.0
Validation	50.0
Test	0.0

> ✎ With smaller raw data sets, model stability can become an important issue. In this case, increasing the number of cases devoted to the Training partition is a reasonable course of action.

8. Right-click the **Data Partition** node and select **Run**.

Copyright © 2011, SAS Institute Inc., Cary, North Carolina, USA. ALL RIGHTS RESERVED.

9. Select **Yes** in the Confirmation window. SAS Enterprise Miner runs the Data Partition node.

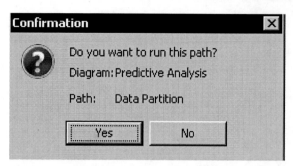

Only the Data Partition node should run, because it is the only "new" element in the process flow. In general, SAS Enterprise Miner only runs elements of diagrams that are new or that are affected by changes earlier in the process flow.

When the Data Partition process is complete, a Run Status window appears.

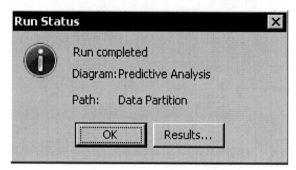

Copyright © 2011, SAS Institute Inc., Cary, North Carolina, USA. ALL RIGHTS RESERVED.

10. Select **Results** in the Run Status window to view the results.

The Results - Node: Data Partition window provides a basic metadata summary of the raw data that feeds the node and, more importantly, a frequency table that shows the distribution of the target variable, **TARGET_B**, in the raw, training, and validation data sets.

```
Summary Statistics for Class Targets

Data=DATA

               Numeric    Formatted    Frequency
Variable        Value       Value        Count      Percent        Label

TARGET_B          0           0           4843         50       Target Gift Flag
TARGET_B          1           1           4843         50       Target Gift Flag


Data=TRAIN

               Numeric    Formatted    Frequency
Variable        Value       Value        Count      Percent        Label

TARGET_B          0           0           2422       50.0103     Target Gift Flag
TARGET_B          1           1           2421       49.9897     Target Gift Flag


Data=VALIDATE

               Numeric    Formatted    Frequency
Variable        Value       Value        Count      Percent        Label

TARGET_B          0           0           2421       49.9897     Target Gift Flag
TARGET_B          1           1           2422       50.0103     Target Gift Flag
```

The Partition node attempts to maintain the proportion of zeros and ones in the Training and Validation partitions. The proportions are not exactly the same due to an odd number of zeros' and ones' cases in the raw data.

The analysis data was selected and partitioned. You are ready to build predictive models.

Copyright © 2011, SAS Institute Inc., Cary, North Carolina, USA. ALL RIGHTS RESERVED.

3.2 Cultivating Decision Trees

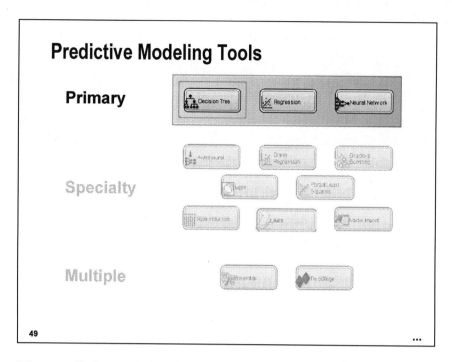

Many predictive modeling tools are found in SAS Enterprise Miner. The tools can be loosely grouped into three categories: primary, specialty, and multiple models. The *primary* tools interface with the three most commonly used predictive modeling methods: decision tree, regression, and neural network.

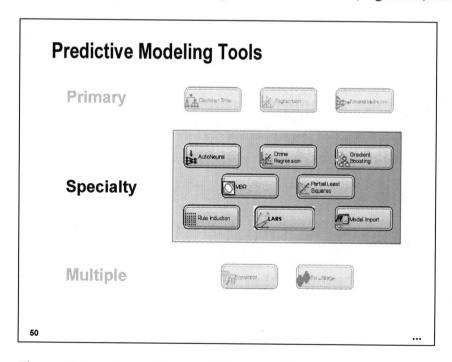

The *specialty* tools are either specializations of the primary tools or tools designed to solve specific problem types.

Copyright © 2011, SAS Institute Inc., Cary, North Carolina, USA. ALL RIGHTS RESERVED.

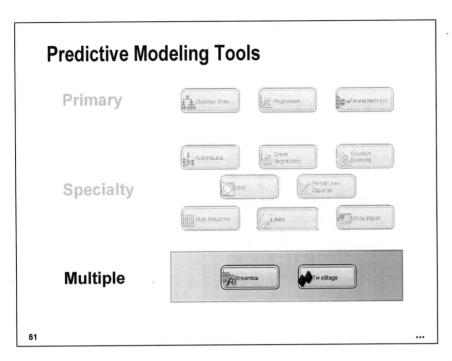

Multiple model tools are used to combine or produce more than one predictive model. The Ensemble tool is briefly described in a later chapter. The Two Stage tool is discussed in the Advanced Predictive Modeling Using SAS® Enterprise Miner™ course.

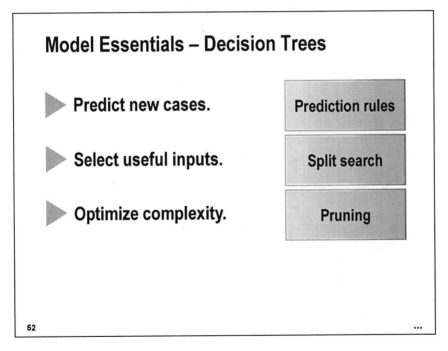

Decision trees provide an excellent introduction to predictive modeling. Decision trees, similar to all modeling methods described in this course, address each of the modeling essentials described in the introduction. Cases are scored using *prediction rules*. A *split-search* algorithm facilitates input selection. Model complexity is addressed by *pruning*.

The following simple prediction problem illustrates each of these model essentials:

Copyright © 2011, SAS Institute Inc., Cary, North Carolina, USA. ALL RIGHTS RESERVED.

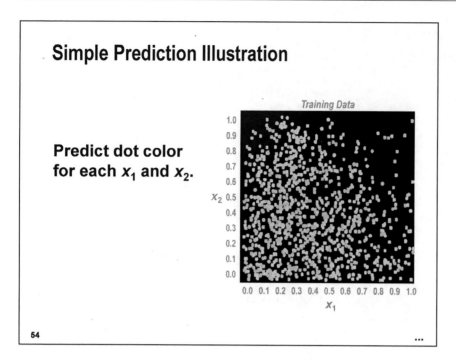

Consider a data set with two inputs and a binary target. The inputs, x_1 and x_2, locate the case in the unit square. The target outcome is represented by a color; yellow is primary and blue is secondary. The analysis goal is to predict the outcome based on the location in the unit square.

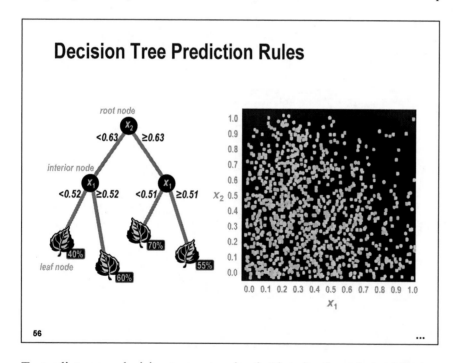

To predict cases, decision trees use rules that involve the values of the input variables.

The rules are arranged hierarchically in a tree-like structure with nodes connected by lines. The nodes represent decision rules, and the lines order the rules. The first rule, at the base (top) of the tree, is named the *root node*. Subsequent rules are named *interior nodes*. Nodes with only one connection are *leaf nodes*.

Copyright © 2011, SAS Institute Inc., Cary, North Carolina, USA. ALL RIGHTS RESERVED.

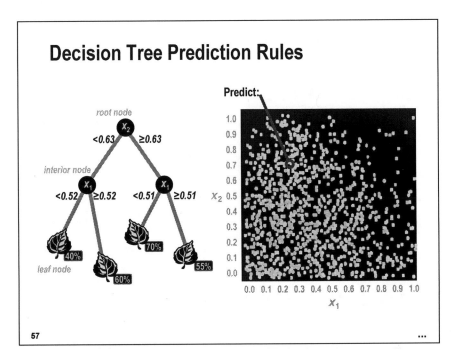

To score a new case, examine the input values and apply the rules defined by the decision tree.

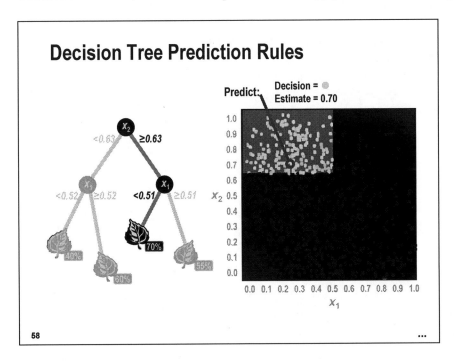

The input values of a new case eventually lead to a single leaf in the tree. A tree leaf provides a decision (for example, classify as yellow) and an estimate (for example, the primary-target proportion).

Copyright © 2011, SAS Institute Inc., Cary, North Carolina, USA. ALL RIGHTS RESERVED.

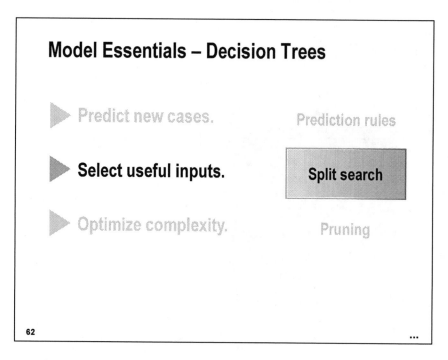

To select useful inputs, trees use a *split-search* algorithm. Decision trees confront the curse of dimensionality by ignoring irrelevant inputs.

 Curiously, trees have no built-in method for ignoring redundant inputs. Because trees can be trained quickly and have a simple structure, this is usually not an issue for model creation. However, it can be an issue for model deployment, in that trees might somewhat arbitrarily select from a set of correlated inputs. To avoid this problem, you must use an algorithm that is external to the tree to manage input redundancy.

Copyright © 2011, SAS Institute Inc., Cary, North Carolina, USA. ALL RIGHTS RESERVED.

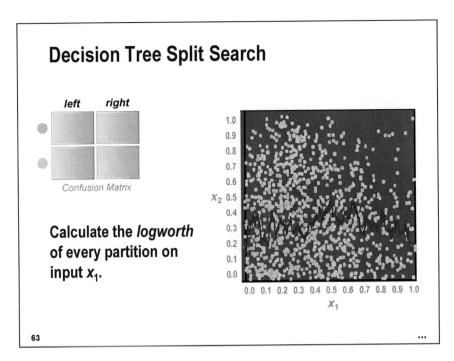

Understanding the default algorithm for building trees enables you to better use the Tree tool and interpret your results. The description presented here assumes a binary target, but the algorithm for interval targets is similar. (The algorithm for categorical targets with more than two outcomes is more complicated and is not discussed.)

The first part of the algorithm is called the *split search*. The split search starts by selecting an input for partitioning the available training data. If the measurement scale of the selected input is *interval*, each unique value serves as a potential split point for the data. If the input is *categorical*, the average value of the target is taken within each categorical input level. The averages serve the same role as the unique interval input values in the discussion that follows.

For a selected input and fixed split point, two groups are generated. Cases with input values less than the split point are said to *branch left*. Cases with input values greater than the split point are said to *branch right*. The groups, combined with the target outcomes, form a 2x2 contingency table with columns specifying branch direction (left or right) and rows specifying target value (0 or 1). A Pearson chi-squared statistic is used to quantify the independence of counts in the table's columns. Large values for the chi-squared statistic suggest that the proportion of zeros and ones in the left branch is different than the proportion in the right branch. A large difference in outcome proportions indicates a good split.

Because the Pearson chi-squared statistic can be applied to the case of multiway splits and multi-outcome targets, the statistic is converted to a probability value or *p*-value. The *p*-value indicates the likelihood of obtaining the observed value of the statistic assuming identical target proportions in each branch direction. For large data sets, these *p*-values can be very close to zero. For this reason, the quality of a split is reported by *logworth* = -*log*(chi-squared *p*-value).

     At least one logworth must exceed a threshold for a split to occur with that input. By default, this threshold corresponds to a chi-squared *p*-value of 0.20 or a logworth of approximately 0.7.

Copyright © 2011, SAS Institute Inc., Cary, North Carolina, USA. ALL RIGHTS RESERVED.

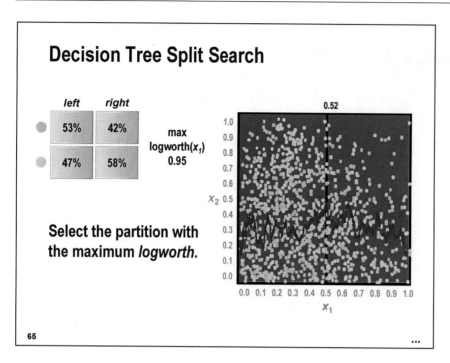

The best split for an input is the split that yields the highest logworth.

Copyright © 2011, SAS Institute Inc., Cary, North Carolina, USA. ALL RIGHTS RESERVED.

Additional Split-Search Details (Self Study)

Several peripheral factors make the split search somewhat more complicated than what is described above.

First, the tree algorithm settings disallow certain partitions of the data. Settings, such as the minimum number of observations required for a split search and the minimum number of observations in a leaf, force a minimum number of cases in a split partition. This minimum number of cases reduces the number of potential partitions for each input in the split search.

Second, when you calculate the independence of columns in a contingency table, it is possible to obtain significant (large) values of the chi-squared statistic even when there are no differences in the outcome proportions between split branches. As the number of possible split points increases, the likelihood of obtaining significant values also increases. In this way, an input with a multitude of unique input values has a greater chance of accidentally having a large logworth than an input with only a few distinct input values.

Statisticians face a similar problem when they combine the results from multiple statistical tests. As the number of tests increases, the chance of a false positive result likewise increases. To maintain overall confidence in the statistical findings, statisticians inflate the p-values of each test by a factor equal to the number of tests being conducted. If an inflated p-value shows a significant result, then the significance of the overall results is assured. This type of p-value adjustment is known as a *Bonferroni correction*.

Because each split point corresponds to a statistical test, Bonferroni corrections are automatically applied to the logworth calculations for an input. These corrections, called *Kass adjustments* (named after the inventor of the default tree algorithm used in SAS Enterprise Miner), penalize inputs with many split points by reducing the logworth of a split by an amount equal to the log of the number of distinct input values. This is equivalent to the Bonferroni correction because subtracting this constant from logworth is equivalent to multiplying the corresponding chi-squared p-value by the number of split points. The adjustment enables a fairer comparison of inputs with many and few levels later in the split-search algorithm.

Third, for inputs with missing values, two sets of Kass-adjusted logworths are actually generated. For the first set, cases with missing input values are included in the left branch of the contingency table and logworths are calculated. For the second set of logworths, missing value cases are moved to the right branch. The best split is then selected from the set of possible splits with the missing values in the left and right branches, respectively.

Copyright © 2011, SAS Institute Inc., Cary, North Carolina, USA. ALL RIGHTS RESERVED.

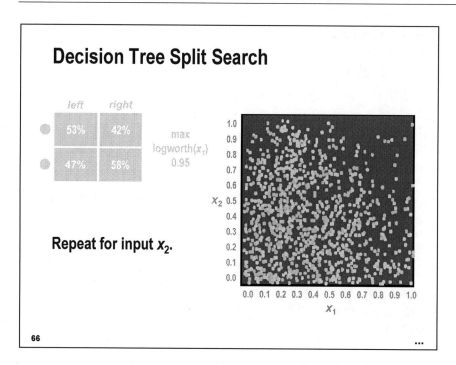

The partitioning process is repeated for every input in the training data. Inputs whose adjusted logworth fails to exceed the threshold are excluded from consideration.

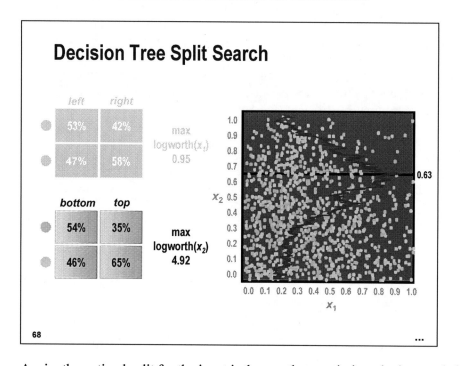

Again, the optimal split for the input is the one that maximizes the logworth function.

Copyright © 2011, SAS Institute Inc., Cary, North Carolina, USA. ALL RIGHTS RESERVED.

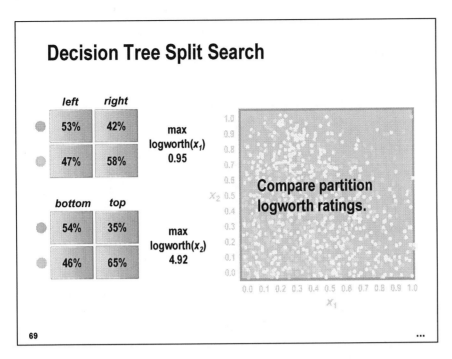

After you determine the best split for every input, the tree algorithm compares each best split's corresponding logworth. The split with the highest adjusted logworth is deemed best.

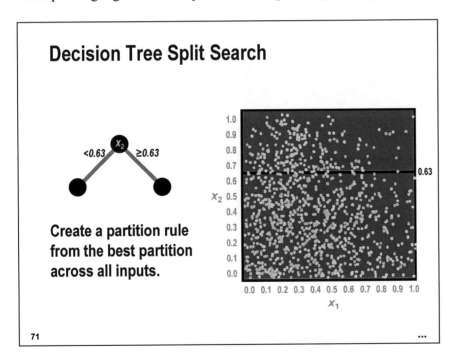

The training data is partitioned using the best split rule.

Copyright © 2011, SAS Institute Inc., Cary, North Carolina, USA. ALL RIGHTS RESERVED.

Decision Tree Split Search

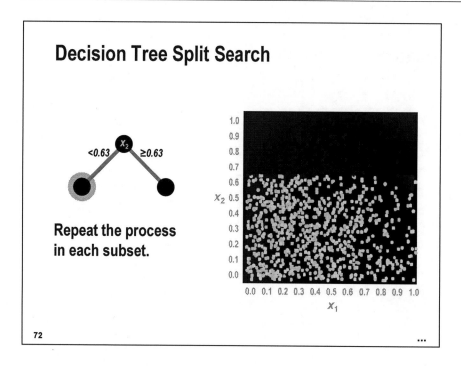

Repeat the process in each subset.

72   ...

Decision Tree Split Search

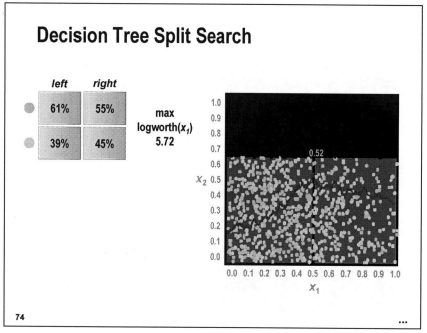

left   right

| 61% | 55% |
| 39% | 45% |

max logworth(x_1) 5.72

74   ...

Copyright © 2011, SAS Institute Inc., Cary, North Carolina, USA. ALL RIGHTS RESERVED.

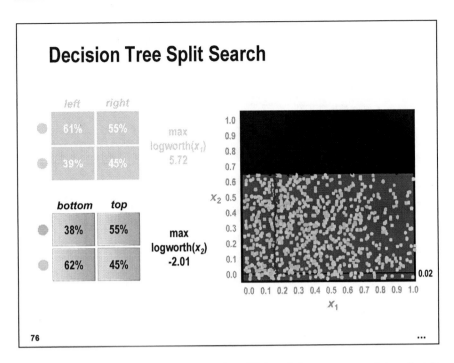

The logworth of the x_2 split is negative. This might seem surprising, but it results from several adjustments made to the logworth calculation. (The Kass adjustment was described previously. Another, called the *depth adjustment*, is outlined in a Self-Study section.)

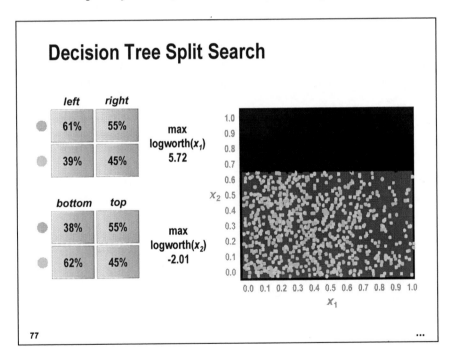

Copyright © 2011, SAS Institute Inc., Cary, North Carolina, USA. ALL RIGHTS RESERVED.

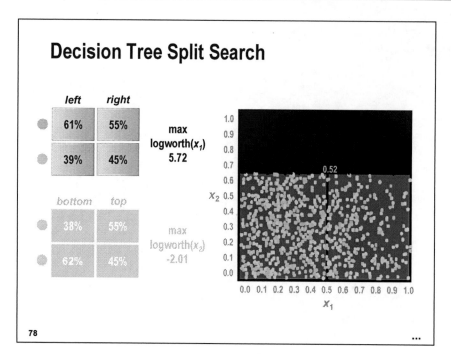

The split search continues within each leaf. Logworths are compared as before.

Additional Split-Search Details (Self-Study)

Because the significance of secondary and subsequent splits depends on the significance of the previous splits, the algorithm again faces a multiple comparison problem. To compensate for this problem, the algorithm increases the threshold by an amount related to the number of splits above the current split. For binary splits, the threshold is increased by $log_{10}(2)\, d \approx 0.3 \cdot d$, where d is the depth of the split on the decision tree.

    By increasing the threshold for each depth (or equivalently decreasing the logworths), the tree algorithm makes it increasingly easy for an input's splits to be excluded from consideration.

Copyright © 2011, SAS Institute Inc., Cary, North Carolina, USA. ALL RIGHTS RESERVED.

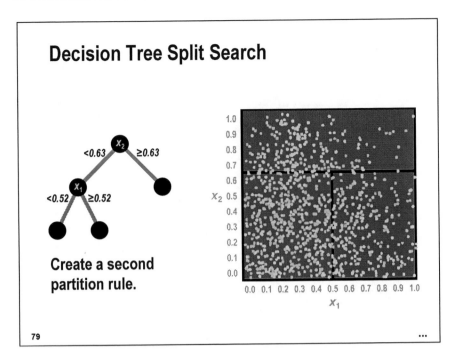

The data is partitioned according to the best split, which creates a second partition rule. The process repeats in each leaf until there are no more splits whose adjusted logworth exceeds the depth-adjusted thresholds. This process completes the split-search portion of the tree algorithm.

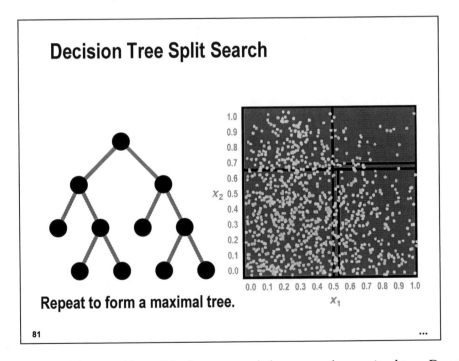

The resulting partition of the input space is known as the *maximal tree*. Development of the maximal tree is based exclusively on statistical measures of split worth on the training data. It is likely that the maximal tree will fail to generalize well on an independent set of validation data.

Copyright © 2011, SAS Institute Inc., Cary, North Carolina, USA. ALL RIGHTS RESERVED.

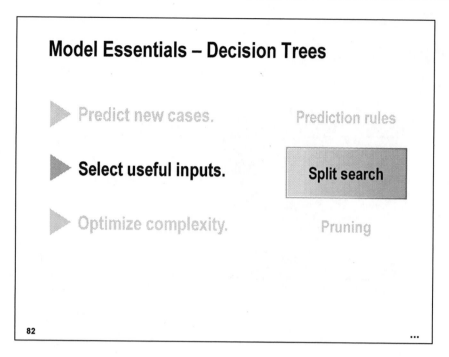

The split-search algorithm can easily cut through the curse of dimensionality and select useful modeling inputs. Because it is simply an algorithm, many variations are possible. (Some variations are discussed at the end of this chapter.)

The demonstration illustrates the use of the split-search algorithm to construct a decision tree model.

Copyright © 2011, SAS Institute Inc., Cary, North Carolina, USA. ALL RIGHTS RESERVED.

Constructing a Decision Tree Predictive Model

This four-part demonstration illustrates the interactive construction of a decision tree model and builds on the process flows of previous demonstrations.

Preparing for Interactive Tree Construction

Follow these steps to prepare the Decision Tree tool for interactive tree construction.

1. Select the **Model** tab. The Decision Tree tool is second from the left.

2. Drag a **Decision Tree** tool into the diagram workspace. Place the node next to the **Data Partition** node.

3. Connect the **Data Partition** node to the **Decision Tree** node.

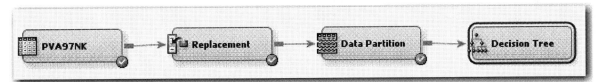

The Decision Tree tool can build predictive models autonomously or interactively. To build a model autonomously, simply run the Decision Tree node. Building models interactively, however, is more informative and is helpful when you first learn about the node, and even when you are more expert at predictive modeling.

Copyright © 2011, SAS Institute Inc., Cary, North Carolina, USA. ALL RIGHTS RESERVED.

4. Select **Interactive** ⇨ [...] from the Decision Tree node's Properties panel.

Property	Value
General	
Node ID	Tree
Imported Data	[...]
Exported Data	[...]
Notes	[...]
Train	
Variables	[...]
Interactive	[...]
Use Frozen Tree	No
Use Multiple Targets	No
⊟ Splitting Rule	
Interval Criterion	ProbF
Nominal Criterion	ProbChisq
Ordinal Criterion	Entropy
Significance Level	0.2
Missing Values	Use in search
Use Input Once	No
Maximum Branch	2
Maximum Depth	6
Minimum Categorical	5
⊟ Node	
Leaf Size	5

Copyright © 2011, SAS Institute Inc., Cary, North Carolina, USA. ALL RIGHTS RESERVED.

The SAS Enterprise Miner Interactive Decision Tree application appears.

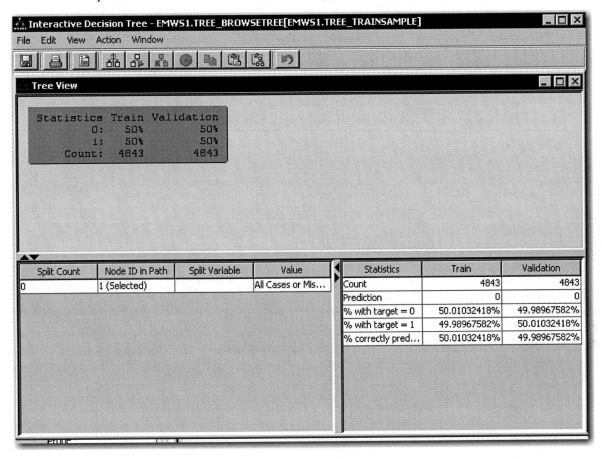

Copyright © 2011, SAS Institute Inc., Cary, North Carolina, USA. ALL RIGHTS RESERVED.

Creating a Splitting Rule

Decision tree models involve recursive partitioning of the training data in an attempt to isolate concentrations of cases with identical target values. The blue box in the Tree window represents the unpartitioned training data. The statistics show the distribution of **Target_B**.

Use the following steps to create an initial splitting rule:

1. Right-click the purple box and select **Split Node** from the menu. The Split Node 1 dialog box appears.

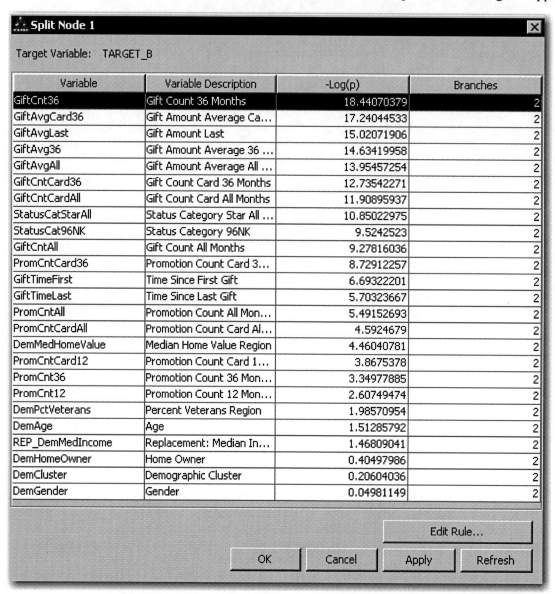

The Split Node dialog box shows the relative value, -Log(p) or *logworth*, of partitioning the training data using the indicated input. As the logworth increases, the partition better isolates cases with identical target values.

Gift Count 36 Months has the highest logworth, followed by **Gift Amount Average Card 36 Months** and **Gift Amount Last**. You can choose to split the data on the selected input or edit the rule for more information.

Copyright © 2011, SAS Institute Inc., Cary, North Carolina, USA. ALL RIGHTS RESERVED.

2. Select **Edit Rule**. The GiftCnt36 - Interval Splitting Rule dialog box appears.

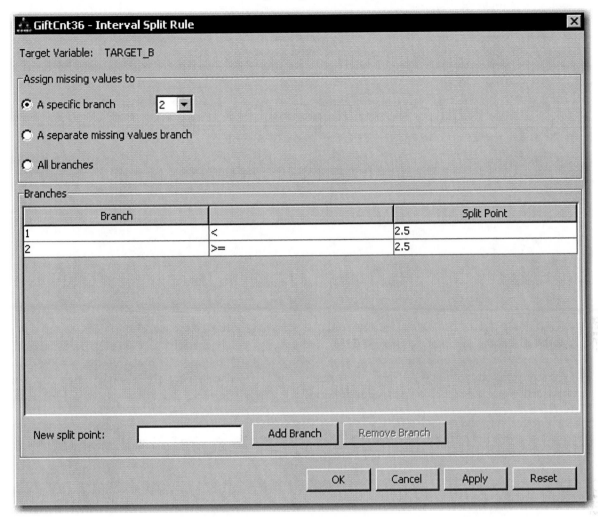

This dialog box shows how the training data is partitioned using the input **Gift Count 36 Months**. Two branches are created. The first branch contains cases with a 36-month gift count less than 2.5, and the second branch contains cases with a 36-month gift count greater than or equal to 2.5. In other words, with cases that have a 36-month gift count of zero, one or two branch left and three or more branch right. In addition, any cases with a missing or unknown 36-month gift count are placed in the first branch.

 The interactive tree assigns any cases with missing values to the branch that maximizes the purity or logworth of the split by default. For **GiftCnt36**, this rule assigns cases with missing values to branch 2.

Copyright © 2011, SAS Institute Inc., Cary, North Carolina, USA. ALL RIGHTS RESERVED.

3. Select **Apply**. The GiftCnt36 - Interval Splitting Rule dialog box remains open, and the Tree View window is updated.

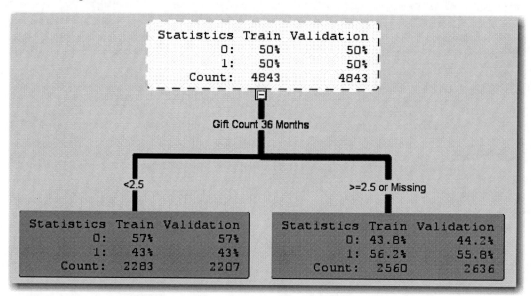

The training data is partitioned into two subsets. The first subset, corresponding to cases with a 36-month gift count less than 2.5, has a higher than average concentration of **TARGET_B**=0 cases. The second subset, corresponding to cases with a 36-month gift count greater than 2.5, has a higher than average concentration of **TARGET_B**=1 cases. The second branch has slightly more cases than the first, which is indicated by the **N in node** field.

The partition of the data also represents your first (non-trivial) predictive model. This model assigns to all cases in the left branch a predicted **TARGET_B** value equal to 0.43 and to all cases in the right branch a predicted **TARGET_B** value equal to 0.56.

     In general, decision tree predictive models assign all cases in a leaf the same predicted target value. For binary targets, this equals the percentage of cases in the target variable's primary outcome (usually the **target=1** outcome).

Copyright © 2011, SAS Institute Inc., Cary, North Carolina, USA. ALL RIGHTS RESERVED.

Adding More Splits

Use the following steps to interactively add more splits to the decision tree:

1. Select the lower left partition. The Split Node dialog box is updated to show the possible partition variables and their respective logworths.

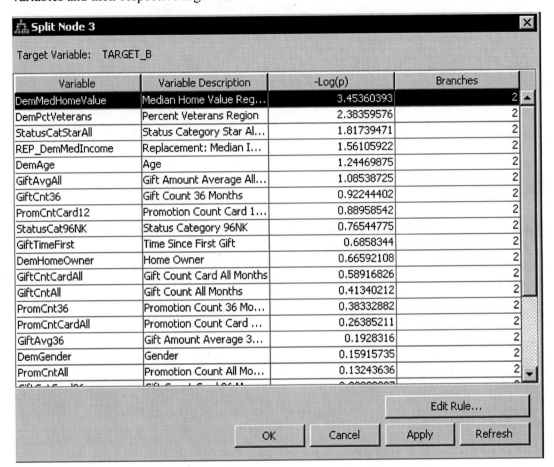

The input with the highest logworth is **Median Home Value Region**.

Copyright © 2011, SAS Institute Inc., Cary, North Carolina, USA. ALL RIGHTS RESERVED.

2. Select **Edit Rule**. The DemMedHomeValue - Interval Splitting Rule dialog box appears.

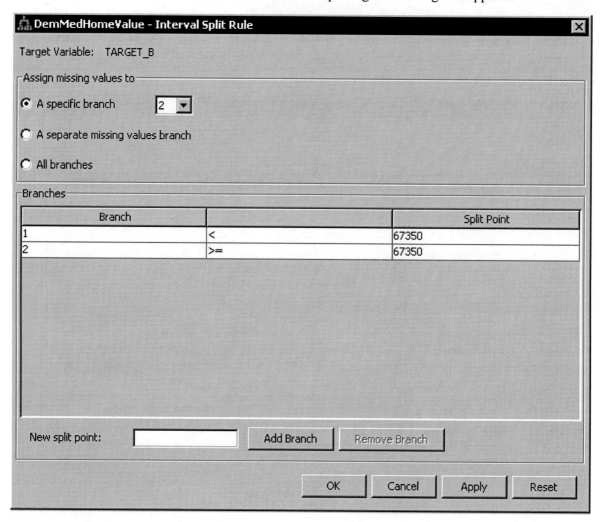

Branch 1 contains all cases with a median home value less than 67350. Branch 2 contains all cases that are equal to or greater than 67350.

Copyright © 2011, SAS Institute Inc., Cary, North Carolina, USA. ALL RIGHTS RESERVED.

3. Select **Apply**. The Tree View window is updated to show the additional split.

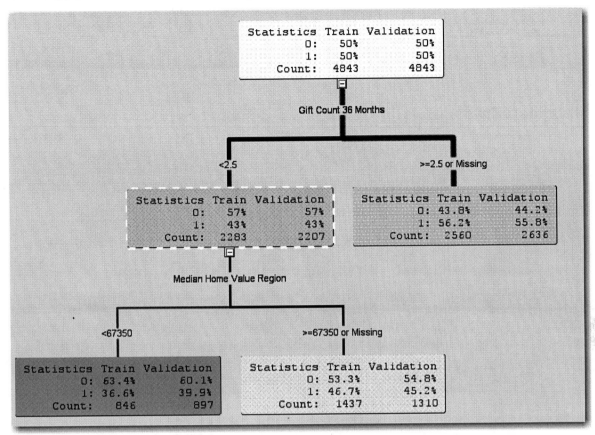

Both left and right leaves contain a lower-than-average proportion of cases with **TARGET_B**=1.

4. Repeat the process for the branch that corresponds to cases with **Gift Count 36 Month** in excess of 2.5.

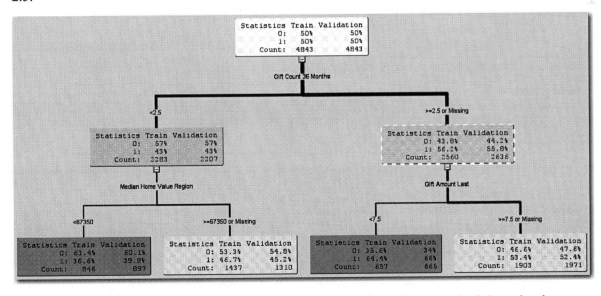

The right-branch cases are split using the **Gift Amount Last** input. This time, both branches have a higher-than-average concentration of **TARGET_B**=1 cases.

Copyright © 2011, SAS Institute Inc., Cary, North Carolina, USA. ALL RIGHTS RESERVED.

It is important to remember that the logworth of each split, reported above, and the predicted **TARGET_B** values are generated using the *training data only*. The main focus is on selecting useful input variables for the first predictive model. A diminishing marginal usefulness of input variables is expected, given the split-search discussion at the beginning of this chapter. This prompts the question: Where do you stop splitting? The validation data provides the necessary information to answer this question.

Changing a Splitting Rule

The bottom left split on **Median Home Value** at 67350 was found to be optimal in a statistical sense, but it might seem strange to someone simply looking at the tree. (Why not split at the more socially acceptable value of 70000?) You can use the Splitting Rule window to edit where a split occurs.

Use the following steps to define your own splitting rule for an input.

1. Select the node above the label **Median Home Value Region**.

2. Right-click this node and select **Split Node** from the menu. The Split Node window appears.

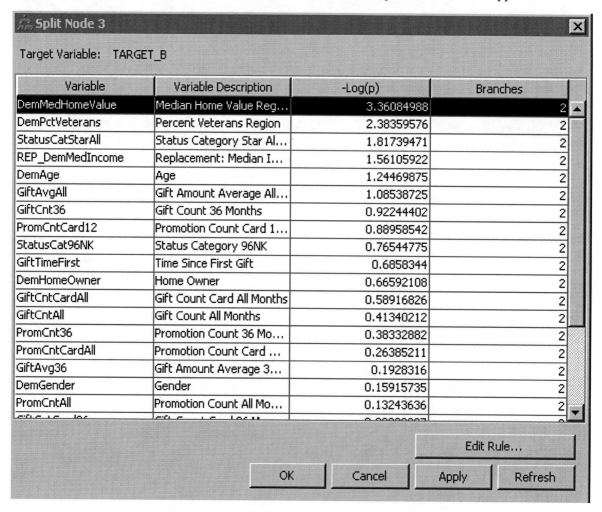

Variable	Variable Description	-Log(p)	Branches
DemMedHomeValue	Median Home Value Reg...	3.36084988	2
DemPctVeterans	Percent Veterans Region	2.38359576	2
StatusCatStarAll	Status Category Star Al...	1.81739471	2
REP_DemMedIncome	Replacement: Median I...	1.56105922	2
DemAge	Age	1.24469875	2
GiftAvgAll	Gift Amount Average All...	1.08538725	2
GiftCnt36	Gift Count 36 Months	0.92244402	2
PromCntCard12	Promotion Count Card 1...	0.88958542	2
StatusCat96NK	Status Category 96NK	0.76544775	2
GiftTimeFirst	Time Since First Gift	0.6858344	2
DemHomeOwner	Home Owner	0.66592108	2
GiftCntCardAll	Gift Count Card All Months	0.58916826	2
GiftCntAll	Gift Count All Months	0.41340212	2
PromCnt36	Promotion Count 36 Mo...	0.38332882	2
PromCntCardAll	Promotion Count Card ...	0.26385211	2
GiftAvg36	Gift Amount Average 3...	0.1928316	2
DemGender	Gender	0.15915735	2
PromCntAll	Promotion Count All Mo...	0.13243636	2

Copyright © 2011, SAS Institute Inc., Cary, North Carolina, USA. ALL RIGHTS RESERVED.

3. Select **Edit Rule**. The DemMedHomeValue - Interval Splitting Rule dialog box appears.

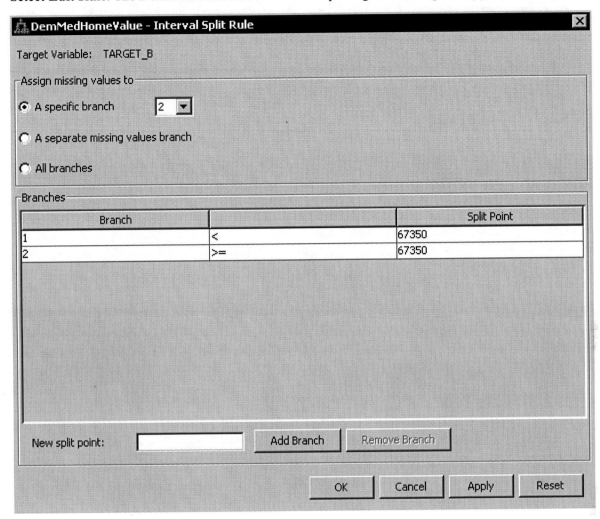

Copyright © 2011, SAS Institute Inc., Cary, North Carolina, USA. ALL RIGHTS RESERVED.

4. Type **70000** in the **New split point** field.

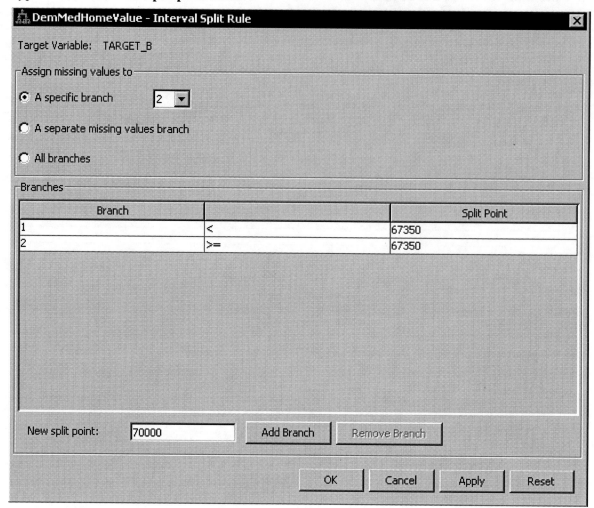

Copyright © 2011, SAS Institute Inc., Cary, North Carolina, USA. ALL RIGHTS RESERVED.

5. Select **Add Branch**. The Interval Splitting Rule dialog box shows three branches.

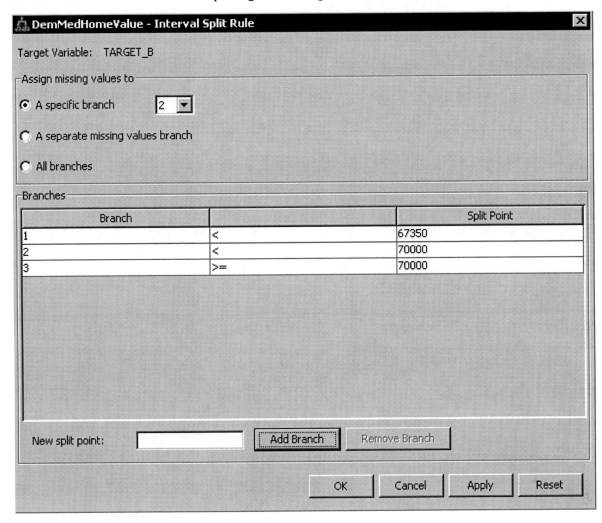

Copyright © 2011, SAS Institute Inc., Cary, North Carolina, USA. ALL RIGHTS RESERVED.

6. Select **Branch 1** by highlighting the row.

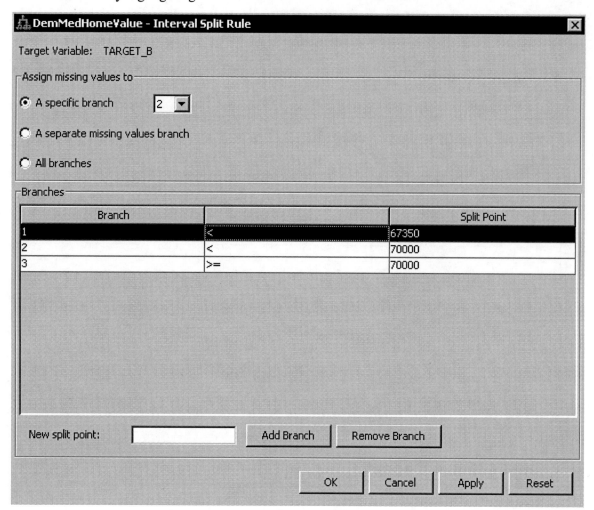

Copyright © 2011, SAS Institute Inc., Cary, North Carolina, USA. ALL RIGHTS RESERVED.

7. Select **Remove Branch**.

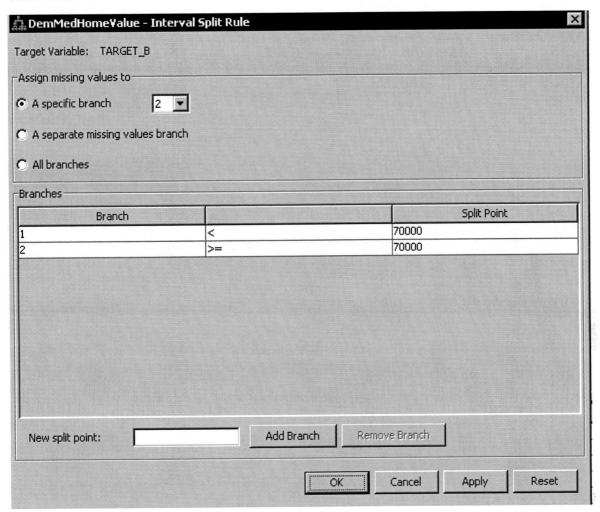

The split point for the partition is moved to 70000.

In general, to change a Decision Tree split point, add the new split point first and then remove the unwanted split point.

Copyright © 2011, SAS Institute Inc., Cary, North Carolina, USA. ALL RIGHTS RESERVED.

8. Select **OK** to close the Interval Splitting Rule dialog box and to update the Tree View window.

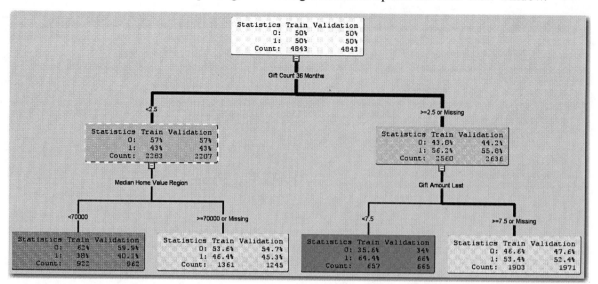

Overriding the statistically optimal split point slightly changed the concentration of cases in both nodes.

Copyright © 2011, SAS Institute Inc., Cary, North Carolina, USA. ALL RIGHTS RESERVED.

Creating the Maximal Tree

As demonstrated thus far, the process of building the decision tree model is one of carefully considering and selecting each split sequentially. There are other, more automated ways to grow a tree.

Follow these steps to automatically grow a tree with the SAS Enterprise Miner Interactive Tree tool:

1. Select the root node of the tree.

2. Right-click and select **Train Node** from the menu. The tree is grown until stopping rules prohibit further growth.

   Stopping rules were discussed previously and are in the Self-Study section at the end of this chapter.

   It is difficult to see the entire tree without scrolling. However, you can zoom into the Tree View window to examine the basic shape of the tree.

3. Select **Options** ⇨ **Zoom** ⇨ **50%** from the main menu. The tree view is scaled to provide the general shape of the maximal tree.

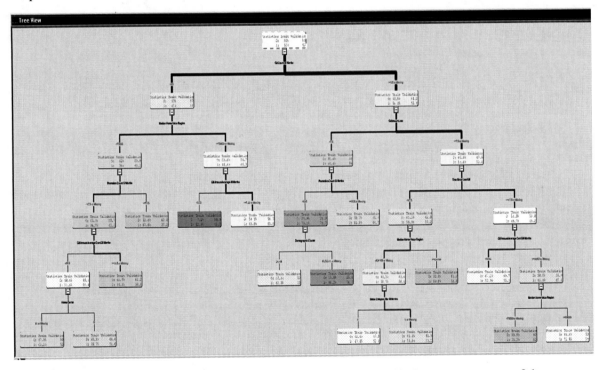

Plots and tables contained in the Interactive Tree tool provide a preliminary assessment of the maximal tree.

Copyright © 2011, SAS Institute Inc., Cary, North Carolina, USA. ALL RIGHTS RESERVED.

4.   Select **View** ⇨ **Subtree Assessment Plot**.

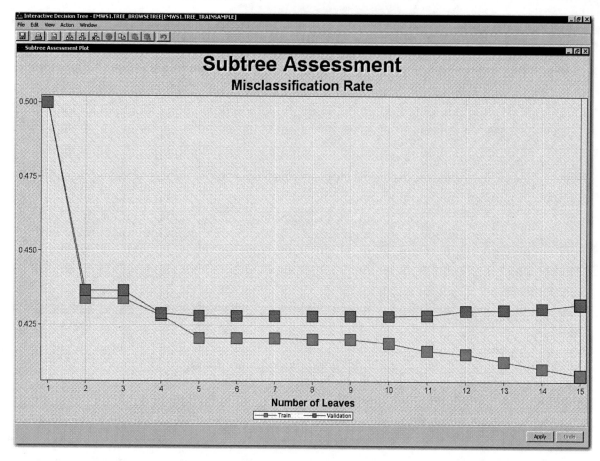

Looking at the plot for training data, even though the majority of the improvement in fit occurs over the first few splits, it appears that the maximal, fifteen-leaf tree generates a lower misclassification rate than any of its simpler predecessors. The plot on training data seems to indicate that the maximal tree is preferred for assigning predictions to cases. However, when looking only at the results from the training data, this plot is misleading.

Using the same sample of data both to evaluate input variable usefulness and to assess model performance commonly leads to overfit models. This is the mistake that the Mosteller and Tukey quotation cautioned you about. Looking at an assessment plot based on validation data provides the solution.

You created a predictive model that assigns one of 15 predicted target values to each case. Your next task is to investigate how well this model generalizes to another similar, but independent, sample: the validation data.

5.   Select **File** ⇨ **Exit** to close the Interactive Tree application.

The Interactive Tree results are now available from the Decision Tree node in the SAS Enterprise Miner flow.

Copyright © 2011, SAS Institute Inc., Cary, North Carolina, USA. ALL RIGHTS RESERVED.

3.3 Optimizing the Complexity of Decision Trees

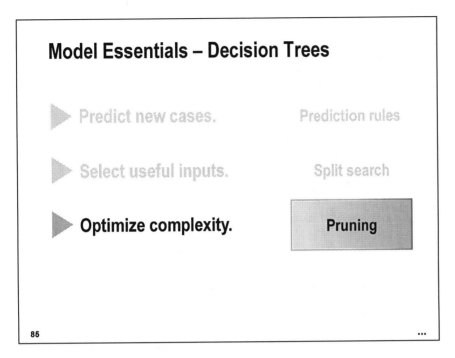

The maximal tree represents the most complicated model you are willing to construct from a set of training data. To avoid potential overfitting, many predictive modeling procedures offer some mechanism for adjusting model complexity. For decision trees, this process is known as *pruning*.

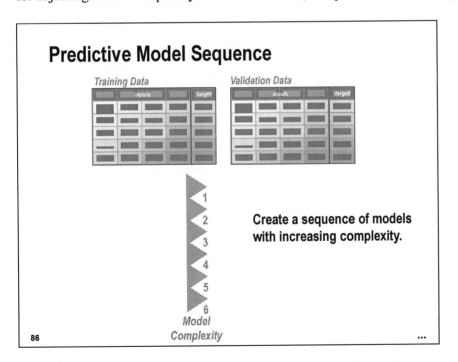

The general principle underlying complexity optimization is creating a sequence of related models of increasing complexity from training data and using validation data to select the optimal model.

Copyright © 2011, SAS Institute Inc., Cary, North Carolina, USA. ALL RIGHTS RESERVED.

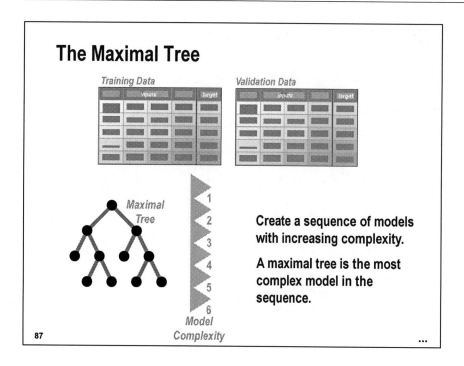

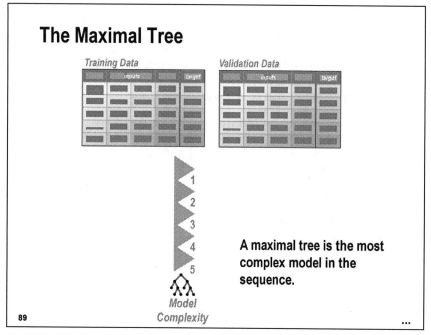

The maximal tree that you generated earlier represents the most complex model in the sequence.

Copyright © 2011, SAS Institute Inc., Cary, North Carolina, USA. ALL RIGHTS RESERVED.

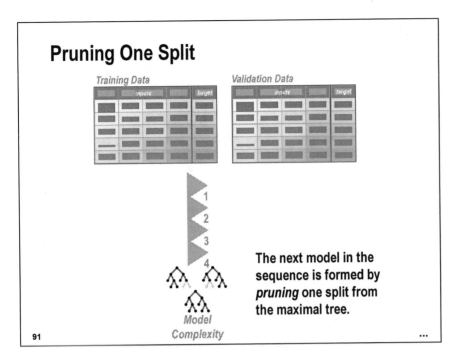

The predictive model sequence consists of *subtrees* obtained from the maximal tree by removing splits. The first batch of subtrees is obtained by *pruning* (that is, removing) one split from the maximal tree. This process results in several models with one less leaf than the maximal tree.

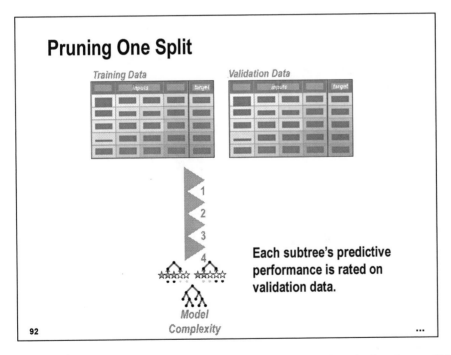

The subtrees are compared using a model rating statistic calculated on validation data. (Choices for model fit statistics are discussed later.)

Copyright © 2011, SAS Institute Inc., Cary, North Carolina, USA. ALL RIGHTS RESERVED.

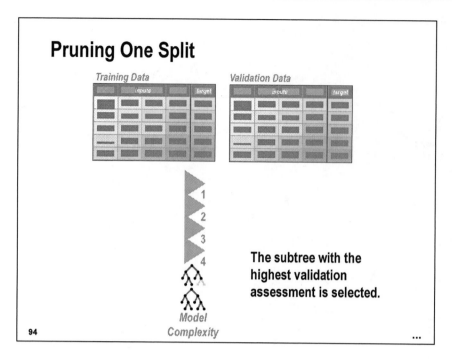

The subtree with the best validation assessment statistics is selected to represent a particular level of model complexity.

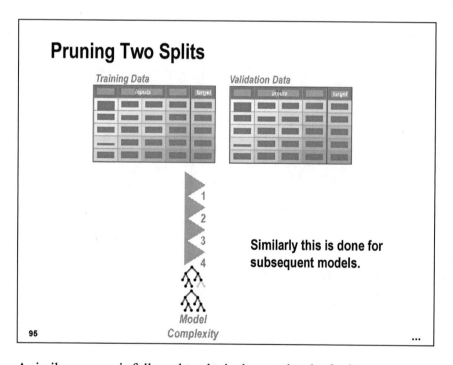

A similar process is followed to obtain the next batch of subtrees.

Copyright © 2011, SAS Institute Inc., Cary, North Carolina, USA. ALL RIGHTS RESERVED.

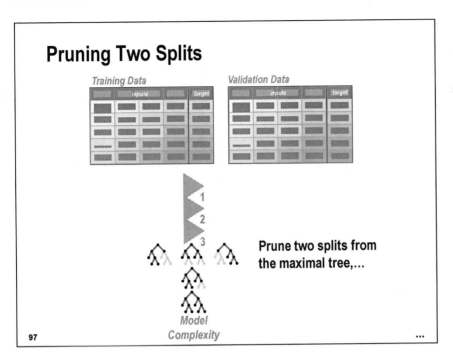

This time the subtrees are formed by removing two splits from the maximal tree.

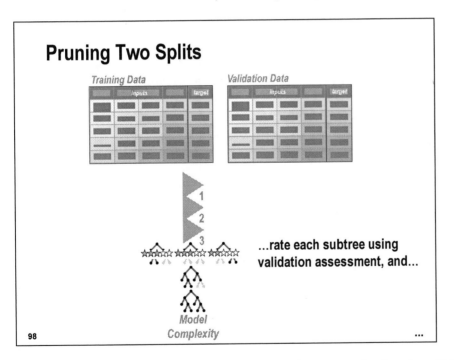

Once again, the predictive rating of each subtree is compared using the validation data.

Copyright © 2011, SAS Institute Inc., Cary, North Carolina, USA. ALL RIGHTS RESERVED.

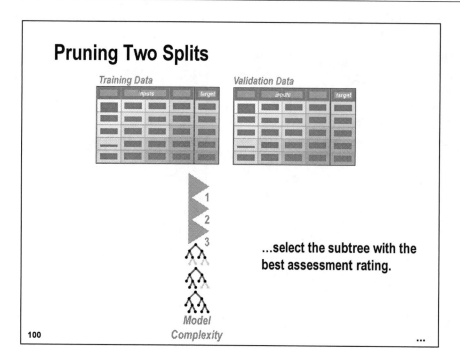

The subtree with the highest predictive rating is chosen to represent the given level of model complexity.

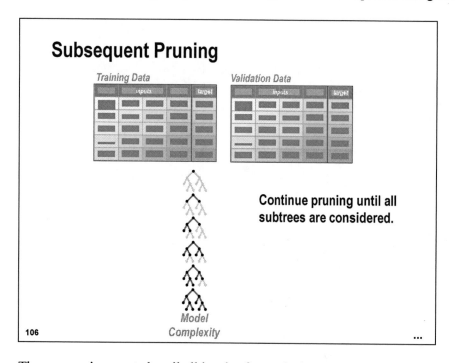

The process is repeated until all levels of complexity are represented by subtrees.

Copyright © 2011, SAS Institute Inc., Cary, North Carolina, USA. ALL RIGHTS RESERVED.

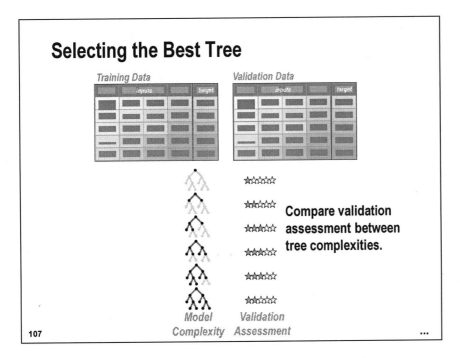

Consider the validation assessment rating for each of the subtrees.

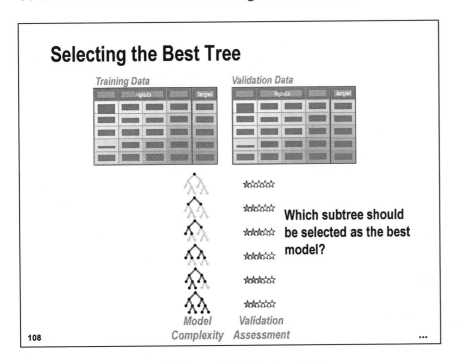

Which of the sequence of subtrees is the best model?

Copyright © 2011, SAS Institute Inc., Cary, North Carolina, USA. ALL RIGHTS RESERVED.

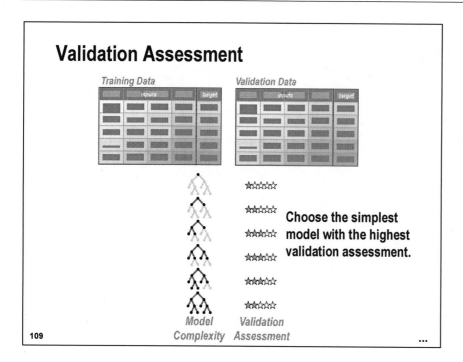

In SAS Enterprise Miner, the simplest model with the highest validation assessment is considered best.

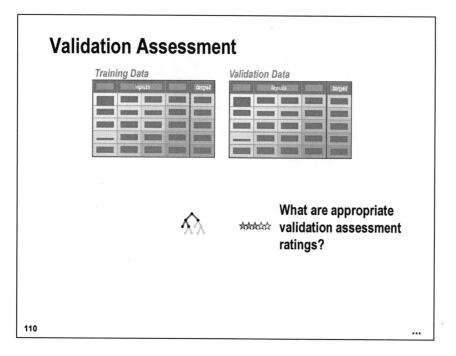

Of course, you must finally define what is meant by *validation assessment ratings*.

Copyright © 2011, SAS Institute Inc., Cary, North Carolina, USA. ALL RIGHTS RESERVED.

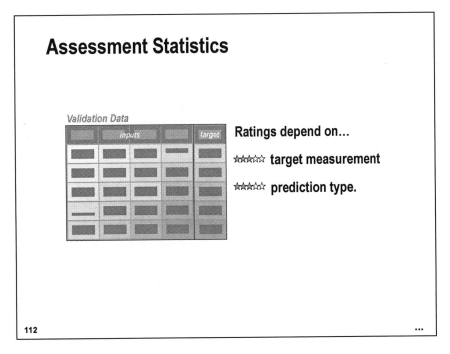

Two factors determine the appropriate validation assessment rating, or more properly, *assessment statistic*:

- the target measurement scale
- the prediction type

An appropriate statistic for a binary target might not make sense for an interval target. Similarly, models tuned for decision predictions might make poor estimate predictions.

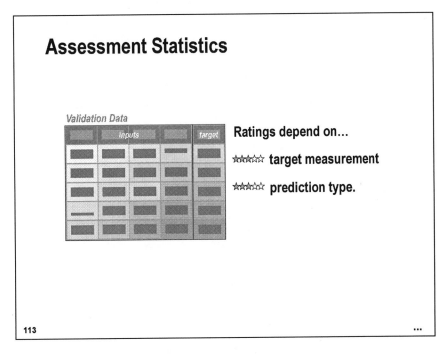

For this discussion, a binary target is assumed with a primary outcome (**target=1**) and a secondary outcome (**target=0**). The appropriate assessment measure for interval targets is noted below.

Copyright © 2011, SAS Institute Inc., Cary, North Carolina, USA. ALL RIGHTS RESERVED.

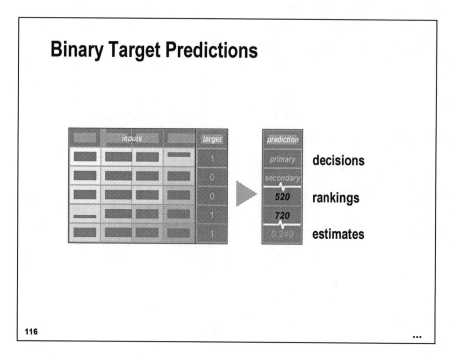

Different summary statistics correspond to each of the three prediction types:

- decisions
- rankings
- estimates

The statistic that you should use to judge a model depends on the type of prediction that you want.

Copyright © 2011, SAS Institute Inc., Cary, North Carolina, USA. ALL RIGHTS RESERVED.

Decision Optimization

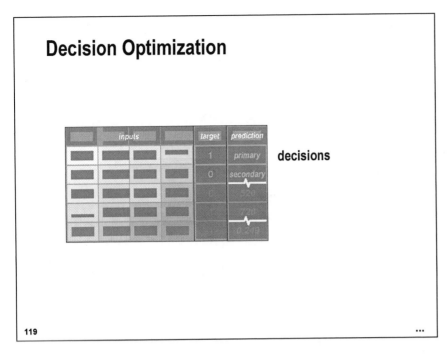

119

Consider decision predictions first. With a binary target, you typically consider two decision types:

- the primary decision, corresponding to the primary outcome
- the secondary decision, corresponding to the secondary outcome

Decision Optimization – Accuracy

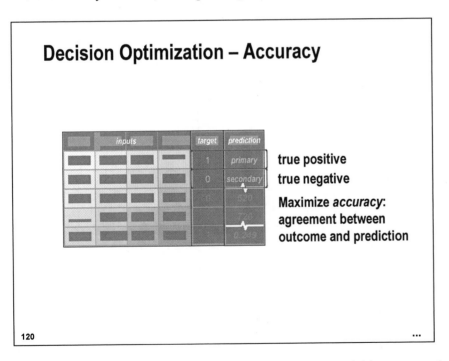

120

Matching the primary decision with the primary outcome yields a correct decision called a *true positive*. Likewise, matching the secondary decision to the secondary outcome yields a correct decision called a *true negative*. Decision predictions can be rated by their *accuracy*, that is, the proportion of agreement between prediction and outcome.

Copyright © 2011, SAS Institute Inc., Cary, North Carolina, USA. ALL RIGHTS RESERVED.

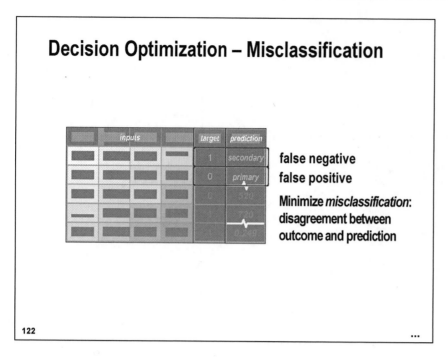

Mismatching the secondary decision with the primary outcome yields an incorrect decision called a *false negative*. Likewise, mismatching the primary decision to the secondary outcome yields an incorrect decision called a *false positive*. A decision prediction can be rated by its *misclassification*, that is, the proportion of disagreement between the prediction and the outcome.

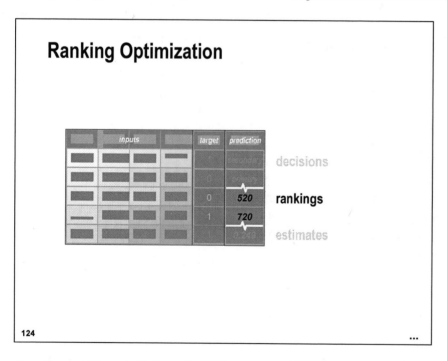

Consider ranking predictions for binary targets. With ranking predictions, a score is assigned to each case. The basic idea is to rank the cases based on their likelihood of being a primary or secondary outcome. Likely primary outcomes receive high scores and likely secondary outcomes receive low scores.

Copyright © 2011, SAS Institute Inc., Cary, North Carolina, USA. ALL RIGHTS RESERVED.

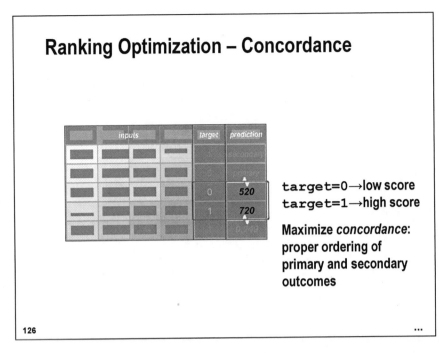

When a pair of primary and secondary cases is correctly ordered, the pair is said to be in *concordance*. Ranking predictions can be rated by their degree of concordance, that is, the proportion of such pairs whose scores are correctly ordered.

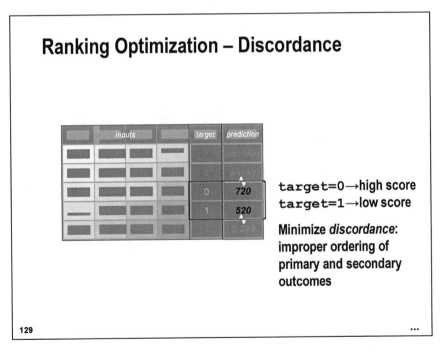

When a pair of primary and secondary cases is incorrectly ordered, the pair is said to be in *discordance*. Ranking predictions can be rated by their degree of discordance, that is, the proportion of such pairs whose scores are incorrectly ordered.

Copyright © 2011, SAS Institute Inc., Cary, North Carolina, USA. ALL RIGHTS RESERVED.

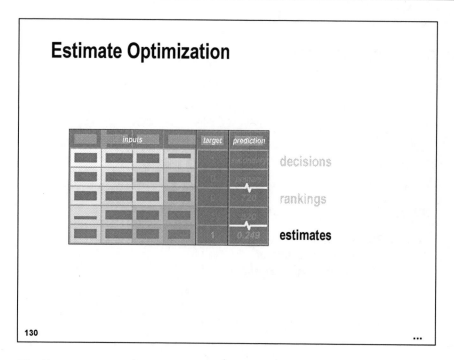

Finally, consider estimate predictions. For a binary target, *estimate predictions* are the probability of the primary outcome for each case. Primary outcome cases should have a high predicted probability; secondary outcome cases should have a low predicted probability.

Copyright © 2011, SAS Institute Inc., Cary, North Carolina, USA. ALL RIGHTS RESERVED.

Estimate Optimization – Squared Error

(target – estimate)²

Minimize *squared error*:
squared difference between
target and prediction

132   ...

The squared difference between a target and an estimate is called the *squared error*.

Averaged over all cases, squared error is a ***fundamental*** statistical measure of model performance.

$$Average\ square\ error = \frac{1}{N}\sum_{i=1}^{N}(y_i - \hat{y}_i)^2$$

where, for the ith case, y_i is the actual target value and $\hat{y}_i$ is the predicted target value.

When calculated in an unbiased fashion, the average square error is related to the amount of bias in a predictive model. A model with a lower average square error is less biased than a model with a higher average square error.

> Because SAS Enterprise Miner enables the target variable to have more than two outcomes, the actual formula used to calculate average square error is slightly different (but equivalent, for a binary target). Suppose the target variable has L outcomes given by $(C_1, C_2, ...C_L)$, then

$$Average\ square\ error = \frac{1}{N \cdot L}\sum_{i=1}^{N}\sum_{j=1}^{L}\left(I(y_i = C_j) - \hat{p}_{ij}\right)^2$$

> where, for the ith case, y_i is the actual target value, $\hat{p}_{ij}$ is the predicted target value for the jth class, and the following:

$$I(y_i = C_j) = \begin{cases} 1 & y_i = C_j \\ 0 & y_i \neq C_j \end{cases}$$

Copyright © 2011, SAS Institute Inc., Cary, North Carolina, USA. ALL RIGHTS RESERVED.

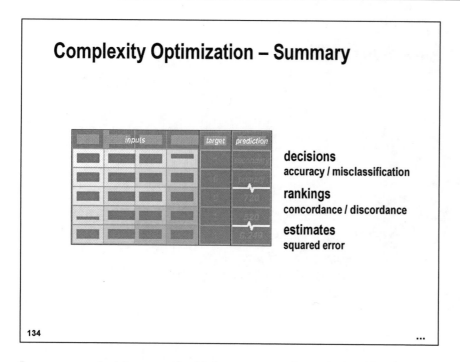

In summary, decisions require high accuracy or low misclassification, rankings require high concordance or low discordance, and estimates require low (average) squared error.

Copyright © 2011, SAS Institute Inc., Cary, North Carolina, USA. ALL RIGHTS RESERVED.

Assessing a Decision Tree

Use the following steps to perform an assessment of the maximal tree on the validation sample:

1. Select the **Decision Tree** node. In the Decision Tree node's Train properties, change **Use Frozen Tree** from No to **Yes**.

    The Frozen Tree property prevents the maximal tree from being changed by other property settings when the flow is run.

2. Right-click the **Decision Tree** node and run it. Select **Results**.

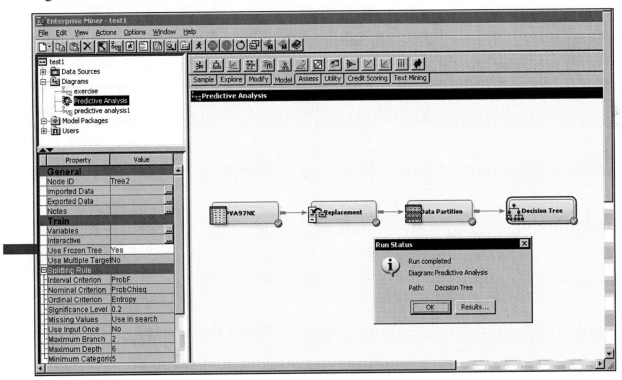

Copyright © 2011, SAS Institute Inc., Cary, North Carolina, USA. ALL RIGHTS RESERVED.

The Results window appears.

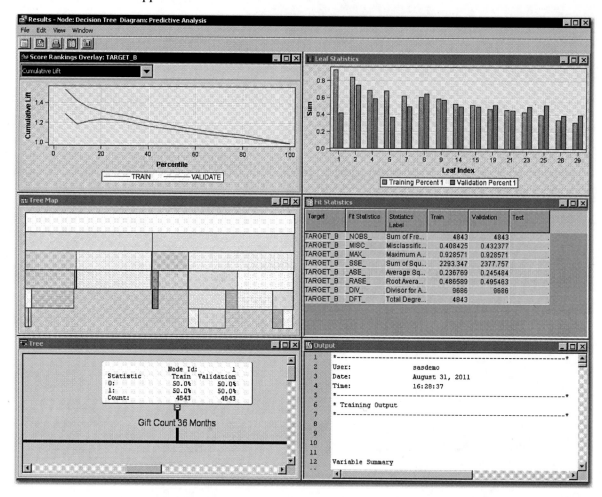

The Results window contains a variety of diagnostic plots and tables, including a cumulative lift chart, a tree map, and a table of fit statistics. The diagnostic tools shown in the results vary with the measurement level of the target variable. Some of the diagnostic tools contained in the results shown above are described in the following Self-Study section.

The saved tree diagram is in the bottom left corner of the Results window. You can verify this by maximizing the tree plot.

Copyright © 2011, SAS Institute Inc., Cary, North Carolina, USA. ALL RIGHTS RESERVED.

4. The main focus of this part of the demonstration is on assessing the performance of a 15-leaf tree, created with the Interactive Decision Tree tool, on the validation sample. Notice that several of the diagnostics shown in the results of the Decision Tree node use the validation data as a basis.

   Select **View** ⇨ **Model** ⇨ **Subtree Assessment Plot**.

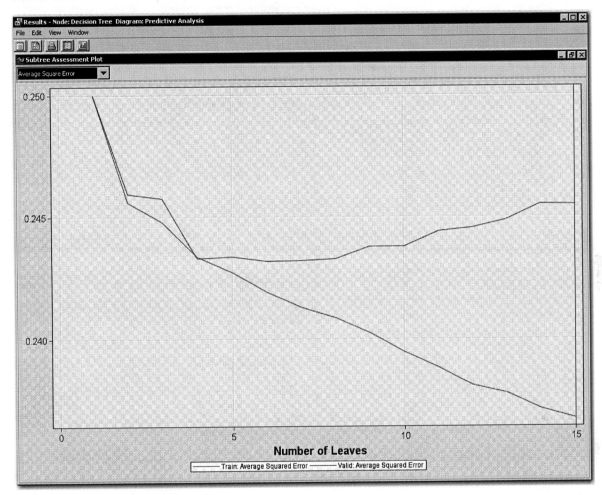

The plot shows the Average Square Error corresponding to each subtree as the data is sequentially split.

This plot is similar to the one generated with the Interactive Decision Tree tool, and it confirms suspicions about the optimality of the 15-leaf tree. The performance on the training sample becomes monotonically better as the tree becomes more complex. However, the performance on the validation sample only improves up to a tree of, approximately, four or five leaves, and then diminishes as model complexity increases.

   The validation performance shows evidence of model overfitting. Over the range of one to approximately four leaves, the precision of the model improves with the increase in complexity. A marginal increase in complexity over this range results in better accommodation of the systematic variation or signal in data. Precision diminishes as complexity increases past this range; the additional complexity accommodates idiosyncrasies in the training sample, and the model extrapolates less well.

Copyright © 2011, SAS Institute Inc., Cary, North Carolina, USA. ALL RIGHTS RESERVED.

Both axes of the Iteration Plot, shown above, require some explanation.

Average Square Error:

The formula for average square error was given previously. For any decision tree in the sequence, necessary inputs for calculating this statistic are the actual target value and the prediction. Recall that predictions generated by trees are the proportion of cases with the primary outcome (**TARGET_B**=1) in each terminal leaf. This value is calculated for both the training and validation data sets.

Number of leaves:

Starting with the four-leaf tree that you constructed earlier, it is possible to create a sequence of simpler trees by removing partitions. For example, a three-leaf tree can be constructed from your four-leaf tree by removing either the left partition (involving **Median Home Value**) or the right partition (involving **Gift Amount Last**). Removing either split might affect the generated average square error. The subtree with the lowest average square error (measured, by default, on the validation data) is the split that remains. To create simpler trees, the process is repeated by, once more, starting with the four-leaf tree that you constructed and removing more leaves. For example, the two-leaf tree is created from the four-leaf tree by removing two splits, and so on.

5. To further explore validation performance, select the arrow in the upper left corner of the Subtree Assessment Plot, and switch the assessment statistic to **Misclassification Rate**.

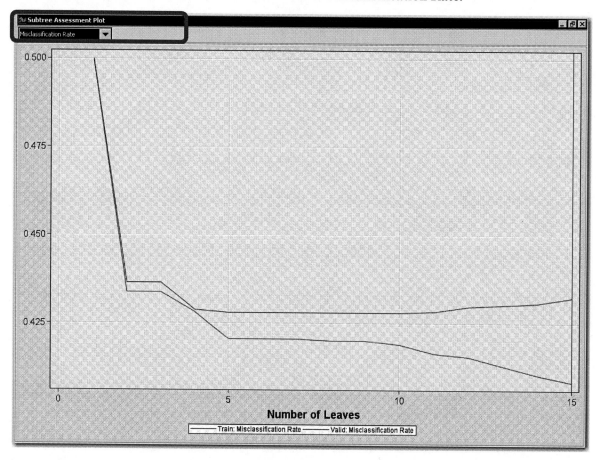

The validation performance under Misclassification Rate is similar to the performance under Average Square Error. The optimal tree appears to have, roughly, four or five leaves.

Copyright © 2011, SAS Institute Inc., Cary, North Carolina, USA. ALL RIGHTS RESERVED.

Proportion misclassified:

> The name *decision tree model* comes from the decision that is made at the leaf or terminal node. In SAS Enterprise Miner, this decision, by default, is a classification based on the *predicted target value*. A predicted target value in excess of 0.5 results in a primary outcome classification, and a predicted target value less than 0.5 results in a secondary outcome classification. Within a leaf, the predicted target value decides the classification for all cases regardless of each case's actual outcome. Clearly, this classification will be inaccurate for all cases that are not in the assigned class. The fraction of cases for which the wrong decision (classification) was made is the proportion misclassified. This value is calculated for both the training and validation data sets.

6. The current Decision Tree node will be renamed and saved for reference. Close the Decision Tree Results window.

7. Right-click on the **Decision Tree** node and select **Rename**. Name the node **Maximal Tree**.

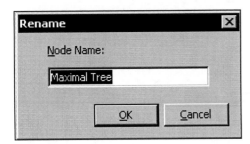

The current process flow should look similar to the following:

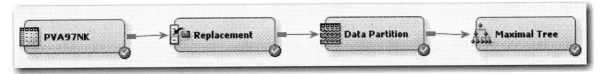

The next step is to generate the optimal tree using the default Decision Tree properties in SAS Enterprise Miner.

Pruning a Decision Tree

The optimal tree in the sequence can be identified using tools contained in the Decision Tree node. The relevant properties are listed under the Subtree heading.

1. Drag another **Decision Tree** node from the Model tab into the diagram.

   Connect it to the **Data Partition** node so that your diagram looks similar to what is shown below.

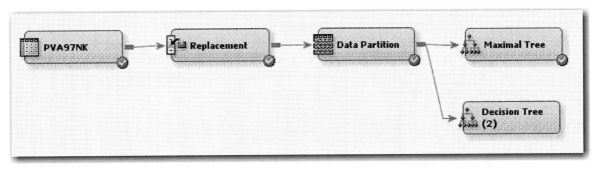

Copyright © 2011, SAS Institute Inc., Cary, North Carolina, USA. ALL RIGHTS RESERVED.

2. Select the new **Decision Tree** node and scroll down in the Decision Tree properties to the **Subtree** section. The main tree pruning properties are listed under the Subtree heading.

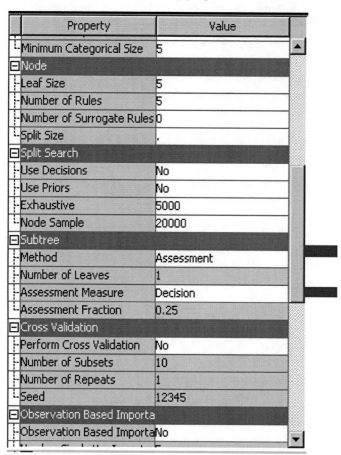

Property	Value
Minimum Categorical Size	5
Node	
Leaf Size	5
Number of Rules	5
Number of Surrogate Rules	0
Split Size	.
Split Search	
Use Decisions	No
Use Priors	No
Exhaustive	5000
Node Sample	20000
Subtree	
Method	Assessment
Number of Leaves	1
Assessment Measure	Decision
Assessment Fraction	0.25
Cross Validation	
Perform Cross Validation	No
Number of Subsets	10
Number of Repeats	1
Seed	12345
Observation Based Importa	
Observation Based Importa	No

The default method used to prune the maximal tree is Assessment. This means that algorithms in SAS Enterprise Miner choose the best tree in the sequence based on some optimality measure.

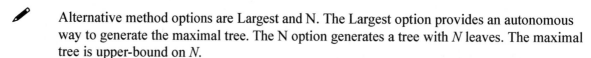

Alternative method options are Largest and N. The Largest option provides an autonomous way to generate the maximal tree. The N option generates a tree with N leaves. The maximal tree is upper-bound on N.

The Assessment Measure property specifies the optimality measure used to select the best tree in the sequence. The default measure is Decision. The default measure varies with the measurement level of the target variable, and other settings in SAS Enterprise Miner.

Metadata plays an important role in how SAS Enterprise Miner functions. Recall that a binary target variable was selected for the project. Based on this, SAS Enterprise Miner assumes that you want a tree that is optimized for making the best *decisions* (as opposed to the best rankings or best probability estimates). That is, under the current project settings, SAS Enterprise Miner chooses, by default, the tree with the lowest misclassification rate on the validation sample.

3. Right-click on the new **Decision Tree** node and select **Run**.

4. After the Decision Tree node runs, select **Results**.

Copyright © 2011, SAS Institute Inc., Cary, North Carolina, USA. ALL RIGHTS RESERVED.

5. In the Result window, select **View** ⇨ **Model** ⇨ **Subtree Assessment Plot**.

    The Subtree Assessment Plot shows model performance under Average Square Error by default. However, this is not the criterion used to select the optimal tree.

6. Change the basis of the plot to **Misclassification Rate**.

    The five-leaf tree has the lowest associated misclassification rate on the validation sample.

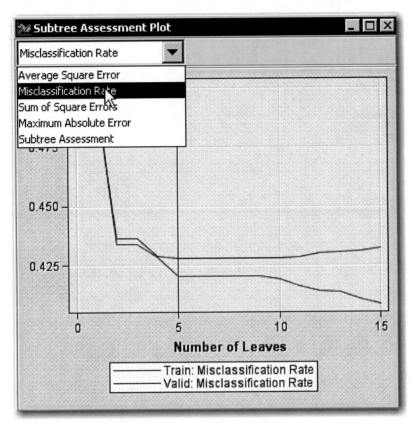

Notice that the first part of the process when generating the optimal tree is very similar to the process followed in the Interactive Decision Tree tool. The maximal, 15-leaf tree is generated. The maximal tree is then sequentially pruned so that the sequence consists of the best 15-leaf tree, the best 14-leaf tree, and so on. *Best* is defined at any point, for example, eight, in the sequence as the eight-leaf tree with the lowest Validation Misclassification Rate among all candidate eight-leaf trees. The tree in the sequence with the lowest overall validation misclassification rate is selected.

Copyright © 2011, SAS Institute Inc., Cary, North Carolina, USA. ALL RIGHTS RESERVED.

The optimal tree generated by the Decision Tree node is found in the bottom left corner of the Results window.

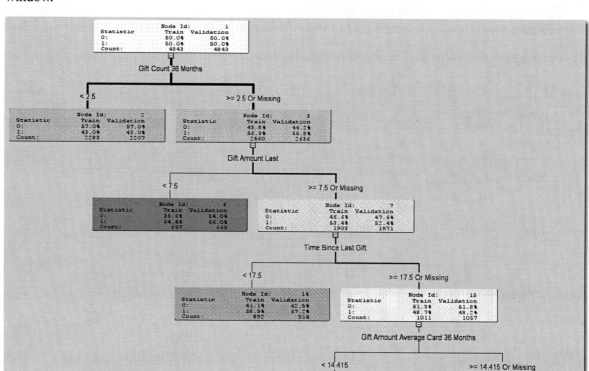

7. Close the Results window of the Decision Tree node.

Alternative Assessment Measures

The Decision Tree generated above is optimized for decisions, that is, to make the best classification of cases into donors and non-donors. What if instead of classification, the primary objective of the project is to assess the *probability of donation*? The discussion above describes how the different assessment measures correspond to the optimization of different modeling objectives.

Generate a tree that is optimized for generating probability estimates. The main purpose is to explore how different modeling objectives can change the optimal model specification.

1. Navigate to the **Model** tab. Drag a new **Decision Tree** into the process flow.

2. Right-click the new **Decision Tree** node and select **Rename**.

3. Name the new Decision Tree node **Probability Tree**.

4. Connect the **Data Partition** node to the **Probability Tree** node.

5. Recall that an appropriate assessment measure for generating optimal probability estimates is Average Square Error.

Copyright © 2011, SAS Institute Inc., Cary, North Carolina, USA. ALL RIGHTS RESERVED.

6. Scroll down in the properties of the Probability Tree node to **Subtree**.

7. Change the Assessment Measure property to **Average Square Error**.

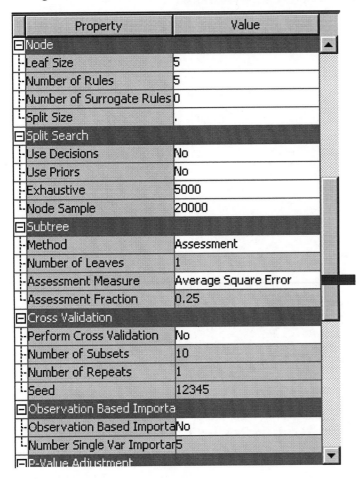

Property	Value
⊟ Node	
├ Leaf Size	5
├ Number of Rules	5
├ Number of Surrogate Rules	0
└ Split Size	.
⊟ Split Search	
├ Use Decisions	No
├ Use Priors	No
├ Exhaustive	5000
└ Node Sample	20000
⊟ Subtree	
├ Method	Assessment
├ Number of Leaves	1
├ Assessment Measure	Average Square Error
└ Assessment Fraction	0.25
⊟ Cross Validation	
├ Perform Cross Validation	No
├ Number of Subsets	10
├ Number of Repeats	1
└ Seed	12345
⊟ Observation Based Importa	
├ Observation Based Importa	No
└ Number Single Var Importar	5
⊟ P-Value Adjustment	

8. Run the Probability Tree node.

9. After it runs, select **Results**.

Copyright © 2011, SAS Institute Inc., Cary, North Carolina, USA. ALL RIGHTS RESERVED.

10. In the Results window, select **View** ⇨ **Model** ⇨ **Subtree Assessment Plot**.

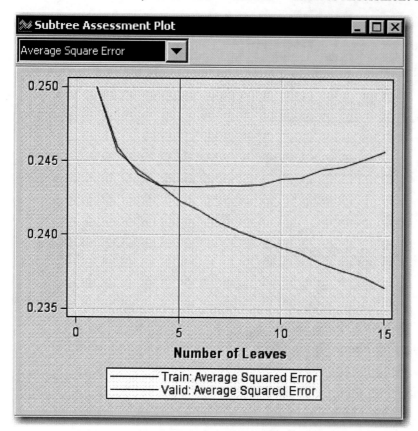

A five-leaf tree is also optimal under the Validation Average Square Error criterion. However, viewing the Tree plot reveals that, although the optimal Decision (Misclassification) Tree and the optimal Probability Tree have the same number of leaves, they are not identical trees.

Copyright © 2011, SAS Institute Inc., Cary, North Carolina, USA. ALL RIGHTS RESERVED.

11. Maximize the Tree plot at the lower left corner of the Results window.

The tree shown below is a different five-leaf tree than the tree optimized under Validation Misclassification.

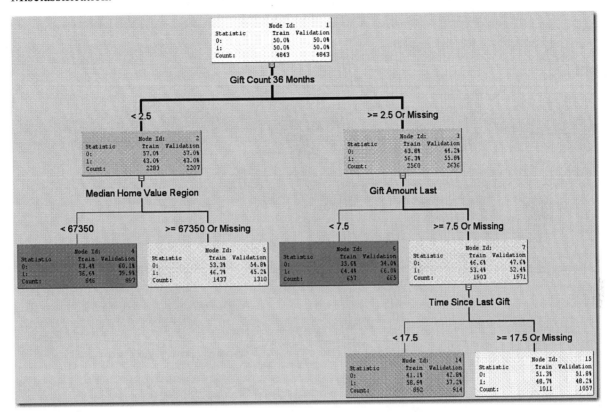

It is important to remember how the assessment measures work in model selection. In the first step, cultivating (or growing or splitting) the tree, the important measure is *logworth*. Splits of the data are made based on logworth to isolate subregions of the input space with high proportions of donors and non-donors. Splitting continues until a boundary associated with a stopping rule is reached. This process generates the maximal tree.

The maximal tree is then sequentially pruned. Each subtree in the pruning sequence is chosen based on the selected assessment measure. For example, the eight-leaf tree in the Decision (Misclassification) Tree pruning sequence is the eight-leaf tree with the lowest misclassification rate on the validation sample among all candidate eight-leaf trees. The eight-leaf tree in the Probability Tree pruning sequence is the eight-leaf tree with the lowest average square error on the validation sample among all candidate eight-leaf trees. This is how the change in assessment measure can generate a change in the optimal specification.

 In order to minimize clutter in the diagram, the Maximal Tree node is deleted and does not appear in the notes for the remainder of the course.

Copyright © 2011, SAS Institute Inc., Cary, North Carolina, USA. ALL RIGHTS RESERVED.

3.4 Understanding Additional Diagnostic Tools (Self-Study)

Several additional plots and tables contained in the Decision Tree node Results window are designed to assist in interpreting and evaluating a decision tree. The most useful are demonstrated on the next several pages.

Copyright © 2011, SAS Institute Inc., Cary, North Carolina, USA. ALL RIGHTS RESERVED.

Understanding Additional Plots and Tables (Optional)

Tree Map

The Tree Map window is intended to be used in conjunction with the Tree window to gauge the relative size of each leaf.

1. Select the small rectangle in the lower right corner of the Tree map.

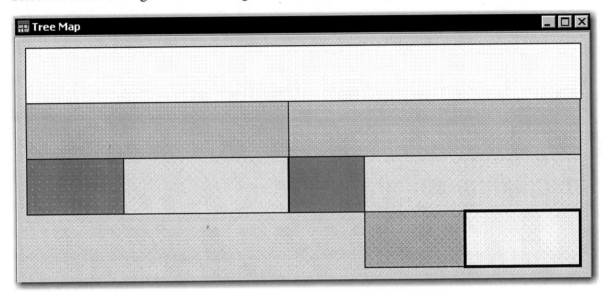

Copyright © 2011, SAS Institute Inc., Cary, North Carolina, USA. ALL RIGHTS RESERVED.

The lower right leaf in the tree is also selected.

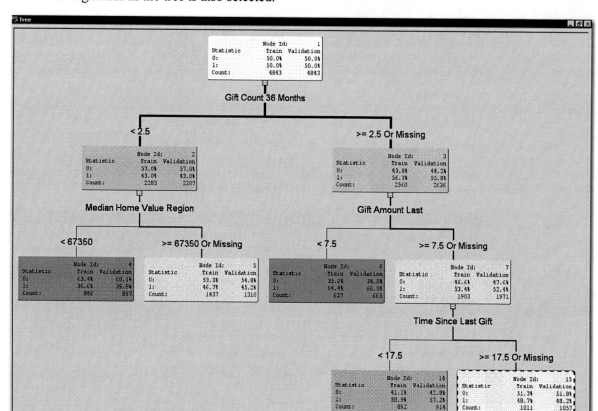

The size of the small rectangle in the tree map indicates the fraction of the training data present in the corresponding leaf. It appears that only a small fraction of the training data finds its way to this leaf.

Leaf Statistic Bar Chart

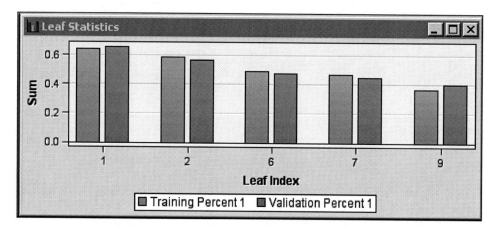

This window compares the blue predicted outcome percentages in the left bars (from the training data) to the red observed outcome percentages in the right bars (from the validation data).

This plot reveals how well training data response rates are reflected in the validation data. Ideally, the bars should be of the same height. Differences in bar heights are usually the result of small case counts in the corresponding leaf.

Copyright © 2011, SAS Institute Inc., Cary, North Carolina, USA. ALL RIGHTS RESERVED.

Variable Importance

The following steps open the Variable Importance window.

Select **View** ⇨ **Model** ⇨ **Variable Importance**. The Variable Importance window appears.

Variable Name	Label	Number of Splitting Rules	Importance	Validation Importance	Ratio of Validation to Training Importance
GiftCnt36	Gift Count 36 Months	1	1	1	1
GiftAvgLast	Gift Amount Last	1	0.524135	0.671883	1.281891
DemMedHomeValue	Median Home Value Region	1	0.50277	0.10861	0.216024
GiftTimeLast	Time Since Last Gift	1	0.480916	0.445303	0.925948
DemPctVeterans	Percent Veterans Region	0	0	0	.
GiftAvg36	Gift Amount Average 36 Months	0	0	0	.
GiftAvgCard36	Gift Amount Average Card 36 Months	0	0	0	.
DemAge	Age	0	0	0	.
GiftAvgAll	Gift Amount Average All Months	0	0	0	.
GiftCntAll	Gift Count All Months	0	0	0	.
GiftCntCard36	Gift Count Card 36 Months	0	0	0	.
GiftCntCardAll	Gift Count Card All Months	0	0	0	.
GiftTimeFirst	Time Since First Gift	0	0	0	.
PromCntCardAll	Promotion Count Card All Months	0	0	0	.
PromCnt12	Promotion Count 12 Months	0	0	0	.
PromCnt36	Promotion Count 36 Months	0	0	0	.
PromCntAll	Promotion Count All Months	0	0	0	.
PromCntCard12	Promotion Count Card 12 Months	0	0	0	.
PromCntCard36	Promotion Count Card 36 Months	0	0	0	.
StatusCatStarAll	Status Category Star All Months	0	0	0	.
REP_DemMedIncome	Replacement: Median Income Region	0	0	0	.
DemCluster	Demographic Cluster	0	0	0	.
DemGender	Gender	0	0	0	.
DemHomeOwner	Home Owner	0	0	0	.
StatusCat96NK	Status Category 96NK	0	0	0	.

The Variable Importance window provides insight into the importance of inputs in the decision tree. The magnitude of the importance statistic relates to the amount of variability in the target *explained* by the corresponding input relative to the input at the top of the table. For example, **Gift Amount Last** explains 52.4% of the variability explained by **Gift Count 36 Months**.

Copyright © 2011, SAS Institute Inc., Cary, North Carolina, USA. ALL RIGHTS RESERVED.

The Score Rankings Overlay Plot

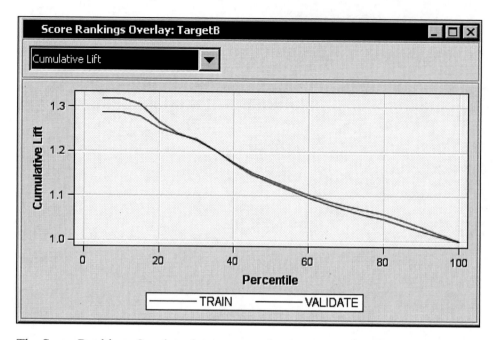

The Score Rankings Overlay plot presents what is commonly called a *cumulative lift chart*. Cases in the training and validation data are ranked, based on decreasing predicted target values. A fraction of the ranked data is selected (given by the decile value). The proportion of cases with the primary target value in this fraction is compared to the proportion of cases with the primary target value overall (given by the cumulative lift value). A useful model shows high lift in low deciles in both the training and validation data.

For example, the Score Ranking plot shows that in the top 20% of cases (ranked by predicted probability), the training and validation lifts are approximately 1.26. This means that the proportion of primary outcome cases in this top 20% is about 26% more likely to have the primary outcome than a randomly selected 20% of cases.

Fit Statistics

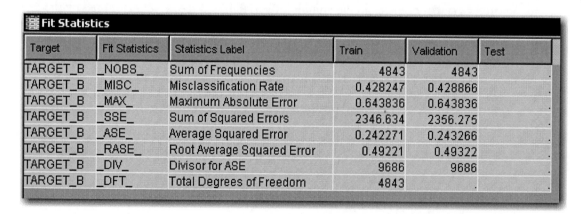

Target	Fit Statistics	Statistics Label	Train	Validation	Test
TARGET_B	_NOBS_	Sum of Frequencies	4843	4843	
TARGET_B	_MISC_	Misclassification Rate	0.428247	0.428866	
TARGET_B	_MAX_	Maximum Absolute Error	0.643836	0.643836	
TARGET_B	_SSE_	Sum of Squared Errors	2346.634	2356.275	
TARGET_B	_ASE_	Average Squared Error	0.242271	0.243266	
TARGET_B	_RASE_	Root Average Squared Error	0.49221	0.49322	
TARGET_B	_DIV_	Divisor for ASE	9686	9686	
TARGET_B	_DFT_	Total Degrees of Freedom	4843		

The Fit Statistics window is used to compare various models built within SAS Enterprise Miner. The misclassification and average square error statistics are of most interest for this analysis.

Copyright © 2011, SAS Institute Inc., Cary, North Carolina, USA. ALL RIGHTS RESERVED.

The Output Window

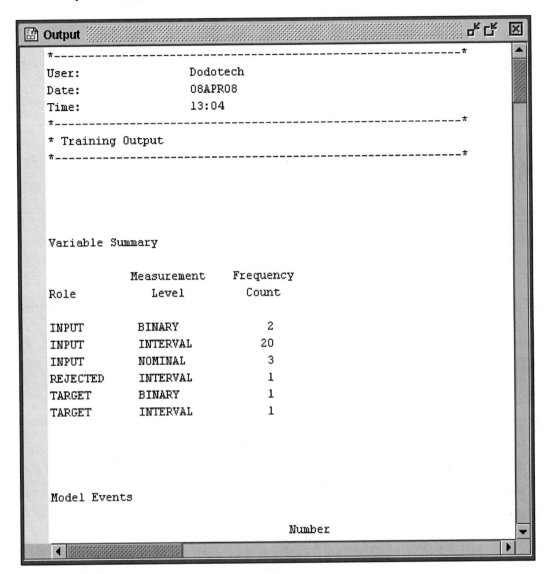

The Output window provides information generated by the SAS procedures that are used to generate the analysis results. For the decision tree, this information includes variable importance, tree leaf report, model fit statistics, classification information, and score rankings.

Copyright © 2011, SAS Institute Inc., Cary, North Carolina, USA. ALL RIGHTS RESERVED.

3.5 Autonomous Tree Growth Options (Self-Study)

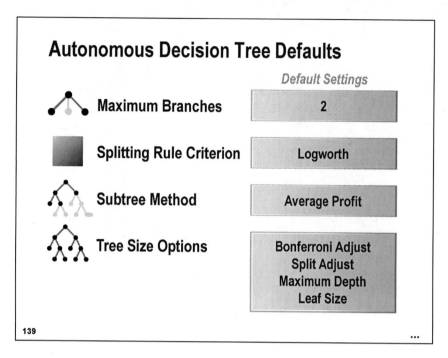

The behavior of the tree algorithm in SAS Enterprise Miner is governed by many parameters that can be divided into four groups:

- the number of splits to create at each partitioning opportunity
- the metric used to compare different splits
- the method used to prune the tree model
- the rules used to stop the autonomous tree growing process

The defaults for these parameters generally yield good results for an initial prediction.

Copyright © 2011, SAS Institute Inc., Cary, North Carolina, USA. ALL RIGHTS RESERVED.

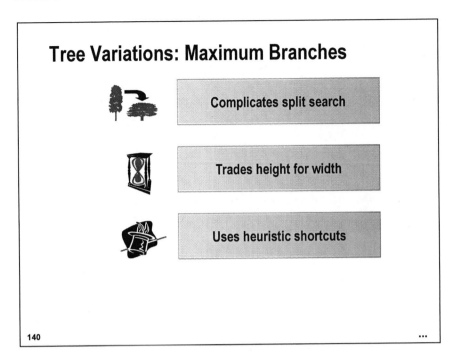

Tree Variations: Maximum Branches

Complicates split search

Trades height for width

Uses heuristic shortcuts

140

SAS Enterprise Miner accommodates a multitude of variations in the default tree algorithm. The first involves the use of multiway splits instead of binary splits.

Theoretically, there is no clear advantage in doing this. Any multiway split can be obtained using a sequence of binary splits. The primary change is cosmetic. Trees with multiway splits tend to be wider than trees with only binary splits.

The inclusion of multiway splits complicates the split-search algorithm. A simple linear search becomes a search whose complexity increases geometrically in the number of splits allowed from a leaf. To combat this complexity explosion, the Tree tool in SAS Enterprise Miner resorts to heuristic search strategies.

Copyright © 2011, SAS Institute Inc., Cary, North Carolina, USA. ALL RIGHTS RESERVED.

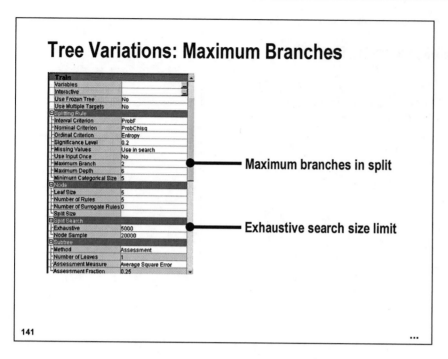

Two fields in the Properties panel affect the number of splits in a tree. The Maximum Branch property sets an upper limit on the number of branches emanating from a node. When this number is greater than the default of 2, the number of possible splits rapidly increases. To save computation time, a limit is set in the Exhaustive property as to how many possible splits are explicitly examined. When this number is exceeded, a heuristic algorithm is used in place of the exhaustive search described above.

The heuristic algorithm alternately merges branches and reassigns consolidated groups of observations to different branches. The process stops when a binary split is reached. Among all considered candidate splits, the one with the best worth is chosen. The heuristic algorithm initially assigns each consolidated group of observations to a different branch, even if the number of such branches is more than the limit allowed in the final split. At each merge step, the two branches that degrade the worth of the partition the least are merged. After the two branches are merged, the algorithm considers reassigning consolidated groups of observations to different branches. Each consolidated group is considered in turn, and the process stops when no group is reassigned.

Copyright © 2011, SAS Institute Inc., Cary, North Carolina, USA. ALL RIGHTS RESERVED.

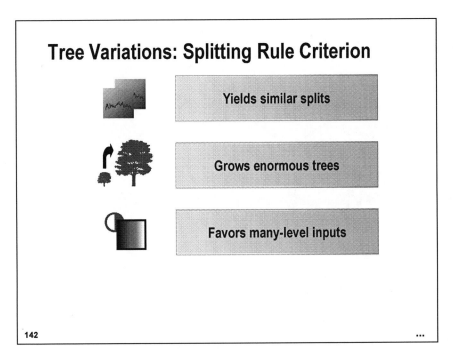

Tree Variations: Splitting Rule Criterion

Yields similar splits

Grows enormous trees

Favors many-level inputs

142

In addition to changing the number of splits, you can also change how the splits are evaluated in the split-search phase of the tree algorithm. For categorical targets, SAS Enterprise Miner offers three separate split-worth criteria. Changing from the chi-squared default criterion typically yields similar splits if the number of distinct levels in each input is similar. If not, the other split methods tend to favor inputs with more levels due to the multiple comparison problem discussed above. You can also cause the chi-squared method to favor inputs with more levels by turning off the Bonferroni adjustments.

Because Gini reduction and entropy reduction criteria lack the significance threshold feature of the chi-squared criterion, they tend to grow enormous trees. Pruning and selecting a tree complexity based on validation profit limit this problem to some extent.

Copyright © 2011, SAS Institute Inc., Cary, North Carolina, USA. ALL RIGHTS RESERVED.

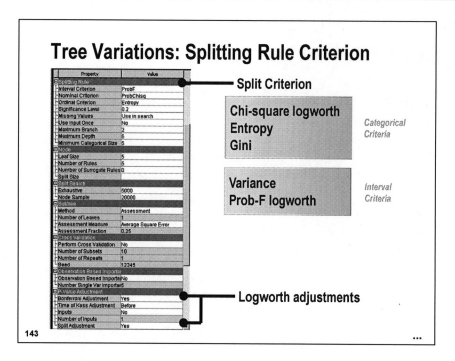

A total of five choices in SAS Enterprise Miner can evaluate split worth. Three (chi-squared logworth, entropy, and Gini) are used for categorical targets, and the remaining two (variance and ProbF logworth) are reserved for interval targets.

Both chi-squared and ProbF logworths are adjusted (by default) for multiple comparisons. It is possible to deactivate this adjustment.

The split worth for the entropy, Gini, and variance options are calculated as shown below. Let a set of cases S be partitioned into p subsets $S_1, \ldots, S_p$ so that

$$S = \bigcup_{i=1}^{p} S_i$$

Let the number of cases in S equal N and the number of cases in each subset S_i equal n_i. Then the worth of a particular partition of S is given by the following:

$$worth = I(S) - \sum_{i=1}^{p} w_i I(S_i)$$

where $w_i = n_i/N$ (the proportion of cases in subset S_i), and for the specified split worth measure, $I(\cdot)$ has the following value:

$$I(\cdot) = \sum_{classes} p_{class} \cdot \log_2 p_{class} \qquad \text{Entropy}$$

$$I(\cdot) = 1 - \sum_{classes} p_{class}^2 \qquad \text{Gini}$$

$$I(\cdot) = \frac{1}{N_{node}} \sum_{cases} (Y_{case} - \overline{Y})^2 \qquad \text{Variance}$$

Each worth statistic measures the change in $I(S)$ from node to branches. In the Variance calculation, $\overline{Y}$ is the average of the target value in the node with Y_{case} as a member.

Copyright © 2011, SAS Institute Inc., Cary, North Carolina, USA. ALL RIGHTS RESERVED.

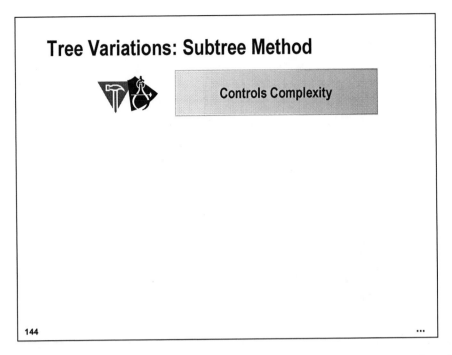

SAS Enterprise Miner features two settings for regulating the complexity of subtree: modify the pruning process or the Subtree method.

By changing the model assessment measure to average square error, you can construct what is known as a *class probability tree*. It can be shown that this action minimizes the imprecision of the tree. Analysts sometimes use this model assessment measure to select inputs for a flexible predictive model such as neural networks.

You can deactivate pruning entirely by changing the subtree to **Largest**. You can also specify that the tree be built with a fixed number of leaves.

Copyright © 2011, SAS Institute Inc., Cary, North Carolina, USA. ALL RIGHTS RESERVED.

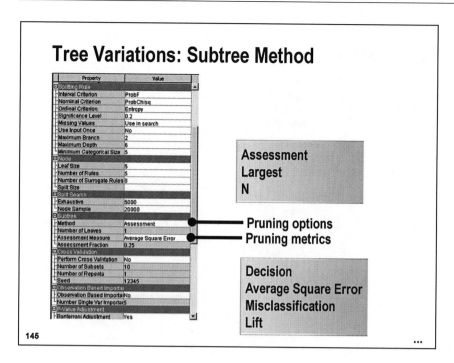

The pruning options are controlled by two properties: Method and Assessment Measure.

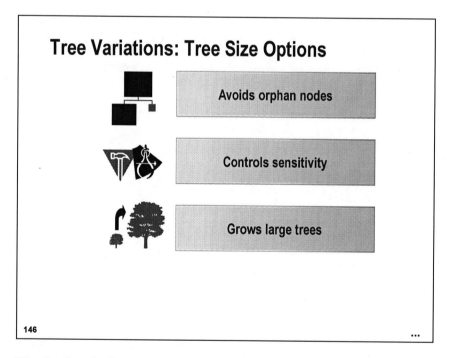

The family of adjustments that you modify most often when building trees are the rules that limit the growth of the tree. Changing the minimum number of observations required for a split search and the minimum number of observations in a leaf prevents the creation of leaves with only one or a handful of cases. Changing the significance level and the maximum depth allows for larger trees that can be more sensitive to complex input and target associations. The growth of the tree is still limited by the depth adjustment made to the threshold.

Copyright © 2011, SAS Institute Inc., Cary, North Carolina, USA. ALL RIGHTS RESERVED.

Tree Variations: Tree Size Options

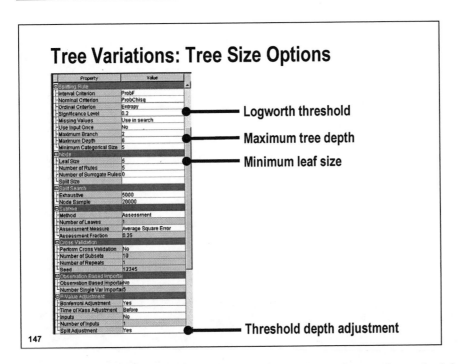

Changing the logworth threshold changes the minimum logworth required for a split to be considered by the tree algorithm (when using the chi-squared or ProbF measures). Increasing the minimum leaf size avoids orphan nodes. For large data sets, you might want to increase the maximum leaf setting to obtain additional modeling resolution. If you want big trees and insist on using the chi-squared split-worth criterion, deactivate the Split Adjustment option.

Copyright © 2011, SAS Institute Inc., Cary, North Carolina, USA. ALL RIGHTS RESERVED.

Exercises

1. Initial Data Exploration

A supermarket is offering a new line of organic products. The supermarket's management wants to determine which customers are likely to purchase these products.

The supermarket has a customer loyalty program. As an initial buyer incentive plan, the supermarket provided coupons for the organic products to all of the loyalty program participants and collected data that includes whether these customers purchased any of the organic products.

The **ORGANICS** data set contains 13 variables and over 22,000 observations. The variables in the data set are shown below with the appropriate roles and levels:

Name	Model Role	Measurement Level	Description
ID	ID	Nominal	Customer loyalty identification number
DemAffl	Input	Interval	Affluence grade on a scale from 1 to 30
DemAge	Input	Interval	Age, in years
DemCluster	Rejected	Nominal	Type of residential neighborhood
DemClusterGroup	Input	Nominal	Neighborhood group
DemGender	Input	Nominal	M = male, F = female, U = unknown
DemRegion	Input	Nominal	Geographic region
DemTVReg	Input	Nominal	Television region
PromClass	Input	Nominal	Loyalty status: tin, silver, gold, or platinum
PromSpend	Input	Interval	Total amount spent
PromTime	Input	Interval	Time as loyalty card member
TargetBuy	Target	Binary	Organics purchased? 1 = Yes, 0 = No
TargetAmt	Rejected	Interval	Number of organic products purchased

✎   Although two target variables are listed, these exercises concentrate on the binary variable **TargetBuy**.

a. Create a new diagram named **Organics**.

Copyright © 2011, SAS Institute Inc., Cary, North Carolina, USA. ALL RIGHTS RESERVED.

b. Define the data set **AAEM.ORGANICS** as a data source for the project.

   1) Set the model roles for the analysis variables as shown above.

   2) Examine the distribution of the target variable. What is the proportion of individuals who purchased organic products? _____

   3) The variable **DemClusterGroup** contains collapsed levels of the variable **DemCluster**. Presume that, based on previous experience, you believe that **DemClusterGroup** is sufficient for this type of modeling effort. Set the model role for **DemCluster** to **Rejected**.

   4) As noted above, only **TargetBuy** will be used for this analysis and should have a role of **Target**. Can **TargetAmt** be used as an input for a model used to predict **TargetBuy**? Why or why not? _____

   _____

   5) Finish the **Organics** data source definition.

c. Add the **AAEM.ORGANICS** data source to the Organics diagram workspace.

d. Add a **Data Partition** node to the diagram and connect it to the **Data Source** node. Assign 50% of the data for training and 50% for validation.

e. Add a **Decision Tree** node to the workspace and connect it to the **Data Partition** node.

f. Create a decision tree model autonomously. Use average square error as the model assessment statistic.

   1) How many leaves are in the optimal tree? _____

   2) Which variable was used for the first split? _____

   What were the competing splits for this first split? _____

g. Add a second **Decision Tree** node to the diagram and connect it to the **Data Partition** node.

   1) In the Properties panel of the new Decision Tree node, change the maximum number of branches from a node to **3** to enable three-way splits.

   2) Create a decision tree model. Use average square error as the model assessment statistic.

   3) How many leaves are in the optimal tree? _____

h. Based on average square error, which of the decision tree models appears to be better? _____

   _____

Copyright © 2011, SAS Institute Inc., Cary, North Carolina, USA. ALL RIGHTS RESERVED.

3.6 Chapter Summary

Predictive modeling fulfills some of the promise of data mining. Past observation of target events coupled with past input measurements enables some degree of assistance for the prediction of future target event values, conditioned on current input measurements. All of this depends on the stationarity of the process being modeled.

A predictive model must perform three essential tasks:

1. It must be able to systematically predict new cases, based on input measurements. These predictions might be decisions, rankings, or estimates.

2. A predictive model must be able to thwart the curse of dimensionality and successfully select a limited number of useful inputs. This is accomplished by systematically ignoring irrelevant and redundant inputs.

3. A predictive model must adjust its complexity to avoid overfitting or underfitting. In SAS Enterprise Miner, this adjustment is accomplished by splitting the raw data into a training data set for building the model and a validation data set for gauging model performance. The performance measure used to gauge performance depends on the prediction type. Decisions can be evaluated by accuracy or misclassification, rankings by concordance or discordance, and estimates by average square error.

Decision trees are a simple but potentially useful example of a predictive model. They score new cases by creating prediction rules. They select useful inputs via a split-search algorithm. They optimize complexity by building and pruning a maximal tree. A decision tree model can be built interactively, automatically, or autonomously. For autonomous models, the Decision Tree Properties panel provides options to control the size and shape of the final tree.

Decision Tree Tools Review

 Partition raw data into training and validation sets.

 Interactively grow trees using the Tree Desktop application. You can control rules, selected inputs, and tree complexity.

Autonomously grow decision trees based on property settings. Settings include branch count, split rule criterion, subtree method, and tree size options.

149

Copyright © 2011, SAS Institute Inc., Cary, North Carolina, USA. ALL RIGHTS RESERVED.

3.7 Solutions

Solutions to Exercises

1. **Initial Data Exploration**

   a. Create a new diagram named **Organics**.

   1) Select **File** ⇨ **New** ⇨ **Diagram**. The Create New Diagram window appears.

   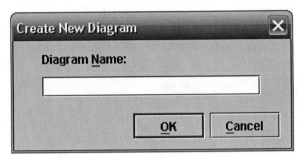

   2) Type **Organics** in the **Diagram Name** field.

   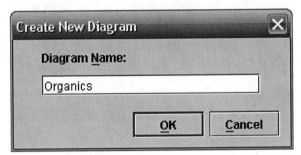

   3) Select **OK**.

   b. Define the data set **AAEM.ORGANICS** as a data source for the project.

   1) Set the model roles for the analysis variables.

   2) Examine the distribution of the target variable. What is the proportion of individuals who purchased organic products?

   a) Select **File** ⇨ **New** ⇨ **Data Source**. The Data Source Wizard window appears.

   b) Select **Next**. The wizard proceeds to Step 2.

   c) Type **AAEM.ORGANICS** in the **Table** field.

Copyright © 2011, SAS Institute Inc., Cary, North Carolina, USA. ALL RIGHTS RESERVED.

d) Select **Next**. The wizard proceeds to Step 3.

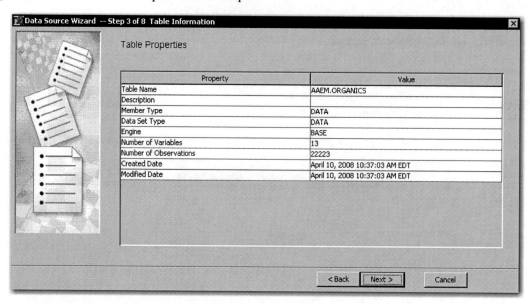

e) Select **Next**. The wizard proceeds to Step 4.

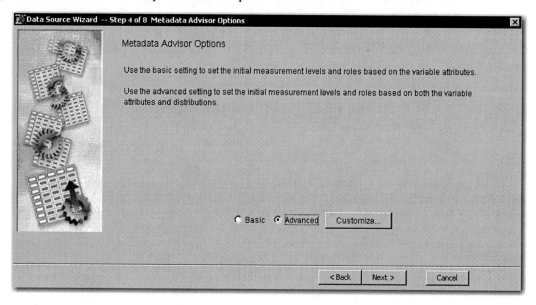

f) Select the **Advanced** radio button and select **Customize**. The Advanced Advisor Options window appears.

Copyright © 2011, SAS Institute Inc., Cary, North Carolina, USA. ALL RIGHTS RESERVED.

g) Type **2** as the Class Levels Count Threshold value.

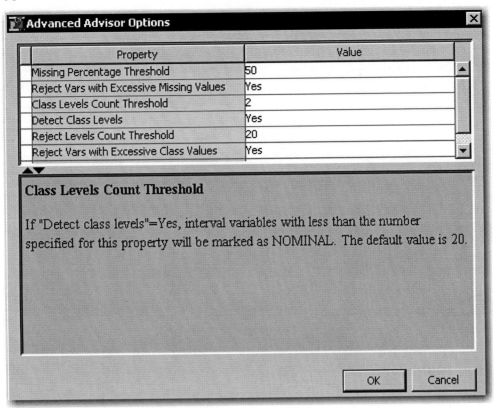

h) Select **OK**. The Advanced Advisor Options window closes and you are returned to Step 4 of the Data Source Wizard.

i) Select **Next**. The wizard proceeds to Step 5.

> By customizing the Advanced Metadata Advisor, most of the roles and levels are correctly set.

Copyright © 2011, SAS Institute Inc., Cary, North Carolina, USA. ALL RIGHTS RESERVED.

j) Select **Role ⇨ Rejected** for **TargetAmt**.

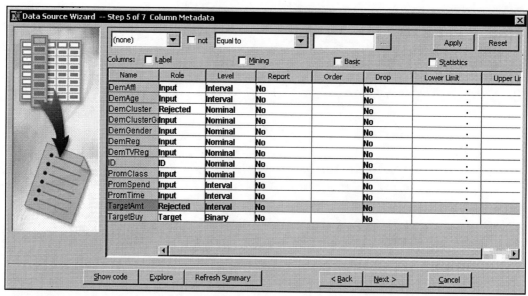

k) Select **TargetBuy** and select **Explore**. The Explore window appears.

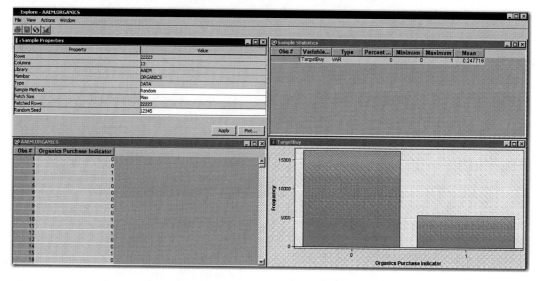

The proportion of individuals who purchased organic products appears to be 25%.

l) Close the Explore window.

3) The variable **DemClusterGroup** contains collapsed levels of the variable **DemCluster**. Presume that, based on previous experience, you believe that **DemClusterGroup** is sufficient for this type of modeling effort. Set the model role for **DemCluster** to **Rejected**.

This is already done using the Advanced Metadata Advisor. Otherwise, select **Role ⇨ Rejected** for **DemCluster**.

Copyright © 2011, SAS Institute Inc., Cary, North Carolina, USA. ALL RIGHTS RESERVED.

4) As noted above, only **TargetBuy** will be used for this analysis and should have a role of Target. Can **TargetAmt** be used as an input for a model used to predict **TargetBuy**? Why or why not?

   No, using TargetAmt as an input is not possible. It is measured at the same time as TargetBuy and therefore has no *causal* relationship to TargetBuy.

5) Finish the **Organics** data source definition.

   a) Select **Next**. The wizard proceeds to Step 6.

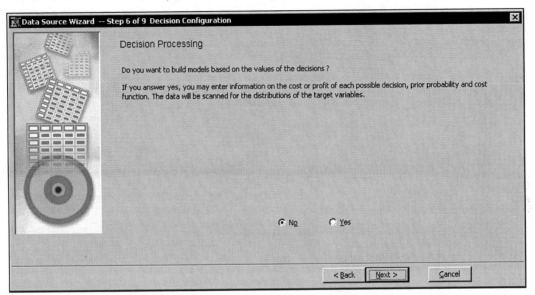

   b) Select **Next** to proceed to the sample data window. No sample data is created. Select **Next**.

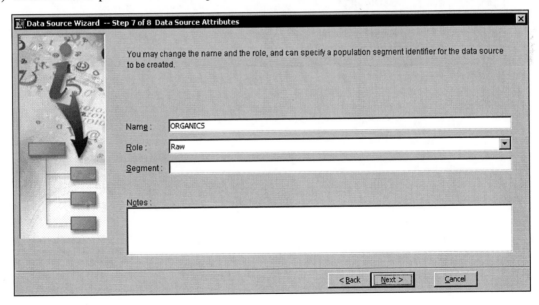

Copyright © 2011, SAS Institute Inc., Cary, North Carolina, USA. ALL RIGHTS RESERVED.

c) Select **Next**.

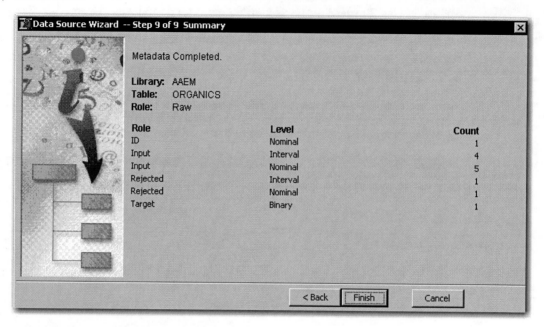

d) Select **Finish**. The wizard closes and the **Organics** data source is ready for use in the Project Panel.

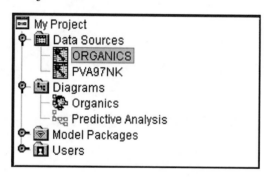

Copyright © 2011, SAS Institute Inc., Cary, North Carolina, USA. ALL RIGHTS RESERVED.

c. Add the **AAEM.ORGANICS** data source to the Organics diagram workspace.

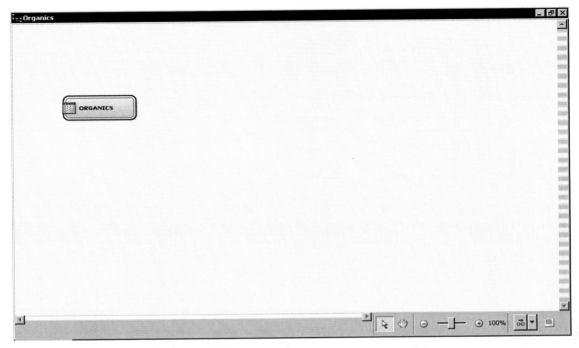

d. Add a **Data Partition** node to the diagram and connect it to the **Data Source** node. Assign 50% of the data for training and 50% for validation.

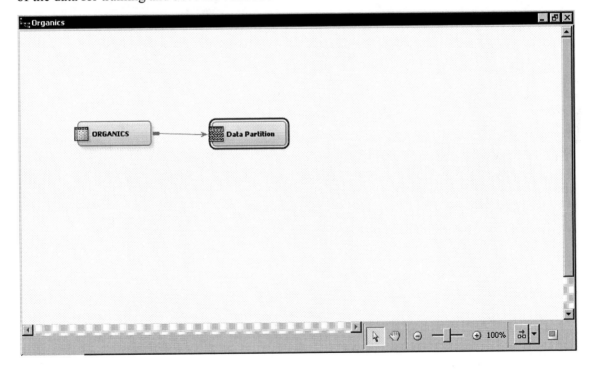

Copyright © 2011, SAS Institute Inc., Cary, North Carolina, USA. ALL RIGHTS RESERVED.

1) Type **50** as the Training and Validation values under Data Set Allocations.

2) Type **0** as the Test value.

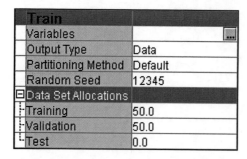

e. Add a **Decision Tree** node to the workspace and connect it to the **Data Partition** node.

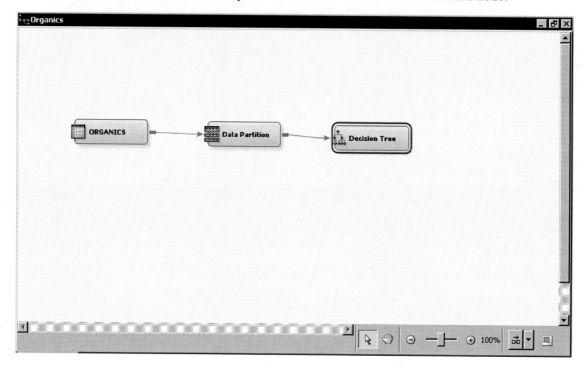

Copyright © 2011, SAS Institute Inc., Cary, North Carolina, USA. ALL RIGHTS RESERVED.

f. Create a decision tree model autonomously. Use average square error as the model assessment statistic.

- Select **Average Square Error** as the Assessment Measure property.

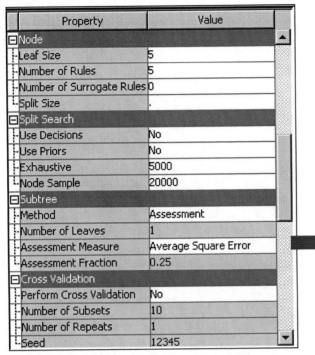

- Right-click on the **Decision Tree** node and select **Run** from the Option menu.
- Select **Yes** in the Confirmation window.

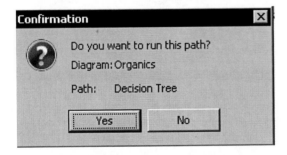

1) How many leaves are in the optimal tree?

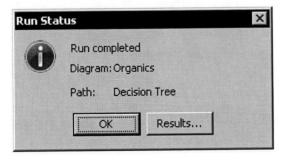

Copyright © 2011, SAS Institute Inc., Cary, North Carolina, USA. ALL RIGHTS RESERVED.

a) When the Decision Tree node run finishes, select **Results** from the Run Status window. The Results window appears.

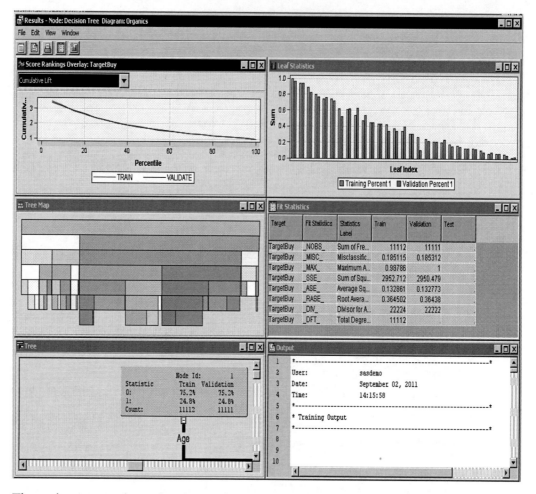

The easiest way to determine the number of leaves in your tree is via the iteration plot.

Copyright © 2011, SAS Institute Inc., Cary, North Carolina, USA. ALL RIGHTS RESERVED.

b) Select **View** ⇨ **Model** ⇨ **Subtree Assessment Plot** from the Result window menu. The Iteration Plot window appears.

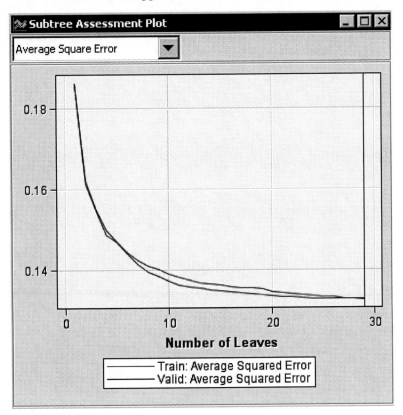

Using average square error as the assessment measure results in a tree with 29 leaves.

2) Which variable was used for the first split? What were the competing splits for this first split?

✎   These questions are best answered using interactive training.

a) Close the Results window for the Decision Tree model.

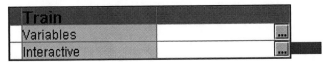

b) Select the Interactive ellipsis (**...**) from the Decision Tree node's Properties panel.

Copyright © 2011, SAS Institute Inc., Cary, North Carolina, USA. ALL RIGHTS RESERVED.

The SAS Enterprise Miner Interactive Decision Tree window appears.

Copyright © 2011, SAS Institute Inc., Cary, North Carolina, USA. ALL RIGHTS RESERVED.

c) Right-click the root node and select **Split Node** from the Option menu. The Split Node 1 window appears with information that answers the two questions.

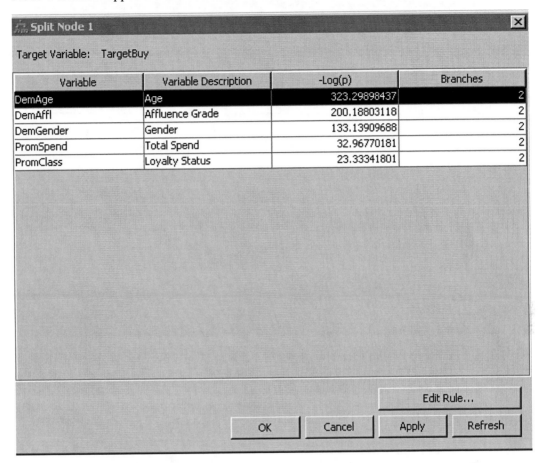

Age is used for the first split.

Competing splits are Affluence Grade, Gender, Total Spend, and Loyalty Status.

Copyright © 2011, SAS Institute Inc., Cary, North Carolina, USA. ALL RIGHTS RESERVED.

g. Add a second **Decision Tree** node to the diagram and connect it to the **Data Partition** node.

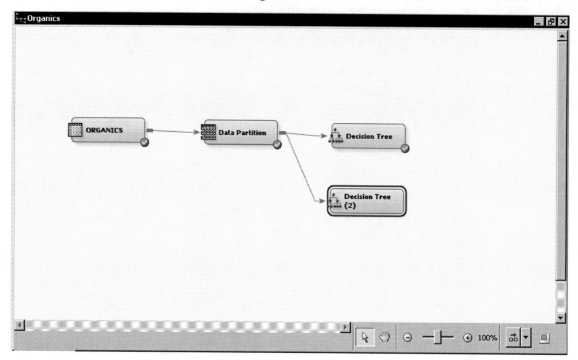

1) In the Properties panel of the new Decision Tree node, change the maximum number of branches from a node to **3** to enable three-way splits.

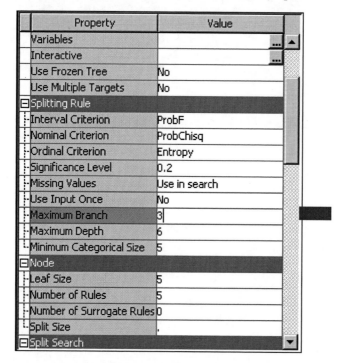

2) Create a decision tree model again. Use average square error as the model assessment statistic.

Copyright © 2011, SAS Institute Inc., Cary, North Carolina, USA. ALL RIGHTS RESERVED.

3) How many leaves are in the optimal tree?

Based on the discussion above, the optimal tree with three-way splits has 33 leaves. This is verified on the subtree assessment plot.

h. Based on average square error, which of the decision tree models appears to be better?

1) Select the first **Decision Tree** node.

2) Right-click and select **Results** from the Option menu. The Results window appears.

3) Examine the Average Squared Error row of the Fit Statistics window.

Target	Fit Statistics	Statistics Label	Train	Validation
TargetBuy	_ASE_	Average Squared Error	0.132861	0.132773

4) Close the Results window.

5) Repeat the process for the Decision Tree (2) model.

Target	Fit Statistics ▲	Statistics Label	Train	Validation	Test
TargetBuy	_ASE_	Average Sq...	0.133009	0.132662	

It appears that the second tree with three-way splits has the lower validation average square error and is the better model.

Copyright © 2011, SAS Institute Inc., Cary, North Carolina, USA. ALL RIGHTS RESERVED.

Solutions to Student Activities (Polls/Quizzes)

3.01 Quiz – Correct Answer

Match the Predictive Modeling Application
to the Decision Type.

Predictive Modeling Application	Decision Type
C Loss Reserving	A. Decision
B Risk Profiling	B. Ranking
B Credit Scoring	C. Estimate
A Fraud Detection	
C Revenue Forecasting	
A Voice Recognition	

26

Copyright © 2011, SAS Institute Inc., Cary, North Carolina, USA. ALL RIGHTS RESERVED.

Chapter 4   Introduction to Predictive Modeling: Regressions

Copyright © 2011, SAS Institute Inc., Cary, North Carolina, USA. ALL RIGHTS RESERVED.

Copyright © 2011, SAS Institute Inc., Cary, North Carolina, USA. ALL RIGHTS RESERVED.

4.1   Introduction

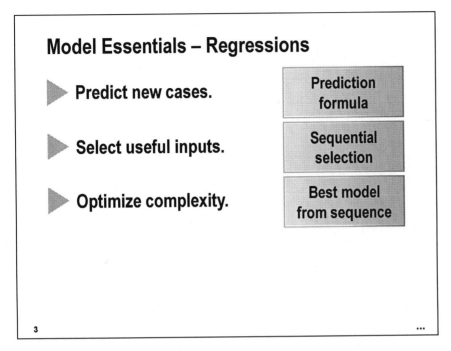

Regressions offer a different approach to prediction compared to decision trees. Regressions, as parametric models, assume a specific association structure between inputs and target. By contrast, trees, as predictive algorithms, do not assume any association structure; they simply seek to isolate concentrations of cases with like-valued target measurements.

The regression approach to the model essentials in SAS Enterprise Miner is outlined in the following pages. Cases are scored using a simple mathematical *prediction formula*. One of several heuristic *sequential selection* techniques is used to pick from a collection of possible inputs and creates a series of models with increasing complexity. Fit statistics calculated from validation data select the *best model from the sequence*.

Copyright © 2011, SAS Institute Inc., Cary, North Carolina, USA. ALL RIGHTS RESERVED.

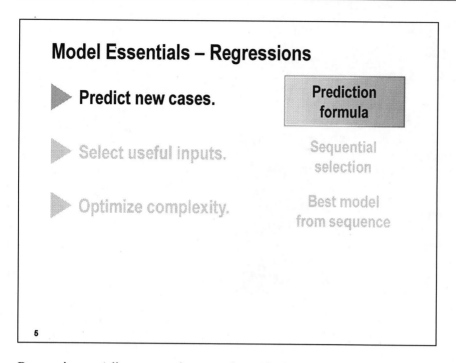

Regressions predict cases using a mathematical equation that involves the values of the input variables.

Copyright © 2011, SAS Institute Inc., Cary, North Carolina, USA. ALL RIGHTS RESERVED.

Linear Regression Prediction Formula

$$\hat{y} = \hat{w}_0 + \hat{w}_1 \cdot x_1 + \hat{w}_2 \cdot x_2$$

input measurement

prediction estimate

intercept parameter estimate estimate

Choose intercept and parameter estimates to *minimize*:

squared error function

$$\sum_{\substack{training \\ data}} (y_i - \hat{y}_i)^2$$

6   ...

In standard linear regression, a prediction estimate for the target variable is formed from a simple linear combination of the inputs. The intercept centers the range of predictions, and the remaining parameter estimates determine the trend strength (or slope) between each input and the target. The simple structure of the model forces changes in predicted values to occur in only a single direction (a vector in the space of inputs with elements equal to the parameter estimates).

Intercept and *parameter estimates* are chosen to minimize the squared error between the predicted and observed target values (least squares estimation). The prediction estimates can be viewed as a linear approximation to the expected (average) value of a target conditioned on observed input values.

Linear regressions are usually deployed for targets with an interval measurement scale.

Copyright © 2011, SAS Institute Inc., Cary, North Carolina, USA. ALL RIGHTS RESERVED.

Logistic Regression Prediction Formula

$$\log\left(\frac{\hat{p}}{1-\hat{p}}\right) = \hat{w}_0 + \hat{w}_1 \cdot x_1 + \hat{w}_2 \cdot x_2 \quad \textit{logit scores}$$

8   ...

Logistic regressions are closely related to linear regressions. In logistic regression, the expected value of the target is transformed by a link function to restrict its value to the unit interval. In this way, model predictions can be viewed as primary outcome probabilities. A linear combination of the inputs generates a *logit score*, the log of the odds of primary outcome, in contrast to the linear regression's direct prediction of the target.

    If your interest is ranking predictions, linear and logistic regressions yield virtually identical results.

Copyright © 2011, SAS Institute Inc., Cary, North Carolina, USA. ALL RIGHTS RESERVED.

Logit Link Function

$$\log\left(\frac{\hat{p}}{1-\hat{p}}\right) = \hat{w}_0 + \hat{w}_1 \cdot x_1 + \hat{w}_2 \cdot x_2 \quad \textit{logit scores}$$

logit link function

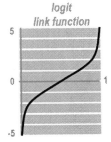

The logit link function transforms probabilities (between 0 and 1) to logit scores (between $-\infty$ and $+\infty$).

9

...

For binary prediction, any monotonic function that maps the unit interval to the real number line can be considered as a link. The logit link function is one of the most common. Its popularity is due, in part, to the interpretability of the model.

Logit Link Function

$$\log\left(\frac{\hat{p}}{1-\hat{p}}\right) = \hat{w}_0 + \hat{w}_1 \cdot x_1 + \hat{w}_2 \cdot x_2 = \text{logit}(\hat{p})$$

$$\hat{p} = \frac{1}{1 + e^{-\text{logit}(\hat{p})}}$$

To obtain prediction estimates, the logit equation is solved for $\hat{p}$.

11

...

The predictions can be decisions, rankings, or estimates. The logit equation produces a ranking or logit score. To get a decision, you need a threshold. The easiest way to get a meaningful threshold is to convert the prediction ranking to a prediction estimate. You can obtain a prediction estimate using a straightforward transformation of the logit score, the logistic function. The *logistic function* is simply the inverse of the logit function. You can obtain the logistic function by solving the logit equation for *p*.

Copyright © 2011, SAS Institute Inc., Cary, North Carolina, USA. ALL RIGHTS RESERVED.

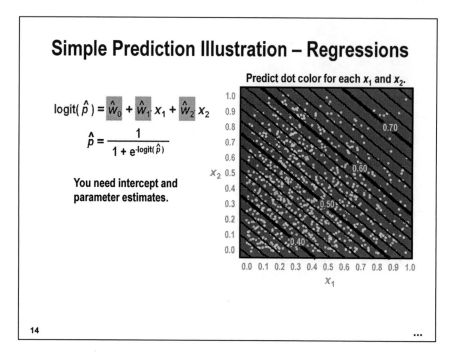

To demonstrate the properties of a logistic regression model, consider the two-color prediction problem introduced in Chapter 3. As before, the goal is to predict the target color, based on the location in the unit square. To make use of the prediction formulation, you need estimates of the intercept and other model parameters.

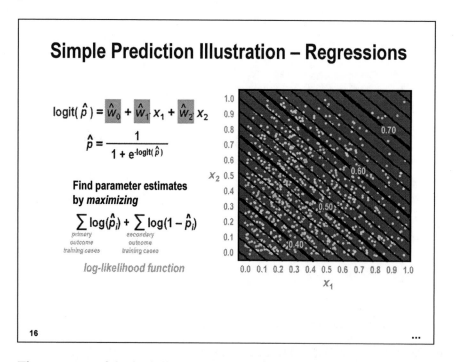

The presence of the logit link function complicates parameter estimation. Least squares estimation is abandoned in favor of maximum likelihood estimation. The likelihood function is the joint probability density of the data treated as a function of the parameters. The maximum likelihood estimates are the values of the parameters that maximize the probability of obtaining the training sample.

Copyright © 2011, SAS Institute Inc., Cary, North Carolina, USA. ALL RIGHTS RESERVED.

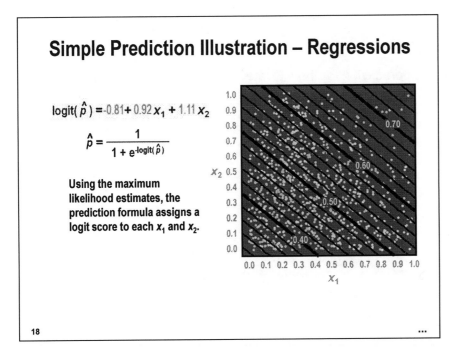

Simple Prediction Illustration – Regressions

$$\text{logit}(\hat{p}) = -0.81 + 0.92\,x_1 + 1.11\,x_2$$

$$\hat{p} = \frac{1}{1 + e^{-\text{logit}(\hat{p})}}$$

Using the maximum likelihood estimates, the prediction formula assigns a logit score to each x_1 and x_2.

18   ...

Parameter estimates are obtained by maximum likelihood estimation. These estimates can be used in the logit and logistic equations to obtain predictions. The plot on the right shows the prediction estimates from the logistic equation. One of the attractions of a standard logistic regression model is the simplicity of its predictions. The contours are simple straight lines. (In higher dimensions, they would be hyperplanes.)

Copyright © 2011, SAS Institute Inc., Cary, North Carolina, USA. ALL RIGHTS RESERVED.

4.01 Multiple Choice Poll

What is the logistic regression prediction for the indicated point?

a. 0.243

b. 0.56

c. yellow

d. It depends.

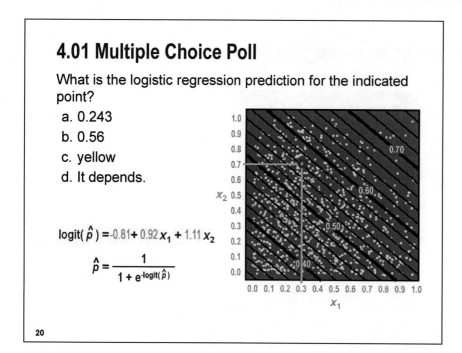

$$\text{logit}(\hat{p}) = -0.81 + 0.92\,x_1 + 1.11\,x_2$$

$$\hat{p} = \frac{1}{1 + e^{-\text{logit}(\hat{p})}}$$

20

To score a new case, the values of the inputs are plugged into the logit or logistic equation. This action creates a logit score or prediction estimate. Typically, if the prediction estimate is greater than 0.5 (or equivalently, the logit score is positive), cases are usually classified to the primary outcome. (This assumes an equal misclassification cost.)

The answer to the question posed is, of course, it depends.

- Answer A , the logit score, is reasonable if the goal is ranking.

- Answer B, the prediction estimate from the logistic equation, is appropriate if the goal is estimation.

- Answer C, a classification, is a good choice if the goal is deciding dot color.

Copyright © 2011, SAS Institute Inc., Cary, North Carolina, USA. ALL RIGHTS RESERVED.

Regressions: Beyond the Prediction Formula

▶ **Manage missing values.**

▶ **Interpret the model.**

▶ **Handle extreme or unusual values.**

▶ **Use nonnumeric inputs.**

▶ **Account for nonlinearities.**

22   ...

While the prediction formula would seem to be the final word in scoring a new case with a regression model, there are actually several additional issues that must be addressed.

- What should be done when one of the input values used in the prediction formula is missing? You might be tempted to simply treat the missing value as zero and skip the term involving the missing value. While this approach can generate a prediction, this prediction is usually biased beyond reason.

- How do you interpret the logistic regression model? Certain inputs influence the prediction more than others. A means to quantify input importance is needed.

- How do you score cases with unusual values? Regression models make their best predictions for cases near the centers of the input distributions. If an input can have (on rare occasion) extreme or *outlying* values, the regression should respond appropriately.

- What value should be used in the prediction formula when the input is not a number? Categorical inputs are common in predictive modeling. They did not present a problem for the rule-based predictions of decision trees, but regression predictions come from algebraic formulas that require numeric inputs. (You cannot multiply marital status by a number.) A method to include nonnumeric data in regression is needed.

- What happens when the relationship between the inputs and the target (or rather logit of the target) is not a straight line? It is preferable to be able to build regression models in the presence of nonlinear (and even nonadditive) input target associations.

Copyright © 2011, SAS Institute Inc., Cary, North Carolina, USA. ALL RIGHTS RESERVED.

Regressions: Beyond the Prediction Formula

▶ **Manage missing values.**

▷ Interpret the model.

▷ Handle extreme or unusual values.

▷ Use nonnumeric inputs.

▷ Account for nonlinearities.

23   ...

✎   The above issues affect both model construction and model deployment. The first of these, handling missing values, is dealt with immediately. The remaining issues are addressed, in turn, at the end of this chapter.

Missing Values and Regression Modeling

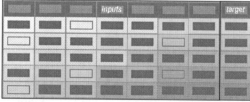

Training Data

Problem 1: Training data cases with missing values on inputs used by a regression model are ignored.

24   ...

Missing values present two distinct problems. The first relates to model construction. The default method for treating missing values in most regression tools in SAS Enterprise Miner is *complete-case analysis*. In complete-case analysis, only those cases without any missing values are used in the analysis.

Copyright © 2011, SAS Institute Inc., Cary, North Carolina, USA. ALL RIGHTS RESERVED.

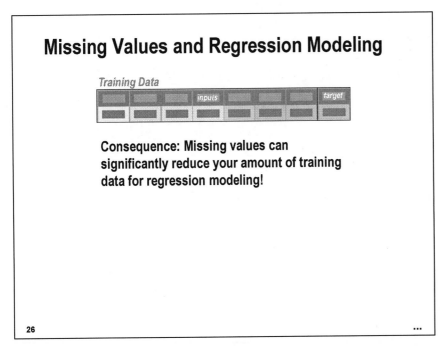

Even a smattering of missing values can cause an enormous loss of data in high dimensions. For instance, suppose that each of the k input variables is missing at random with probability α. In this situation, the expected proportion of complete cases is as follows:

$$(1-\alpha)^k$$

Therefore, a 1% probability of missing ($\alpha=.01$) for 100 inputs retains only 37% of the data for analysis, 200 keeps 13%, and 400 preserves 2%. If the "missingness" were increased to 5% ($\alpha=.05$), then less than 1% of the data would be available with 100 inputs.

Copyright © 2011, SAS Institute Inc., Cary, North Carolina, USA. ALL RIGHTS RESERVED.

Missing Values and the Prediction Formula

$$\text{logit}(\hat{p}) = -0.81 + 0.92 \cdot x_1 + 1.11 \cdot x_2$$

Predict: (x1, x2) = (0.3, ?)

Problem 2: Prediction formulas cannot score cases with missing values.

27   ...

Missing Values and the Prediction Formula

$$\text{logit}(\hat{p}) = ?$$

Problem 2: Prediction formulas cannot score cases with missing values.

30   ...

The second missing value problem relates to model deployment or using the prediction formula. How would a model built on the complete cases score a new case if it had a missing value? To decline to score, new incomplete cases would be practical only if there were a very small number of missing values.

Copyright © 2011, SAS Institute Inc., Cary, North Carolina, USA. ALL RIGHTS RESERVED.

Missing Value Issues

Manage missing values.

Problem 1: Training data cases with missing
values on inputs used by a regression model
are ignored.

Problem 2: Prediction formulas cannot
score cases with missing values.

31   ...

A remedy is needed for the two problems of missing values. The appropriate remedy depends on the
reason for the missing values.

Copyright © 2011, SAS Institute Inc., Cary, North Carolina, USA. ALL RIGHTS RESERVED.

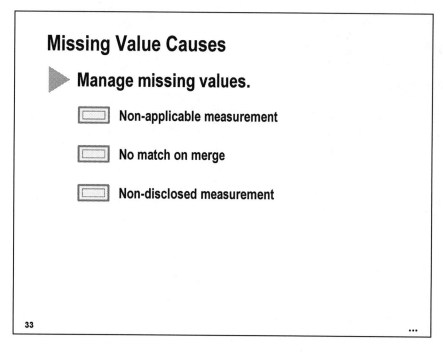

Missing values arise for a variety of reasons. For example, the time since the last donation to a card campaign is meaningless if someone did not donate to a card campaign. In the **PVA97NK** data set, several demographic inputs have missing values in unison. The probable cause was no address match for the donor. Finally, certain information, such as an individual's total wealth, is closely guarded and is often not disclosed.

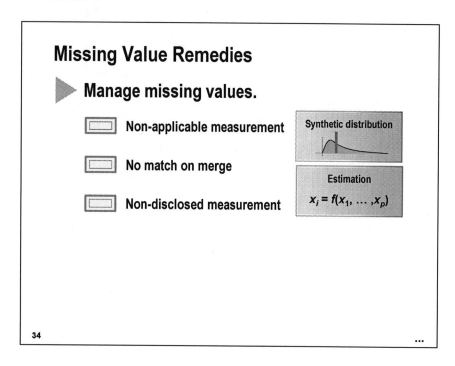

Copyright © 2011, SAS Institute Inc., Cary, North Carolina, USA. ALL RIGHTS RESERVED.

The primary remedy for missing values in regression models is a missing value replacement strategy. Missing value replacement strategies fall into one of two categories.

Synthetic distribution methods	use a one-size-fits-all approach to handle missing values. Any case with a missing input measurement has the missing value replaced with a fixed number. The net effect is to modify an input's distribution to include a point mass at the selected fixed number. The location of the point mass in synthetic distribution methods is not arbitrary. Ideally, it should be chosen to have minimal impact on the magnitude of an input's association with the target. With many modeling methods, this can be achieved by locating the point mass at the input's mean value.
Estimation methods	eschew the one-size-fits-all approach and provide tailored imputations for each case with missing values. This is done by viewing the missing value problem as a prediction problem. That is, you can train a model to predict an input's value from other inputs. Then, when an input's value is unknown, you can use this model to predict or estimate the unknown missing value. This approach is best suited for missing values that result from a lack of knowledge, that is, no-match or nondisclosure, but it is not appropriate for not-applicable missing values.

Because a predicted response might be different for cases with a missing input value, a binary imputation indicator variable is often added to the training data. Adding this variable enables a model to adjust its predictions in the situation where "missingness" itself is correlated with the target.

Copyright © 2011, SAS Institute Inc., Cary, North Carolina, USA. ALL RIGHTS RESERVED.

Managing Missing Values

The demonstrations in this chapter build on the demonstrations of Chapters 2 and 3. At this point, the process flow diagram has the following structure:

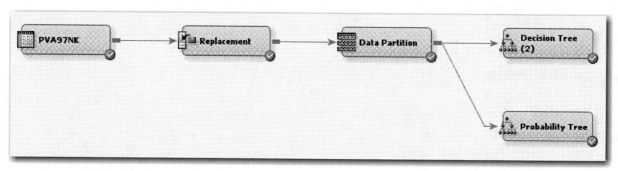

Data Assessment

Continue the analysis at the Data Partition node. As discussed above, regression requires that a case have a complete set of input values for both training and scoring. Follow these steps to examine the data status after the partition.

1. Select the **Data Partition** node.

2. Select **Exported Data** ⇨ **...** from the Data Partition node property sheet.

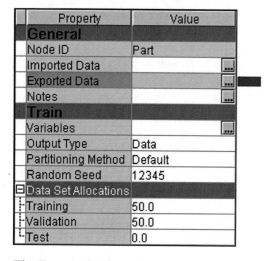

The Exported Data window appears.

Copyright © 2011, SAS Institute Inc., Cary, North Carolina, USA. ALL RIGHTS RESERVED.

3. Select the **TRAIN** data port and select **Explore**.

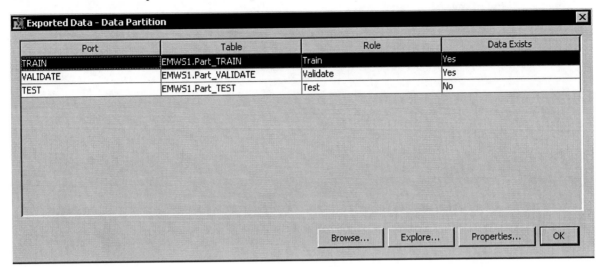

Copyright © 2011, SAS Institute Inc., Cary, North Carolina, USA. ALL RIGHTS RESERVED.

There are several inputs with a noticeable frequency of missing values, for example, **Age** and the replaced value of median income.

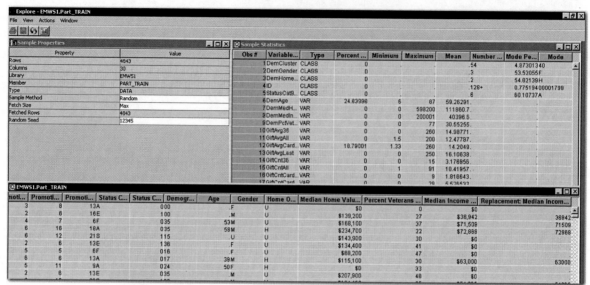

Median Home Valu...	Percent Veterans ...	Median Income ...	Replacement: Median Incom...
$0	0	$0	.
$139,200	27	$38,942	38942
$168,100	37	$71,509	71509
$234,700	22	$72,868	72868
$143,900	30	$0	.
$134,400	41	$0	.
$68,200	47	$0	.
$115,100	30	$63,000	63000
$0	33	$0	.
$207,900	48	$0	.
$104,400	35	$54,385	54385

There are several ways to proceed:

- ***Do nothing.*** If there are very few cases with missing values, this is a viable option. The difficulty with this approach comes when the model must predict a new case that contains a missing value. Omitting the missing term from the parametric equation usually produces an extremely biased prediction.

Copyright © 2011, SAS Institute Inc., Cary, North Carolina, USA. ALL RIGHTS RESERVED.

- *Impute* a synthetic value for the missing value. For example, if an interval input contains a missing value, replace the missing value with the mean of the nonmissing values for the input. This eliminates the incomplete case problem but modifies the input's distribution. This can bias the model predictions.

  Making the missing value imputation process part of the modeling process allays the modified distribution concern. Any modifications made to the training data are also made to the validation data and the remainder of the modeling population. A model trained with the modified training data will not be biased if the same modifications are made to any other data set that the model might encounter (and the data has a similar pattern of missing values).

- Create a *missing indicator* for each input in the data set. Cases often contain missing values for a reason. If the reason for the missing value is in some way related to the target variable, useful predictive information is lost.

  The missing indicator is 1 when the corresponding input is missing and 0 otherwise. Each missing indicator becomes an input to the model. This enables modeling of the association between the target and a missing value on an input.

4. Close the Explore and Exported Data windows.

Imputation

To address missing values in the **PVA97NK** data set, use the following steps to impute synthetic data values and create missing value indicators:

1. Select the **Modify** tab.

2. Drag an **Impute** tool into the diagram workspace.

3. Connect the **Data Partition** node to the **Impute** node. In the display, below, the Decision Tree modeling nodes are repositioned for clarity.

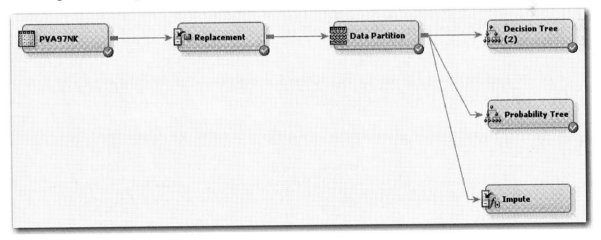

Copyright © 2011, SAS Institute Inc., Cary, North Carolina, USA. ALL RIGHTS RESERVED.

4.   Select the **Impute** node and examine the Properties panel.

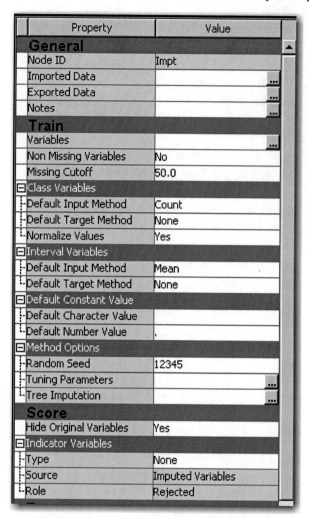

The defaults of the Impute node are as follows:

- For interval inputs, replace any missing values with the mean of the nonmissing values.

- For categorical inputs, replace any missing values with the most frequent category.

✎   These are acceptable default values and are used throughout the rest of the course.

With these settings, each input with missing values generates a new input. The new input named IMP_*original_input_name* will have missing values replaced by a synthetic value and nonmissing values copied from the original input.

Copyright © 2011, SAS Institute Inc., Cary, North Carolina, USA. ALL RIGHTS RESERVED.

Missing Indicators

Use the steps below to create missing value indicators. The settings for missing value indicators are found in the Score property group.

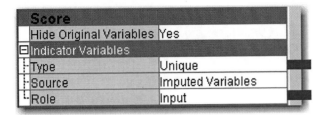

1.   Select **Indicator Variables** ⇨ **Type** ⇨ **Unique**.

2.   Select **Indicator Variables** ⇨ **Role** ⇨ **Input**.

With these settings, new inputs named M_*original_input_name* are added to the training data to indicate the synthetic data values.

Imputation Results

Run the Impute node and review the Results window. Three inputs had missing values.

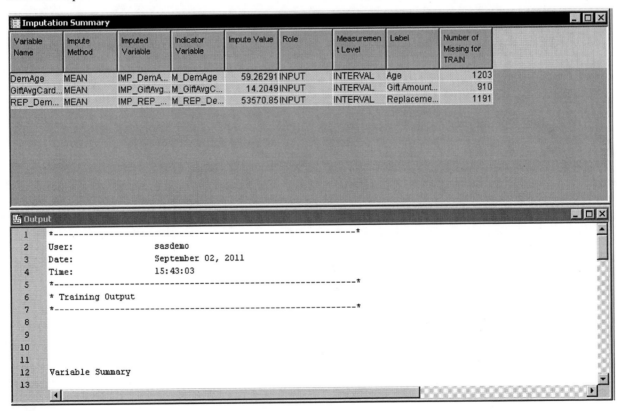

With all of the missing values imputed, the entire training data set is available for building the logistic regression model. In addition, a method is in place for scoring new cases with missing values. (See Chapter 7.)

Copyright © 2011, SAS Institute Inc., Cary, North Carolina, USA. ALL RIGHTS RESERVED.

Running the Regression Node

There are several tools in SAS Enterprise Miner to fit regression or regression-like models. By far, the most commonly used (and, arguably, the most useful) is the *Regression tool*.

Use the following steps to build a simple regression model.

1. Select the **Model** tab.

2. Drag a **Regression** tool into the diagram workspace.

3. Connect the **Impute** node to the **Regression** node.

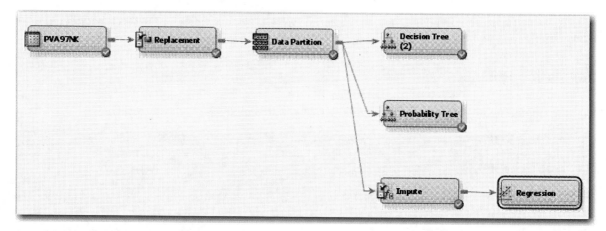

The Regression node can create several types of regression models, including linear and logistic. The type of default regression type is determined by the target's measurement level.

Copyright © 2011, SAS Institute Inc., Cary, North Carolina, USA. ALL RIGHTS RESERVED.

4. Run the Regression node and view the results. The Results - Node: Regression Diagram window appears.

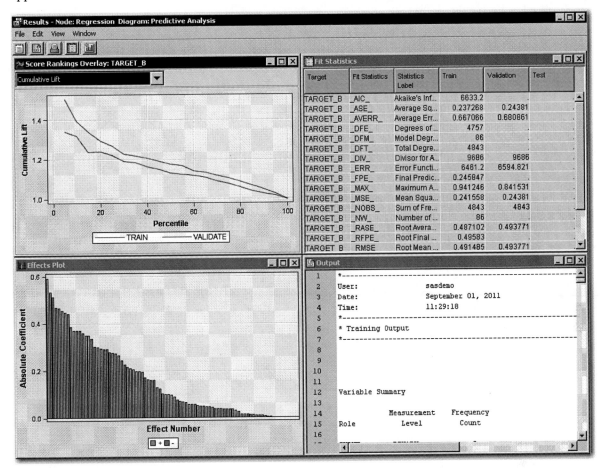

5. Maximize the Output window by double-clicking its title bar.

The initial lines of the Output window summarize the roles of variables used (or not) by the Regression node.

```
Variable Summary

                    Measurement    Frequency
Role                   Level          Count

INPUT               BINARY             5
INPUT               INTERVAL          20
INPUT               NOMINAL            3
REJECTED            INTERVAL           2
TARGET              BINARY             1
```

The fit model has 28 inputs that predict a binary target.

Copyright © 2011, SAS Institute Inc., Cary, North Carolina, USA. ALL RIGHTS RESERVED.

Ignore the output related to model events and predicted and decision variables. The next lines give more information about the model, including the training data set name, target variable name, number of target categories, and most importantly, the number of model parameters.

```
                          Model Information

        Training Data Set        EMWS2.IMPT_TRAIN.VIEW
        DMDB Catalog             WORK.REG_DMDB
        Target Variable          TargetB (Target Gift Flag)
        Target Measurement Level    Ordinal
        Number of Target Categories  2
        Error                    MBernoulli
        Link Function            Logit
        Number of Model Parameters   86
        Number of Observations      4843
```

Based on the introductory material about logistic regression that is presented above, you might expect to have a number of model parameters equal to the number of input variables. This ignores the fact that a single nominal input (for example, **DemCluster**) can generate scores of model parameters.

Next, consider maximum likelihood procedure, overall model fit, and the Type 3 Analysis of Effects.

The Type 3 Analysis tests the statistical significance of adding the indicated input to a model that already contains other listed inputs. A value near 0 in the Pr > ChiSq column approximately indicates a significant input; a value near 1 indicates an extraneous input.

Type 3 Analysis of Effects

Effect	DF	Wald Chi-Square	Pr > ChiSq
DemCluster	53	58.9098	0.2682
DemGender	2	0.5088	0.7754
DemHomeOwner	1	0.1630	0.6864
DemMedHomeValue	1	2.4464	0.1178
DemPctVeterans	1	5.2502	0.0219
GiftAvg36	1	1.6709	0.1961
GiftAvgAll	1	0.0339	0.8540
GiftAvgLast	1	0.0026	0.9593
GiftCnt36	1	1.2230	0.2688
GiftCntAll	1	0.1308	0.7176
GiftCntCard36	1	1.0244	0.3115
GiftCntCardAll	1	0.0061	0.9380
GiftTimeFirst	1	1.6064	0.2050
GiftTimeLast	1	21.5351	<.0001
IMP_DemAge	1	0.0701	0.7911
IMP_GiftAvgCard36	1	0.0476	0.8273
IMP_REP_DemMedIncome	1	0.1408	0.7074
M_DemAge	1	3.0616	0.0802
M_GiftAvgCard36	1	0.9190	0.3377
M_REP_DemMedIncome	1	0.6228	0.4300
PromCnt12	1	3.2335	0.0721
PromCnt36	1	1.0866	0.2972
PromCntAll	1	1.9715	0.1603
PromCntCard12	1	0.0294	0.8639
PromCntCard36	1	0.0049	0.9441
PromCntCardAll	1	2.9149	0.0878
StatusCat96NK	5	11.3434	0.0450
StatusCatStarAll	1	1.7487	0.1860

Copyright © 2011, SAS Institute Inc., Cary, North Carolina, USA. ALL RIGHTS RESERVED.

The statistical significance measures a range from <0.0001 (highly significant) to 0.9593 (highly dubious). Results such as this suggest that certain inputs can be eliminated without affecting the predictive prowess of the model.

6. Restore the Output window to its original size by double-clicking its title bar. Maximize the Fit Statistics window.

Target	Fit Statistics	Statistics Label	Train	Validation
TARGET_B	_AIC_	Akaike's Information Criterion	6633.2	
TARGET_B	_ASE_	Average Squared Error	0.237268	0.24381
TARGET_B	_AVERR_	Average Error Function	0.667066	0.680861
TARGET_B	_DFE_	Degrees of Freedom for Error	4757	
TARGET_B	_DFM_	Model Degrees of Freedom	86	
TARGET_B	_DFT_	Total Degrees of Freedom	4843	
TARGET_B	_DIV_	Divisor for ASE	9686	9686
TARGET_B	_ERR_	Error Function	6461.2	6594.821
TARGET_B	_FPE_	Final Prediction Error	0.245847	
TARGET_B	_MAX_	Maximum Absolute Error	0.941246	0.841531
TARGET_B	_MSE_	Mean Square Error	0.241558	0.24381
TARGET_B	_NOBS_	Sum of Frequencies	4843	4843
TARGET_B	_NW_	Number of Estimate Weights	86	
TARGET_B	_RASE_	Root Average Sum of Squares	0.487102	0.493771
TARGET_B	_RFPE_	Root Final Prediction Error	0.49583	
TARGET_B	_RMSE_	Root Mean Squared Error	0.491485	0.493771
TARGET_B	_SBC_	Schwarz's Bayesian Criterion	7190.935	
TARGET_B	_SSE_	Sum of Squared Errors	2298.179	2361.545
TARGET_B	_SUMW_	Sum of Case Weights Times Freq	9686	9686
TARGET_B	_MISC_	Misclassification Rate	0.411522	0.431964

If the decision predictions are of interest, model fit can be judged by misclassification. If estimate predictions are the focus, model fit can be assessed by average squared error. There appears to be some discrepancy between the values of these two statistics in the train and validation data. This indicates a possible overfit of the model. It can be mitigated by using an input selection procedure.

7. Close the Results window.

Copyright © 2011, SAS Institute Inc., Cary, North Carolina, USA. ALL RIGHTS RESERVED.

4.2 Selecting Regression Inputs

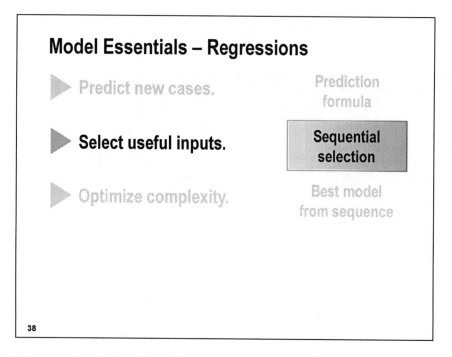

The second task that all predictive models should perform is input selection. One way to find the optimal set of inputs for a regression is simply to try every combination. Unfortunately, the number of models to consider using this approach increases exponentially in the number of available inputs. Such an exhaustive search is impractical for realistic prediction problems.

An alternative to the exhaustive search is to restrict the search to a sequence of improving models. While this might not find the single best model, it is commonly used to find models with good predictive performance. The Regression node in SAS Enterprise Miner provides three sequential selection methods.

Copyright © 2011, SAS Institute Inc., Cary, North Carolina, USA. ALL RIGHTS RESERVED.

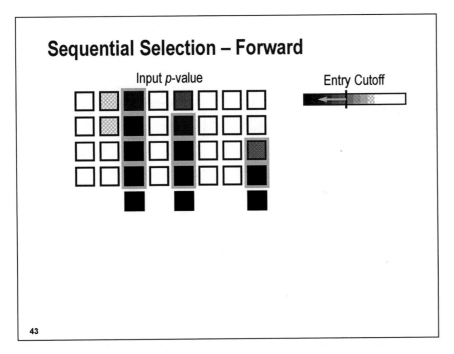

Forward selection creates a sequence of models of increasing complexity. The sequence starts with the baseline model, a model predicting the overall average target value for all cases. The algorithm searches the set of one-input models and selects the model that most improves on the baseline model. It then searches the set of two-input models that contain the input selected in the previous step and selects the model showing the most significant improvement. By adding a new input to those selected in the previous step, a nested sequence of increasingly complex models is generated. The sequence terminates when no significant improvement can be made.

Improvement is quantified by the usual statistical measure of significance, the p-value. Adding terms in this nested fashion always increases a model's overall fit statistic. By calculating the change in the fit statistic and assuming that the change conforms to a chi-squared distribution, a significance probability, or p-value, can be calculated. A large fit statistic change (corresponding to a large chi-squared value) is unlikely due to chance. Therefore, a small p-value indicates a significant improvement. When no p-value is below a predetermined entry cutoff, the forward selection procedure terminates.

Copyright © 2011, SAS Institute Inc., Cary, North Carolina, USA. ALL RIGHTS RESERVED.

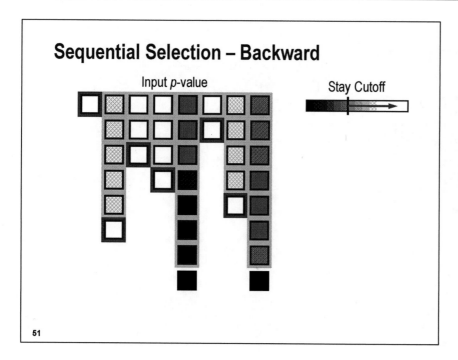

In contrast to forward selection, *backward selection* creates a sequence of models of ***decreasing*** complexity. The sequence starts with a saturated model, which is a model that contains all available inputs, and therefore, has the highest possible fit statistic. Inputs are sequentially removed from the model. At each step, the input chosen for removal least reduces the overall model fit statistic. This is equivalent to removing the input with the highest p-value. The sequence terminates when all remaining inputs have a p-value that is less than the predetermined stay cutoff.

Copyright © 2011, SAS Institute Inc., Cary, North Carolina, USA. ALL RIGHTS RESERVED.

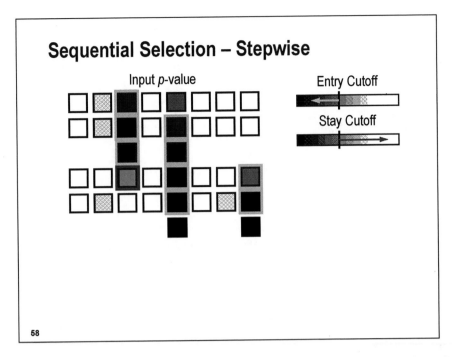

Sequential Selection – Stepwise

58

Stepwise selection combines elements from both the forward and backward selection procedures. The method begins in the same way as the forward procedure, sequentially adding inputs with the smallest p-value below the entry cutoff. After each input is added, however, the algorithm reevaluates the statistical significance of all included inputs. If the p-value of any of the included inputs exceeds the stay cutoff, the input is removed from the model and reentered into the pool of inputs that are available for inclusion in a subsequent step. The process terminates when all inputs available for inclusion in the model have p-values in excess of the entry cutoff and all inputs already included in the model have p-values below the stay cutoff.

4.02 Poll

The three sequential selection methods for building regression models can never lead to the same model for the same set of data.

○ True
○ False

60

Copyright © 2011, SAS Institute Inc., Cary, North Carolina, USA. ALL RIGHTS RESERVED.

Selecting Inputs

Implementing a sequential selection method in the Regression node requires a minor change to the Regression node settings.

1. Select **Selection Model** ⇨ **Stepwise** on the Regression node property sheet.

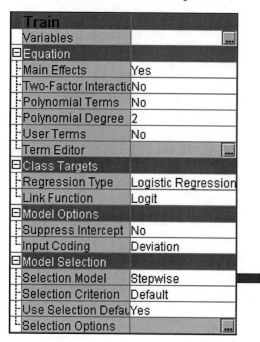

Train	
Variables	[...]
⊟Equation	
Main Effects	Yes
Two-Factor Interactic	No
Polynomial Terms	No
Polynomial Degree	2
User Terms	No
Term Editor	[...]
⊟Class Targets	
Regression Type	Logistic Regression
Link Function	Logit
⊟Model Options	
Suppress Intercept	No
Input Coding	Deviation
⊟Model Selection	
Selection Model	Stepwise
Selection Criterion	Default
Use Selection Defau	Yes
Selection Options	[...]

The Regression node is now configured to use stepwise selection to choose inputs for the model.

2. Run the Regression node and view the results.

3. Maximize the Output window.

4. Hold down the **CTRL** key and type **G**. The Go To Line window appears.

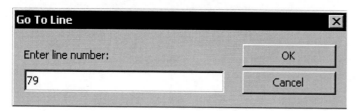

Go To Line	✕
Enter line number:	OK
79	Cancel

5. Type **79** in the **Enter line number** field and select **OK**. Scroll down one page from line 79.

Copyright © 2011, SAS Institute Inc., Cary, North Carolina, USA. ALL RIGHTS RESERVED.

The stepwise procedure starts with Step 0, an intercept-only regression model. The value of the intercept parameter is chosen so that the model predicts the overall target mean for every case. The parameter estimate and the training data target measurements are combined in an objective function. The objective function is determined by the model form and the error distribution of the target. The value of the objective function for the intercept-only model is compared to the values obtained in subsequent steps for more complex models. A large decrease in the objective function for the more complex model indicates a significantly better model.

```
                        Step 0: Intercept entered.
                          The DMREG Procedure
                   Newton-Raphson Ridge Optimization
                       Without Parameter Scaling
                                      Parameter Estimates                1


                           Optimization Start

Active Constraints          0  Objective Function   3356.9116922
Max Abs Gradient Element  5.707879E-12


                          Optimization Results

Iterations              0  Function Calls              3
Hessian Calls           1  Active Constraints            0
Objective Function   3356.9116922  Max Abs Gradient Element      5.707879E-12
Ridge                   0  Actual Over Pred Change       0

Convergence criterion (ABSGCONV=0.00001) satisfied.

   Likelihood Ratio Test for Global Null Hypothesis: BETA=0

   -2 Log Likelihood     Likelihood
 Intercept   Intercept &    Ratio
   Only      Covariates   Chi-Square     DF    Pr > ChiSq

  6713.823    6713.823      0.0000     0       .

                   Analysis of Maximum Likelihood Estimates

                  Standard     Wald        Standardized
Parameter   DF   Estimate    Error   Chi-Square  Pr > ChiSq    Estimate  Exp(Est)

Intercept   1   -0.00041    0.0287     0.00      0.9885          1.000
```

Copyright © 2011, SAS Institute Inc., Cary, North Carolina, USA. ALL RIGHTS RESERVED.

Step 1 adds one input to the intercept-only model. The input and corresponding parameter are chosen to produce the largest decrease in the objective function. To estimate the values of the model parameters, the modeling algorithm makes an initial guess for their values. The initial guess is combined with the training data measurements in the objective function. Based on statistical theory, the objective function is assumed to take its minimum value at the correct estimate for the parameters. The algorithm decides whether changing the values of the initial parameter estimates can decrease the value of the objective function. If so, the parameter estimates are changed to decrease the value of the objective function and the process iterates. The algorithm continues iterating until changes in the parameter estimates fail to substantially decrease the value of the objective function.

```
                         Step 1: Effect GiftCnt36 entered.


                              The DMREG Procedure
                        Newton-Raphson Ridge Optimization
                            Without Parameter Scaling


                                          Parameter Estimates              2


                               Optimization Start

Active Constraints          0   Objective Function   3356.9116922
Max Abs Gradient Element  89.678463762
                                     Ratio
                                    Between
                                    Actual
                      Objective    Max Abs         and
           Function   Active  Objective   Function  Gradient        Predicted
Iter Restarts Calls Constraints  Function   Change   Element  Ridge    Change
  1     0      2        0         3316     41.4036   2.1746    0    1.014
  2     0      3        0         3315      0.0345   0.00690   0    1.002
  3     0      4        0         3315     2.278E-7  4.833E-8  0    1.000

                               Optimization Results

Iterations              3 Function Calls              6
Hessian Calls           4 Active Constraints          0
Objective Function   3315.473573 Max Abs Gradient Element    4.833086E-8
Ridge                   0 Actual Over Pred Change   0.999858035

Convergence criterion (GCONV=1E-6) satisfied.
```

The output next compares the model fit in Step 1 with the model fit in Step 0. The objective functions of both models are multiplied by 2 and differenced. The difference is assumed to have a chi-squared distribution with one degree of freedom. The hypothesis that the two models are identical is tested. A large value for the chi-squared statistic makes this hypothesis unlikely.

The hypothesis test is summarized in the next lines.

```
           Likelihood Ratio Test for Global Null Hypothesis: BETA=0


     -2 Log Likelihood       Likelihood
  Intercept    Intercept &     Ratio
     Only      Covariates    Chi-Square   DF   Pr > ChiSq

   6713.823    6630.947       82.8762     1      <.0001
```

Copyright © 2011, SAS Institute Inc., Cary, North Carolina, USA. ALL RIGHTS RESERVED.

The output summarizes an analysis of the statistical significance of individual model effects. For the one input model, this is similar to the global significance test above.

```
                    Type 3 Analysis of Effects

                        Wald
Effect          DF  Chi-Square  Pr > ChiSq
GiftCnt36        1    79.4757     <.0001
```

Finally, an analysis of individual parameter estimates is made. (The standardized estimates and the odds ratios merit special attention and are discussed in the next section of this chapter.)

```
               Analysis of Maximum Likelihood Estimates

                  Standard    Wald        Standardized
Parameter    DF   Estimate   Error   Chi-Square  Pr > ChiSq   Estimate  Exp(Est)

Intercept     1   -0.3956   0.0526     56.53      <.0001                 0.673
GiftCnt36     1    0.1250   0.0140     79.48      <.0001       0.1474    1.133


     Odds Ratio Estimates
               Point
Effect        Estimate
GiftCnt36      1.133
```

The standardized estimates present the effect of the input on the log-odds of donation. The values are standardized to be independent of the input's unit of measure. This provides a means of ranking the importance of inputs in the model.

The odds ratio estimates indicate by what factor the odds of donation increase for each unit change in the associated input. Combined with knowledge of the range of the input, this provides an excellent way to judge the practical (as opposed to the statistical) importance of an input in the model.

The stepwise selection process continues for eight steps. After the eighth step, neither adding nor removing inputs from the model significantly changes the model fit statistic. At this point, the Output window provides a summary of the stepwise procedure.

6. Go to line 850 and page down one page to view the stepwise summary.

The summary shows the step in which each input was added and the statistical significance of each input in the final eight-input model.

```
NOTE: No (additional) effects met the 0.05 significance level for entry into the model.

                     Summary of Stepwise Selection

          Effect         Number     Score      Wald
  Step    Entered       DF   In   Chi-Square  Chi-Square  Pr > ChiSq

    1    GiftCnt36        1    1    81.6807                  <.0001
    2    GiftTimeLast     1    2    23.2884                  <.0001
    3    DemMedHomeValue  1    3    16.9872                  <.0001
    4    GiftAvgAll       1    4    14.8514                  0.0001
    5    StatusCat96NK    5    5    18.2293                  0.0027
    6    DemPctVeterans   1    6     7.4187                  0.0065
    7    M_GiftAvgCard36  1    7     7.1729                  0.0074
    8    M_DemAge         1    8     4.6501      0.0311
```

Copyright © 2011, SAS Institute Inc., Cary, North Carolina, USA. ALL RIGHTS RESERVED.

The default selection criterion selects the model from Step 8 as the model with optimal complexity. As the next section shows, this might not be the optimal model, based on the fit statistic that is appropriate for your analysis objective.

```
The selected model is the model trained in the last step (Step 8). It consists of the following effects:

Intercept  DemMedHomeValue  DemPctVeterans  GiftAvgAll  GiftCnt36  GiftTimeLast  M_DemAge  M_GiftAvgCard36  StatusCat96NK
```

For convenience, the output from Step 8 is repeated. An excerpt from the analysis of individual parameter estimates is shown below.

```
                    Analysis of Maximum Likelihood Estimates

                      Standard   Wald        Standardized
Parameter        DF  Estimate   Error  Chi-Square  Pr > ChiSq  Estimate  Exp(Est)

Intercept         1   0.2727   0.2024     1.82      0.1779       1.314
DemMedHomeValue   1  1.385E-6  3.009E-7  21.18     <.0001       0.0763    1.000
DemPctVeterans    1   0.00658  0.00261    6.38      0.0115      0.0412    1.007
GiftAvgAll        1  -0.0136   0.00444    9.33      0.0023     -0.0608    0.987
GiftCnt36         1   0.0587   0.0187     9.79      0.0018      0.0692    1.060
GiftTimeLast      1  -0.0376   0.00770   23.90     <.0001      -0.0837    0.963
M_DemAge       0  1   0.0741   0.0344     4.65      0.0311                1.077
M_GiftAvgCard36 0 1   0.1112   0.0411     7.30      0.0069                1.118
StatusCat96NK  A  1  -0.0880   0.0927     0.90      0.3423                0.916
StatusCat96NK  E  1   0.4974   0.1818     7.48      0.0062                1.644
StatusCat96NK  F  1  -0.4570   0.1303    12.30      0.0005                0.633
StatusCat96NK  L  1   0.1456   0.3735     0.15      0.6966                1.157
StatusCat96NK  N  1  -0.1206   0.1323     0.83      0.3621                0.886
```

The parameter with the largest standardized estimate (in absolute value) is **GiftTimeLast**.

Copyright © 2011, SAS Institute Inc., Cary, North Carolina, USA. ALL RIGHTS RESERVED.

7. Restore the Output window and maximize the Fit Statistics window.

Target	Fit Statistics	Statistics Label	Train	Validation
TARGET_B	_AIC_	Akaike's Information Criterion	6563.093	.
TARGET_B	_ASE_	Average Squared Error	0.240919	0.242336
TARGET_B	_AVERR_	Average Error Function	0.674901	0.678517
TARGET_B	_DFE_	Degrees of Freedom for Error	4830	.
TARGET_B	_DFM_	Model Degrees of Freedom	13	.
TARGET_B	_DFT_	Total Degrees of Freedom	4843	.
TARGET_B	_DIV_	Divisor for ASE	9686	9686
TARGET_B	_ERR_	Error Function	6537.093	6572.12
TARGET_B	_FPE_	Final Prediction Error	0.242216	.
TARGET_B	_MAX_	Maximum Absolute Error	0.965413	0.998582
TARGET_B	_MSE_	Mean Square Error	0.241567	0.242336
TARGET_B	_NOBS_	Sum of Frequencies	4843	4843
TARGET_B	_NW_	Number of Estimate Weights	13	
TARGET_B	_RASE_	Root Average Sum of Squares	0.490835	0.492277
TARGET_B	_RFPE_	Root Final Prediction Error	0.492154	.
TARGET_B	_RMSE_	Root Mean Squared Error	0.491495	0.492277
TARGET_B	_SBC_	Schwarz's Bayesian Criterion	6647.402	.
TARGET_B	_SSE_	Sum of Squared Errors	2333.54	2347.27
TARGET_B	_SUMW_	Sum of Case Weights Times Freq	9686	9686
TARGET_B	_MISC_	Misclassification Rate	0.421433	0.42453

The simpler model improves on both the validation misclassification and average squared error measures of model performance.

Copyright © 2011, SAS Institute Inc., Cary, North Carolina, USA. ALL RIGHTS RESERVED.

4.3 Optimizing Regression Complexity

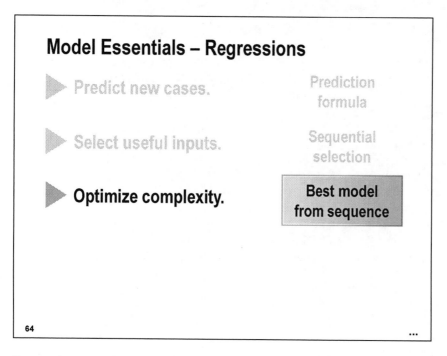

Regression complexity is optimized by choosing the optimal model in the sequential selection sequence.

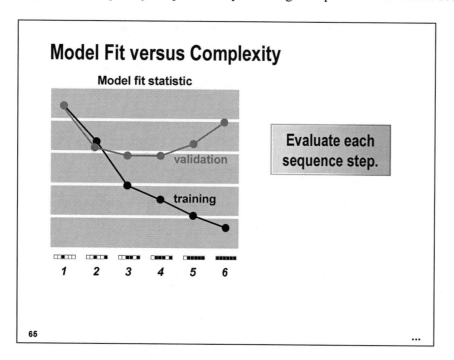

The process involves two steps. First, fit statistics are calculated for the models generated in each step of the selection process. Both the training and validation data sets are used.

Copyright © 2011, SAS Institute Inc., Cary, North Carolina, USA. ALL RIGHTS RESERVED.

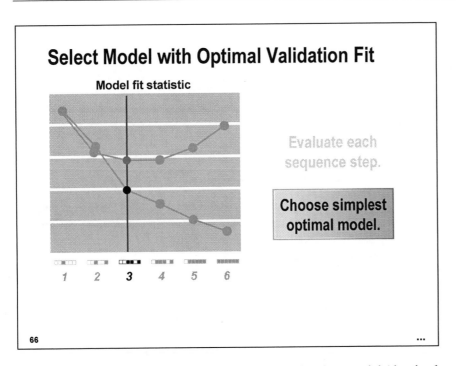

Then, as with the decision tree in Chapter 3, the simplest model (that is, the one with the fewest inputs) with the optimal fit statistic is selected.

Copyright © 2011, SAS Institute Inc., Cary, North Carolina, USA. ALL RIGHTS RESERVED.

 **Optimizing Complexity**

Iteration Plot

The following steps illustrate the use of the iteration plot in the Regression tool Results window.

In the same manner as the decision tree, you can tune a regression model to give optimal performance on the validation data. The basic idea involves calculating a fit statistic for each step in the input selection procedure and selecting the step (and corresponding model) with the optimal fit statistic value. To avoid bias, the fit statistic should be calculated on the validation data set.

1. Select **View** ⇨ **Model** ⇨ **Iteration Plot**. The Iteration Plot window appears.

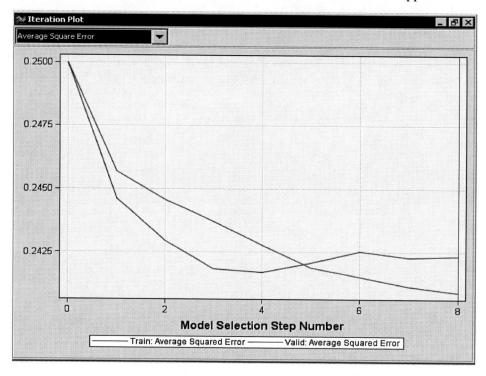

The Iteration Plot window shows (by default) average squared error (training and validation) from the model selected in each step of the stepwise selection process.

    Surprisingly, this plot contradicts the naïve assumption that a model fit statistic calculated on training data will ***always*** be better than the same statistic calculated on validation data. This concept, called the *optimism principle*, is correct only ***on the average***, and usually manifests itself only when overly complex (overly flexible) models are considered. It is not uncommon for training and validation fit statistic plots to cross (possibly several times). These crossings illustrate unquantified variability in the fit statistics.

Apparently, the smallest average squared error occurs in Step 4, rather than in the final model, Step 8. If your analysis objective requires estimates as predictions, the model from Step 4 should provide slightly less biased ones.

Copyright © 2011, SAS Institute Inc., Cary, North Carolina, USA. ALL RIGHTS RESERVED.

2. Select **Select Chart** ⇨ **Misclassification Rate**.

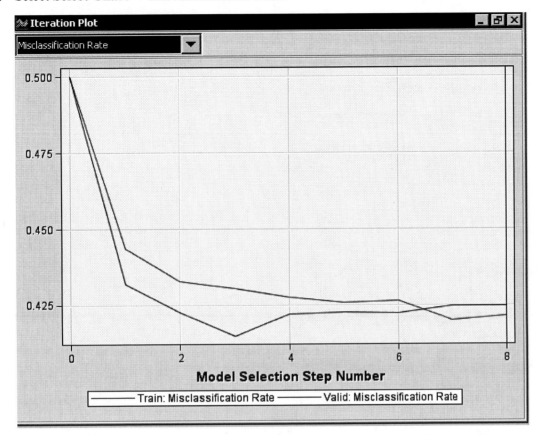

The iteration plot shows that the model with the smallest misclassification rate occurs in Step 3. If your analysis objective requires decision predictions, the predictions from the Step 3 model are as accurate as the predictions from the final Step 8 model.

The selection process stopped at Step 8 to limit the amount of time spent running the stepwise selection procedure. In Step 8, no more inputs had a chi-squared p-value below 0.05. The value 0.05 is a somewhat arbitrary holdover from the days of statistical tables. With the validation data available to gauge overfitting, it is possible to eliminate this restriction and obtain a richer pool of models to consider.

Copyright © 2011, SAS Institute Inc., Cary, North Carolina, USA. ALL RIGHTS RESERVED.

Full Model Selection

Use the following steps to build and evaluate a larger sequence of regression models:

1. Close the Results - Regression window.

2. Select **Use Selection Default** ⇨ **No** from the Regression node Properties panel.

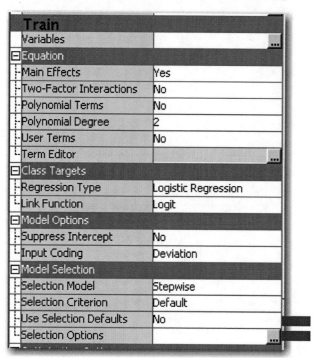

3. Select **Selection Options** ⇨ .

Copyright © 2011, SAS Institute Inc., Cary, North Carolina, USA. ALL RIGHTS RESERVED.

The Selection Options window appears.

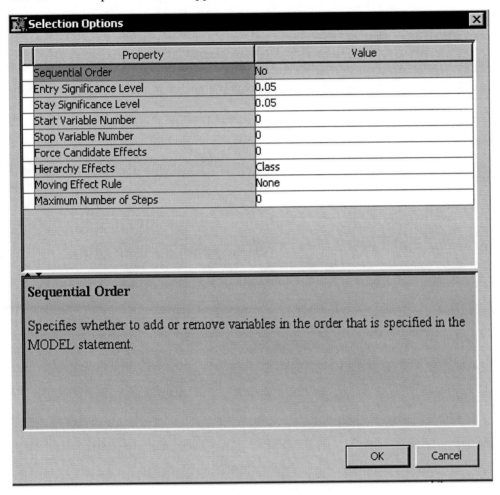

Copyright © 2011, SAS Institute Inc., Cary, North Carolina, USA. ALL RIGHTS RESERVED.

4. Type **1.0** as the Entry Significance Level value.

5. Type **0.5** as the Stay Significance Level value.

    The Entry Significance value enables any input in the model. (The one chosen will have the smallest p-value.) The Stay Significance value keeps any input in the model with a p-value less than 0.5. This second choice is somewhat arbitrary. A smaller value can terminate the stepwise selection process earlier, while a larger value can maintain it longer. A Stay Significance of 1.0 forces stepwise to behave in the manner of a forward selection.

6. Change the **Maximum Number of Steps** to a large value, such as **30**. This enables step-wise regression to run more than zero steps, but no more than 30 steps. If this value is left at 0, an intercept only model is the result.

    In practice, if step-wise regression does not complete, consider increasing this value.

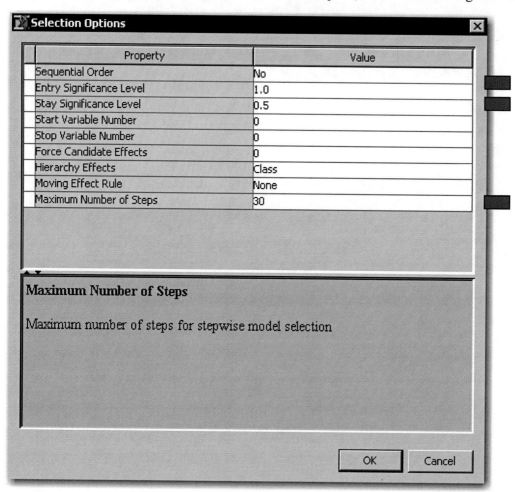

7. Run the Regression node and view the results.

Copyright © 2011, SAS Institute Inc., Cary, North Carolina, USA. ALL RIGHTS RESERVED.

8. Select **View** ⇨ **Model** ⇨ **Iteration Plot**. The Iteration Plot window appears.

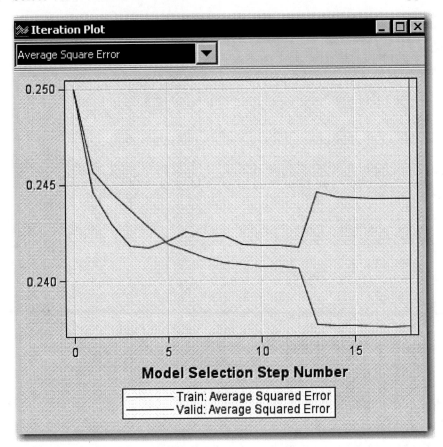

The iteration plot shows the smallest average squared errors occurring in Steps 4 or 12. There is a significant change in average squared error in Step 13, when the **DemCluster** input is added. Inclusion of this nonnumeric input improves training performance but hurts validation performance.

Copyright © 2011, SAS Institute Inc., Cary, North Carolina, USA. ALL RIGHTS RESERVED.

9.   Select **Select Chart** ⇨ **Misclassification Rate**.

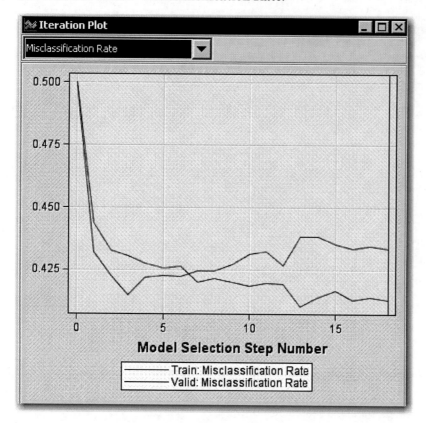

The iteration plot shows that the smallest validation misclassification rates occur at Step 3. Notice that the change in the assessment statistic in Step 13 is much less pronounced.

Best Sequence Model

You can configure the Regression node to select the model with the smallest fit statistic (rather than the final stepwise selection iteration). This method is how SAS Enterprise Miner optimizes complexity for regression models.

1.   Close the Results - Regression window.

2.   If your predictions are decisions, use the following setting:

Select **Selection Criterion** ⇨ **Validation Misclassification**. (Equivalently, you can select **Validation Profit/Loss**. The equivalence is demonstrated in Chapter 6.)

3.   If your predictions are estimates (or rankings), use the following setting:

Select **Selection Criterion** ⇨ **Validation Error**.

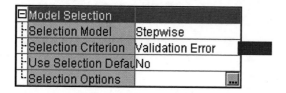

✎   The continuing demonstration assumes validation error selection criteria.

Copyright © 2011, SAS Institute Inc., Cary, North Carolina, USA. ALL RIGHTS RESERVED.

4. Run the **Regression** node and view the results.

5. Select **View** ➪ **Model** ➪ **Iteration Plot**.

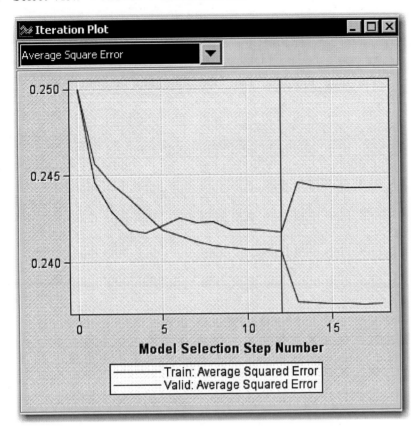

The vertical blue line shows the model with the optimal validation error (Step 12).

6. Go to line 2690 and page down one page.

Parameter	DF	Standard Estimate	Wald Error	Chi-Square	Pr > ChiSq	Standardized Estimate	Exp(Est)
Intercept	1	0.4999	0.2575	3.77	0.0522	1.649	
DemMedHomeValue	1	1.416E-6	3.011E-7	22.12	<.0001	0.0781	1.000
DemPctVeterans	1	0.00651	0.00261	6.23	0.0126	0.0407	1.007
GiftAvg36	1	-0.0101	0.00355	8.02	0.0046	-0.0561	0.990
GiftCnt36	1	0.0574	0.0197	8.53	0.0035	0.0677	1.059
GiftTimeLast	1	-0.0415	0.00829	25.07	<.0001	-0.0923	0.959
M_DemAge	0 1	0.0720	0.0345	4.36	0.0367		1.075
M_GiftAvgCard36	0 1	0.1126	0.0412	7.46	0.0063		1.119
PromCntCard12	1	-0.0381	0.0281	1.85	0.1740	-0.0282	0.963
StatusCat96NK A	1	-0.0353	0.0957	0.14	0.7122		0.965
StatusCat96NK E	1	0.4010	0.1950	4.23	0.0398		1.493
StatusCat96NK F	1	-0.4485	0.1314	11.66	0.0006		0.639
StatusCat96NK L	1	0.1733	0.3743	0.21	0.6433		1.189
StatusCat96NK N	1	-0.0988	0.1353	0.53	0.4649		0.906
StatusCatStarAll	0 1	-0.0701	0.0367	3.64	0.0563		0.932

Analysis of Maximum Likelihood Estimates

Copyright © 2011, SAS Institute Inc., Cary, North Carolina, USA. ALL RIGHTS RESERVED.

While not all the p-values are less than 0.05, the model seems to have a better validation average squared error (and misclassification) than the model selected using the default Significance Level settings.

In short, there is nothing sacred about 0.05. It is not unreasonable to override the defaults of the Regression node to enable selection from a richer collection of potential models. On the other hand, most of the reduction in the fit statistics occurs during inclusion of the first three inputs. If you seek a parsimonious model, it is reasonable to use a smaller value for the Stay Significance parameter.

Copyright © 2011, SAS Institute Inc., Cary, North Carolina, USA. ALL RIGHTS RESERVED.

4.4 Interpreting Regression Models

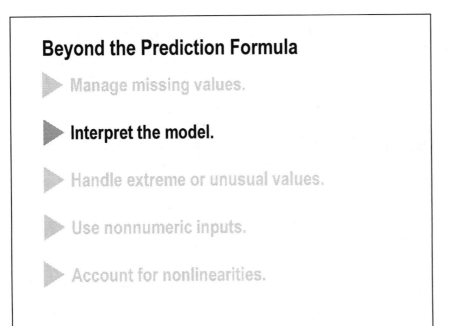

Beyond the Prediction Formula

Manage missing values.

Interpret the model.

Handle extreme or unusual values.

Use nonnumeric inputs.

Account for nonlinearities.

69

After you build a model, you might be asked to interpret the results. Fortunately regression models lend themselves to easy interpretation.

Copyright © 2011, SAS Institute Inc., Cary, North Carolina, USA. ALL RIGHTS RESERVED.

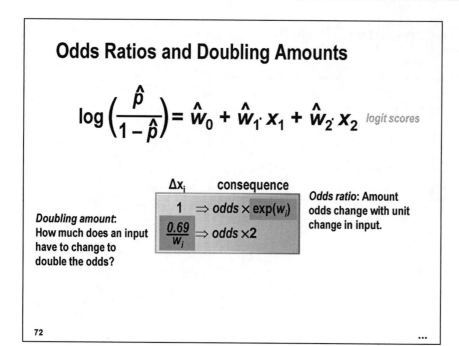

Odds Ratios and Doubling Amounts

$$\log\left(\frac{\hat{p}}{1-\hat{p}}\right) = \hat{w}_0 + \hat{w}_1 \cdot x_1 + \hat{w}_2 \cdot x_2 \quad \textit{logit scores}$$

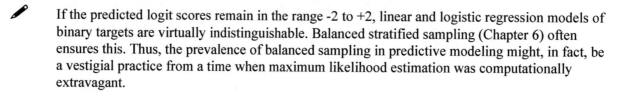

Doubling amount: How much does an input have to change to double the odds?

Δx_i	consequence
1	$\Rightarrow odds \times \exp(w_i)$
$\dfrac{0.69}{w_i}$	$\Rightarrow odds \times 2$

Odds ratio: Amount odds change with unit change in input.

72

...

There are two equivalent ways to interpret a logistic regression model. Both relate changes in input measurements to changes in odds of primary outcome.

- An *odds ratio* expresses the increase in primary outcome odds associated with a unit change in an input. It is obtained by exponentiation of the parameter estimate of the input of interest.

- A *doubling amount* gives the amount of change required for doubling the primary outcome odds. It is equal to $\log(2) \approx 0.69$ divided by the parameter estimate of the input of interest.

✎   If the predicted logit scores remain in the range -2 to +2, linear and logistic regression models of binary targets are virtually indistinguishable. Balanced stratified sampling (Chapter 6) often ensures this. Thus, the prevalence of balanced sampling in predictive modeling might, in fact, be a vestigial practice from a time when maximum likelihood estimation was computationally extravagant.

Copyright © 2011, SAS Institute Inc., Cary, North Carolina, USA. ALL RIGHTS RESERVED.

Interpreting a Regression Model

The following steps demonstrate how to interpret a model using odds ratios:

1. Go to line 2712 of the regression model output.

```
                          Odds Ratio Estimates

                                    Point
             Effect                Estimate

             DemMedHomeValue           1.000
             DemPctVeterans            1.007
             GiftAvg36                0.990
             GiftCnt36                 1.059
             GiftTimeLast             0.959
             M_DemAge        0 vs 1    1.155
             M_GiftAvgCard36   0 vs 1     1.253
             PromCntCard12             0.963
             StatusCat96NK   A vs S    0.957
             StatusCat96NK   E vs S    1.481
             StatusCat96NK   F vs S    0.633
             StatusCat96NK   L vs S    1.179
             StatusCat96NK   N vs S    0.898
             StatusCatStarAll  0 vs 1     0.869
```

This output includes most of situations you will encounter when you build a regression model.

For **GiftAvg36**, the odds ratio estimate equals 0.990. This means that for each additional dollar donated (on average) in the past 36 months, the odds of donation during the 97NK campaign change by a factor of 0.99, a 1% decrease.

For **GiftCnt36**, the odds ratio estimate equals 1.059. This means that for each additional donation in the past 36 months, the odds of donation during the 97NK campaign change by a factor of 1.059, a 5.9% increase.

For **M_DemAge**, the odds ratio (0 versus 1) estimate equals 1.155. This means that cases with a 0 value for **M_DemAge** are 1.155 times more likely to donate than cases with a 1 value for **M_DemAge**.

The unusual value of 1.000 for the **DemMedHomeValue** odds ratio has a simple explanation. Unit (that is, single dollar) changes in home value do not change the odds of response by an amount captured in three significant digits. To obtain a more meaningful value for this input's effect on response odds, you can multiply the parameter estimate by 1000 and exponentiate the result. You then have the change in response odds based on 1000 dollar changes in median home value. Equivalently, you could use the Transform Variables node to replace **DemMedHomeValue** with **DemMedHmVal1000=DemMedHomeValue/1000**, and a unit increase on that new input would represent a $1000 increase in the **DemMedHomeValue**.

2. Close the Results window.

Copyright © 2011, SAS Institute Inc., Cary, North Carolina, USA. ALL RIGHTS RESERVED.

4.5 Transforming Inputs

Beyond the Prediction Formula

▶ Manage missing values.

▶ Interpret the model.

▶ **Handle extreme or unusual values.**

▶ Use nonnumeric inputs.

▶ Account for nonlinearities.

75   ...

Classical regression analysis makes no assumptions about the distribution of inputs. The only assumption is that the expected value of the target (or some function thereof) is a linear combination of fixed input measurements.

Why should you worry about extreme input distributions?

Copyright © 2011, SAS Institute Inc., Cary, North Carolina, USA. ALL RIGHTS RESERVED.

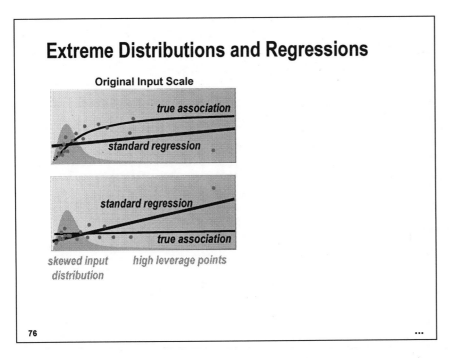

Extreme Distributions and Regressions

Original Input Scale

true association

standard regression

standard regression

true association

skewed input distribution   *high leverage points*

76   ...

There are at least two compelling reasons.

- First, in most real-world applications, the relationship between expected target value and input value does not increase without bound. Rather, it typically tapers off to some horizontal asymptote. Standard regression models are unable to accommodate such a relationship.

- Second, as a point expands from the overall mean of a distribution, the point has more influence, or *leverage*, on model fit. Models built on inputs with extreme distributions attempt to optimize fit for the most extreme points at the cost of fit for the bulk of the data, usually near the input mean. This can result in an exaggeration or an understating of an input's association with the target.

Both of these phenomena are seen in the above slide.

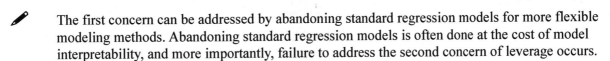

The first concern can be addressed by abandoning standard regression models for more flexible modeling methods. Abandoning standard regression models is often done at the cost of model interpretability, and more importantly, failure to address the second concern of leverage occurs.

Copyright © 2011, SAS Institute Inc., Cary, North Carolina, USA. ALL RIGHTS RESERVED.

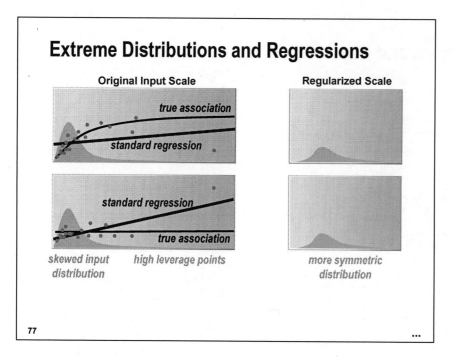

A simpler and, arguably, more effective approach transforms or regularizes offending inputs in order to eliminate extreme values.

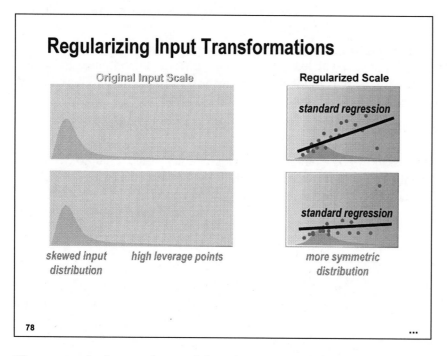

Then, a standard regression model can be accurately fit using the transformed input in place of the original input.

Copyright © 2011, SAS Institute Inc., Cary, North Carolina, USA. ALL RIGHTS RESERVED.

Regularizing Input Transformations

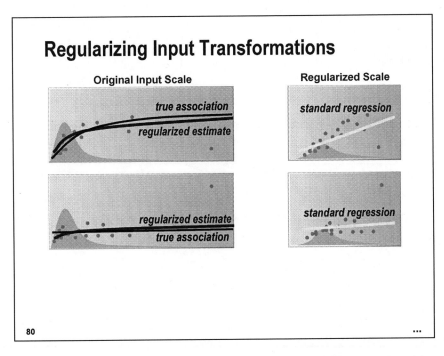

Often this can solve both problems mentioned above. This not only mitigates the influence of extreme cases, but also creates the desired asymptotic association between input and target on the original input scale.

4.03 Multiple Choice Poll

Which statement below is true about transformations of input variables in a regression analysis?

a. They are never a good idea.

b. They help model assumptions match the assumptions of maximum likelihood estimation.

c. They are performed to reduce the bias in model predictions.

d. They typically are done on nominal (categorical) inputs.

Copyright © 2011, SAS Institute Inc., Cary, North Carolina, USA. ALL RIGHTS RESERVED.

 **Transforming Inputs**

Regression models are sensitive to extreme or outlying values in the input space. Inputs with highly skewed or highly kurtotic distributions can be selected over inputs that yield better overall predictions. To avoid this problem, analysts often regularize the input distributions using a simple transformation. The benefit of this approach is improved model performance. The cost, of course, is increased difficulty in model interpretation.

The Transform Variables tool enables you to easily apply standard transformations (in addition to the specialized ones seen in Chapter 9) to a set of inputs.

The Transform Variables Tool

Use the following steps to transform inputs with the Transform Variables tool:

1. Remove the connection between the Data Partition node and the Impute node.

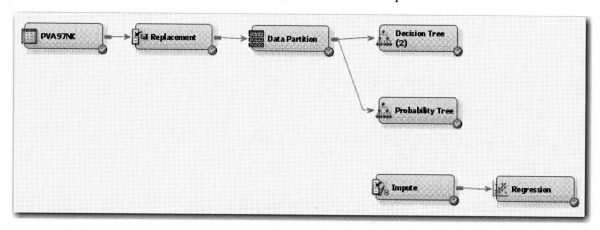

2. Select the **Modify** tab.

3. Drag the **Transform Variables** tool into the diagram workspace.

4. Connect the **Data Partition** node to the **Transform Variables** node.

5. Connect the **Transform Variables** node to the **Impute** node.

Copyright © 2011, SAS Institute Inc., Cary, North Carolina, USA. ALL RIGHTS RESERVED.

6. Adjust the diagram icons for aesthetics. (So that you can see the entire diagram, the zoom level is reduced.)

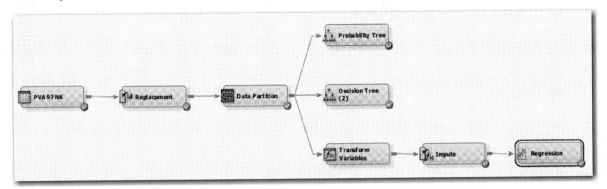

The Transform Variables node is placed before the Impute node to keep the imputed values at the average (or center of mass) of the model inputs.

7. Select **Variables** ⇨ 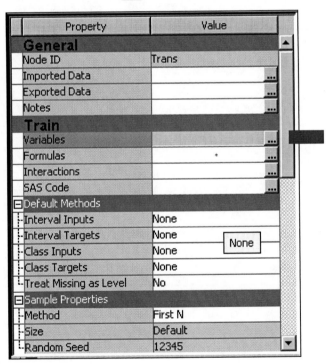 for the property of the Transform Variables node.

The Variables - Trans window appears.

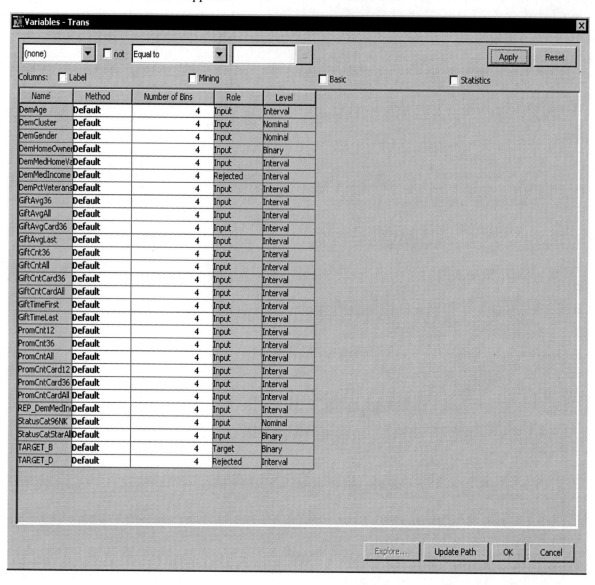

Copyright © 2011, SAS Institute Inc., Cary, North Carolina, USA. ALL RIGHTS RESERVED.

8. Select all inputs with **Gift** in the name.

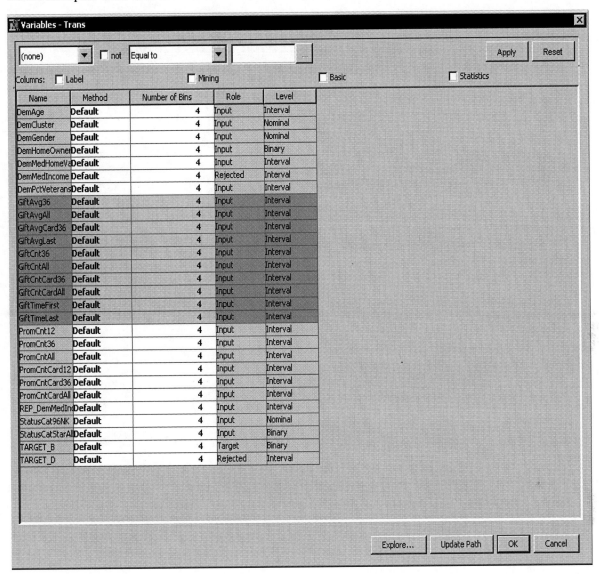

Copyright © 2011, SAS Institute Inc., Cary, North Carolina, USA. ALL RIGHTS RESERVED.

9.   Select **Explore**. The Explore window appears.

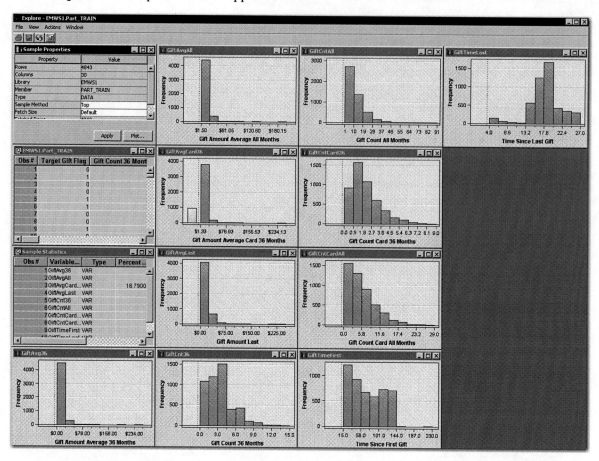

The **GiftAvg** and **GiftCnt** inputs show some degree of skew in their distributions. The **GiftTime** inputs do not. To regularize the skewed distributions, use the log transformation. For these inputs, the order of magnitude of the underlying measure predicts the target rather than the measure itself.

10. Close the Explore window.

Copyright © 2011, SAS Institute Inc., Cary, North Carolina, USA. ALL RIGHTS RESERVED.

11. Deselect the two inputs with **GiftTime** in their names.

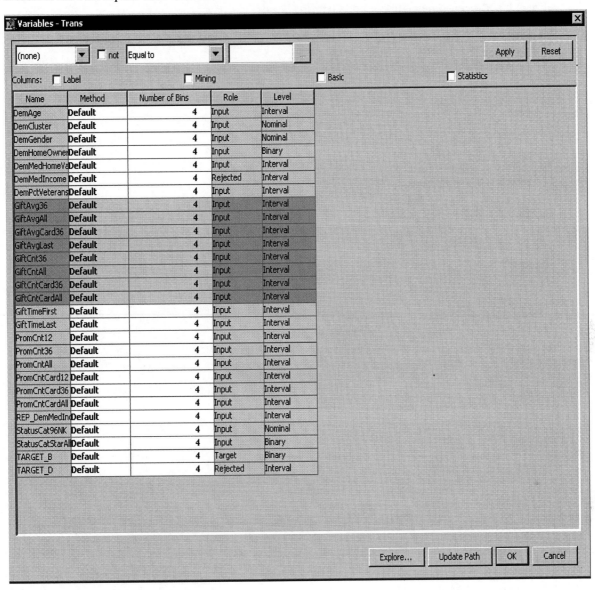

Copyright © 2011, SAS Institute Inc., Cary, North Carolina, USA. ALL RIGHTS RESERVED.

12. Select **Method** ⇨ **Log** for one of the remaining selected inputs. The selected method changes from `Default` to `Log` for the **GiftAvg** and **GiftCnt** inputs.

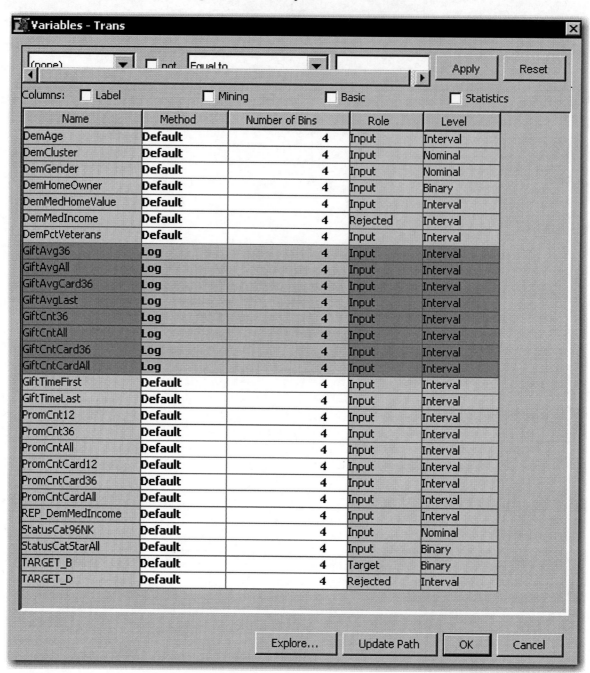

13. Select **OK** to close the Variables - Trans window.

14. Run the Transform Variables node and view the results.

Copyright © 2011, SAS Institute Inc., Cary, North Carolina, USA. ALL RIGHTS RESERVED.

15. Maximize the Output window and go to line 28.

```
                Input
Input Name      Role    Level     Name           Level      Formula

GiftAvg36       INPUT   INTERVAL  LOG_GiftAvg36      INTERVAL  log(GiftAvg36 + 1)
GiftAvgAll      INPUT   INTERVAL  LOG_GiftAvgAll     INTERVAL  log(GiftAvgAll + 1)
GiftAvgCard36   INPUT   INTERVAL  LOG_GiftAvgCard36  INTERVAL  log(GiftAvgCard36 + 1)
GiftAvgLast     INPUT   INTERVAL  LOG_GiftAvgLast    INTERVAL  log(GiftAvgLast + 1)
GiftCnt36       INPUT   INTERVAL  LOG_GiftCnt36      INTERVAL  log(GiftCnt36 + 1)
GiftCntAll      INPUT   INTERVAL  LOG_GiftCntAll     INTERVAL  log(GiftCntAll + 1)
GiftCntCard36   INPUT   INTERVAL  LOG_GiftCntCard36  INTERVAL  log(GiftCntCard36 + 1)
GiftCntCardAll  INPUT   INTERVAL  LOG_GiftCntCardAll INTERVAL  log(GiftCntCardAll + 1)
```

Notice the Formula column. While a log transformation was specified, the actual transformation used was log(*input* + 1). This default action of the Transform Variables tool avoids problems with 0-values of the underlying inputs.

16. Close the Transform Variables - Results window.

Regressions with Transformed Inputs

The following steps revisit regression, and use the transformed inputs:

1. Run the diagram from the Regression node and view the results.

2. Go to line 3754 of the Output window and page down one page.

```
                        Summary of Stepwise Selection
```

Step	Effect Entered	Removed	Number DF	In	Score Chi-Square	Wald Chi-Square	Pr > ChiSq
1	LOG_GiftCnt36		1	1	95.0275		<.0001
2	GiftTimeLast		1	2	21.1330		<.0001
3	DemMedHomeValue		1	3	17.7373		<.0001
4	LOG_GiftAvgAll		1	4	21.7306		<.0001
5	DemPctVeterans		1	5	7.0742		0.0078
6	StatusCat96NK		5	6	13.7906		0.0170
7	LOG_GiftCntCard36		1	7	5.9966		0.0143
8	M_DemAge		1	8	5.0301		0.0249
9	DemCluster		53	9	61.2167		0.2049
10	StatusCatStarAll		1	10	1.2431		0.2649
11	PromCntCard12		1	11	1.4604		0.2269
12	PromCntAll		1	12	1.0022		0.3168
13	LOG_GiftCntAll		1	13	2.2990		0.1295
14	PromCnt12		1	14	0.8158		0.3664
15	PromCntCardAll		1	15	1.8875		0.1695
16		PromCntCard12	1	14		0.0358	0.8500
17	M_REP_DemMedIncome		1	15		0.6075	0.4357
18	LOG_GiftAvg36		1	16		0.4691	0.4934
19	M_LOG_GiftAvgCard36		1	17		0.6226	0.4301
20	GiftTimeFirst		1	18		0.3972	0.5285
21		GiftTimeFirst	1	17		0.3971	0.5286

```
The selected model, based on the CHOOSE=VERROR criterion, is the model trained in Step 4. It consists of
the following effects:

Intercept DemMedHomeValue GiftTimeLast LOG_GiftAvgAll LOG_GiftCnt36
```

Copyright © 2011, SAS Institute Inc., Cary, North Carolina, USA. ALL RIGHTS RESERVED.

The stepwise selection process took 21 steps, and the selected model came from Step 4. Notice that half of the selected inputs are log transformations of the original gift variables.

3. Go to line 3800 to view more statistics from the selected model.

```
                      Analysis of Maximum Likelihood Estimates

                      Standard    Wald        Standardized
Parameter        DF   Estimate    Error  Chi-Square  Pr > ChiSq   Estimate  Exp(Est)

Intercept        1    0.8251     0.2921     7.98      0.0047                 2.282
DemMedHomeValue  1    1.448E-6   3.002E-7   23.26    <.0001       0.0798     1.000
GiftTimeLast     1   -0.0341     0.00756    20.33    <.0001      -0.0758     0.966
LOG_GiftAvgAll   1   -0.3469     0.0747     21.58    <.0001      -0.0895     0.707
LOG_GiftCnt36    1    0.3736     0.0728     26.34    <.0001       0.0998     1.453


        Odds Ratio Estimates

                    Point
Effect             Estimate

DemMedHomeValue     1.000
GiftTimeLast        0.966
LOG_GiftAvgAll      0.707
LOG_GiftCnt36       1.453
```

4. Select **View** ⇨ **Model** ⇨ **Iteration Plot**.

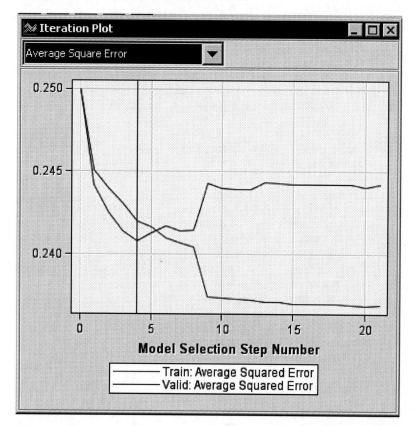

The selected model (based on minimum error) occurs in Step 4. The value of average squared error for this model is slightly lower than that for the model with the untransformed inputs.

Copyright © 2011, SAS Institute Inc., Cary, North Carolina, USA. ALL RIGHTS RESERVED.

5. Select **Select Chart** ⇨ **Misclassification Rate**.

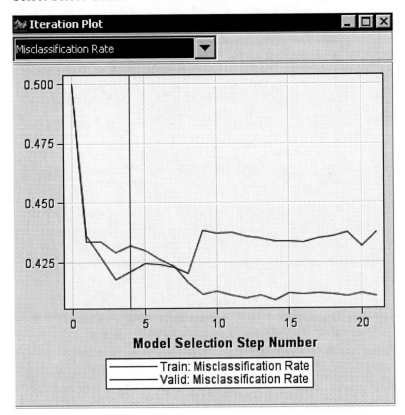

The misclassification rate with the transformed input model is nearly the same as that for the untransformed input model. The model with the lowest misclassification rate comes from Step 3. If you want to optimize on the misclassification rate, you must change this property in the Regression node's property sheet.

6. Close the Results window.

Copyright © 2011, SAS Institute Inc., Cary, North Carolina, USA. ALL RIGHTS RESERVED.

4.6 Categorical Inputs

Beyond the Prediction Formula

▷ Manage missing values.

▷ Interpret the model.

▷ Handle extreme or unusual values.

▶ **Use nonnumeric inputs.**

▷ Account for nonlinearities.

86

...

Using nonnumeric or categorical inputs presents another problem for regressions. As was seen in the earlier demonstrations, inclusion of a categorical input with excessive levels can lead to overfitting.

Nonnumeric Input Coding

Level	D_A	D_B	D_C	D_D	D_E	D_F	D_G	D_H	D_I
A	1	0	0	0	0	0	0	0	0
B	0	1	0	0	0	0	0	0	0
C	0	0	1	0	0	0	0	0	0
D	0	0	0	1	0	0	0	0	0
E	0	0	0	0	1	0	0	0	0
F	0	0	0	0	0	1	0	0	0
G	0	0	0	0	0	0	1	0	0
H	0	0	0	0	0	0	0	1	0
I	0	0	0	0	0	0	0	0	1

88

...

Copyright © 2011, SAS Institute Inc., Cary, North Carolina, USA. ALL RIGHTS RESERVED.

Coding Redundancy

Level	D_A	D_B	D_C	D_D	D_E	D_F	D_G	D_H	D_I
A	1	0	0	0	0	0	0	0	0
B	0	1	0	0	0	0	0	0	0
C	0	0	1	0	0	0	0	0	0
D	0	0	0	1	0	0	0	0	0
E	0	0	0	0	1	0	0	0	0
F	0	0	0	0	0	1	0	0	0
G	0	0	0	0	0	0	1	0	0
H	0	0	0	0	0	0	0	1	0
I	0	0	0	0	0	0	0	0	1

89

To represent these nonnumeric inputs in a model, you must convert them to some sort of numeric values. This conversion is most commonly done by creating design variables (or *dummy* variables), with each design variable representing approximately one level of the categorical input. (The total number of design variables required is, in fact, one less than the number of inputs.) A single categorical input can vastly increase a model's degrees of freedom, which, in turn, increases the chances of a model overfitting.

Coding Consolidation

Level	D_A	D_B	D_C	D_D	D_E	D_F	D_G	D_H	D_I
A	1	0	0	0	0	0	0	0	0
B	0	1	0	0	0	0	0	0	0
C	0	0	1	0	0	0	0	0	0
D	0	0	0	1	0	0	0	0	0
E	0	0	0	0	1	0	0	0	0
F	0	0	0	0	0	1	0	0	0
G	0	0	0	0	0	0	1	0	0
H	0	0	0	0	0	0	0	1	0
I	0	0	0	0	0	0	0	0	1

90

Copyright © 2011, SAS Institute Inc., Cary, North Carolina, USA. ALL RIGHTS RESERVED.

Coding Consolidation

Level	D_{ABCD}	D_B	D_C	D_D	D_{EF}	D_F	D_{GH}	D_H	D_I
A	1	0	0	0	0	0	0	0	0
B	1	1	0	0	0	0	0	0	0
C	1	0	1	0	0	0	0	0	0
D	1	0	0	1	0	0	0	0	0
E	0	0	0	0	1	0	0	0	0
F	0	0	0	0	1	1	0	0	0
G	0	0	0	0	0	0	1	0	0
H	0	0	0	0	0	0	1	1	0
I	0	0	0	0	0	0	0	0	1

91

There are many remedies to this problem. One of the simplest remedies is to use domain knowledge to reduce the number of levels of the categorical input. In this way, level-groups are encoded in the model in place of the original levels.

Copyright © 2011, SAS Institute Inc., Cary, North Carolina, USA. ALL RIGHTS RESERVED.

Recoding Categorical Inputs

In Chapter 2, you used the Replacement tool to eliminate an inappropriate value in the median income input. This demonstration shows how to use the Replacement tool to facilitate combining input levels of a categorical input.

1. Remove the connection between the Transform Variables node and the Impute node.

2. Select the **Modify** tab.

3. Drag a **Replacement** tool into the diagram workspace.

4. Connect the **Transform Variables** node to the **Replacement** node.

5. Connect the **Replacement** node to the **Impute** node.

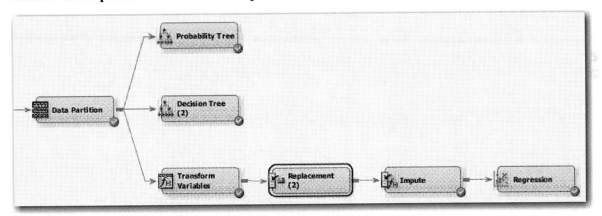

You need to change some of the node's default settings so that the replacements are limited to a single categorical input.

6. In the Interval Variables property group, select **Default Limits Method ⇨ None**.

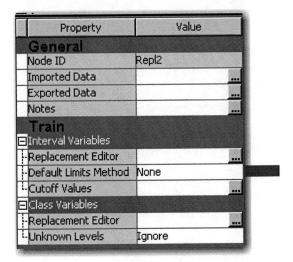

Copyright © 2011, SAS Institute Inc., Cary, North Carolina, USA. ALL RIGHTS RESERVED.

7. In the Class Variables property group, select **Replacement Editor** ⇨ 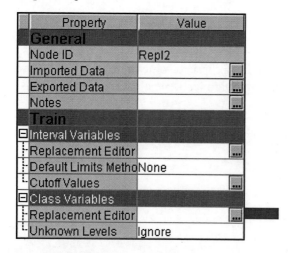 from the Replacement node Properties panel.

The Replacement Editor appears.

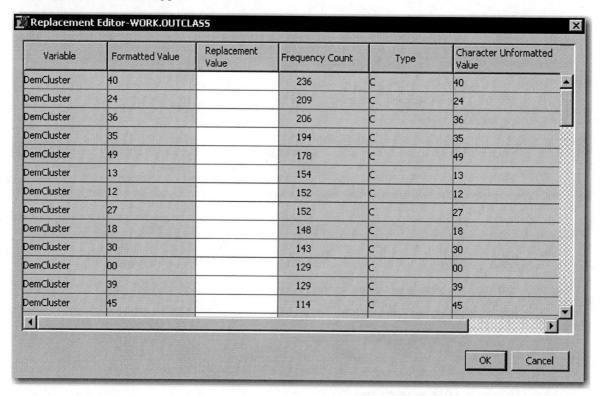

The categorical input Replacement Editor lists all levels of each binary, ordinal, and nominal input. You can use the Replacement column to reassign values to any of the levels.

The input with the largest number of levels is **DemCluster,** which has so many levels that consolidating the levels using the Replacement Editor would be an arduous task. (Another, autonomous method for consolidating the levels of **DemCluster** is presented as a special topic in Chapter 9.)

For this demonstration, you combine the levels of another input, **StatusCat96NK.**

Copyright © 2011, SAS Institute Inc., Cary, North Carolina, USA. ALL RIGHTS RESERVED.

8. Scroll the Replacement Editor to view the levels of **StatusCat96NK**.

Replacement Editor-WORK.OUTCLASS

Variable	Formatted Value	Replacement Value	Frequency Count	Type	Character Unformatted Value
DemGender	M		2002	C	M
DemGender	U		249	C	U
DemGender	_UNKNOWN_	_DEFAULT_	.	C	
DemHomeOwner	H		2655	C	H
DemHomeOwner	U		2188	C	U
DemHomeOwner	_UNKNOWN_	_DEFAULT_	.	C	
StatusCat96NK	A		2911	C	A
StatusCat96NK	S		1168	C	S
StatusCat96NK	F		342	C	F
StatusCat96NK	N		286	C	N
StatusCat96NK	E		115	C	E
StatusCat96NK	L		21	C	L
StatusCat96NK	_UNKNOWN_	_DEFAULT_	.	C	
StatusCatStarAll	1		2590	N	
StatusCatStarAll	0		2253	N	
StatusCatStarAll	_UNKNOWN_	_DEFAULT_	.	N	
TARGET_B	0		2422	N	
TARGET_B	1		2421	N	
TARGET_B	_UNKNOWN_	_DEFAULT_	.	N	

OK   Cancel

The input has six levels, plus a level to represent unknown values (which do not occur in the training data). The levels of **StatusCat96NK** will be consolidated as follows:

- Levels A and S (active and star donors) indicate consistent donors and are grouped into a single level, A.
- Levels F and N (first-time and new donors) indicate new donors and are grouped into a single level, N.
- Levels E and L (inactive and lapsing donors) indicate lapsing donors and are grouped into a single level L.

Copyright © 2011, SAS Institute Inc., Cary, North Carolina, USA. ALL RIGHTS RESERVED.

9. Type **A** as the Replacement level for **StatusCat96NK** levels A and S.

10. Type **N** as the Replacement level for **StatusCat96NK** levels F and N.

11. Type **L** as the Replacement level for **StatusCat96NK** levels L and E.

StatusCat96NK	A	A	2911
StatusCat96NK	S	A	1168
StatusCat96NK	F	N	342
StatusCat96NK	N	N	286
StatusCat96NK	E	L	115
StatusCat96NK	L	L	21
StatusCat96NK	_UNKNOWN_	_DEFAULT_	.

12. Select **OK** to close the Replacement Editor.

Copyright © 2011, SAS Institute Inc., Cary, North Carolina, USA. ALL RIGHTS RESERVED.

13. Run the Replacement node and view the results. (Partial Results Shown)

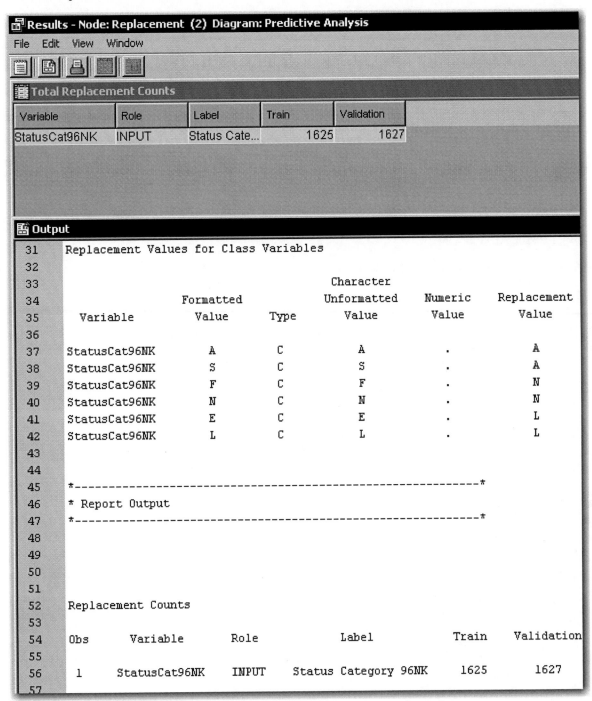

The Total Replacement Counts window shows the number of replacements that occur in the training and validation data.

Copyright © 2011, SAS Institute Inc., Cary, North Carolina, USA. ALL RIGHTS RESERVED.

14. Select **View** ⇨ **Model** ⇨ **Replaced Levels**. The Replaced Levels window appears.

Variable	Formatted Value	Type	Character Unformatted Value	Numeric Value	Replacement Value	Label
StatusCat9...	A	C	A		.A	Status Cate...
StatusCat9...	S	C	S		.A	Status Cate...
StatusCat9...	F	C	F		.N	Status Cate...
StatusCat9...	N	C	N		.N	Status Cate...
StatusCat9...	E	C	E		.L	Status Cate...
StatusCat9...	L	C	L		.L	Status Cate...

The replaced level values are consistent with expectations.

15. Close the Results window.

16. Run the Regression node and view the results.

17. Go to line 3659 of the Output window and page down.

Summary of Stepwise Selection

Step	Effect Entered	Removed	Number DF	In	Score Chi-Square	Wald Chi-Square	Pr > ChiSq
1	LOG_GiftCnt36		1	1	95.0275		<.0001
2	GiftTimeLast		1	2	21.1330		<.0001
3	DemMedHomeValue		1	3	17.7373		<.0001
4	LOG_GiftAvgAll		1	4	21.7306		<.0001
5	DemPctVeterans		1	5	7.0742		0.0078
6	REP_StatusCat96NK		2	6	9.7073		0.0078
7	LOG_GiftCntCard36		1	7	6.2112		0.0127
8	M_DemAge		1	8	4.8754		0.0272
9	DemCluster		53	9	61.7834		0.1910
10	StatusCatStarAll		1	10	1.6743		0.1957
11	PromCntCard12		1	11	1.3961		0.2374
12	PromCntAll		1	12	1.1442		0.2848
13	LOG_GiftCntAll		1	13	1.8685		0.1717
14	PromCnt12		1	14	0.6761		0.4109
15	PromCntCardAll		1	15	2.0585		0.1514
16		PromCntCard12	1	14		0.0216	0.8830
17	LOG_GiftAvg36		1	15	0.7608		0.3831
18	M_LOG_GiftAvgCard36		1	16	0.7343		0.3915
19	M_REP_DemMedIncome		1	17	0.5853		0.4443
20	GiftTimeFirst		1	18	0.3821		0.5365
21		GiftTimeFirst	1	17		0.3821	0.5365

The **REP_StatusCat96NK** input (created from the original **StatusCat96NK** input) is included in Step 6 of the Stepwise Selection process. The three-level input is represented by two degrees of freedom.

18. Close the Results window.

Copyright © 2011, SAS Institute Inc., Cary, North Carolina, USA. ALL RIGHTS RESERVED.

4.7 Polynomial Regressions (Self-Study)

Beyond the Prediction Formula

▶ Manage missing values.

▶ Interpret the model.

▶ Handle extreme or unusual values.

▶ Use nonnumeric inputs.

▶ **Account for nonlinearities.**

95   ...

The Regression tool assumes (by default) a linear and additive association between the inputs and the logit of the target. If the true association is more complicated, such an assumption might result in biased predictions. For decisions and rankings, this bias can (in some cases) be unimportant. For estimates, this bias appears as a higher value for the validation average squared error fit statistic.

Standard Logistic Regression

$$\log\left(\frac{\hat{p}}{1-\hat{p}}\right) = \hat{w}_0 + \hat{w}_1 x_1 + \hat{w}_2 x_2$$

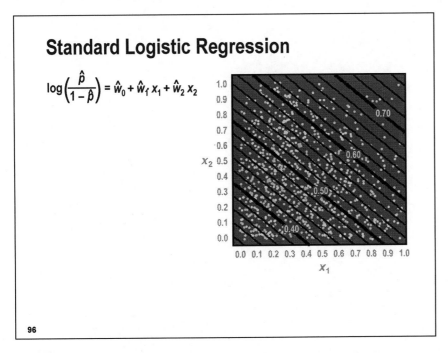

In the dot color problem, the (standard logistic regression) assumption that the concentration of yellow dots increases toward the upper right corner of the unit square seems to be suspect.

Copyright © 2011, SAS Institute Inc., Cary, North Carolina, USA. ALL RIGHTS RESERVED.

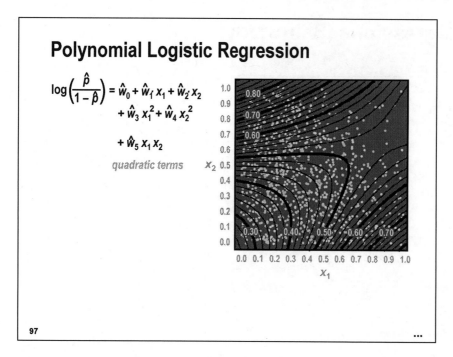

Polynomial Logistic Regression

$$\log\left(\frac{\hat{p}}{1-\hat{p}}\right) = \hat{w}_0 + \hat{w}_1 x_1 + \hat{w}_2 x_2$$
$$+ \hat{w}_3 x_1^2 + \hat{w}_4 x_2^2$$
$$+ \hat{w}_5 x_1 x_2$$

quadratic terms

97 ...

When minimizing prediction bias is important, you can increase the flexibility of a regression model by adding polynomial combinations of the model inputs. This enables predictions to better match the true input/target association. It also increases the chances of overfitting while simultaneously reducing the interpretability of the predictions. Therefore, polynomial regression must be approached with some care.

In SAS Enterprise Miner, adding polynomial terms can be done selectively or autonomously.

Copyright © 2011, SAS Institute Inc., Cary, North Carolina, USA. ALL RIGHTS RESERVED.

Adding Polynomial Regression Terms Selectively

This demonstration shows you how to use the Term Editor window to selectively add polynomial regression terms.

You can modify the existing Regression node or add a new Regression node. If you add a new node, you must configure the Polynomial Regression node to perform the same tasks as the original. An alternative is to make a copy of the existing node.

1. Right-click the **Regression** node and select **Copy** from the menu.

2. Right-click the diagram workspace and select **Paste** from the menu. A new Regression node is added with the label **Regression (2)** to distinguish it from the existing one.

3. Select the **Regression (2)** node. The properties are identical to the existing node.

4. Rename the new regression node **Polynomial Regression (2)**. The (2) is retained to help with model identification in later chapters.

5. Connect the **Polynomial Regression (2)** node to the **Impute** node.

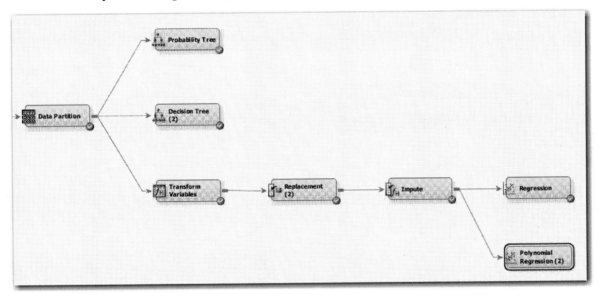

To add polynomial terms to the model, you use the Term Editor. To use the Term Editor, you need to enable User Terms.

Copyright © 2011, SAS Institute Inc., Cary, North Carolina, USA. ALL RIGHTS RESERVED.

6. Select **User Terms** ⇨ **Yes** in the Polynomial Regression (2) property panel.

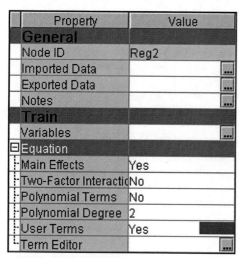

The Term Editor is now unlocked and can be used to add specific polynomial terms to the regression model.

3. Select **Term Editor** ⇨ 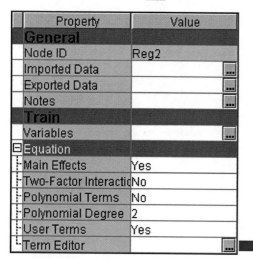 from the Polynomial Regression Properties panel.

Copyright © 2011, SAS Institute Inc., Cary, North Carolina, USA. ALL RIGHTS RESERVED.

The Terms window appears.

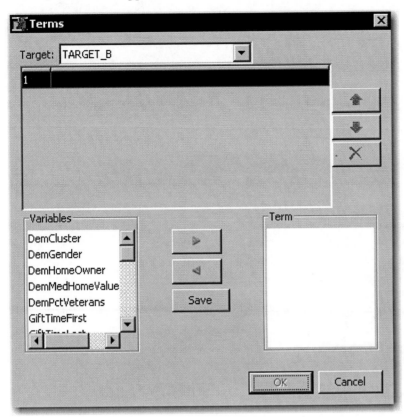

Copyright © 2011, SAS Institute Inc., Cary, North Carolina, USA. ALL RIGHTS RESERVED.

Interaction Terms

Suppose that you suspect an interaction between the home value and the time since the last gift. (Perhaps a recent change in property values affected the donation patterns.)

1. Select **DemMedHomeValue** in the Variables panel of the Terms dialog box.

2. Select the Add button, 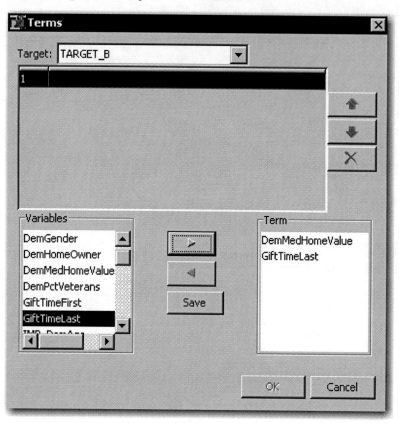 . The **DemMedHomeValue** input is added to the Term panel.

3. Repeat the previous step to add **GiftTimeLast**.

4. Select **Save**.

Copyright © 2011, SAS Institute Inc., Cary, North Carolina, USA. ALL RIGHTS RESERVED.

An interaction between the selected inputs is now available for consideration by the Regression node.

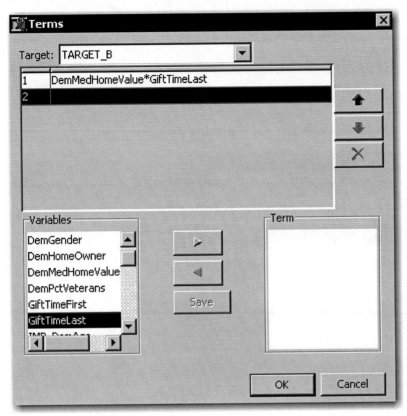

Copyright © 2011, SAS Institute Inc., Cary, North Carolina, USA. ALL RIGHTS RESERVED.

Quadratic Terms

Similarly, suppose that you suspect a parabola-shaped relationship between the logit of donation probability and median home value.

1. Select **DemMedHomeValue**.

2. Select the Add button. The **DemMedHomeValue** input is added to the Term panel.

3. Select ▷ again. Another **DemMedHomeValue** input is added to the Term panel.

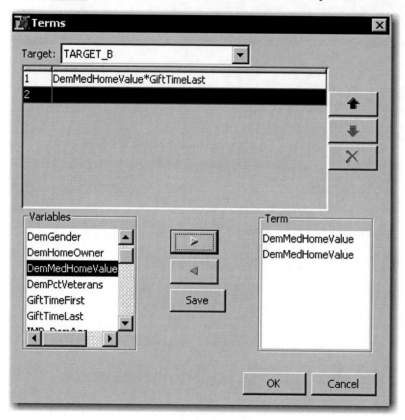

4. Select **Save**. A quadratic median home value term is available for consideration by the model.

Copyright © 2011, SAS Institute Inc., Cary, North Carolina, USA. ALL RIGHTS RESERVED.

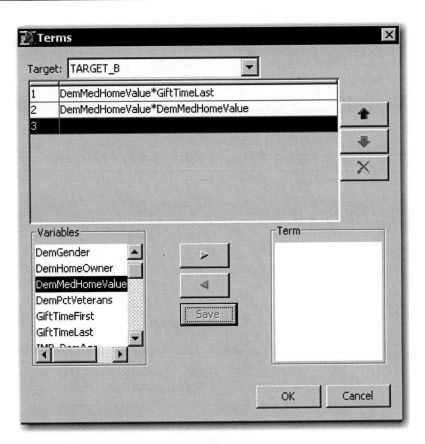

5. Select **OK** to close the Terms dialog box.

6. Run the Polynomial Regression node and view the results.

Copyright © 2011, SAS Institute Inc., Cary, North Carolina, USA. ALL RIGHTS RESERVED.

7. Go to line 3752 in the Output window.

Summary of Stepwise Selection

Step	Effect Entered	Removed	Number DF	In	Score Chi-Square	Wald Chi-Square	Pr > ChiSq
1	LOG_GiftCnt36		1	1	95.0275		<.0001
2	GiftTimeLast		1	2	21.1330		<.0001
3	DemMedHomeValue*GiftTimeLast		1	3	19.6032		<.0001
4	LOG_GiftAvgAll		1	4	21.8432		<.0001
5	DemPctVeterans		1	5	7.0965		0.0077
6	REP_StatusCat96NK		2	6	9.7708		0.0076
7	LOG_GiftCntCard36		1	7	6.2012		0.0128
8	M_DemAge		1	8	4.9143		0.0266
9	DemMedHomeValue*DemMedHomeValue		1	9	3.6530		0.0560
10	StatusCatStarAll		1	10	1.8153		0.1779
11	PromCntCard12		1	11	1.2570		0.2622
12	PromCntAll		1	12	1.3799		0.2401
13		StatusCatStarAll	1	11		0.4504	0.5021
14	DemCluster		53	12	58.7308		0.2736
15	LOG_GiftCntAll		1	13	1.0539		0.3046
16	StatusCatStarAll		1	14	1.2548		0.2626
17	PromCnt12		1	15	0.6591		0.4169
18	PromCntCardAll		1	16	2.0806		0.1492
19		PromCntCard12	1	15		0.0180	0.8931
20	LOG_GiftAvg36		1	16	0.7426		0.3888
21	M_REP_DemMedIncome		1	17	0.6424		0.4228
22	M_LOG_GiftAvgCard36		1	18	0.6013		0.4381
23	GiftTimeFirst		1	19	0.3946		0.5299
24		GiftTimeFirst	1	18		0.3945	0.5299

The stepwise selection summary shows the interaction term added in Step 3 and the quadratic term in Step 9.

8. Close the Results window.

This raises the obvious question: How do you know which nonlinear terms to include in a model? Unfortunately, there is no simple solution to this question in SAS Enterprise Miner, other than including all polynomial and interaction terms in the selection process.

Copyright © 2011, SAS Institute Inc., Cary, North Carolina, USA. ALL RIGHTS RESERVED.

Adding Polynomial Regression Terms Autonomously (Self-Study)

SAS Enterprise Miner has the ability to add *every* polynomial combination of inputs to a regression model. Obviously, this feature must be used with some care, because the number of polynomial input combinations increases rapidly with input count.

For instance, the **PVA97NK** data set has 20 interval inputs. If you want to consider every quadratic combination of these 20 inputs, your selection procedure must sequentially plod through more than 200 inputs. This is not an overwhelming task for today's fast computers.

Follow these steps to explore a full two-factor stepwise selection process:

1. Select **Two-Factor Interaction** ⇨ **Yes** in the Polynomial Regression Properties panel.

2. Select **Polynomial Terms** ⇨ **Yes** in the Polynomial Regression Properties panel.

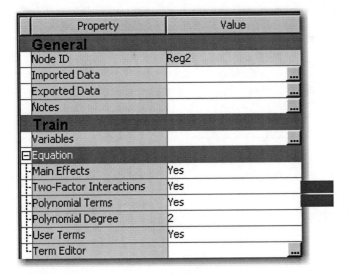

3. Run the Polynomial Regression (2) node and view the results. (In general, this might take longer than most activities.)

Copyright © 2011, SAS Institute Inc., Cary, North Carolina, USA. ALL RIGHTS RESERVED.

4. Go to line 1774 of the Output window.

Summary of Stepwise Selection

Step	Effect Entered	Removed	DF	Number In	Score Chi-Square	Wald Chi-Square	Pr > ChiSq
1	LOG_GiftCnt36*LOG_GiftCntCardAll		1	1	101.0902		<.0001
2	GiftTimeLast*LOG_GiftAvgLast		1	2	33.9163		<.0001
3	DemMedHomeValue*DemPctVeterans		1	3	25.2441		<.0001
4	REP_StatusCat96NK		2	4	10.2804		0.0059
5	DemHomeOwner*M_LOG_GiftAvgCard36		1	5	5.8659		0.0154
6	DemCluster*DemGender		106	6	134.9632		0.0302
7	GiftTimeLast*PromCnt12		1	7	5.6507		0.0174
8	LOG_GiftCntCard36*PromCnt12		1	8	3.7134		0.0540
9	LOG_GiftAvgAll		1	9	5.8292	0.0158	
10	DemCluster		50	10	64.6125	0.0801	
11		DemCluster	53	9		39.8737	0.9086

    Surprisingly, the selection process takes only 11 steps. This is the result of the 106 degree-of-freedom **DemCluster** and **DemGender** interaction in Step 6. As the iteration plot shows below, the model is hopelessly overfit after this step. Inputs with many levels are problematic for predictive models. It is a good practice to reduce the impact of these inputs either by consolidating the levels or by simply excluding them from the analysis.

5. Scroll down in the Output Window.

The selected model, based on the CHOOSE=VERROR criterion, is the model trained in Step 3. It consists of the following effects:

Intercept DemMedHomeValue*DemPctVeterans GiftTimeLast*LOG_GiftAvgLast LOG_GiftCnt36*LOG_GiftCntCardAll

The selected model includes only three terms!

Copyright © 2011, SAS Institute Inc., Cary, North Carolina, USA. ALL RIGHTS RESERVED.

6. Select **View** ⇨ **Model** ⇨ **Iteration Plot**.

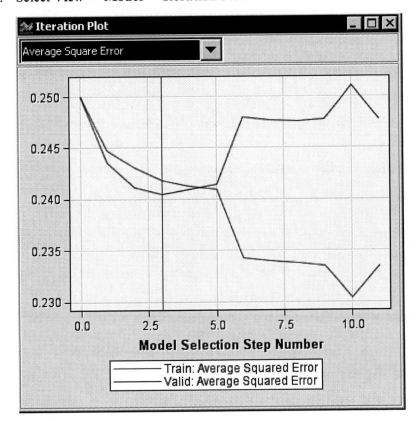

The validation average squared error of the three-term model is lower than any other model considered to this point.

Copyright © 2011, SAS Institute Inc., Cary, North Carolina, USA. ALL RIGHTS RESERVED.

 **Exercises**

1. **Predictive Modeling Using Regression**

   a. Return to the Chapter 3 Organics diagram. Attach the StatExplore tool to the **ORGANICS** data source and run it.

   b. In preparation for regression, is any missing values imputation needed? _____

   If yes, should you do this imputation before generating the decision tree models? _____

   Why or why not? _____

   c. Add an **Impute** node to the diagram and connect it to the **Data Partition** node. Set the node to impute **U** for unknown class variable values and the overall mean for unknown interval variable values. Create imputation indicators for all imputed inputs.

   d. Add a **Regression** node to the diagram and connect it to the **Impute** node.

   e. Choose stepwise as the selection model and the validation error as the selection criterion.

   f. Run the Regression node and view the results.

   Which variables are included in the final model? _____

   Which variables are important in this model? _____

   What is the validation ASE? _____

   g. In preparation for regression, are any transformations of the data warranted? _____

   Why or why not? _____

   h. Disconnect the **Impute** node from the **Data Partition** node.

   i. Add a **Transform Variables** node to the diagram and connect it to the **Data Partition** node.

   j. Connect the **Transform Variables** node to the **Impute** node.

   k. Apply a log transformation to the **DemAffl** and **PromTime** inputs.

   l. Run the **Transform Variables** node. Explore the exported training data. Did the transformations result in less skewed distributions? _____

   m. Rerun the **Regression** node.

   Do the selected variables change? _____

   How about the validation ASE? _____

   n. Create a full second-degree polynomial model. How does the validation average squared error for the polynomial model compare to the original model? _____

Copyright © 2011, SAS Institute Inc., Cary, North Carolina, USA. ALL RIGHTS RESERVED.

4.8 Chapter Summary

Regression models are a prolific and useful way to create predictions. New cases are scored using a prediction formula. Inputs are selected via a sequential selection process. Model complexity is controlled by fit statistics calculated on validation data.

To use regression models, there are several issues with which to contend that go beyond the predictive modeling essentials:

1. A mechanism for handling missing input values must be included in the model development process.

2. A reliable way to interpret the results is needed.

3. Methods for handling extreme or outlying predictions should be included.

4. The level-count of a categorical should be reduced to avoid overfitting.

5. The model complexity might need to be increased beyond what is provided by standard regression methods.

One approach to this is polynomial regression. Polynomial regression models can be fit manually with specific interactions in mind. They can also be fit autonomously by selecting polynomial terms from a list of all polynomial candidates.

Copyright © 2011, SAS Institute Inc., Cary, North Carolina, USA. ALL RIGHTS RESERVED.

Regression Tools Review

 Replace missing values for interval (means) and categorical data (mode). Create a unique replacement indicator.

 Create linear and logistic regression models. Select inputs with a sequential selection method and appropriate fit statistic. Interpret models with odds ratios.

 Regularize distributions of inputs. Typical transformations control for input skewness via a log transformation.

101

continued...

Regression Tools Review

 Consolidate levels of a nonnumeric input using the Replacement Editor window.

 Add polynomial terms to a regression either by hand or by an autonomous exhaustive search.

102

Copyright © 2011, SAS Institute Inc., Cary, North Carolina, USA. ALL RIGHTS RESERVED.

4.9 Solutions

Solutions to Exercises

1. **Predictive Modeling Using Regression**

   a. Return to the Chapter 3 Organics diagram in the **My Project** project. Use the StatExplore tool on the **ORGANICS** data source.

   1) Add the **StatExplore** node from the Explore tab into the diagram. Connect the **StatExplore** node to the **ORGANICS** node as shown.

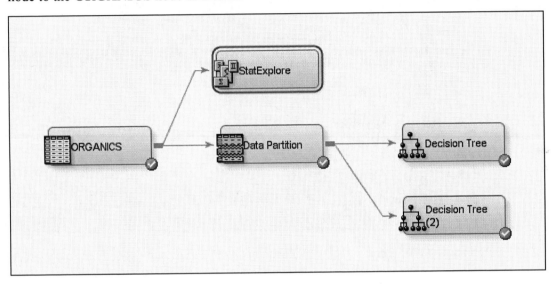

Copyright © 2011, SAS Institute Inc., Cary, North Carolina, USA. ALL RIGHTS RESERVED.

2) Run the StatExplore node and view the results.

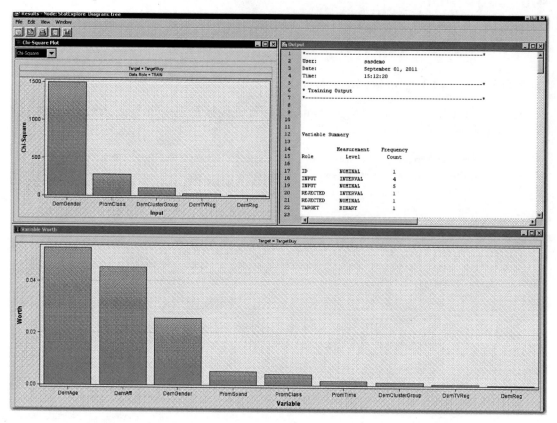

b. In preparation for regression, is any missing values imputation needed? If yes, should you do this imputation before generating the decision tree models? Why or why not?

Go to line 37 in the Output window. Several of the class inputs have missing values.

					Mode		Mode2
	Number of						
Variable	Role	Levels	Missing	Mode	Percentage	Mode	Percentage

Class Variable Summary Statistics

Variable	Role	Levels	Number of Missing	Mode	Mode Percentage	Mode2	Mode2 Percentage
DemClusterGroup	INPUT	8	674	C	20.55	D	19.70
DemGender	INPUT	4	2512	F	54.67	M	26.17
DemReg	INPUT	6	465	South East	38.85	Midlands	30.33
DemTVReg	INPUT	14	465	London	27.85	Midlands	14.05
PromClass	INPUT	4	0	Silver	38.57	Tin	29.19
TargetBuy	TARGET	2	0	0	75.23	1	24.77

Go to line 65 of the Output window. Most of the Interval inputs also have missing values.

Interval Variable Summary Statistics

Variable	ROLE	Mean	Std. Deviation	Non Missing	Missing	Minimum	Median	Maximum
DemAffl	INPUT	8.71	3.42	21138	1085	0.00	8	34.00
DemAge	INPUT	53.80	13.21	20715	1508	18.00	54	79.00
PromSpend	INPUT	4420.59	7559.05	22223	0	0.01	2000	296313.85
PromTime	INPUT	6.56	4.66	21942	281	0.00	5	39.00

You do not need to impute before the Decision Tree node. Decision trees have built-in ways to handle missing values. (See Chapter 3.)

Copyright © 2011, SAS Institute Inc., Cary, North Carolina, USA. ALL RIGHTS RESERVED.

c. Add an **Impute** node from the **Modify** tab into the diagram and connect it to the **Data Partition** node. Set the node to impute **U** for unknown class variable values and the overall mean for unknown interval variable values. Create imputation indicators for all imputed inputs.

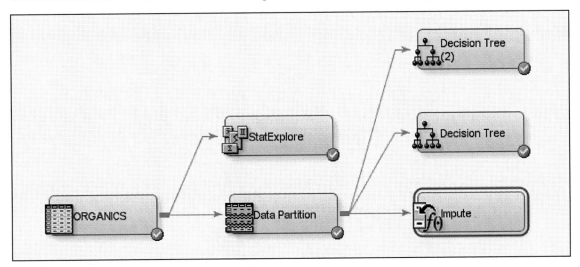

1) Select **Default Input Method** ⇨ **Default Constant Value**.

2) Type **U** for the Default Character Value.

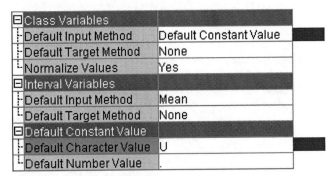

Class Variables	
Default Input Method	Default Constant Value
Default Target Method	None
Normalize Values	Yes
Interval Variables	
Default Input Method	Mean
Default Target Method	None
Default Constant Value	
Default Character Value	U
Default Number Value	.

3) Select **Indicator Variable** ⇨ **Type** ⇨ **Unique**.

4) Select **Indicator Variable** ⇨ **Role** ⇨ **Input**.

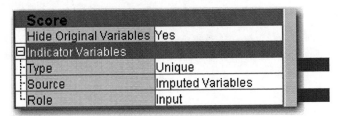

Score	
Hide Original Variables	Yes
Indicator Variables	
Type	Unique
Source	Imputed Variables
Role	Input

Copyright © 2011, SAS Institute Inc., Cary, North Carolina, USA. ALL RIGHTS RESERVED.

d. Add a **Regression** node to the diagram and connect it to the **Impute** node.

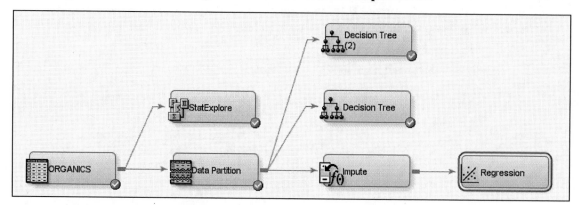

e. Choose stepwise as the selection model and the validation error as the selection criterion.

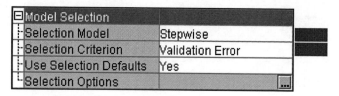

f. Run the Regression node and view the results. Which variables are included in the final model? Which variables are important in this model? What is the validation ASE?

1) The Results window appears.

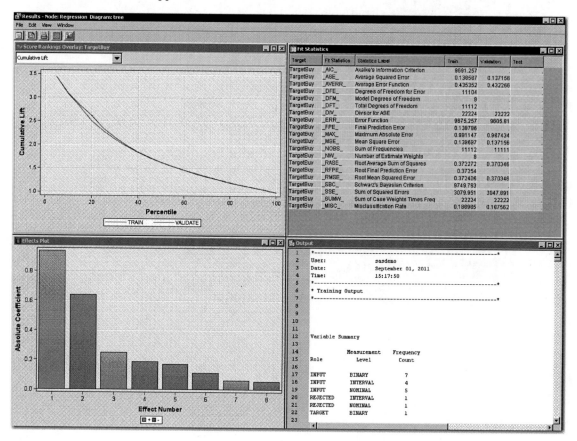

Copyright © 2011, SAS Institute Inc., Cary, North Carolina, USA. ALL RIGHTS RESERVED.

2) Go to line 664 in the Output window.

```
The selected model, based on the CHOOSE=VERROR criterion, is the model trained in
Step 6. It consists of the following effects:

Intercept IMP_DemAffl IMP_DemAge IMP_DemGender M_DemAffl M_DemAge M_DemGender
```

3) The odds ratios indicate the effect that each input has on the logit score.

```
                              Point
Effect                       Estimate
IMP_DemAffl                    1.283
IMP_DemAge                     0.947
IMP_DemGender     F vs U        6.967
IMP_DemGender     M vs U        2.899
M_DemAffl         0 vs 1       0.708
M_DemAge          0 vs 1       0.796
M_DemGender       0 vs 1        0.685
```

4) The validation ASE is given in the Fit Statistics window.

Fit Statistics

Target	Fit Statistics	Statistics Label	Train	Validation
TargetBuy	_AIC_	Akaike's Information Criterion	9691.257	.
TargetBuy	_ASE_	Average Squared Error	0.138587	0.137156
TargetBuy	_AVERR_	Average Error Function	0.435352	0.432266
TargetBuy	_DFE_	Degrees of Freedom for Error	11104	.
TargetBuy	_DFM_	Model Degrees of Freedom	8	.
TargetBuy	_DFT_	Total Degrees of Freedom	11112	.
TargetBuy	_DIV_	Divisor for ASE	22224	22222
TargetBuy	_ERR_	Error Function	9675.257	9605.81
TargetBuy	_FPE_	Final Prediction Error	0.138786	.
TargetBuy	_MAX_	Maximum Absolute Error	0.991147	0.987434
TargetBuy	_MSE_	Mean Square Error	0.138687	0.137156
TargetBuy	_NOBS_	Sum of Frequencies	11112	11111
TargetBuy	_NW_	Number of Estimate Weights	8	.
TargetBuy	_RASE_	Root Average Sum of Squares	0.372272	0.370346
TargetBuy	_RFPE_	Root Final Prediction Error	0.37254	.
TargetBuy	_RMSE_	Root Mean Squared Error	0.372406	0.370346
TargetBuy	_SBC_	Schwarz's Bayesian Criterion	9749.783	.
TargetBuy	_SSE_	Sum of Squared Errors	3079.951	3047.891
TargetBuy	_SUMW_	Sum of Case Weights Times Freq	22224	22222
TargetBuy	_MISC_	Misclassification Rate	0.188985	0.187562

Copyright © 2011, SAS Institute Inc., Cary, North Carolina, USA. ALL RIGHTS RESERVED.

g. In preparation for regression, are any transformations of the data warranted? Why or why not?

1) Open the Variables window of the Regression node.

2) Select the imputed interval inputs.

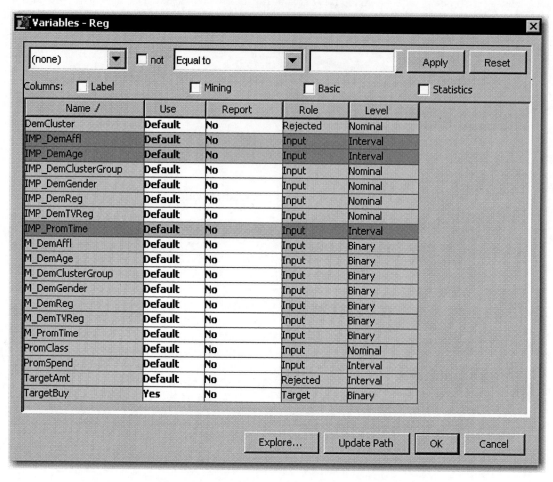

Copyright © 2011, SAS Institute Inc., Cary, North Carolina, USA. ALL RIGHTS RESERVED.

3) Select **Explore**. The Explore window appears.

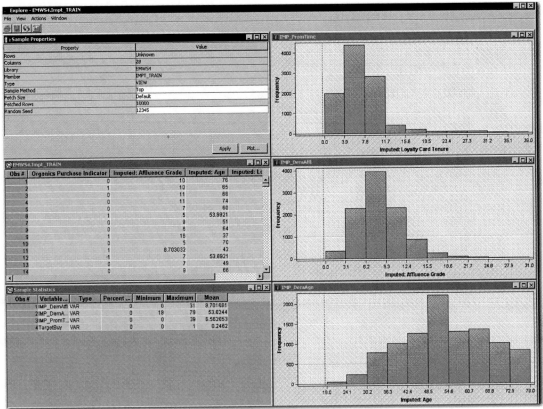

Both Card Tenure and Affluence Grade have moderately skewed distributions. Applying a log transformation to these inputs might improve the model fit.

h. Disconnect the **Impute** node from the **Data Partition** node.

i. Add a **Transform Variables** node from the **Modify tab** to the diagram and connect it to the **Data Partition** node.

j. Connect the **Transform Variables** node to the **Impute** node.

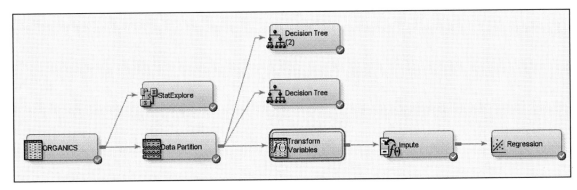

Copyright © 2011, SAS Institute Inc., Cary, North Carolina, USA. ALL RIGHTS RESERVED.

k. Apply a log transformation to the DemAffl and PromTime inputs.

1) Open the Variables window of the Transform Variables node.

2) Select **Method** ⇨ **Log** for the DemAffl and PromTime inputs.

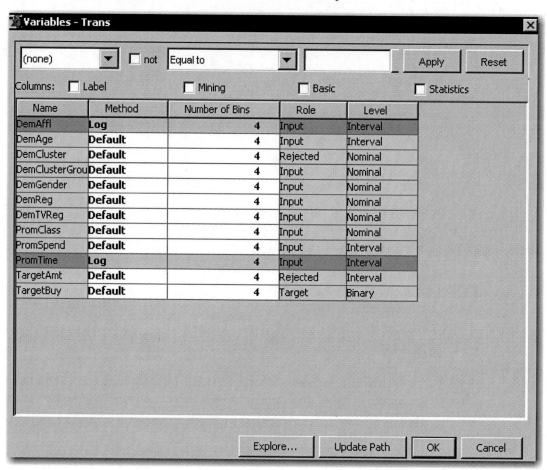

3) Select **OK** to close the Variables window.

Copyright © 2011, SAS Institute Inc., Cary, North Carolina, USA. ALL RIGHTS RESERVED.

l. Run the **Transform Variables** node. Explore the exported training data. Did the transformations result in less skewed distributions?

   1) The easiest way to explore the created inputs is to open the Variables window in the subsequent Impute node. Make sure that you update the Impute node before opening its Variables window.

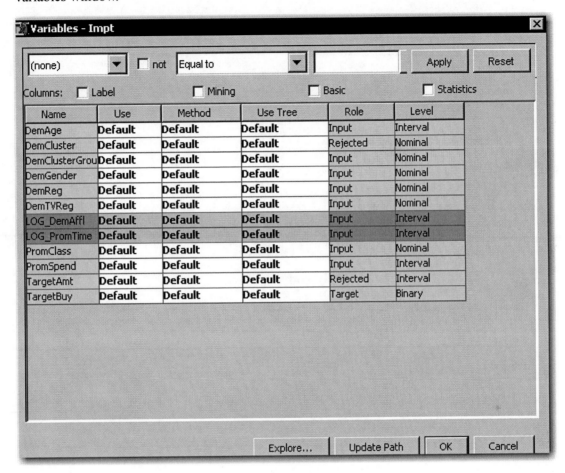

Copyright © 2011, SAS Institute Inc., Cary, North Carolina, USA. ALL RIGHTS RESERVED.

2) With the **LOG_DemAffl** and **LOG_PromTime** inputs selected, select **Explore**.

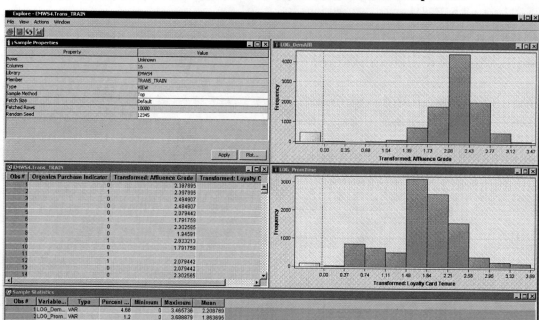

The distributions are nicely symmetric.

m. Rerun the **Regression** node. Do the selected variables change? How about the validation ASE?

1) Go to line 664 of the Output window.

> The selected model, based on the CHOOSE=VERROR criterion, is the model trained in Step 6.
> It consists of the following effects:
>
> Intercept IMP_DemAge IMP_DemGender IMP_LOG_DemAffl M_DemAge M_DemGender M_LOG_DemAffl

2) **IMP_LOG_DemAffl** and **M_LOG_DemAffl** replace **IMP_DemAffl** and **M_DemAffl**, respectively.

Copyright © 2011, SAS Institute Inc., Cary, North Carolina, USA. ALL RIGHTS RESERVED.

3) Apparently the log transformation actually increased the validation ASE slightly.

Target	Fit Statistics	Statistics Label	Train	Validation
TargetBuy	_AIC_	Akaike's Information Criterion	9758.609	.
TargetBuy	_ASE_	Average Squared Error	0.139545	0.138204
TargetBuy	_AVERR_	Average Error Function	0.438382	0.43599
TargetBuy	_DFE_	Degrees of Freedom for Error	11104	.
TargetBuy	_DFM_	Model Degrees of Freedom	8	.
TargetBuy	_DFT_	Total Degrees of Freedom	11112	.
TargetBuy	_DIV_	Divisor for ASE	22224	22222
TargetBuy	_ERR_	Error Function	9742.609	9688.581
TargetBuy	_FPE_	Final Prediction Error	0.139746	.
TargetBuy	_MAX_	Maximum Absolute Error	0.992317	0.994405
TargetBuy	_MSE_	Mean Square Error	0.139646	0.138204
TargetBuy	_NOBS_	Sum of Frequencies	11112	11111
TargetBuy	_NW_	Number of Estimate Weights	8	
TargetBuy	_RASE_	Root Average Sum of Squares	0.373557	0.371759
TargetBuy	_RFPE_	Root Final Prediction Error	0.373826	.
TargetBuy	_RMSE_	Root Mean Squared Error	0.373692	0.371759
TargetBuy	_SBC_	Schwarz's Bayesian Criterion	9817.136	.
TargetBuy	_SSE_	Sum of Squared Errors	3101.251	3071.178
TargetBuy	_SUMW_	Sum of Case Weights Times Freq	22224	22222
TargetBuy	_MISC_	Misclassification Rate	0.187815	0.186122

n. Create a full second-degree polynomial model. How does the validation average squared error for the polynomial model compare to the original model?

1) Add another Regression node to the diagram and rename it **Polynomial Regression**.

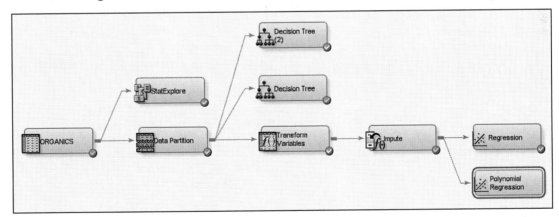

Copyright © 2011, SAS Institute Inc., Cary, North Carolina, USA. ALL RIGHTS RESERVED.

2) Make the indicated changes to the Polynomial Regression Properties panel and run the node.

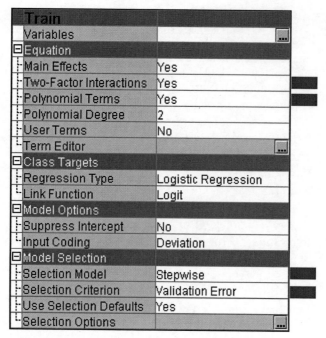

3) Go to line 1598 of the results output window.

```
The selected model, based on the CHOOSE=VERROR criterion, is the model trained in Step 7.
It consists of the following effects:

Intercept IMP_DemAge IMP_DemGender IMP_LOG_DemAffl M_DemAge M_DemGender*M_LOG_DemAffl
IMP_DemAge*IMP_DemAge IMP_LOG_DemAffl*IMP_LOG_DemAffl
```

4) The Polynomial Regression node adds additional interaction terms.

Copyright © 2011, SAS Institute Inc., Cary, North Carolina, USA. ALL RIGHTS RESERVED.

5) Examine the Fit Statistics window.

Target	Fit Statistics	Statistics Label	Train	Validation
TargetBuy	_AIC_	Akaike's Information Criterion	9529.938	
TargetBuy	_ASE_	Average Squared Error	0.136407	0.134038
TargetBuy	_AVERR_	Average Error Function	0.428003	0.421824
TargetBuy	_DFE_	Degrees of Freedom for Error	11103	
TargetBuy	_DFM_	Model Degrees of Freedom	9	
TargetBuy	_DFT_	Total Degrees of Freedom	11112	
TargetBuy	_DIV_	Divisor for ASE	22224	22222
TargetBuy	_ERR_	Error Function	9511.938	9373.784
TargetBuy	_FPE_	Final Prediction Error	0.136628	
TargetBuy	_MAX_	Maximum Absolute Error	0.985718	0.986233
TargetBuy	_MSE_	Mean Square Error	0.136517	0.134038
TargetBuy	_NOBS_	Sum of Frequencies	11112	11111
TargetBuy	_NW_	Number of Estimate Weights	9	
TargetBuy	_RASE_	Root Average Sum of Squares	0.369333	0.366112
TargetBuy	_RFPE_	Root Final Prediction Error	0.369632	
TargetBuy	_RMSE_	Root Mean Squared Error	0.369482	0.366112
TargetBuy	_SBC_	Schwarz's Bayesian Criterion	9595.78	
TargetBuy	_SSE_	Sum of Squared Errors	3031.498	2978.59
TargetBuy	_SUMW_	Sum of Case Weights Times Freq	22224	22222
TargetBuy	_MISC_	Misclassification Rate	0.190245	0.188282

The additional terms reduce the validation ASE slightly.

Copyright © 2011, SAS Institute Inc., Cary, North Carolina, USA. ALL RIGHTS RESERVED.

Solutions to Student Activities (Polls/Quizzes)

4.01 Multiple Choice Poll – Correct Answer

What is the logistic regression prediction for the indicated point?

a. 0.243
b. 0.56
c. yellow
d. It depends.

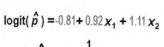

$$\text{logit}(\hat{p}) = -0.81 + 0.92\, x_1 + 1.11\, x_2$$

$$\hat{p} = \frac{1}{1 + e^{-\text{logit}(\hat{p})}}$$

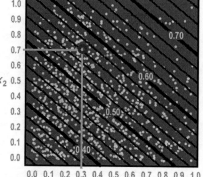

21

4.02 Poll – Correct Answer

The three sequential selection methods for building regression models can never lead to the same model for the same set of data.

○ True
◉ False

61

Copyright © 2011, SAS Institute Inc., Cary, North Carolina, USA. ALL RIGHTS RESERVED.

4.03 Multiple Choice Poll – Correct Answer

Which statement below is true about transformations of input variables in a regression analysis?

a. They are never a good idea.

b. They help model assumptions match the assumptions of maximum likelihood estimation.

c. They are performed to reduce the bias in model predictions.

d. They typically are done on nominal (categorical) inputs.

83

Copyright © 2011, SAS Institute Inc., Cary, North Carolina, USA. ALL RIGHTS RESERVED.

Copyright © 2011, SAS Institute Inc., Cary, North Carolina, USA. ALL RIGHTS RESERVED.

Chapter 5 Introduction to Predictive Modeling: Neural Networks and Other Modeling Tools

Copyright © 2011, SAS Institute Inc., Cary, North Carolina, USA. ALL RIGHTS RESERVED.

Copyright © 2011, SAS Institute Inc., Cary, North Carolina, USA. ALL RIGHTS RESERVED.

5.1   Introduction

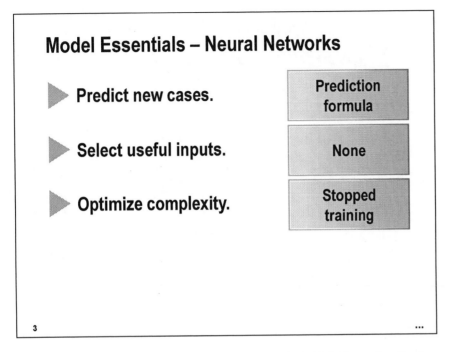

With its exotic sounding name, a neural network model (formally, for the models discussed in this course, *multi-layer perceptrons*) is often regarded as a mysterious and powerful predictive tool. Perhaps surprisingly, the most typical form of the model is, in fact, a natural extension of a regression model.

The prediction formula used to predict new cases is similar to a regression's, but with an interesting and flexible addition. This addition enables a properly trained neural network to model virtually any association between input and target variables. Flexibility comes at a price, however, because the problem of input selection is not easily addressed by a neural network. The inability to select inputs is offset (somewhat) by a complexity optimization algorithm named *stopped training*. Stopped training can reduce the chances of overfitting, even in the presence of redundant and irrelevant inputs.

Copyright © 2011, SAS Institute Inc., Cary, North Carolina, USA. ALL RIGHTS RESERVED.

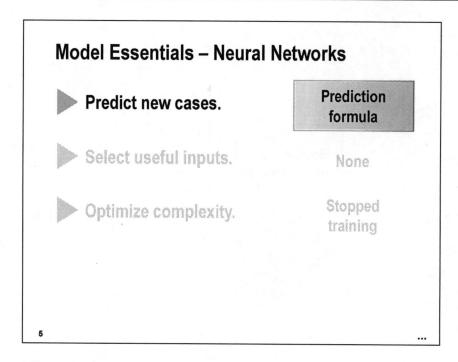

Like regressions, neural networks predict cases using a mathematical equation involving the values of the input variables.

Copyright © 2011, SAS Institute Inc., Cary, North Carolina, USA. ALL RIGHTS RESERVED.

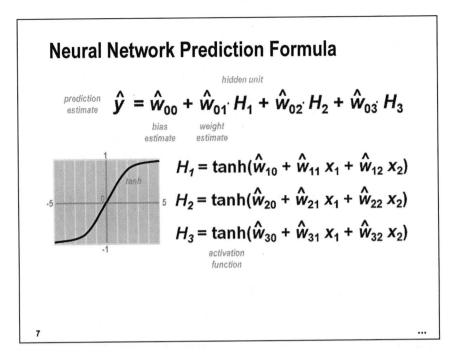

Neural Network Prediction Formula

hidden unit

prediction estimate $\quad \hat{y} = \hat{w}_{00} + \hat{w}_{01} H_1 + \hat{w}_{02} H_2 + \hat{w}_{03} H_3$

bias estimate   *weight estimate*

$H_1 = \tanh(\hat{w}_{10} + \hat{w}_{11} x_1 + \hat{w}_{12} x_2)$

$H_2 = \tanh(\hat{w}_{20} + \hat{w}_{21} x_1 + \hat{w}_{22} x_2)$

$H_3 = \tanh(\hat{w}_{30} + \hat{w}_{31} x_1 + \hat{w}_{32} x_2)$

activation function

7   ...

A neural network can be thought of as a regression model on a set of derived inputs, called *hidden units*. In turn, the hidden units can be thought of as regressions on the original inputs. The hidden unit "regressions" include a default link function (in neural network language, an *activation function*), the hyperbolic tangent. The hyperbolic tangent is a shift and rescaling of the logistic function introduced in Chapter 4.

Because of a neural network's biological roots, its components receive different names from corresponding components of a regression model. Instead of an intercept term, a neural network has a *bias* term. Instead of parameter estimates, a neural network has *weight estimates*.

What makes neural networks interesting is their ability to approximate virtually any continuous association between the inputs and the target. You simply specify the correct number of hidden units and find reasonable values for the weights. Specifying the correct number of hidden units involves some trial and error. Finding reasonable values for the weights is done by least squares estimation (for interval-valued targets).

Copyright © 2011, SAS Institute Inc., Cary, North Carolina, USA. ALL RIGHTS RESERVED.

Neural Network Binary Prediction Formula

$$\log\left(\frac{\hat{p}}{1-\hat{p}}\right) = \hat{w}_{00} + \hat{w}_{01} H_1 + \hat{w}_{02} H_2 + \hat{w}_{03} H_3$$

*logit
link function*

$$H_1 = \tanh(\hat{w}_{10} + \hat{w}_{11} x_1 + \hat{w}_{12} x_2)$$

$$H_2 = \tanh(\hat{w}_{20} + \hat{w}_{21} x_1 + \hat{w}_{22} x_2)$$

$$H_3 = \tanh(\hat{w}_{30} + \hat{w}_{31} x_1 + \hat{w}_{32} x_2)$$

8   ...

When the target variable is binary, as in the demonstration data, the main neural network regression equation receives the same logit link function featured in logistic regression. As with logistic regression, the weight estimation process changes from least squares to maximum likelihood.

Copyright © 2011, SAS Institute Inc., Cary, North Carolina, USA. ALL RIGHTS RESERVED.

Neural Network Diagram

$$\log\left(\frac{\hat{p}}{1-\hat{p}}\right) = \hat{w}_{00} + \hat{w}_{01} H_1 + \hat{w}_{02} H_2 + \hat{w}_{03} H_3$$

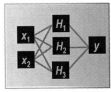

$$H_1 = \tanh(\hat{w}_{10} + \hat{w}_{11} x_1 + \hat{w}_{12} x_2)$$

$$H_2 = \tanh(\hat{w}_{20} + \hat{w}_{21} x_1 + \hat{w}_{22} x_2)$$

$$H_3 = \tanh(\hat{w}_{30} + \hat{w}_{31} x_1 + \hat{w}_{32} x_2)$$

input layer   hidden layer   target layer

9   ...

Multi-layer perceptron models were originally inspired by neurophysiology and the interconnections between neurons, and they are often represented by a network diagram instead of an equation. The basic model form arranges neurons in layers. The first layer, called the *input layer*, connects to a layer of neurons called a *hidden layer*, which, in turn, connects to a final layer called the *target* or *output layer*. Each element in the diagram has a counterpart in the network equation. The blocks in the diagram correspond to inputs, hidden units, and target variables. The block interconnections correspond to the network equation weights.

Copyright © 2011, SAS Institute Inc., Cary, North Carolina, USA. ALL RIGHTS RESERVED.

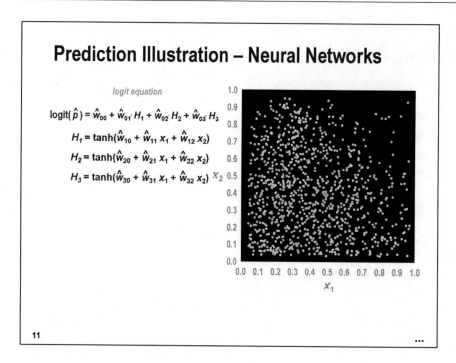

To demonstrate the properties of a neural network model, consider again the two-color prediction problem. As always, the goal is to predict the target color based on the location in the unit square.

As with regressions, the predictions can be decisions, rankings, or estimates. The logit equation produces a ranking or logit score.

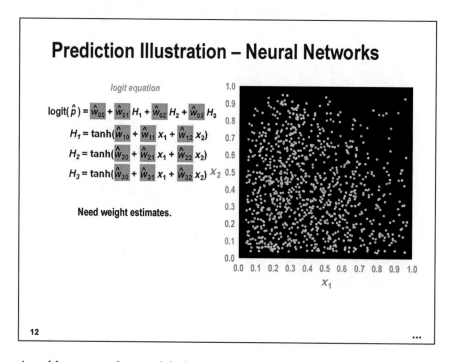

As with a regression model, the primary task is to obtain parameter, or in the neural network case, weight estimates that result in accurate predictions. A major difference between a neural network and a regression model, however, is the number of values to be estimated and the complicated relationship between the weights.

Copyright © 2011, SAS Institute Inc., Cary, North Carolina, USA. ALL RIGHTS RESERVED.

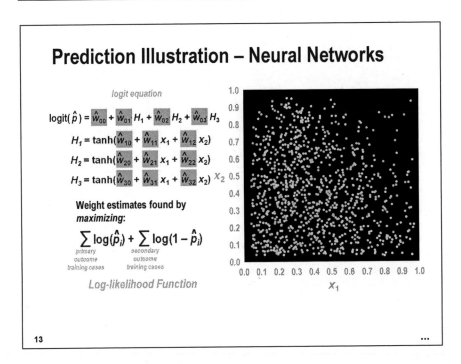

Prediction Illustration – Neural Networks

logit equation

$$\text{logit}(\hat{p}) = \hat{w}_{00} + \hat{w}_{01}\,H_1 + \hat{w}_{02}\,H_2 + \hat{w}_{03}\,H_3$$

$$H_1 = \tanh(\hat{w}_{10} + \hat{w}_{11}\,x_1 + \hat{w}_{12}\,x_2)$$

$$H_2 = \tanh(\hat{w}_{20} + \hat{w}_{21}\,x_1 + \hat{w}_{22}\,x_2)$$

$$H_3 = \tanh(\hat{w}_{30} + \hat{w}_{31}\,x_1 + \hat{w}_{32}\,x_2)$$

Weight estimates found by *maximizing:*

$$\sum \log(\hat{p}_i) + \sum \log(1 - \hat{p}_i)$$

primary outcome training cases   secondary outcome training cases

Log-likelihood Function

13   ...

For a binary target, the weight estimation process is driven by an attempt to maximize the log-likelihood function. Unfortunately, in the case of a neural network model, the maximization process is complicated by local optima as well as a tendency to create overfit models. A technique illustrated in the next section (usually) overcomes these difficulties and produces a reasonable model.

Copyright © 2011, SAS Institute Inc., Cary, North Carolina, USA. ALL RIGHTS RESERVED.

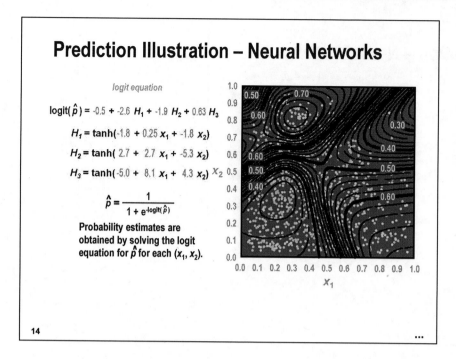

Even a relatively simple neural network with three hidden units permits elaborate associations between the inputs and the target. While the model might be simple, explanation of the model is decidedly not. This lack of explicability is frequently cited as a major disadvantage of a neural network. Of course, complex input/target associations are difficult to explain no matter what technique is used to model them. Neural networks should not be faulted, assuming that they correctly modeled this association.

After the prediction formula is established, obtaining a prediction is strictly a matter of plugging the input measurements into the hidden unit expressions. In the same way as with regression models, you can obtain a prediction estimate using the logistic function.

Copyright © 2011, SAS Institute Inc., Cary, North Carolina, USA. ALL RIGHTS RESERVED.

Neural Nets: Beyond the Prediction Formula

▶ **Manage missing values.**

▶ **Handle extreme or unusual values.**

▶ **Use non-numeric inputs.**

▶ Account for nonlinearities.

▶ Interpret the model.

16

Neural networks share some of the same prediction complications with their regression kin.

The most prevalent problem is missing values. Like regressions, neural networks require a complete record for estimation and scoring. Neural networks resolve this complication in the same way that regression does, by imputation.

Extreme or unusual values also present a problem for neural networks. The problem is mitigated somewhat by the hyperbolic tangent activation functions in the hidden units. These functions squash extreme input values between -1 and +1.

Nonnumeric inputs pose less of a complication to a properly tuned neural network than they do to regressions. This is mainly due to the complexity optimization process described in the next section.

Unlike standard regression models, neural networks easily accommodate nonlinear and nonadditive associations between inputs and target. In fact, the main challenge is over-accommodation, that is, falsely discovering nonlinearities and interactions.

Interpreting a neural network model can be difficult, and while it is an issue, it is one with no easy solution.

Copyright © 2011, SAS Institute Inc., Cary, North Carolina, USA. ALL RIGHTS RESERVED.

Training a Neural Network

Several tools in SAS Enterprise Miner include the term *neural* in their name. The Neural Network tool is the most useful of these. (The AutoNeural and DM Neural tools are described later in the chapter.)

1.   Select the **Model** tab.

2.   Drag a **Neural Network** tool into the diagram workspace.

3.   Connect the **Impute** node to the **Neural Network** node.

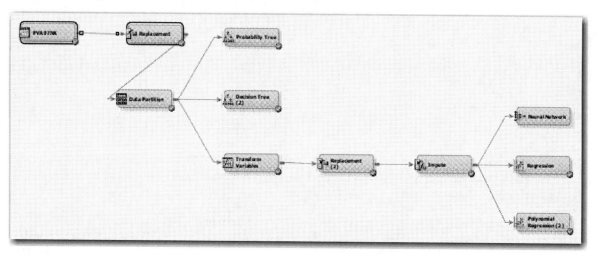

With the diagram configured as shown, the Neural Network node takes advantage of the transformations, replacements, and imputations prepared for the Regression node.

The neural network has a default option for so-called "preliminary training."

Copyright © 2011, SAS Institute Inc., Cary, North Carolina, USA. ALL RIGHTS RESERVED.

4. Select **Optimization** ⇨ ... from the Neural Network Properties panel.

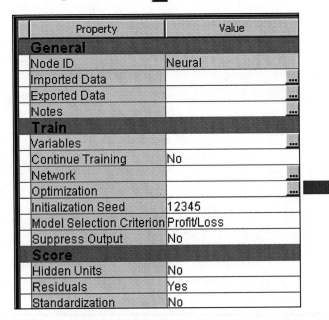

5. Select **Enable** ⇨ **No** under the Preliminary Training options.

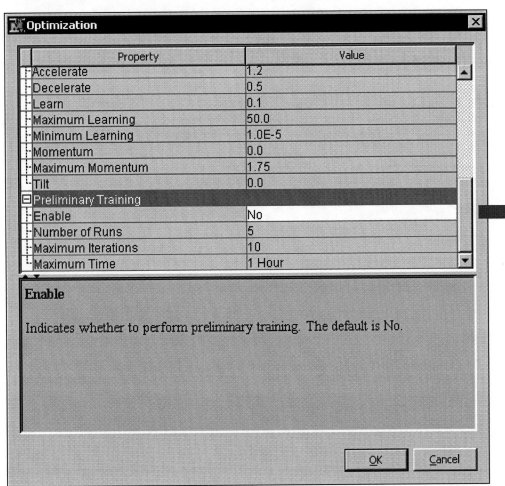

Copyright © 2011, SAS Institute Inc., Cary, North Carolina, USA. ALL RIGHTS RESERVED.

6. Run the Neural Network node and view the results.

The Results - Node: Neural Network Diagram window appears.

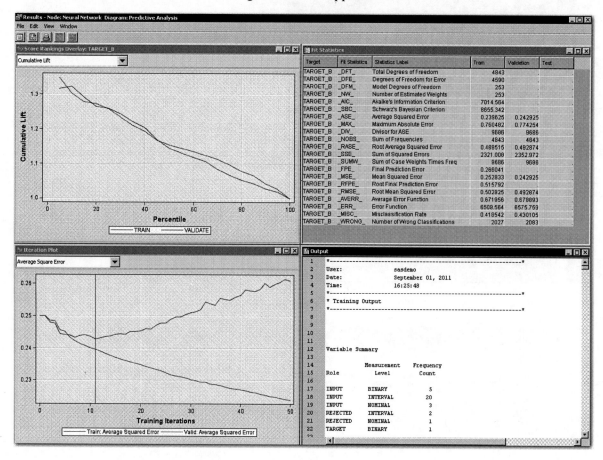

Copyright © 2011, SAS Institute Inc., Cary, North Carolina, USA. ALL RIGHTS RESERVED.

7. Maximize the Fit Statistics window.

Target	Fit Statistics	Statistics Label	Train	Validation	Test
TARGET_B	_DFT_	Total Degre...	4843	.	
TARGET_B	_DFE_	Degrees of ...	4590	.	
TARGET_B	_DFM_	Model Degr...	253	.	
TARGET_B	_NW_	Number of ...	253	.	
TARGET_B	_AIC_	Akaike's Inf...	7014.564	.	
TARGET_B	_SBC_	Schwarz's ...	8655.342	.	
TARGET_B	_ASE_	Average Sq...	0.239625	0.242925	
TARGET_B	_MAX_	Maximum A...	0.760482	0.774254	
TARGET_B	_DIV_	Divisor for A...	9686	9686	
TARGET_B	_NOBS_	Sum of Fre...	4843	4843	
TARGET_B	_RASE_	Root Avera...	0.489515	0.492874	
TARGET_B	_SSE_	Sum of Squ...	2321.008	2352.972	
TARGET_B	_SUMW_	Sum of Cas...	9686	9686	
TARGET_B	_FPE_	Final Predic...	0.266041	.	
TARGET_B	_MSE_	Mean Squa...	0.252833	0.242925	
TARGET_B	_RFPE_	Root Final ...	0.515792	.	
TARGET_B	_RMSE_	Root Mean ...	0.502825	0.492874	
TARGET_B	_AVERR_	Average Err...	0.671956	0.678893	
TARGET_B	_ERR_	Error Functi...	6508.564	6575.759	
TARGET_B	_MISC_	Misclassific...	0.418542	0.430105	
TARGET_B	_WRONG_	Number of ...	2027	2083	

The average squared error and misclassification are similar to the values observed from regression models in the previous chapter. Notice that the model contains 253 weights. This is a large model.

Copyright © 2011, SAS Institute Inc., Cary, North Carolina, USA. ALL RIGHTS RESERVED.

8. Go to line 54 of the Output window. There you can find a table of the initial values for the neural network weights.

```
                        The NEURAL Procedure

                        Optimization Start
                       Parameter Estimates

                                                    Gradient
                                                    Objective
       N Parameter                      Estimate    Function

       1 DemMedHomeValue_H11           -0.004746           0
       2 DemPctVeterans_H11            -0.011042           0
       3 GiftTimeFirst_H11             -0.026889           0
       4 GiftTimeLast_H11              -0.024545           0
       5 IMP_DemAge_H11                 0.008120           0
       6 IMP_LOG_GiftAvgCard36_H11      0.055146           0
       7 IMP_REP_DemMedIncome_H11      -0.167987           0
       8 LOG_GiftAvg36_H11              0.087440           0
       9 LOG_GiftAvgAll_H11             0.063190           0
                            .
                            .
                            .
     250 H11_TargetB1                         0    -0.004814
     251 H12_TargetB1                         0  -0.000030480
     252 H13_TargetB1                         0     0.001641
     253 BIAS_TargetB1                -0.000413  1.178583E-15
```

Despite the huge number of weights, the model shows no signs of overfitting.

9. Go to line 415. You can find a summary of the model optimization (maximizing the likelihood estimates of the model weights).

```
                          Optimization Results

Iterations                         50  Function Calls              136
Gradient Calls                     62  Active Constraints            0
Objective Function         0.6368394579  Max Abs Gradient Element  0.0076065979
Slope of Search Direction  -0.000752598

QUANEW needs more than 50 iterations or 2147483647 function calls.

WARNING: QUANEW Optimization cannot be completed.
```

Notice the warning message. It can be interpreted to mean that the model-fitting process did not converge.

10. Close the Results - Neural Network window.

Copyright © 2011, SAS Institute Inc., Cary, North Carolina, USA. ALL RIGHTS RESERVED.

11. Reopen the Optimization window and examine the Optimization options in the Properties panel for the Neural Network node.

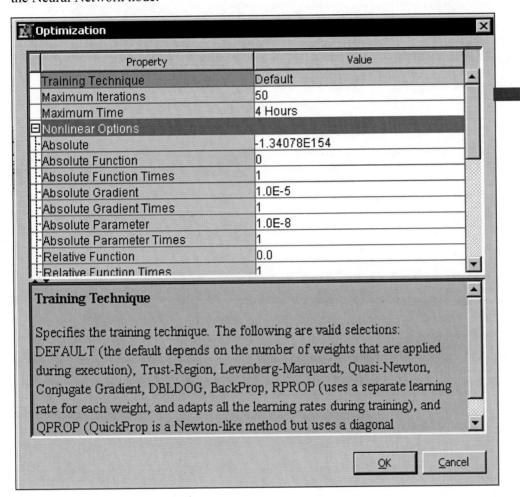

The maximum number of iterations, by default, is 50. Apparently, this is not enough for the network training process to converge.

12. Type **100** for the Maximum Iterations property.

13. Run the Neural Network node and examine the results.

14. Maximize the Output window. Go to line 465. You are again warned that the optimization process still failed to converge (even after 100 iterations).

```
QUANEW needs more than 100 iterations or 2147483647 function calls

WARNING: QUANEW Optimization cannot be completed.
```

Copyright © 2011, SAS Institute Inc., Cary, North Carolina, USA. ALL RIGHTS RESERVED.

15. Maximize the Fit Statistics window.

Target	Fit Statistics	Statistics Label	Train	Validation
TARGET_B	_DFT_	Total Degrees of Freedom	4843	
TARGET_B	_DFE_	Degrees of Freedom for Error	4590	
TARGET_B	_DFM_	Model Degrees of Freedom	253	
TARGET_B	_NW_	Number of Estimated Weights	253	
TARGET_B	_AIC_	Akaike's Information Criterion	7014.564	
TARGET_B	_SBC_	Schwarz's Bayesian Criterion	8655.342	
TARGET_B	_ASE_	Average Squared Error	0.239625	0.242925
TARGET_B	_MAX_	Maximum Absolute Error	0.760482	0.774254
TARGET_B	_DIV_	Divisor for ASE	9686	9686
TARGET_B	_NOBS_	Sum of Frequencies	4843	4843
TARGET_B	_RASE_	Root Average Squared Error	0.489515	0.492874
TARGET_B	_SSE_	Sum of Squared Errors	2321.008	2352.972
TARGET_B	_SUMW_	Sum of Case Weights Times Freq	9686	9686
TARGET_B	_FPE_	Final Prediction Error	0.266041	
TARGET_B	_MSE_	Mean Squared Error	0.252833	0.242925
TARGET_B	_RFPE_	Root Final Prediction Error	0.515792	
TARGET_B	_RMSE_	Root Mean Squared Error	0.502825	0.492874
TARGET_B	_AVERR_	Average Error Function	0.671956	0.678893
TARGET_B	_ERR_	Error Function	6508.564	6575.759
TARGET_B	_MISC_	Misclassification Rate	0.418542	0.430105
TARGET_B	_WRONG_	Number of Wrong Classifications	2027	2083

Curiously, increasing the maximum number of iterations changes none of the fit statistics. How can this be? The answer is found in the Iteration Plot window.

Copyright © 2011, SAS Institute Inc., Cary, North Carolina, USA. ALL RIGHTS RESERVED.

16. Examine the Iteration Plot window.

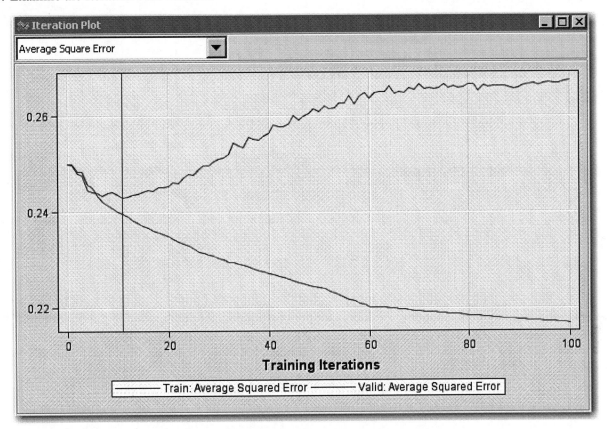

The iteration plot shows the average squared error versus optimization iteration. A massive divergence in training and validation average squared error occurs near iteration 14, indicated by the vertical blue line.

The rapid divergence of the training and validation fit statistics is cause for concern. This primarily results from a huge number of weights in the fitted neural network model. The huge number of weights comes from the use of all inputs in the model. Reducing the number of modeling inputs reduces the number of modeling weights and possibly improves model performance.

17. Close the Results window.

Copyright © 2011, SAS Institute Inc., Cary, North Carolina, USA. ALL RIGHTS RESERVED.

5.2 Input Selection

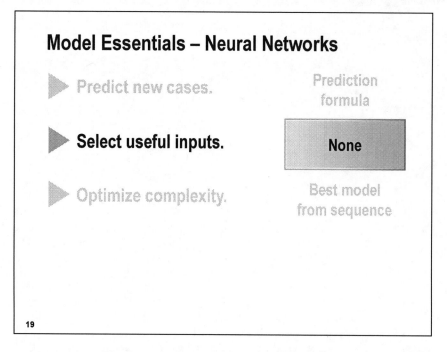

The Neural Network tool in SAS Enterprise Miner lacks a built-in method for selecting useful inputs. While sequential selection procedures such as stepwise are known for neural networks, the computational costs of their implementation tax even fast computers. Therefore, these procedures are not part of SAS Enterprise Miner. You can solve this problem by using an external process to select useful inputs. In this demonstration, you use the variables selected by the standard regression model. (In Chapter 9, several other approaches are shown.)

5.01 Multiple Answer Poll

Which of the following are true about neural networks in SAS Enterprise Miner?

a. Neural networks are universal approximators.

b. Neural networks have no internal, automated process for selecting useful inputs.

c. Neural networks are easy to interpret and thus are very useful in highly regulated industries.

d. Neural networks cannot model nonlinear relationships.

Copyright © 2011, SAS Institute Inc., Cary, North Carolina, USA. ALL RIGHTS RESERVED.

Selecting Neural Network Inputs

This demonstration shows how to use a logistic regression to select inputs for a neural network.

Additional dimension reduction techniques are discussed in Chapter 9.

1. Delete the connection between the Impute node and the Neural Network node.

2. Connect the **Regression** node to the **Neural Network** node.

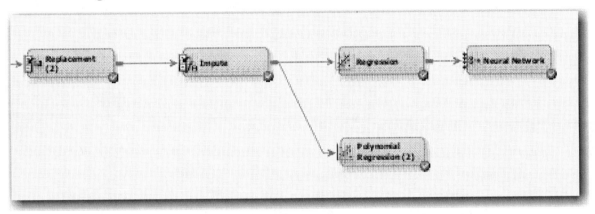

3. Right-click the **Neural Network** node and select **Update** from the shortcut menu.

Copyright © 2011, SAS Institute Inc., Cary, North Carolina, USA. ALL RIGHTS RESERVED.

4. Open the Variables dialog box for the Neural Network node. Select the check box next to **Label** and resize the fields for better visibility.

Only the inputs selected by the Regression node's stepwise procedure are not rejected.

5. Close the Variables dialog box.

Copyright © 2011, SAS Institute Inc., Cary, North Carolina, USA. ALL RIGHTS RESERVED.

6. Run the Neural Network node and view the results.

The Fit Statistics window shows an improvement in model fit using only 19 weights.

Target	Fit Statistics	Statistics Label	Train	Validation
Fit Statistics				
TARGET_B	_DFT_	Total Degrees of Freedom	4843	.
TARGET_B	_DFE_	Degrees of Freedom for Error	4824	.
TARGET_B	_DFM_	Model Degrees of Freedom	19	.
TARGET_B	_NW_	Number of Estimated Weights	19	.
TARGET_B	_AIC_	Akaike's Information Criterion	6573.409	.
TARGET_B	_SBC_	Schwarz's Bayesian Criterion	6696.629	.
TARGET_B	_ASE_	Average Squared Error	0.240983	0.240441
TARGET_B	_MAX_	Maximum Absolute Error	0.777	0.78162
TARGET_B	_DIV_	Divisor for ASE	9686	9686
TARGET_B	_NOBS_	Sum of Frequencies	4843	4843
TARGET_B	_RASE_	Root Average Squared Error	0.4909	0.490348
TARGET_B	_SSE_	Sum of Squared Errors	2334.159	2328.913
TARGET_B	_SUMW_	Sum of Case Weights Times Freq	9686	9686
TARGET_B	_FPE_	Final Prediction Error	0.242881	.
TARGET_B	_MSE_	Mean Squared Error	0.241932	0.240441
TARGET_B	_RFPE_	Root Final Prediction Error	0.49283	.
TARGET_B	_RMSE_	Root Mean Squared Error	0.491866	0.490348
TARGET_B	_AVERR_	Average Error Function	0.674727	0.673563
TARGET_B	_ERR_	Error Function	6535.409	6524.13
TARGET_B	_MISC_	Misclassification Rate	0.427421	0.421639
TARGET_B	_WRONG_	Number of Wrong Classifications	2070	2042

The validation and training average squared errors are nearly identical.

Copyright © 2011, SAS Institute Inc., Cary, North Carolina, USA. ALL RIGHTS RESERVED.

5.3 Stopped Training

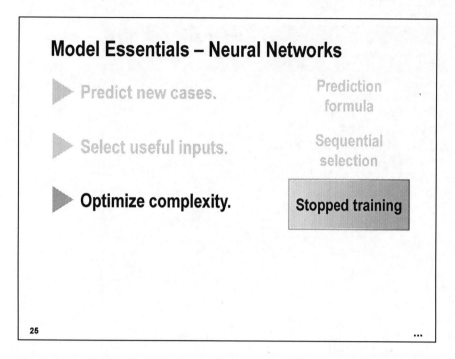

As was seen in the first demonstration, complexity optimization is an integral part of neural network modeling. Other modeling methods selected an optimal model from a sequence of possible models. In the demonstration, only one model was estimated (a neural network with three hidden units), so what was being compared?

SAS Enterprise Miner treats each iteration in the optimization process as a separate model. The iteration with the smallest value of the selected fit statistic is chosen as the final model. This method of model optimization is called *stopped training*.

Copyright © 2011, SAS Institute Inc., Cary, North Carolina, USA. ALL RIGHTS RESERVED.

Fit Statistic versus Optimization Iteration

initial hidden unit weights

$\text{logit}(\hat{p}) = 0 + \boxed{0}H_1 + \boxed{0}H_2 + \boxed{0}H_3$

$H_1 = \tanh(-1.5 - .03x_1 - .07x_2)$

$H_2 = \tanh(.79 - .17x_1 - .16x_2)$

$H_3 = \tanh(.57 + .05x_1 + .35x_2)$

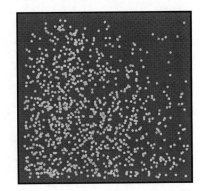

26   ...

Copyright © 2011, SAS Institute Inc., Cary, North Carolina, USA. ALL RIGHTS RESERVED.

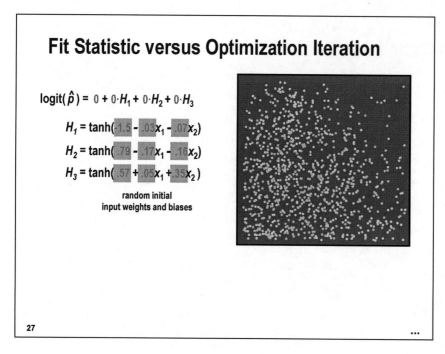

To begin model optimization, model weights are given initial values. The weights multiplying the hidden units in the logit equation are set to zero, and the bias in the logit equation is set equal to the logit(π_1), where π_1 equals the primary outcome proportion. The remaining weights (corresponding to the hidden units) are given random initial values (near zero).

This "model" assigns each case a prediction estimate: $\hat{p}_i = \pi_1$. An initial fit statistic is calculated on training and validation data. For a binary target, this is proportional to the log likelihood function:

$$\sum_{\substack{primary \\ outcomes}} \log(\hat{p}_i(\hat{\mathbf{w}})) + \sum_{\substack{sec\,ondary \\ outcomes}} \log(1 - \hat{p}_i(\hat{\mathbf{w}}))$$

where

$\hat{p}_i$ is the predicted target value.

$\hat{\mathbf{w}}$ is the current estimate of the model parameters.

Training proceeds by updating the parameter estimates in a manner that decreases the value of the objective function.

Copyright © 2011, SAS Institute Inc., Cary, North Carolina, USA. ALL RIGHTS RESERVED.

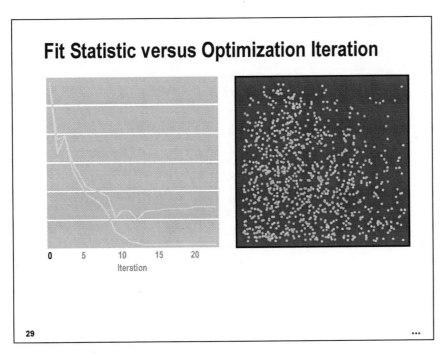

As stated above, in the initial step of the training procedure, the neural network model is set up to predict the overall average response rate for all cases.

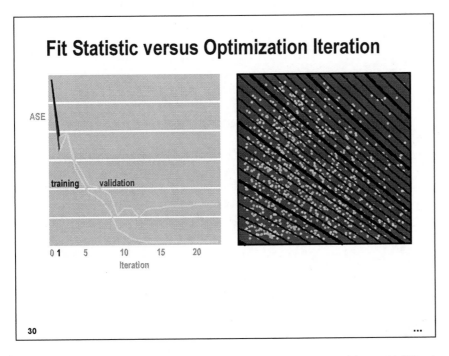

One step substantially decreases the value average squared error (ASE). Amazingly, the model that corresponds to this one-iteration neural network closely resembles the standard regression model, as seen from the fitted isoclines.

Copyright © 2011, SAS Institute Inc., Cary, North Carolina, USA. ALL RIGHTS RESERVED.

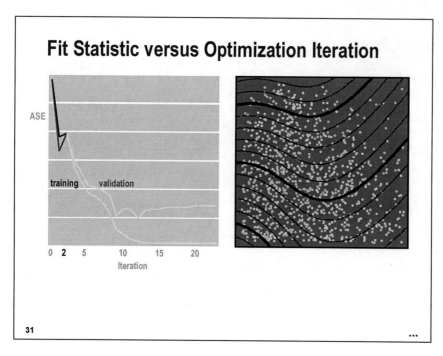

The second iteration step goes slightly astray. The model actually becomes slightly worse on the training and validation data.

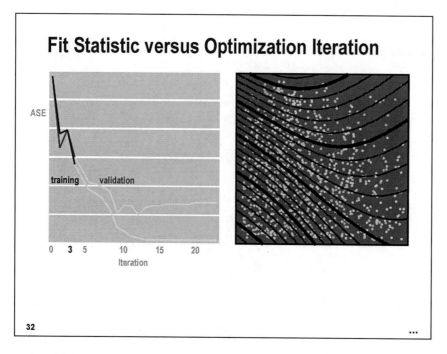

Things are back on track in the third iteration step. The fitted model is already exhibiting nonlinear and nonadditive predictions. Half of the improvement in ASE is realized by the third step.

Copyright © 2011, SAS Institute Inc., Cary, North Carolina, USA. ALL RIGHTS RESERVED.

Fit Statistic versus Optimization Iteration

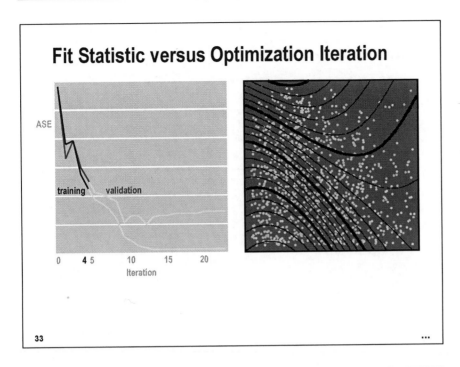

33

Fit Statistic versus Optimization Iteration

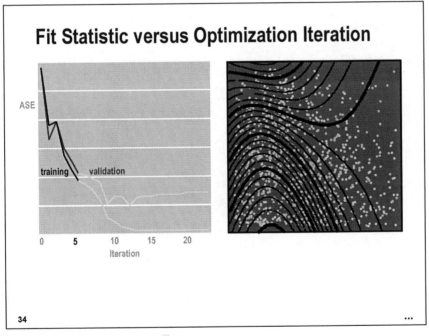

34

Copyright © 2011, SAS Institute Inc., Cary, North Carolina, USA. ALL RIGHTS RESERVED.

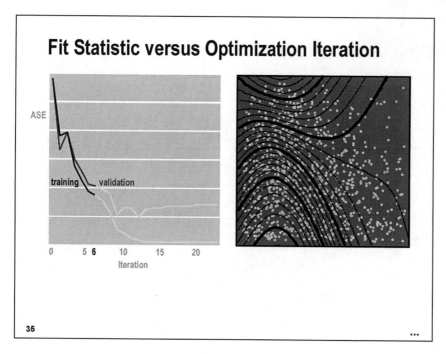

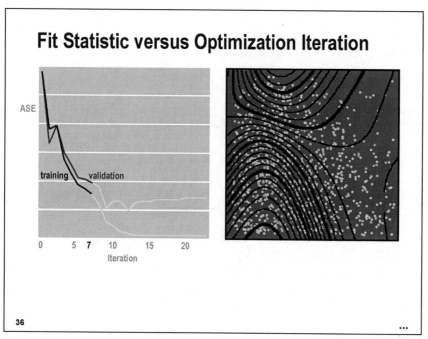

Copyright © 2011, SAS Institute Inc., Cary, North Carolina, USA. ALL RIGHTS RESERVED.

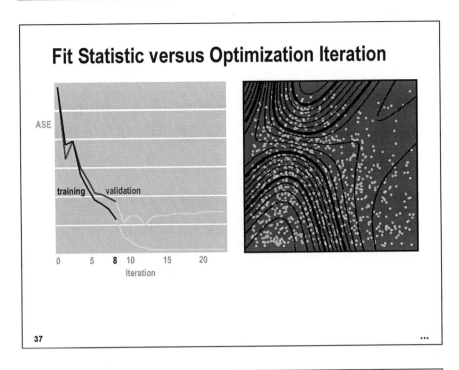

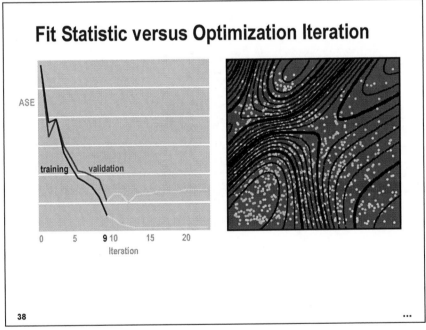

Most of the improvement in validation ASE occurred by the ninth step. (Training ASE continues to improve until convergence in Step 23.) The predictions are close to their final form.

Copyright © 2011, SAS Institute Inc., Cary, North Carolina, USA. ALL RIGHTS RESERVED.

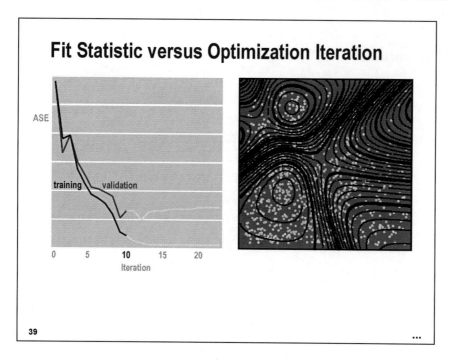

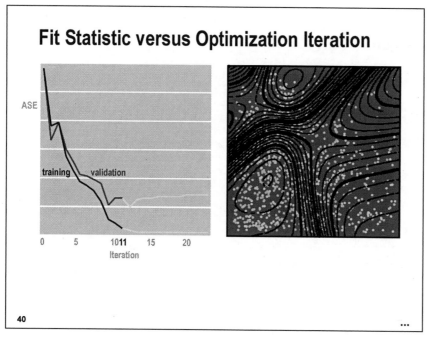

Copyright © 2011, SAS Institute Inc., Cary, North Carolina, USA. ALL RIGHTS RESERVED.

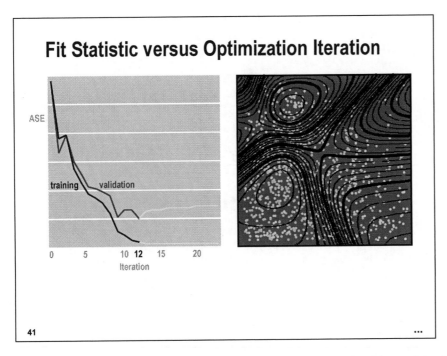

Step 12 brings the minimum value for validation ASE. While this model will ultimately be chosen as the final model, SAS Enterprise Miner continues to train until the likelihood objective function changes by a negligible amount on the training data.

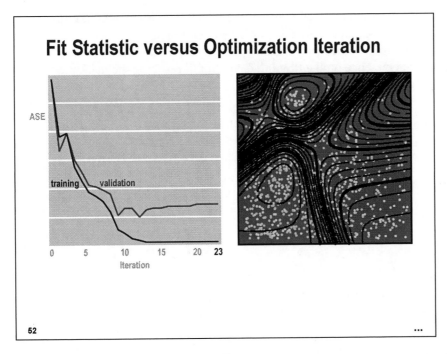

In Step 23, training is declared complete due to lack of change in the objective function from Step 22. Notice that between Step 13 and Step 23, ASE actually increased for the validation data. This is a sign of overfitting.

Copyright © 2011, SAS Institute Inc., Cary, North Carolina, USA. ALL RIGHTS RESERVED.

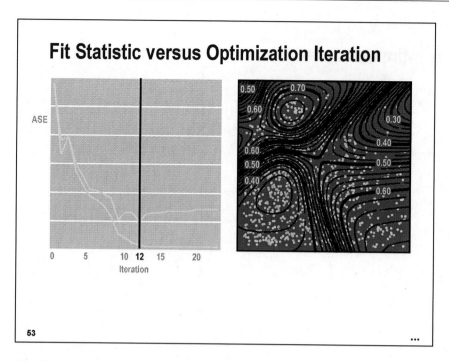

Fit Statistic versus Optimization Iteration

53

The Neural Network tool selects the modeling weights from iteration 13 for the final model. In this iteration, the validation ASE is minimized. You can also configure the Neural Network tool to select the iteration with minimum misclassification or maximum profit for final weight estimates.

    The name *stopped training* comes from the fact that the final model is selected as if training were stopped on the optimal iteration. Detecting when this optimal iteration occurs (while actually training) is somewhat problematic. To avoid stopping too early, the Neural Network tool continues to train until convergence on the training data or until reaching the maximum iteration count, whichever comes first.

Copyright © 2011, SAS Institute Inc., Cary, North Carolina, USA. ALL RIGHTS RESERVED.

Increasing Network Flexibility

Stopped training helps to ensure that a neural network does not overfit (even when the number of network weights is large). Further improvement in neural network performance can be realized by increasing the number of hidden units from the default of three. There are two ways to explore alternative network sizes:

- manually, by changing the number of weights by hand
- automatically, by using the AutoNeural tool

Changing the number of hidden units manually involves trial-and-error guessing of the "best" number of hidden units. Several hidden unit counts were tried in advance. One of the better selections is demonstrated.

1. Select **Network** ⇨ **...** from the Neural Network properties panel.

Property	Value
General	
Node ID	Neural
Imported Data	...
Exported Data	...
Notes	...
Train	
Variables	...
Continue Training	No
Network	...
Optimization	...
Initialization Seed	12345
Model Selection Crite	Profit/Loss
Suppress Output	No

Copyright © 2011, SAS Institute Inc., Cary, North Carolina, USA. ALL RIGHTS RESERVED.

The Network window appears.

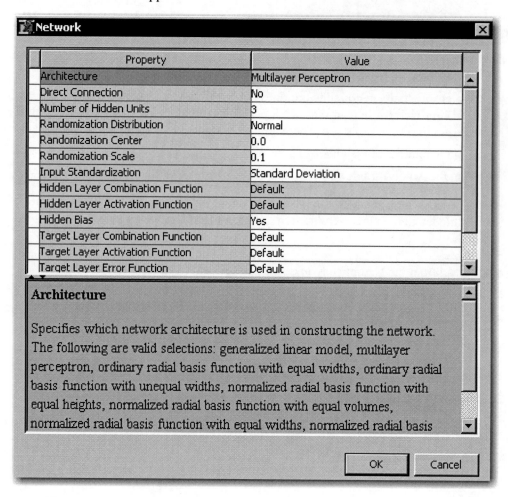

2. Type **6** as the **Number of Hidden Units** value.

3. Select **OK**.

4. Run the Neural Network node and view the results.

Copyright © 2011, SAS Institute Inc., Cary, North Carolina, USA. ALL RIGHTS RESERVED.

The Fit Statistics window shows good model performance on both the average squared error and misclassification scales.

Target	Fit Statistics	Statistics Label	Train	Validation
TARGET_B	_DFT_	Total Degrees of Freedom	4843	.
TARGET_B	_DFE_	Degrees of Freedom for Error	4806	.
TARGET_B	_DFM_	Model Degrees of Freedom	37	.
TARGET_B	_NW_	Number of Estimated Weights	37	.
TARGET_B	_AIC_	Akaike's Information Criterion	6601.6	.
TARGET_B	_SBC_	Schwarz's Bayesian Criterion	6841.556	.
TARGET_B	_ASE_	Average Squared Error	0.240623	0.23988
TARGET_B	_MAX_	Maximum Absolute Error	0.857328	0.869935
TARGET_B	_DIV_	Divisor for ASE	9686	9686
TARGET_B	_NOBS_	Sum of Frequencies	4843	4843
TARGET_B	_RASE_	Root Average Squared Error	0.490533	0.489776
TARGET_B	_SSE_	Sum of Squared Errors	2330.673	2323.478
TARGET_B	_SUMW_	Sum of Case Weights Times Freq	9686	9686
TARGET_B	_FPE_	Final Prediction Error	0.244328	.
TARGET_B	_MSE_	Mean Squared Error	0.242475	0.23988
TARGET_B	_RFPE_	Root Final Prediction Error	0.494295	.
TARGET_B	_RMSE_	Root Mean Squared Error	0.492418	0.489776
TARGET_B	_AVERR_	Average Error Function	0.673921	0.672391
TARGET_B	_ERR_	Error Function	6527.6	6512.78
TARGET_B	_MISC_	Misclassification Rate	0.427421	0.422878
TARGET_B	_WRONG_	Number of Wrong Classifications	2070	2048

Copyright © 2011, SAS Institute Inc., Cary, North Carolina, USA. ALL RIGHTS RESERVED.

The iteration plot shows optimal validation average squared error occurring on iteration 5.

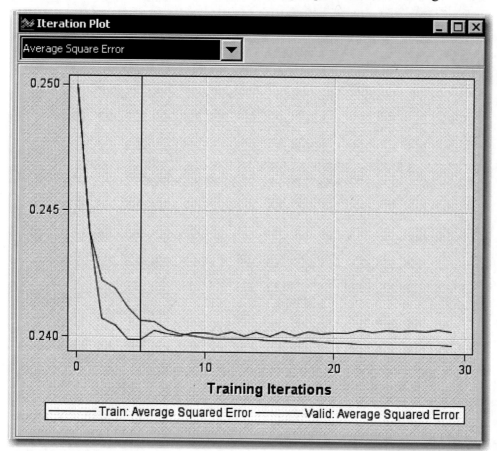

Unfortunately, there is little else of interest to describe this model. (In Chapter 9, a method is shown to give some insight into describing the cases with high primary outcome probability.)

Copyright © 2011, SAS Institute Inc., Cary, North Carolina, USA. ALL RIGHTS RESERVED.

Using the AutoNeural Tool (Self-Study)

The AutoNeural tool offers an automatic way to explore alternative network architectures and hidden unit counts. This demonstration shows how to explore neural networks with increasing hidden unit counts.

1. Select the **Model** tab.

2. Drag the **AutoNeural** tool into the diagram workspace.

3. Connect the **Regression** node to the **AutoNeural** node as shown.

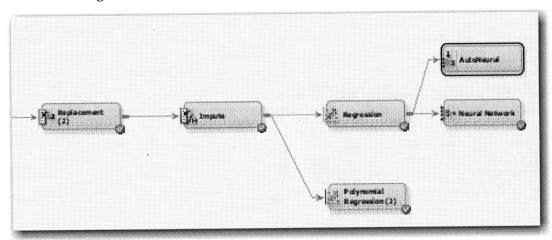

Some changes must be made to the AutoNeural node's default settings.

4. Confirm that this setting is in effect: **Train Action** ⇨ **Search**. This configures the AutoNeural node to sequentially increase the network complexity.

5. Select **Number of Hidden Units** ⇨ **1**. With this option, each iteration adds one hidden unit.

6. Select **Tolerance** ⇨ **Low**. This prevents preliminary training from occurring.

7. Select **Direct** ⇨ **No**. This deactivates direct connections between the inputs and the target.

8. Select **Normal** ⇨ **No**. This deactivates the normal distribution activation function.

Copyright © 2011, SAS Institute Inc., Cary, North Carolina, USA. ALL RIGHTS RESERVED.

9. Select **Sine** ⇨ **No**. This deactivates the sine activation function.

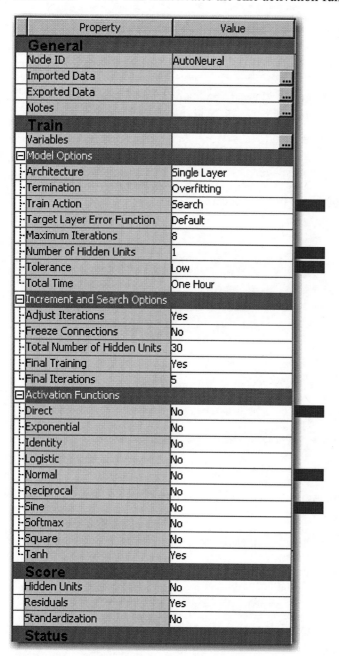

Property	Value
General	
Node ID	AutoNeural
Imported Data	...
Exported Data	...
Notes	...
Train	
Variables	...
Model Options	
Architecture	Single Layer
Termination	Overfitting
Train Action	Search
Target Layer Error Function	Default
Maximum Iterations	8
Number of Hidden Units	1
Tolerance	Low
Total Time	One Hour
Increment and Search Options	
Adjust Iterations	Yes
Freeze Connections	No
Total Number of Hidden Units	30
Final Training	Yes
Final Iterations	5
Activation Functions	
Direct	No
Exponential	No
Identity	No
Logistic	No
Normal	No
Reciprocal	No
Sine	No
Softmax	No
Square	No
Tanh	Yes
Score	
Hidden Units	No
Residuals	Yes
Standardization	No
Status	

With these settings, each iteration adds one hidden unit to the neural network. Only the hyperbolic tangent activation function is considered.

✎   After each iteration, the existing network weights are ***not*** reinitialized. With this restriction, the influence of additional hidden units decreases. Also, the neural network models that you obtain with the AutoNeural and Neural Network tools are different, even if both networks have the same number of hidden units.

Copyright © 2011, SAS Institute Inc., Cary, North Carolina, USA. ALL RIGHTS RESERVED.

10. Run the AutoNeural node and view the results. The Results - Node: AutoNeural Diagram window appears.

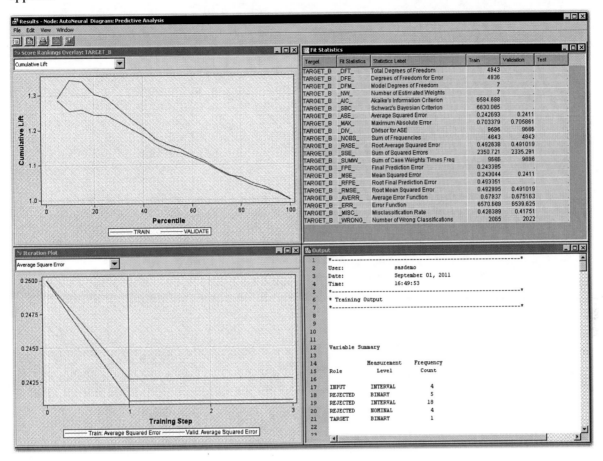

Copyright © 2011, SAS Institute Inc., Cary, North Carolina, USA. ALL RIGHTS RESERVED.

11. Maximize the Fit Statistics window.

Target	Fit Statistics	Statistics Label	Train	Validation
TARGET_B	_DFT_	Total Degrees of Freedom	4843	
TARGET_B	_DFE_	Degrees of Freedom for Error	4836	
TARGET_B	_DFM_	Model Degrees of Freedom	7	
TARGET_B	_NW_	Number of Estimated Weights	7	
TARGET_B	_AIC_	Akaike's Information Criterion	6584.688	
TARGET_B	_SBC_	Schwarz's Bayesian Criterion	6630.085	
TARGET_B	_ASE_	Average Squared Error	0.242693	0.2411
TARGET_B	_MAX_	Maximum Absolute Error	0.703379	0.705861
TARGET_B	_DIV_	Divisor for ASE	9686	9686
TARGET_B	_NOBS_	Sum of Frequencies	4843	4843
TARGET_B	_RASE_	Root Average Squared Error	0.492638	0.491019
TARGET_B	_SSE_	Sum of Squared Errors	2350.721	2335.291
TARGET_B	_SUMW_	Sum of Case Weights Times Freq	9686	9686
TARGET_B	_FPE_	Final Prediction Error	0.243395	
TARGET_B	_MSE_	Mean Squared Error	0.243044	0.2411
TARGET_B	_RFPE_	Root Final Prediction Error	0.493351	
TARGET_B	_RMSE_	Root Mean Squared Error	0.492995	0.491019
TARGET_B	_AVERR_	Average Error Function	0.67837	0.675163
TARGET_B	_ERR_	Error Function	6570.688	6539.625
TARGET_B	_MISC_	Misclassification Rate	0.426389	0.41751
TARGET_B	_WRONG_	Number of Wrong Classifications	2065	2022

The number of weights implies that the selected model has one hidden unit. The average squared error and misclassification rates are quite low.

Copyright © 2011, SAS Institute Inc., Cary, North Carolina, USA. ALL RIGHTS RESERVED.

12. Maximize the Iteration Plot window.

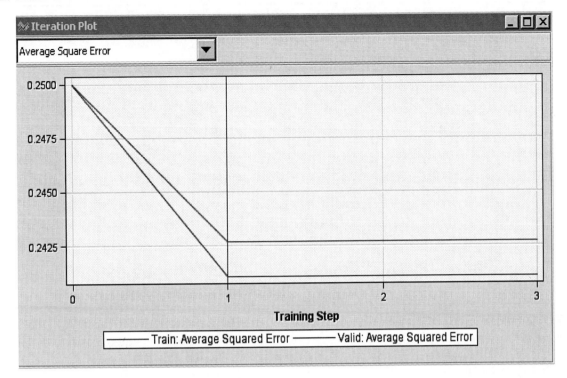

The AutoNeural and Neural Network node's iteration plots differ. The AutoNeural node's iteration plot shows the final fit statistic versus the number of hidden units in the neural network.

13. Maximize the Output window. The Output window describes the AutoNeural process.

14. Go to line 52.

Search # 1 SINGLE LAYER trial # 1 : TANH : Training					
ITER	_AIC_	_AVERR_	_MISC_	_VAVERR_	_VMISC_
0	6727.82	0.69315	0.49990	0.69315	0.50010
1	6725.17	0.69287	0.48462	0.69311	0.48193
2	6587.79	0.67869	0.42866	0.67713	0.42350
3	6584.69	0.67837	0.42639	0.67516	0.41751
4	6584.10	0.67831	0.42804	0.67638	0.43031
5	6575.69	0.67744	0.42660	0.67472	0.42061
6	6572.57	0.67712	0.42763	0.67455	0.42783
7	6571.21	0.67698	0.42866	0.67427	0.42205
8	6570.69	0.67692	0.42845	0.67420	0.42061
8	6570.69	0.67692	0.42845	0.67420	0.42061

These lines show various fit statistics versus training iteration using a single hidden unit network. Training stops at iteration 8 (based on an AutoNeural property setting). Validation misclassification is used to select the best iteration, in this case, Step 3. Weights from this iteration are selected for use in the next step.

Copyright © 2011, SAS Institute Inc., Cary, North Carolina, USA. ALL RIGHTS RESERVED.

15. View output lines 73-99.

```
                Search # 2 SINGLE LAYER trial # 1 : TANH : Training

        _ITER_      _AIC_      _AVERR_      _MISC_      _VAVERR_      _VMISC_

          0       6596.69     0.67837     0.42639      0.67516      0.41751
          1       6587.08     0.67738     0.42866      0.67472      0.42639
          2       6581.99     0.67685     0.42928      0.67405      0.42123
          3       6580.65     0.67671     0.42887      0.67393      0.42391
          4       6579.01     0.67654     0.42763      0.67392      0.42267
          5       6578.27     0.67647     0.43011      0.67450      0.42804
          6       6577.64     0.67640     0.42474      0.67426      0.42453
          7       6577.57     0.67640     0.42680      0.67458      0.42825
          8       6575.88     0.67622     0.42845      0.67411      0.42783
          8       6575.88     0.67622     0.42845      0.67411      0.42783


                    Selected Iteration based on _VMISC_

        _ITER_      _AIC_      _AVERR_      _MISC_      _VAVERR_      _VMISC_

          0       6596.69     0.67837     0.42639      0.67516      0.41751
```

A second hidden unit is added to the neural network model. All weights related to this new hidden unit are set to zero. All remaining weights are set to the values obtained in iteration 3 above. In this way, the two-hidden-unit neural network (Step 0) and the one-hidden-unit neural network (Step 3) have equal fit statistics.

Training of the two-hidden-unit network commences. The training process trains for eight iterations. Iteration 0 has the smallest validation misclassification and is selected to provide the weight values for the next AutoNeural step.

16. Go to line 106.

```
                          Final Training Training

        _ITER_      _AIC_      _AVERR_      _MISC_      _VAVERR_      _VMISC_

          0       6584.69     0.67837     0.42639      0.67516      0.41751
          1       6584.10     0.67831     0.42804      0.67638      0.43031
          2       6573.21     0.67718     0.42783      0.67462      0.42350
          3       6571.19     0.67698     0.42990      0.67437      0.42247
          4       6570.98     0.67695     0.42887      0.67431      0.42308
          5       6570.56     0.67691     0.43052      0.67418      0.42081
          5       6570.56     0.67691     0.43052      0.67418      0.42081


                    Selected Iteration based on _VMISC_

        _ITER_      _AIC_      _AVERR_      _MISC_      _VAVERR_      _VMISC_

          0       6584.69     0.67837     0.42639      0.67516      0.41751
```

The final model training commences. Again iteration zero offers the best validation misclassification.

Copyright © 2011, SAS Institute Inc., Cary, North Carolina, USA. ALL RIGHTS RESERVED.

The next block of output summarizes the training process. Fit statistics from the iteration with the smallest validation misclassification are shown for each step.

```
                          Final Training History

     _step_       _func_ _status_ _iter_ _AVERR_ _MISC_  _AIC_  _VAVERR_ _VMISC_

  SINGLE LAYER 1  TANH   initial    0   0.69315 0.49990 6727.82 0.69315 0.50010
  SINGLE LAYER 1  TANH   keep       3   0.67837 0.42639 6584.69 0.67516 0.41751
  SINGLE LAYER 2  TANH   reject     0   0.67837 0.42639 6596.69 0.67516 0.41751
                         Final      0   0.67837 0.42639 6584.69 0.67516 0.41751


                              Final Model
  Stopping: Termination criteria was satisfied: overfitting based on _VMISC_


  _func_    _AVERR_    _VAVERR_    neurons

   TANH     0.67837    0.67516        1
                                  =======
                                     1
```

The Final Model shows the hidden units added at each step and the corresponding value of the objective function (related to the likelihood).

Copyright © 2011, SAS Institute Inc., Cary, North Carolina, USA. ALL RIGHTS RESERVED.

5.4 Other Modeling Tools (Self-Study)

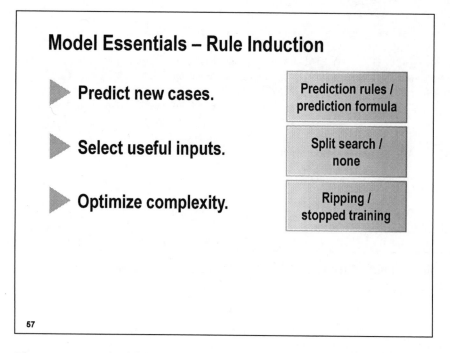

There are several additional modeling tools in SAS Enterprise Miner. This section describes the intended purpose (that is, when you should consider using them), how they perform the modeling essentials, and how they predict the simple example data.

The *Rule Induction tool* combines decision tree and neural network models to predict **nominal** targets. It is intended to be used when one of the nominal target levels is rare.

New cases are predicted using a combination of prediction rules (from decision trees) and a prediction formula (from a neural network, by default). Input selection and complexity optimization are described below.

Copyright © 2011, SAS Institute Inc., Cary, North Carolina, USA. ALL RIGHTS RESERVED.

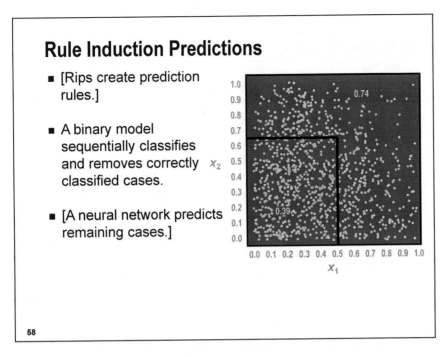

The Rule Induction algorithm has three steps:

- Using a decision tree, the first step attempts to locate "pure" concentrations of cases. These are regions of the input space containing only a single value of the target. The rules identifying these pure concentrations are recorded in the scoring code, and the cases in these regions are removed from the training data.

    The simple example data does not contain any "pure" regions, so the step is skipped.

- The second step attempts to filter easy-to-classify cases. This is done with a sequence of binary target decision trees. The first tree in the sequence attempts to distinguish the most common target level from the others. Cases found in leaves correctly classifying the most common target level are removed from the training data. Using this revised training data, a second tree is built to distinguish the second most common target class from the others. Again, cases in any leaf correctly classifying the second most common target level are removed from the training data. This process continues through the remaining levels of the target.

- In the third step, a neural network is used to predict the remaining cases. All inputs selected for use in the Rule Induction node will be used in the neural network model. Model complexity is controlled by stopped training using classification as the fit statistic.

Copyright © 2011, SAS Institute Inc., Cary, North Carolina, USA. ALL RIGHTS RESERVED.

Model Essentials – Dmine Regression

▶ **Predict new cases.**   Prediction formula

▶ **Select useful inputs.**   Forward selection

▶ **Optimize complexity.**   Stop R-square

59

Dmine regression is designed to provide a regression model with more flexibility than a standard regression model. It should be noted that with increased flexibility comes an increased potential of overfitting.

A regression-like prediction formula is used to score new cases. Forward selection picks the inputs. Model complexity is controlled by a minimum R-squared statistic.

Copyright © 2011, SAS Institute Inc., Cary, North Carolina, USA. ALL RIGHTS RESERVED.

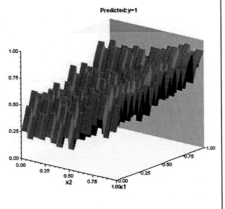

Dmine Regression Predictions

- Interval inputs binned, categorical inputs grouped

- Forward selection picks from binned and original inputs

60

The main distinguishing feature of Dmine regression versus traditional regression is its grouping of categorical inputs and binning of continuous inputs.

- The levels of each categorical input are systematically grouped together using an algorithm that is reminiscent of a decision tree. Both the original and grouped inputs are made available for subsequent input selection.

- All interval inputs are broken into a maximum of 16 bins in order to accommodate nonlinear associations between the inputs and the target. The levels of the maximally binned interval inputs are grouped using the same algorithm for grouping categorical inputs. These binned-and-grouped inputs and the original interval inputs are made available for input selection.

A forward selection algorithm selects from the original, binned, and grouped inputs. Only inputs with an R square of 0.005 or above are eligible for inclusion in the forward selection process. Forward selection on eligible inputs stops when no input improves the R square of the model by the default value 0.0005.

Copyright © 2011, SAS Institute Inc., Cary, North Carolina, USA. ALL RIGHTS RESERVED.

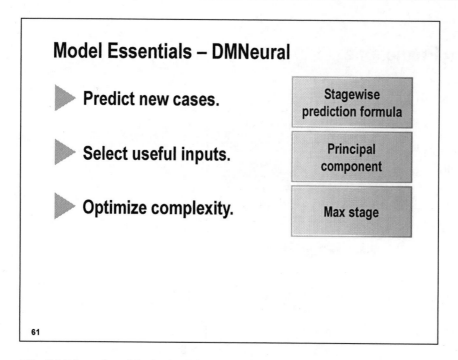

The DMNeural tool is designed to provide a flexible target prediction using an algorithm with some similarities to a neural network. A multi-stage prediction formula scores new cases. The problem of selecting useful inputs is circumvented by a principal components method. Model complexity is controlled by choosing the number of stages in the multi-stage predictions formula.

Copyright © 2011, SAS Institute Inc., Cary, North Carolina, USA. ALL RIGHTS RESERVED.

DMNeural Predictions

- Up to three PCs with highest target R square are selected.

- One of eight continuous transformations are selected and applied to selected PCs.

- The process is repeated three times with residuals from each stage.

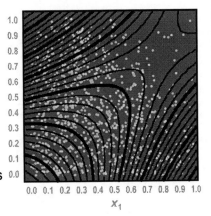

62

The algorithm starts by transforming the original inputs into principal components, which are orthogonal linear transformations of the original variables. The three principal components with the highest target correlation are selected for the next step.

Next, one of eight possible continuous transformations (square, hyperbolic tangent, arctangent, logistic, Gaussian, sine, cosine, exponential) is applied to the three principle component inputs. (For efficiency, the transformation is actually applied to a gridded version of the principle component, where each grid point is weighted by the number of cases near the point.) The transformation with the optimal fit statistic (squared error, by default) is selected. The target is predicted by a regression model using the selected principal components and transformation.

The process in the previous paragraph is repeated on the residual (the difference between the observed and predicted target value) up to the number of times specified in the maximum stage property (three, by default).

Copyright © 2011, SAS Institute Inc., Cary, North Carolina, USA. ALL RIGHTS RESERVED.

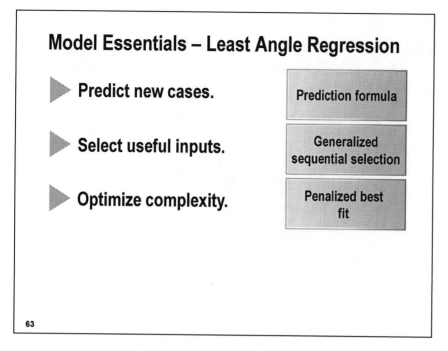

Forward selection, discussed in the previous chapter, provides good motivation for understanding how the Least Angle Regression (LARS) node works. In forward selection, the model-building process starts with an intercept. The best candidate input (the variable whose parameter estimate is most significantly different from zero) is added to create a one-variable model in the first step. The best candidate input variable from the remaining subset of input variables is added to create a two-variable model in the second step, and so on. Notice that an equivalent way to phrase the description of what happens in Step 2 is that the candidate input variable *most highly correlated with the residuals of the one variable model* is added to create a two-variable model in the second step.

The LARS algorithm generalizes forward selection in the following way:

1. Weight estimates are initially set to a value of zero.

2. The slope estimate in the one variable model grows away from zero until some other candidate input has an equivalent correlation with the residuals of that model.

3. Growth of the slope estimate on the first variable stops, and growth on the slope estimate of the second variable begins.

4. This process continues until the least squares solutions for the weights are attained, or some stopping criterion is optimized.

This process can be constrained by putting a threshold on the aggregate magnitude of the parameter estimates. The LARS node provides an option to use the LASSO (Least Absolute Shrinkage and Selection Operator) method for variable subset selection.

The LARS node optimizes the complexity of the model using a penalized best fit criterion. The Schwarz's Bayesian Criterion (SBC) is the default.

Copyright © 2011, SAS Institute Inc., Cary, North Carolina, USA. ALL RIGHTS RESERVED.

Least Angle Regression Predictions

- Inputs are selected using a generalization of forward selection.

- An input combination in the sequence with optimal, penalized validation assessment is selected by default.

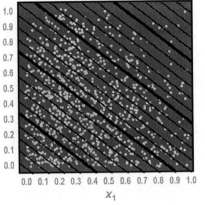

64

The Least Angle Regression node can be useful in a situation where there are many candidate input variables to choose from and the data set is not large. As mentioned above, the best subset model is chosen using SBC by default. SBC and its cousins (AIC, AICC, and others) optimize complexity by penalizing the fit of candidate input variables. That is, for an input to enter the model, it must improve the overall fit (here, diminish the residual sum of squares) of the model enough to overcome a penalty term built into the fit criterion. Other criteria, based on predicted (simulated) residual sums of squares or a validation data set, are available.

Copyright © 2011, SAS Institute Inc., Cary, North Carolina, USA. ALL RIGHTS RESERVED.

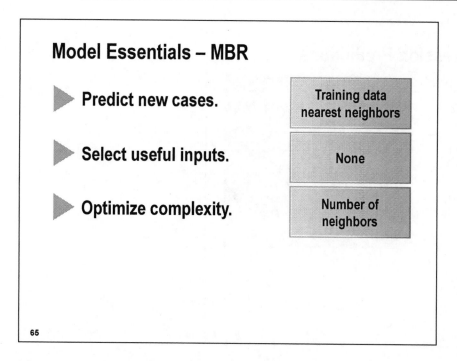

Memory Based Reasoning (MBR) is the implementation of k-nearest neighbor prediction in SAS Enterprise Miner. MBR predictions should be limited to decisions rather than rankings or estimates. Decisions are made based on the prevalence of each target level in the nearest k-cases (16 by default). A majority of primary outcome cases results in a primary decision, and a majority of secondary outcome cases results in a secondary decision. Nearest neighbor algorithms have no means to select inputs and can easily fall victim to the curse of dimensionality. Complexity of the model can be adjusted by changing the number of neighbors considered for prediction.

Copyright © 2011, SAS Institute Inc., Cary, North Carolina, USA. ALL RIGHTS RESERVED.

MBR Prediction Estimates

- Sixteen nearest training data cases predict the target for each point in the input space.

- Scoring requires training data and the PMBR procedure.

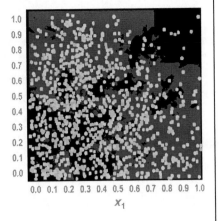

66

By default, the prediction decision made for each point in the input space is determined by the target values of the 16 nearest training data cases. Increasing the number of cases involved in the decision tends to smooth the prediction boundaries, which can be quite complex for small neighbor counts.

Unlike other prediction tools where scoring is performed by DATA step functions independent of the original training data, MBR scoring requires both the original training data set and a specialized SAS procedure, PMBR.

Copyright © 2011, SAS Institute Inc., Cary, North Carolina, USA. ALL RIGHTS RESERVED.

Model Essentials – Partial Least Squares

▶ **Predict new cases.**

▶ **Select useful inputs.**

▶ **Optimize complexity.**

| Prediction formula |
| VIP |
| Sequential factor extraction |

67

In partial least squares regression (PLS) modeling, model weights are chosen to simultaneously account for variability in both the target and the inputs. In general, model fit statistics such as average squared error are worse for a PLS model than for a standard regression model using the same inputs. A distinction of the PLS algorithm, however, is its ability to produce meaningful predictions based on limited data (for example, when there are more inputs than modeling cases). A variable selection method named *variable importance* in the projection arises naturally from the PLS framework.

In PLS, regression latent components, consisting of linear combinations of original inputs, are sequentially added. The final model complexity is chosen by optimizing a model fit statistic on validation data.

Copyright © 2011, SAS Institute Inc., Cary, North Carolina, USA. ALL RIGHTS RESERVED.

Partial Least Squares Predictions

- Input combinations (factors) that optimally account for both predictor and response variation are successively selected.
- Factor count with a minimum validation PRESS statistic is selected.
- Inputs with small VIP are rejected for subsequent diagram nodes.

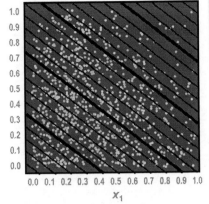

68

The PLS predictions look similar to a standard regression model. In the algorithm, input combinations, called *factors*, which are correlated with both input and target distributions, are selected. This choice is based on a projection given in the SAS/STAT PLS procedure documentation. Factors are sequentially added. The factor count with the lowest validation PRESS statistic (or equivalently, average squared error) is selected. In the PLS tool, the variable importance in the projection (VIP) for each input is calculated. Inputs with VIP less than 0.8 are rejected for subsequent nodes in the process flow.

Copyright © 2011, SAS Institute Inc., Cary, North Carolina, USA. ALL RIGHTS RESERVED.

 **Exercises**

1. **Predictive Modeling Using Neural Networks**

    a. In preparation for a neural network model, is imputation of missing values needed? _____

    Why or why not? _____

    b. In preparation for a neural network model, is data transformation generally needed? _____

    Why or why not? _____

    c. Add a Neural Network tool to the Organics diagram. Connect the **Impute** node to the **Neural Network** node.

    d. Set the model selection criterion to average squared error.

    e. Run the Neural Network node and examine the validation average squared error.

    How does it compare to other models? _____

Copyright © 2011, SAS Institute Inc., Cary, North Carolina, USA. ALL RIGHTS RESERVED.

5.5 Chapter Summary

Neural networks are a powerful extension of standard regression models. They have the ability to model virtually any association between a set of inputs and a target. Being regression-like models, they share some of the same prediction complications faced by regression models (missing values, categorical inputs, extreme values). Their performance is reasonable even without input selection, but it can be marginally improved by selecting inputs with an external variable selection process. Most of their predictive success comes from stopped training, a technique used to prevent overfitting.

Network complexity is marginally influenced by the number of hidden units selected in the model. This number can be selected manually with the Neural Network tool, or it can be selected automatically using the AutoNeural tool.

SAS Enterprise Miner includes several other flexible modeling tools. These specialized tools include Rule Induction, Dmine Regression, DM Neural, and MBR.

Neural Network Tool Review

Create a multi-layer perceptron on selected inputs. Control complexity with stopped training and hidden unit count.

70

Copyright © 2011, SAS Institute Inc., Cary, North Carolina, USA. ALL RIGHTS RESERVED.

5.6 Solutions

Solutions to Exercises

1. **Predictive Modeling Using Neural Networks**

    a. In preparation for a neural network model, is imputation of missing values needed? **Yes.**

       Why or why not? **Neural network models, as well as most models relying on a prediction formula, require a complete record for both modeling and scoring.**

    b. In preparation for a neural network model, is data transformation generally needed? **Not necessarily.**

       Why or why not? **Neural network models create transformations of inputs for use in a regression-like model. However, having input distributions with low skewness and kurtosis tends to result in more stable models.**

    c. Add a Neural Network tool to the Organics diagram. Connect the **Impute** node to the **Neural Network** node.

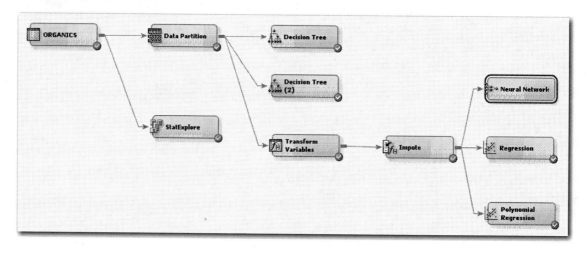

Copyright © 2011, SAS Institute Inc., Cary, North Carolina, USA. ALL RIGHTS RESERVED.

d. Set the model selection criterion to **Average Error**.

Property	Value
General	
Node ID	Neural
Imported Data	...
Exported Data	...
Notes	...
Train	
Variables	...
Continue Training	No
Network	...
Optimization	...
Initialization Seed	12345
Model Selection Criterion	Average Error
Suppress Output	No
Score	
Hidden Units	No
Residuals	Yes
Standardization	No

e. Run the Neural Network node and examine the validation average squared error.

1) The Result window should appear as shown below.

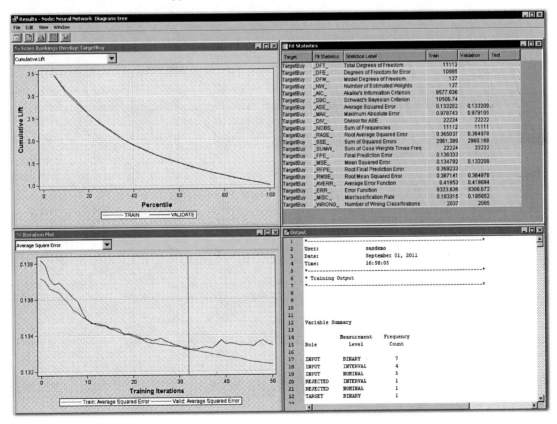

Copyright © 2011, SAS Institute Inc., Cary, North Carolina, USA. ALL RIGHTS RESERVED.

2) Examine the Fit Statistics window.

Target	Fit Statistics	Statistics Label	Train	Validation
TargetBuy	_DFT_	Total Degrees of Freedom	11112	.
TargetBuy	_DFE_	Degrees of Freedom for Error	10985	.
TargetBuy	_DFM_	Model Degrees of Freedom	127	.
TargetBuy	_NW_	Number of Estimated Weights	127	.
TargetBuy	_AIC_	Akaike's Information Criterion	9577.636	.
TargetBuy	_SBC_	Schwarz's Bayesian Criterion	10506.74	.
TargetBuy	_ASE_	Average Squared Error	0.133252	0.133209
TargetBuy	_MAX_	Maximum Absolute Error	0.978743	0.979105
TargetBuy	_DIV_	Divisor for ASE	22224	22222
TargetBuy	_NOBS_	Sum of Frequencies	11112	11111
TargetBuy	_RASE_	Root Average Squared Error	0.365037	0.364978
TargetBuy	_SSE_	Sum of Squared Errors	2961.389	2960.168
TargetBuy	_SUMW_	Sum of Case Weights Times Freq	22224	22222
TargetBuy	_FPE_	Final Prediction Error	0.136333	.
TargetBuy	_MSE_	Mean Squared Error	0.134792	0.133209
TargetBuy	_RFPE_	Root Final Prediction Error	0.369233	.
TargetBuy	_RMSE_	Root Mean Squared Error	0.367141	0.364978
TargetBuy	_AVERR_	Average Error Function	0.41953	0.418894
TargetBuy	_ERR_	Error Function	9323.636	9308.673
TargetBuy	_MISC_	Misclassification Rate	0.183315	0.185852
TargetBuy	_WRONG_	Number of Wrong Classifications	2037	2065

How does it compare to other models? **The validation ASE for the neural network model is slightly smaller than the standard regression model, nearly the same as the polynomial regression, and slightly larger than the decision tree's ASE.**

Copyright © 2011, SAS Institute Inc., Cary, North Carolina, USA. ALL RIGHTS RESERVED.

Solutions to Student Activities (Polls/Quizzes)

5.01 Multiple Answer Poll – Correct Answers

Which of the following are true about neural networks in SAS Enterprise Miner?

(a.) Neural networks are universal approximators.

(b.) Neural networks have no internal, automated process for selecting useful inputs.

c. Neural networks are easy to interpret and thus are very useful in highly regulated industries.

d. Neural networks cannot model nonlinear relationships.

22

Copyright © 2011, SAS Institute Inc., Cary, North Carolina, USA. ALL RIGHTS RESERVED.

Copyright © 2011, SAS Institute Inc., Cary, North Carolina, USA. ALL RIGHTS RESERVED.

Chapter 6   Model Assessment

Copyright © 2011, SAS Institute Inc., Cary, North Carolina, USA. ALL RIGHTS RESERVED.

Copyright © 2011, SAS Institute Inc., Cary, North Carolina, USA. ALL RIGHTS RESERVED.

6.1 Model Fit Statistics

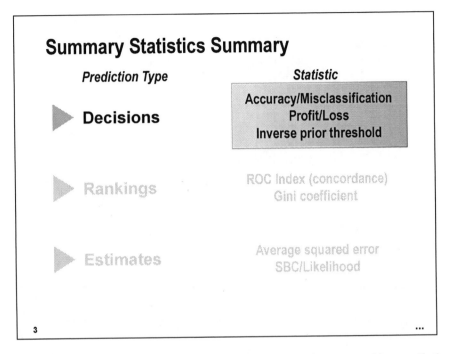

As introduced in Chapter 3, summary statistics can be grouped by prediction type.

For decision prediction, the Model Comparison tool rates model performance based on accuracy or misclassification, profit or loss, and by the Kolmogorov-Smirnov (KS) statistic. Accuracy and misclassification tally the correct or incorrect prediction decisions. Profit is detailed later in this chapter. The Kolmogorov-Smirnov statistic describes the ability of the model to separate the primary and secondary outcomes.

Copyright © 2011, SAS Institute Inc., Cary, North Carolina, USA. ALL RIGHTS RESERVED.

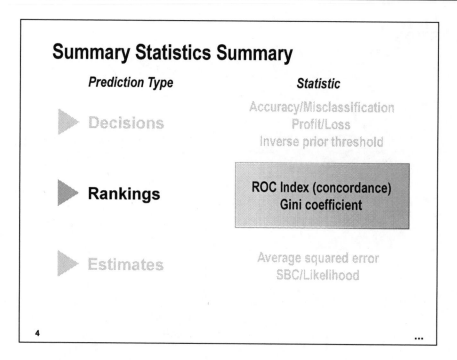

For ranking predictions, the Model Comparison tool gives two closely related measures of model fit. The ROC index is similar to concordance (introduced in Chapter 3). The Gini coefficient (for binary prediction) equals $2 \times (\text{ROC Index} - 0.5)$.

   The ROC index equals the percent of concordant cases plus one-half times the percent tied cases. Recall that a pair of cases, consisting of one primary outcome and one secondary outcome, is *concordant* if the primary outcome case has a higher rank than the secondary outcome case. By contrast, if the primary outcome case has a lower rank, that pair is *discordant*. If the two cases have the same rank, they are said to be tied.

Copyright © 2011, SAS Institute Inc., Cary, North Carolina, USA. ALL RIGHTS RESERVED.

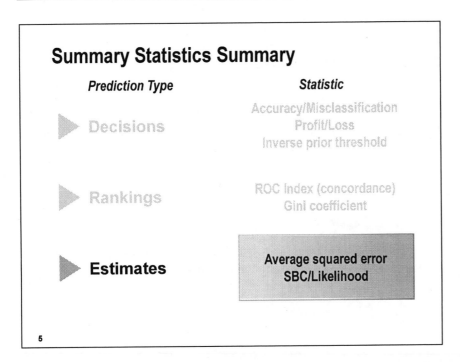

Summary Statistics Summary

Prediction Type	Statistic
Decisions	Accuracy/Misclassification Profit/Loss Inverse prior threshold
Rankings	ROC Index (concordance) Gini coefficient
Estimates	Average squared error SBC/Likelihood

5

For estimate predictions, the Model Comparison tool provides two performance statistics. Average squared error was used to tune many of the models fit in earlier chapters. The Schwarz's Bayesian Criterion (SBC) is a penalized likelihood statistic. The likelihood statistic was used to estimate regression and neural network model parameters and can be thought of as a weighted average squared error.

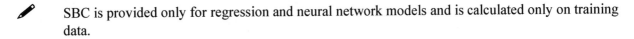 SBC is provided only for regression and neural network models and is calculated only on training data.

Copyright © 2011, SAS Institute Inc., Cary, North Carolina, USA. ALL RIGHTS RESERVED.

Comparing Models with Summary Statistics

After you build several models, it is desirable to compare their performance. The Model Comparison tool collects assessment information from attached modeling nodes and enables you to easily compare model performance measures.

1. Select the **Assess** tab.

2. Drag a **Model Comparison** tool into the diagram workspace.

3. Connect the Regression node first, both Decision Trees, and finally the Neural Network node to the Model Comparison node as shown. (Self-study models are ignored here.)

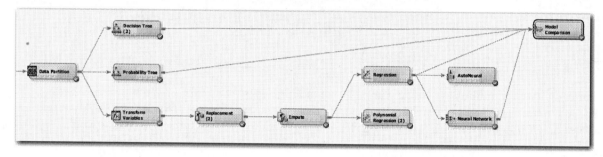

Copyright © 2011, SAS Institute Inc., Cary, North Carolina, USA. ALL RIGHTS RESERVED.

4. Run the Model Comparison node and view the results. The Results window appears.

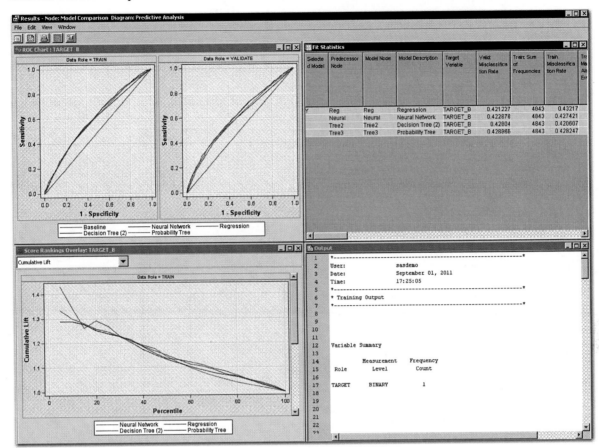

The Results window contains four sub-windows: ROC Chart, Score Rankings Overlay plot, Fit Statistics, and Output.

5. Maximize the Output window. Go to line 29. The Regression model was selected based on the Validation data: Misclassification rate. SAS Enterprise Miner assumes decision processing and selects the model with the lowest Misclassification Rate when there is a Binary Target.

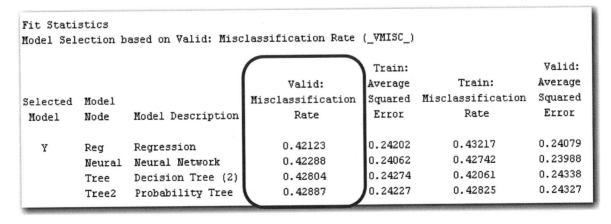

Fit Statistics
Model Selection based on Valid: Misclassification Rate (_VMISC_)

Selected Model	Model Node	Model Description	Valid: Misclassification Rate	Train: Average Squared Error	Train: Misclassification Rate	Valid: Average Squared Error
Y	Reg	Regression	0.42123	0.24202	0.43217	0.24079
	Neural	Neural Network	0.42288	0.24062	0.42742	0.23988
	Tree	Decision Tree (2)	0.42804	0.24274	0.42061	0.24338
	Tree2	Probability Tree	0.42887	0.24227	0.42825	0.24327

Copyright © 2011, SAS Institute Inc., Cary, North Carolina, USA. ALL RIGHTS RESERVED.

6.   Go to line 96 in the Output window.

		Reg	Neural	Tree2	Tree3
96	Data Role=Valid				
97					
98	Statistics	Reg	Neural	Tree2	Tree3
99					
100	Valid: Kolmogorov-Smirnov Statistic	0.16	0.17	0.14	0.14
101	Valid: Average Squared Error	0.24	0.24	0.24	0.24
102	Valid: Roc Index	0.61	0.61	0.58	0.59
103	Valid: Average Error Function	0.67	0.67	.	.
104	Valid: Bin-Based Two-Way Kolmogorov-Smirnov Probability Cutoff	0.55	0.53	0.53	0.54
105	Valid: Cumulative Percent Captured Response	14.33	14.49	13.22	13.22
106	Valid: Percent Captured Response	7.18	6.90	6.60	6.60
107	Valid: Divisor for VASE	9686.00	9686.00	9686.00	9686.00
108	Valid: Error Function	6533.21	6512.78	.	.
109	Valid: Gain	43.06	44.71	32.00	32.00
110	Valid: Gini Coefficient	0.22	0.23	0.17	0.18
111	Valid: Bin-Based Two-Way Kolmogorov-Smirnov Statistic	0.16	0.17	0.14	0.14
112	Valid: Kolmogorov-Smirnov Probability Cutoff	0.54	0.52	0.43	0.49
113	Valid: Cumulative Lift	1.43	1.45	1.32	1.32
114	Valid: Lift	1.44	1.38	1.32	1.32
115	Valid: Maximum Absolute Error	0.86	0.87	0.64	0.64
116	Valid: Misclassification Rate	0.42	0.42	0.43	0.43
117	Valid: Mean Square Error	0.24	0.24	.	.
118	Valid: Sum of Frequencies	4843.00	4843.00	4843.00	4843.00
119	Valid: Root Average Squared Error	0.49	0.49	0.49	0.49
120	Valid: Cumulative Percent Response	71.55	72.37	66.02	66.02
121	Valid: Percent Response	71.90	69.01	66.02	66.02
122	Valid: Root Mean Square Error	0.49	0.49	.	.
123	Valid: Sum of Squared Errors	2332.27	2323.48	2357.33	2356.28
124	Valid: Sum of Case Weights Times Freq	9686.00	9686.00	9686.00	9686.00
125	Valid: Number of Wrong Classifications	.	2048.00	.	.
126					

The output shows numerous fit statistics for the selected models. It appears that the performance of each model, as gauged by fit statistics, is quite similar.

As discussed above, the choice of fit statistics best depends on the predictions of interest.

Prediction Type	Validation Fit Statistic	Direction
Decisions	Misclassification	smallest
	Average Profit/Loss	largest/smallest
	Kolmogorov-Smirnov Statistic	largest
Rankings	ROC Index (concordance)	largest
	Gini Coefficient	largest
Estimates	Average Squared Error	smallest
	Schwarz's Bayesian Criterion	smallest
	Log-Likelihood	largest

Copyright © 2011, SAS Institute Inc., Cary, North Carolina, USA. ALL RIGHTS RESERVED.

6.2 Statistical Graphics

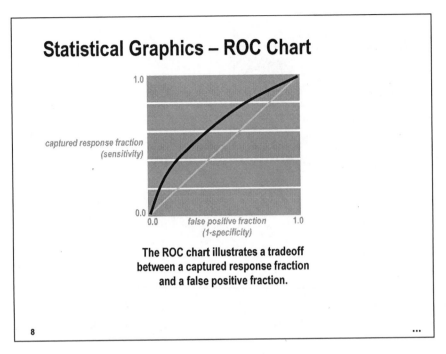

The Model Comparison tool features two charts to aid in model assessment: the ROC chart and the Score Rankings chart. Consider the ROC chart.

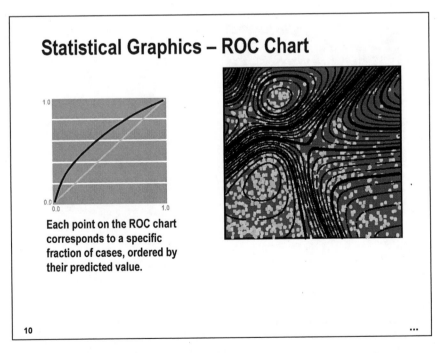

To create a ROC chart, predictions are generated for a set of validation data. For chart generation, the predictions must be rankings or estimates. The validation data is sorted from high to low (either scores or estimates). Each point on the ROC chart corresponds to a specific fraction of the sorted data.

Copyright © 2011, SAS Institute Inc., Cary, North Carolina, USA. ALL RIGHTS RESERVED.

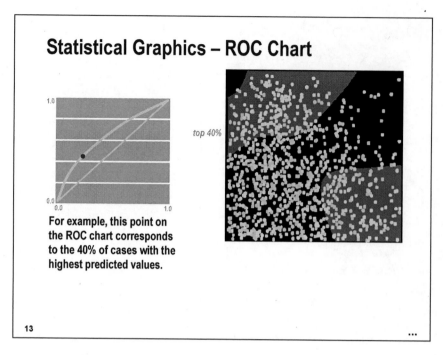

For example, the red point on the ROC chart corresponds to the indicated selection of 40% of the validation data. That is, the points in the gray region on the scatter plot are in the highest 40% of predicted probabilities.

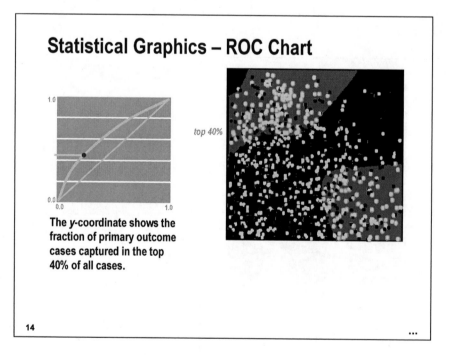

The vertical or *y*-coordinate of the red point indicates the fraction of primary outcome cases "captured" in the gray region (here approximately 45%).

Copyright © 2011, SAS Institute Inc., Cary, North Carolina, USA. ALL RIGHTS RESERVED.

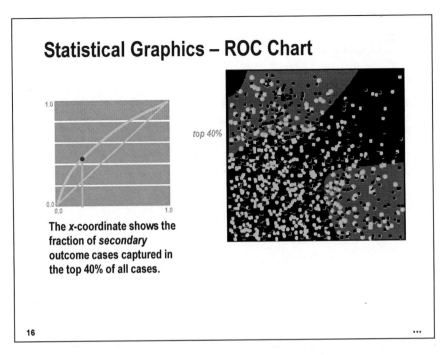

The horizontal or *x*-coordinate of the red point indicates the fraction of secondary outcome cases "captured" in the gray region (here approximately 25%).

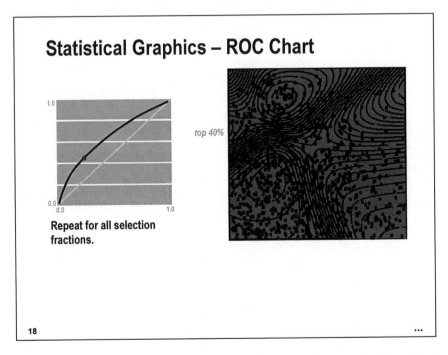

The ROC chart represents the union of similar calculations for all selection fractions.

Copyright © 2011, SAS Institute Inc., Cary, North Carolina, USA. ALL RIGHTS RESERVED.

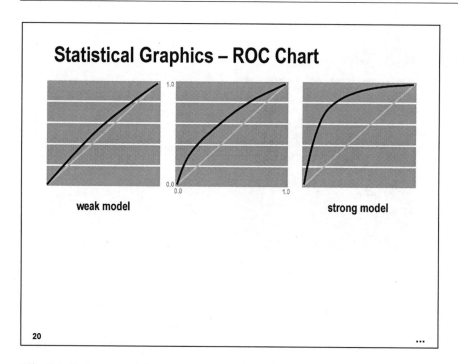

The ROC chart provides a nearly universal diagnostic for predictive models. Models that capture primary and secondary outcome cases in a proportion approximately equal to the selection fraction are weak models (left). Models that capture mostly primary outcome cases without capturing secondary outcome cases are strong models (right).

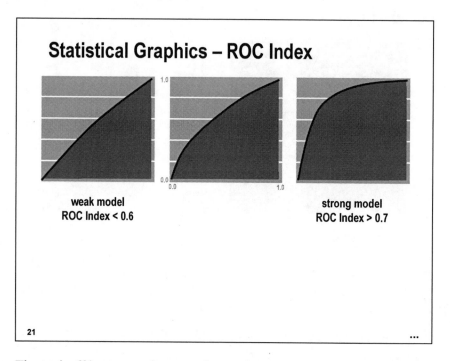

The tradeoff between primary and secondary case capture can be summarized by the area under the ROC curve. In SAS Enterprise Miner, this area is called the *ROC Index*. (In statistical literature, it is more commonly called the *c*-statistic.) Perhaps surprisingly, the ROC Index is closely related to concordance, the measure of correct case ordering.

Copyright © 2011, SAS Institute Inc., Cary, North Carolina, USA. ALL RIGHTS RESERVED.

Comparing Models with ROC Charts

Use the following steps to compare models using ROC charts:

1. Maximize the ROC chart.

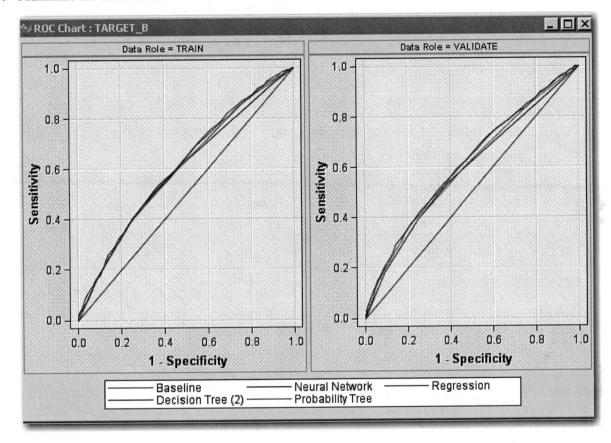

Copyright © 2011, SAS Institute Inc., Cary, North Carolina, USA. ALL RIGHTS RESERVED.

2. Double-click the **Data Role = VALIDATE** plot.

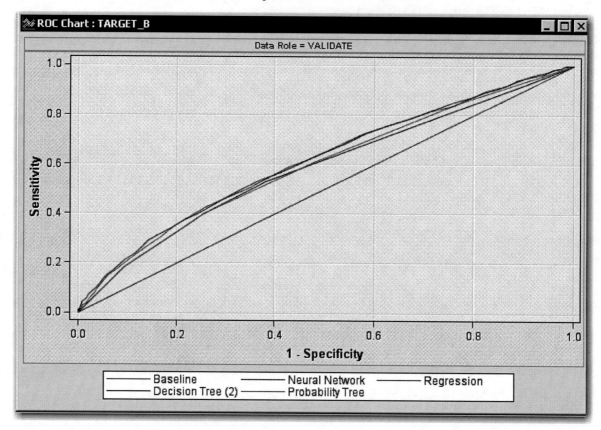

The ROC chart shows little difference between the non-tree models. This is consistent with the values of the ROC Index, which equals the area under the ROC curves.

Copyright © 2011, SAS Institute Inc., Cary, North Carolina, USA. ALL RIGHTS RESERVED.

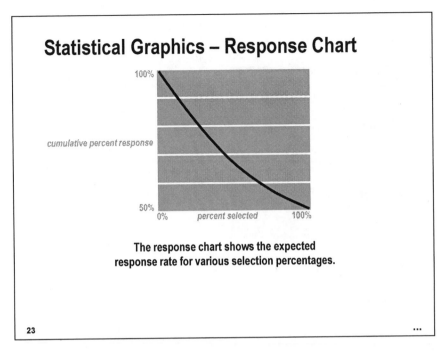

A second category of assessment charts examines response rate. It is the prototype of the so-called Score Rankings charts found in every model Results window.

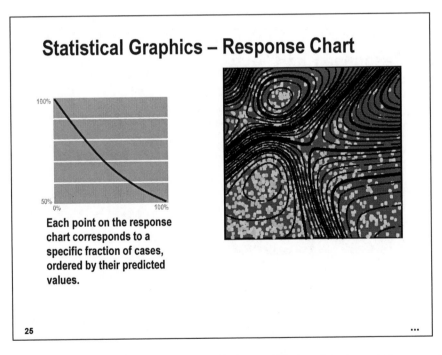

As with ROC charts, a model is applied to validation data to sort the cases from highest to lowest (again, by prediction rankings or estimates). Each point on the response chart corresponds to a selected fraction of cases.

Copyright © 2011, SAS Institute Inc., Cary, North Carolina, USA. ALL RIGHTS RESERVED.

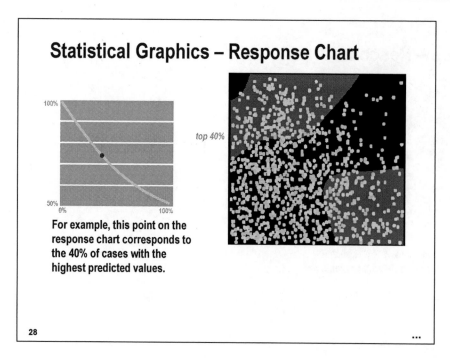

For example, the red point on the Response chart corresponds to the indicated selection of 40% of the validation data. That is, the points in the gray region on the scatter plot are in the highest 40% of predicted probabilities.

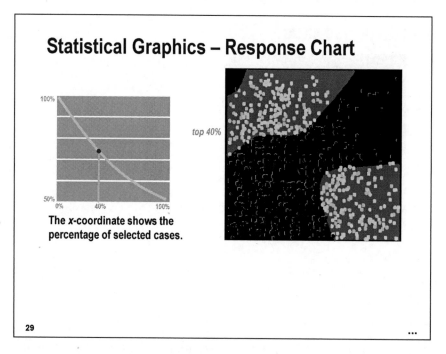

The x-coordinate of the red point is simply the selection fraction (in this case, 40%).

Copyright © 2011, SAS Institute Inc., Cary, North Carolina, USA. ALL RIGHTS RESERVED.

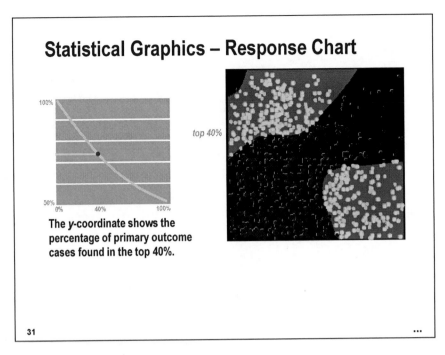

The vertical coordinate for a point on the response chart is the proportion of primary outcome cases in the selected fraction. It is called the *cumulative percent response* in the SAS Enterprise Miner interface and is more widely known as *cumulative gain* in the predictive modeling literature. Dividing cumulative gain by the primary outcome proportion yields a quantity named *lift*.

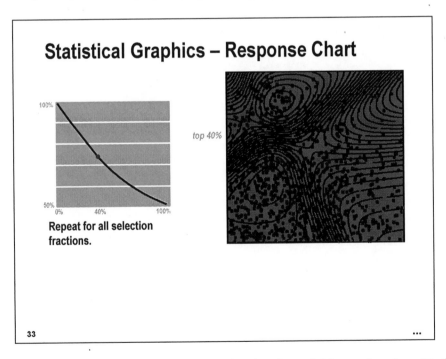

Plotting cumulative gain for all selection fractions yields a *gains chart*. Notice that when all cases are selected, the cumulative gain equals the overall primary outcome proportion.

Copyright © 2011, SAS Institute Inc., Cary, North Carolina, USA. ALL RIGHTS RESERVED.

6.01 Poll

In practice, modelers often use several tools, sometimes both graphical and numerical, to choose a best model.

○ True
○ False

35

Copyright © 2011, SAS Institute Inc., Cary, North Carolina, USA. ALL RIGHTS RESERVED.

Comparing Models with Score Rankings Plots

Use the following steps to compare models with Score Rankings plots:

1. Maximize the Score Rankings Overlay window.

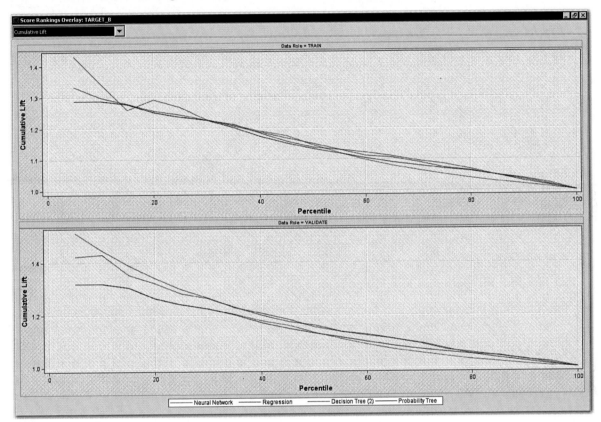

Copyright © 2011, SAS Institute Inc., Cary, North Carolina, USA. ALL RIGHTS RESERVED.

2. Double-click the **Data Role = VALIDATE** plot.

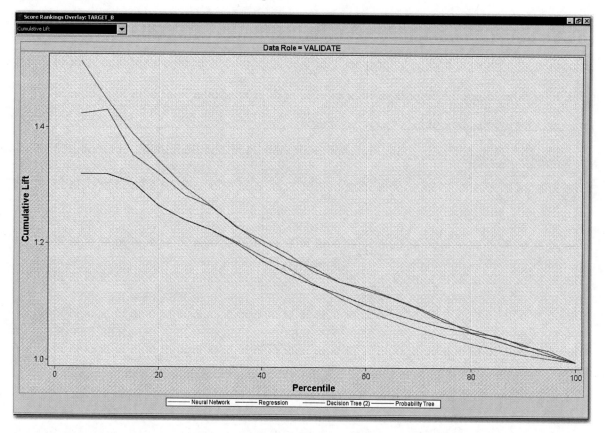

The Score Rankings Overlay plot presents what is commonly called a *cumulative lift chart*. Cases in the training and validation data are ranked based on decreasing predicted target values. A fraction of the ranked data is selected. This fraction, or *decile*, corresponds to the horizontal axis of the chart. The ratio, (proportion of cases with the primary outcome in the selected fraction) to (proportion of cases with the primary outcome overall), is defined as *cumulative lift*. Cumulative lift corresponds to the vertical axis. High values of cumulative lift suggest that the model is doing a good job separating the primary and secondary cases.

As can be seen, the model with the highest cumulative lift depends on the decile; however, none of the models has a cumulative lift over 1.5.

It is instructive to view the actual proportion of cases with the primary outcome (called *gain* or *cumulative percent response*) at each decile.

Copyright © 2011, SAS Institute Inc., Cary, North Carolina, USA. ALL RIGHTS RESERVED.

3. Select **Chart ⇨ Cumulative % Response**. The Score Rankings Overlay plot is updated to show Cumulative Percent Response on the vertical axis.

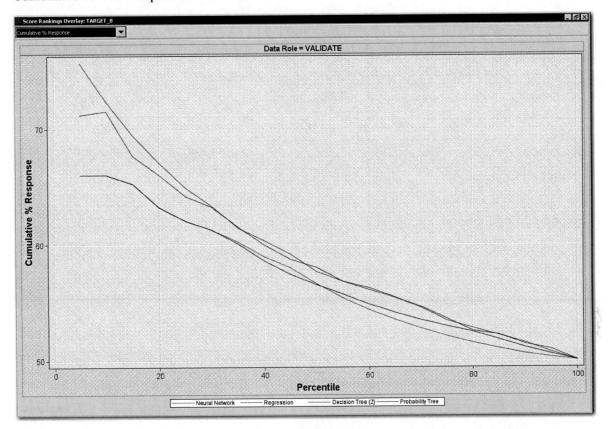

This plot should show the response rate for soliciting the indicated fraction of individuals. Unfortunately, the proportion of responders in the ***training data*** does not equal the true proportion of responders for the **97NK campaign**. The training data under-represents nonresponders by almost a factor of 20!

This under-representation was not an accident. It is a rather standard predictive modeling practice known as *separate sampling*. (*Oversampling*, *balanced sampling*, *choice-based sampling*, *case-control sampling*, and other names are also used.)

Copyright © 2011, SAS Institute Inc., Cary, North Carolina, USA. ALL RIGHTS RESERVED.

Adjusting for Separate Sampling

If you do not adjust for separate sampling, the following occurs:

- Prediction estimates reflect target proportions in the training sample, not the population from which the sample was drawn.

- Score Rankings plots are inaccurate and misleading,

- Decision-based statistics related to misclassification or accuracy misrepresent the model performance on the population.

Fortunately, it is easy to adjust for separate sampling in SAS Enterprise Miner. However, you must rerun the models that you created.

✎   Because this can take some time, it is recommended that you run this demonstration during the discussion about the benefits and consequences of separate sampling.

Follow these steps to integrate sampling information into your analysis:

1. Close the Results - Model Comparison window.

2. Select **Decisions** ⇨ ... in the **PVA97NK** node's Properties panel.

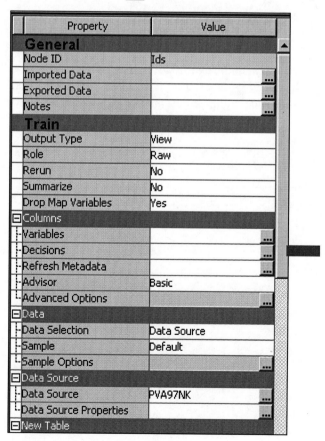

Copyright © 2011, SAS Institute Inc., Cary, North Carolina, USA. ALL RIGHTS RESERVED.

The Decision Processing - PVA97NK dialog box appears.

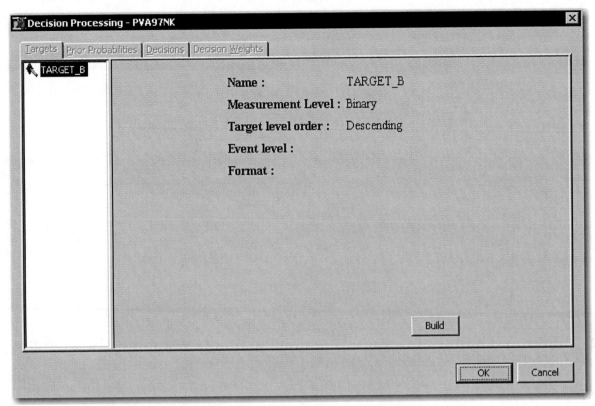

The Decision Processing dialog box enables you to inform SAS Enterprise Miner about the extent of separate sampling in the training data. This is done by defining *prior probabilities*.

3. Select **Build** in the Decision Processing dialog box. SAS Enterprise Miner scans the raw data to determine the proportion of primary and secondary outcomes in the raw data.

Copyright © 2011, SAS Institute Inc., Cary, North Carolina, USA. ALL RIGHTS RESERVED.

4. Select the **Prior Probabilities** tab.

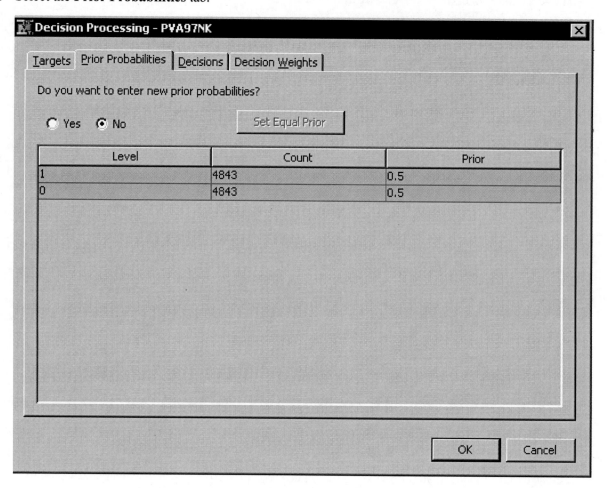

Copyright © 2011, SAS Institute Inc., Cary, North Carolina, USA. ALL RIGHTS RESERVED.

5. Select **Yes**. The dialog box is updated to show the Adjusted Prior column.

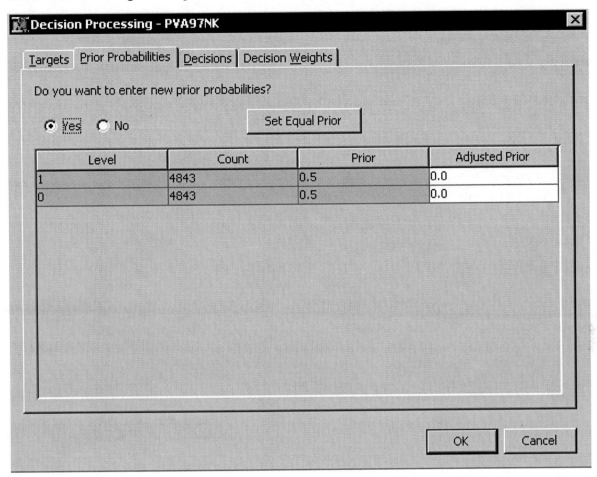

The Adjusted Prior column enables you to specify the proportion of primary and secondary outcomes in the original **PVA97NK** population. When the analysis problem was introduced in Chapter 2, the primary outcome (response) proportion was claimed to be 5%.

Copyright © 2011, SAS Institute Inc., Cary, North Carolina, USA. ALL RIGHTS RESERVED.

6. Type **0.05** as the Adjusted Prior value for the primary outcome, Level 1.

7. Type **0.95** as the Adjusted Prior value for the secondary outcome, Level 0.

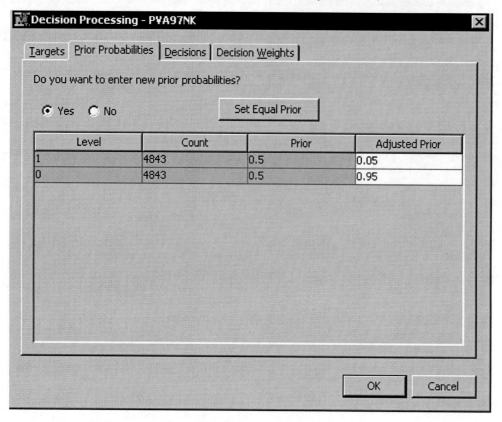

8. Select **OK** to close the Decision Processing dialog box.

Decision Processing and the Neural Network Node

If your diagram was developed according to the instructions in Chapters 2 through 5, one modeling node (the Neural Network) needs a property change to correctly use the decision processing information.

Follow these steps to adjust the Neural Network node settings.

1. Examine the Properties panel for the Neural Network node. The default model selection criterion is Profit/Loss.

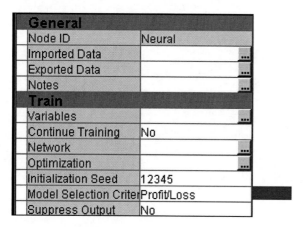

Copyright © 2011, SAS Institute Inc., Cary, North Carolina, USA. ALL RIGHTS RESERVED.

2. Select **Model Selection Criterion** ⇨ **Average Error**.

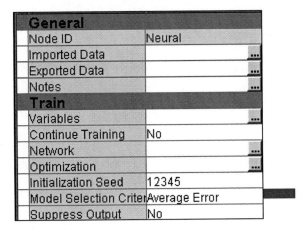

✐   When no decision data is defined, the neural network optimizes complexity using average squared error, even though the default says Profit/Loss. Now that decision data is defined, you must manually change Model Selection Criterion to Average Error.

4. Click on the **Model Comparison** node and examine the properties panel.

Under the **Model Selection** portion of the properties panel, select **Average Squared Error** for **Selection Statistic**, and set the **Selection Table** to **Validation**.

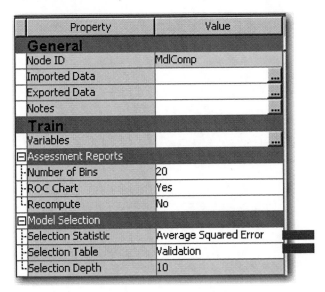

5. Run the diagram from the **Model Comparison** node. This reruns the entire analysis.

Copyright © 2011, SAS Institute Inc., Cary, North Carolina, USA. ALL RIGHTS RESERVED.

Decision Processing and the AutoNeural Node

Decision processing data (prior probabilities and decision weights) is ignored by the AutoNeural node. Predictions from the node are adjusted for priors, but that actual model selection process is based strictly on misclassification (without prior adjustment). This fact can lead to unexpected prediction results when the primary and secondary outcome proportions are not equal. Fortunately, the **PVA97NK** data has an equal proportion of primary and secondary outcomes and gives reasonable results with the AutoNeural node.

    Using the AutoNeural node with training data that does not have equal outcome proportions is reasonable only if your data is not separately sampled *and* your prediction goal is classification.

Copyright © 2011, SAS Institute Inc., Cary, North Carolina, USA. ALL RIGHTS RESERVED.

6.3 Adjusting for Separate Sampling

Outcome Overrepresentation

A common predictive
modeling practice is to build
models from a sample with a
primary outcome proportion
different from the original
population.

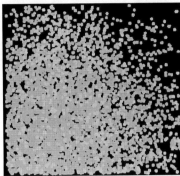

40

A common predictive modeling practice is to build models from a sample with a primary outcome proportion different from the true population proportion. This is typically done when the ratio of primary to secondary outcome cases is small.

Separate Sampling

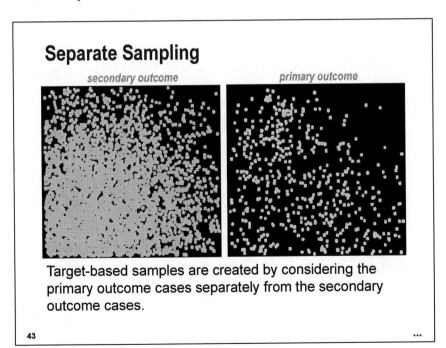

Target-based samples are created by considering the primary outcome cases separately from the secondary outcome cases.

43

Copyright © 2011, SAS Institute Inc., Cary, North Carolina, USA. ALL RIGHTS RESERVED.

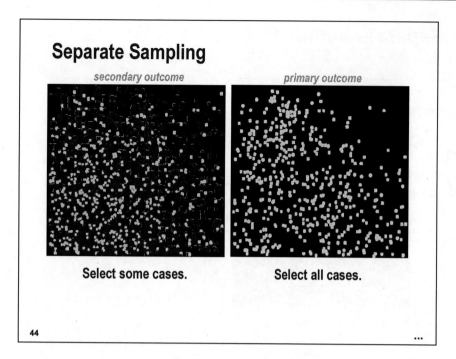

Separate sampling derives its name from the technique used to generate the modeling data, that is, samples are drawn separately based on the target outcome. In the case of a rare primary outcome, usually all primary outcome cases are selected. Then, each primary outcome case is matched by one or (optimally) more secondary outcome cases.

Copyright © 2011, SAS Institute Inc., Cary, North Carolina, USA. ALL RIGHTS RESERVED.

The Modeling Sample

+ Similar predictive power
  with smaller case count

– Must adjust assessment
  statistics and graphics

– Must adjust prediction
  estimates for bias

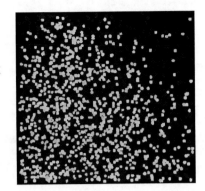

46

...

The advantage of separate sampling is that you are able to obtain (on the average) a model of similar predictive power with a smaller overall case count. This is in concordance with the idea that the amount of information in a data set with a categorical outcome is determined not by the total number of cases in the data set itself, but instead by the number of cases in the rarest outcome category. (For binary target data sets, this is usually the primary outcome.) (Harrell 2006)

This advantage might seem of minimal importance in the age of extremely fast computers. (A model might fit 10 times faster with a reduced data set, but a 10-second model fit versus a 1-second model fit is probably not relevant.) However, the model-fitting process occurs only after the completion of a long, tedious, and error-prone data preparation process. Smaller sample sizes for data preparation are usually welcome.

While it reduces analysis time, separate sampling also introduces some analysis complications.

- Most model fit statistics (especially those related to prediction decisions) and most of the assessment plots are closely tied to the outcome proportions in the training samples. If the outcome proportions in the training and validation samples do not match the outcome proportions in the scoring population, model performance can be greatly misestimated.

- If the outcome proportions in the training sample and scoring populations do not match, model prediction estimates are biased.

Fortunately, SAS Enterprise Miner can adjust assessments and prediction estimates to match the scoring population if you specify *prior probabilities*, the scoring population outcome proportions. This is precisely what was done using the Decisions option in the demonstration.

Copyright © 2011, SAS Institute Inc., Cary, North Carolina, USA. ALL RIGHTS RESERVED.

Adjusting for Separate Sampling (Continued)

The consequences of incorporating prior probabilities in the analysis can be viewed in the Model Comparison node.

1. Select **Results** in the Run Status dialog box. The Results - Model Comparison window appears.

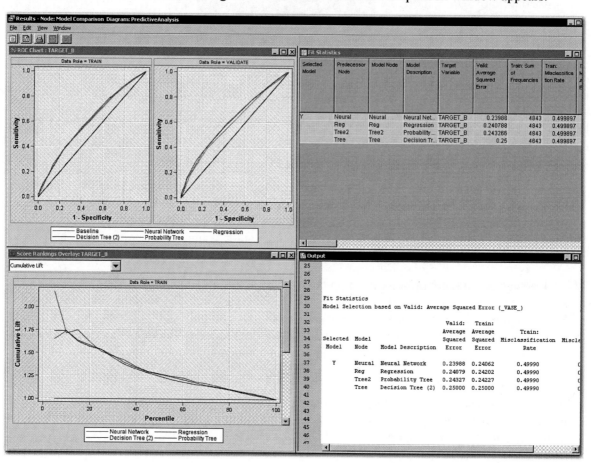

Copyright © 2011, SAS Institute Inc., Cary, North Carolina, USA. ALL RIGHTS RESERVED.

2. Maximize the Score Rankings Overlay window and focus on the Data Role = VALIDATE chart.

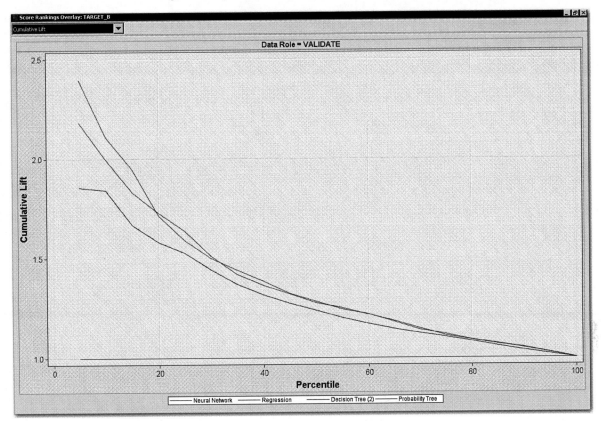

Before you adjusted for priors, none of the models had a cumulative lift over 1.5. Now most of the models have a cumulative lift in excess of 1.5 (at least for some deciles).

 The exception is the Decision Tree model. Its lift is exactly 1 for all percentiles. The reason for this is the inclusion of disparate prior probabilities for a model tuned on misclassification. On the average, cases have a primary outcome probability of 0.05. A low misclassification rate model might be built by simply calling everyone a non-responder.

Copyright © 2011, SAS Institute Inc., Cary, North Carolina, USA. ALL RIGHTS RESERVED.

3. Select **Chart:** ⇨ **Cumulative % Response**.

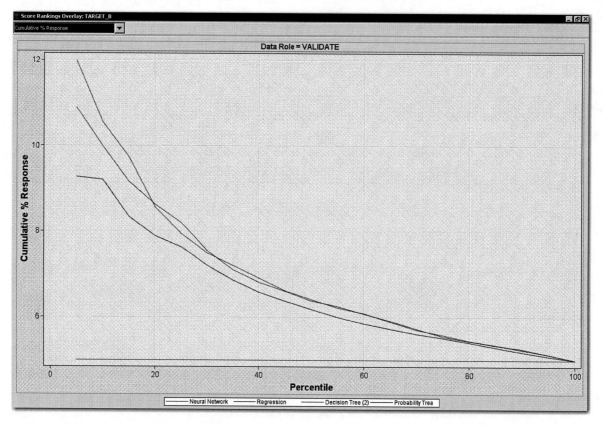

The cumulative percent responses are now adjusted for separate sampling. You have an accurate representation of response proportions by selection fraction.

With this plot, a business analyst could rate the relative performance of each model for different selection fractions. The best selection fraction is usually determined by financial considerations. For example, the charity might have a budget that allows contact with 40% of the available population. Thus, it intuitively makes sense to contact the 40% of the population with the highest chances of responding (as predicted by one of the available models). Another financial consideration, however, is also important, that is, the profit (and loss) associated with a response (and non-response) to a solicitation. To correctly rank the value of a case, response probability estimates must be combined with profit and loss information.

Copyright © 2011, SAS Institute Inc., Cary, North Carolina, USA. ALL RIGHTS RESERVED.

Creating a Profit Matrix

To determine reasonable values for profit and loss information, consider the outcomes and the actions you would take given knowledge of these outcomes. In this case, there are two outcomes (response and non-response) and two corresponding actions (solicit and ignore). Knowing that someone is a responder, you would naturally want to solicit that person; knowing that someone is a non-responder, you would naturally want to ignore that person. (Organizations really do *not* want to send junk mail.) On the other hand, knowledge of an individual's actual behavior is rarely perfect, so mistakes are made, for example, soliciting non-responders (false positives) and ignoring responders (false negatives).

Taken together, there are four outcome/action combinations:

	Solicit	Ignore
Response		
Non-response		

Each of these outcome/action combinations has a profit consequence (where a loss is called, somewhat euphemistically, *a negative profit*). Some of the profit consequences are obvious. For example, if you do not solicit, you do not make any profit. For this analysis, the second column can be immediately set to zero.

	Solicit	Ignore
Response		0
Non-response		0

From the description of the analysis problem, you find that it costs about $0.68 to send a solicitation. Also, the variable **TARGET_D** gives that amount of response (when a donation occurs). The completed profit consequence matrix can be written as shown.

	Solicit	Ignore
Response	**TARGET_D- 0.68**	0
Non-response	-0.68	0

From a statistical perspective, **TARGET_D** is a random variable. Individuals who are identical on every input measurement might give different donation amounts. To simplify the analysis, a summary statistic for **TARGET_D** is plugged into the profit consequence matrix. In general, this value can vary on a case-by-case basis. However, for this course, the overall average of **TARGET_D** is used.

You can obtain the average of **TARGET_D** using the StatExplore node.

1. Select the **Explore** tab.

2. Drag the **StatExplore** tool into the diagram workspace.

Copyright © 2011, SAS Institute Inc., Cary, North Carolina, USA. ALL RIGHTS RESERVED.

3. Connect the **StatExplore** node to the **Data Partition** node.

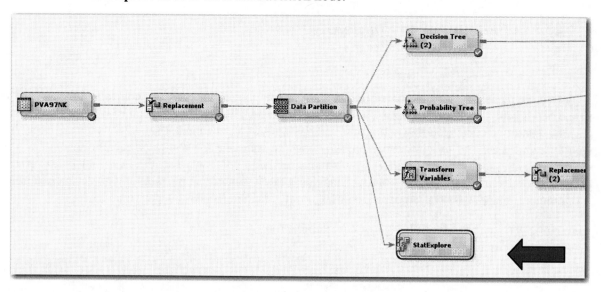

4. Select **Variables** from the Properties panel of the StatExplore node.

Copyright © 2011, SAS Institute Inc., Cary, North Carolina, USA. ALL RIGHTS RESERVED.

The Variables - Stat window appears.

5.   Select **Use** ⇨ **Yes** for the **TARGET_D** variable. It is okay that the role is set to **Rejected** for this node.

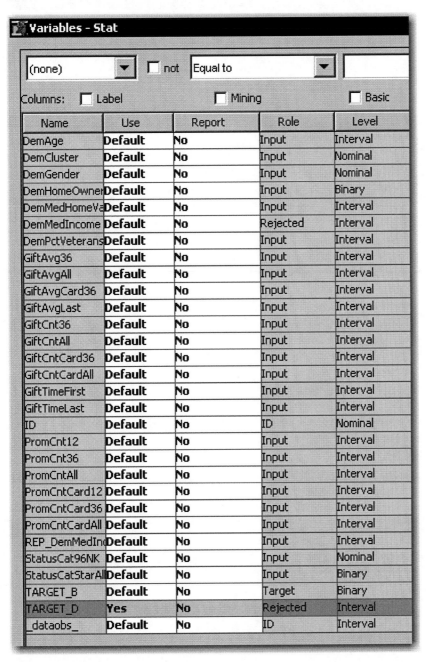

6.   Select **OK** to close the Variables dialog box.

Copyright © 2011, SAS Institute Inc., Cary, North Carolina, USA. ALL RIGHTS RESERVED.

7. Run the StatExplore node and view the results. The Results - StatExplore window appears.

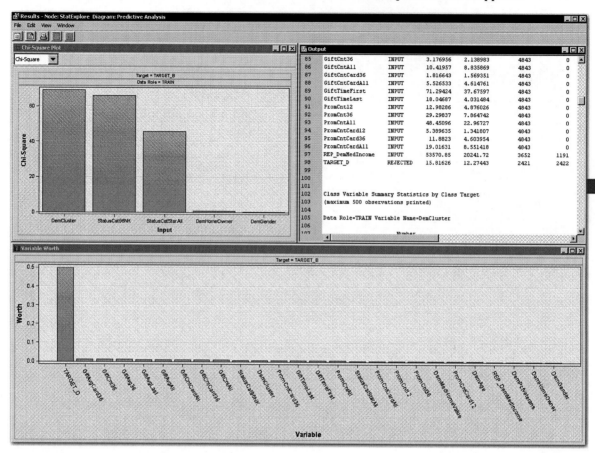

Scrolling the Output window shows the average of **TARGET_D** as $15.82.

8. Close the Results - Stat window.

9. As an alternative to using the Stat Explorer node, explore the **Exported Train** data set from the Data Partition node to see the same result under Sample Statistics as shown below.

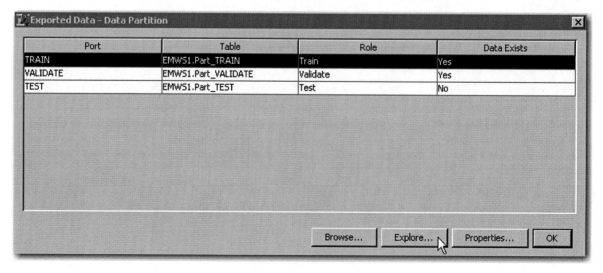

Copyright © 2011, SAS Institute Inc., Cary, North Carolina, USA. ALL RIGHTS RESERVED.

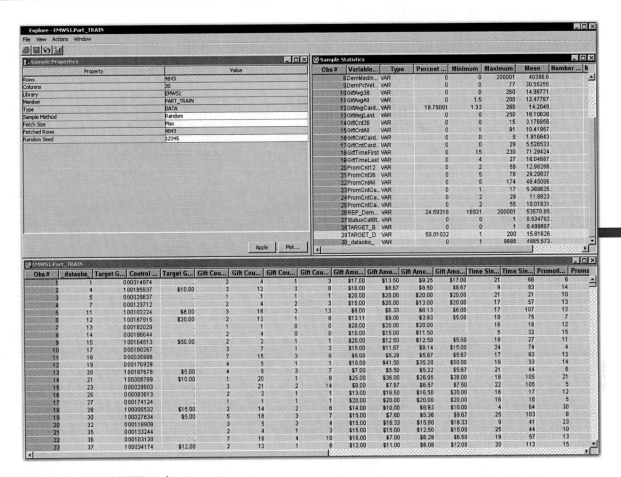

10. Select the **PVA97NK** node.

Copyright © 2011, SAS Institute Inc., Cary, North Carolina, USA. ALL RIGHTS RESERVED.

11. Select the **Decisions** property. The Decision Processing - PVA97NK dialog box appears.

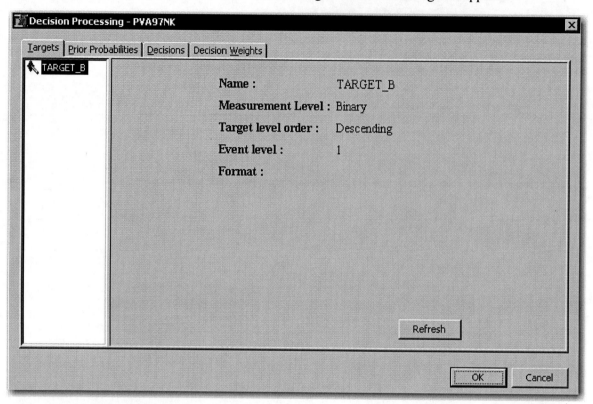

12. Select the **Decisions** tab.

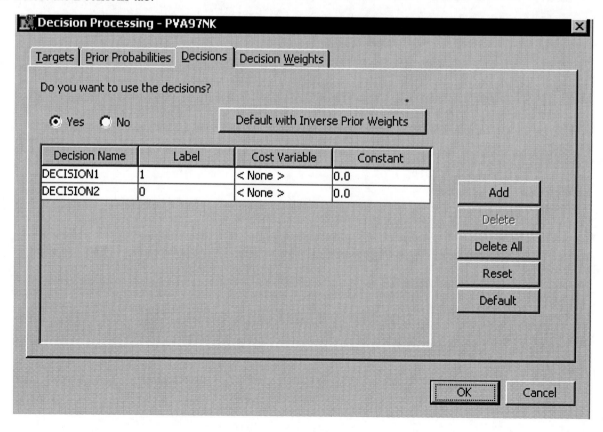

Copyright © 2011, SAS Institute Inc., Cary, North Carolina, USA. ALL RIGHTS RESERVED.

13. Type **Solicit** (in place of the word **DECISION1**) in the first row of the Decision Name column.

14. Type **Ignore** (in place of the word **DECISION2**) in the second row of the Decision Name column.

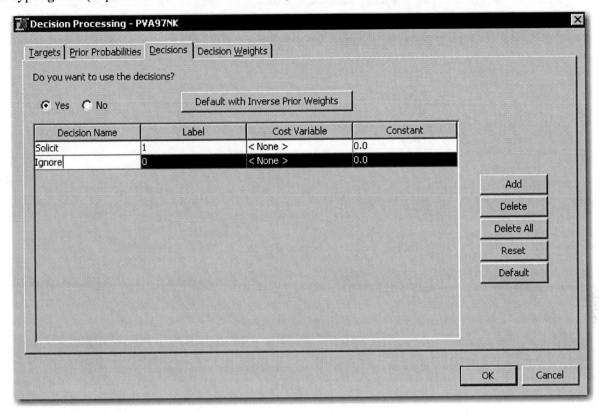

Copyright © 2011, SAS Institute Inc., Cary, North Carolina, USA. ALL RIGHTS RESERVED.

15. Select the **Decision Weights** tab.

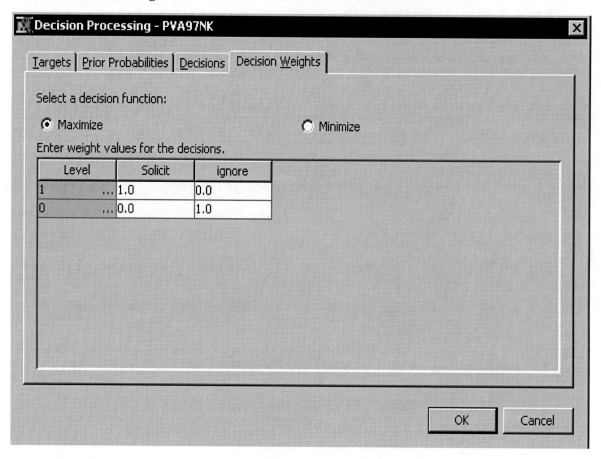

The completed profit consequence matrix for this example is shown below.

	Solicit	Ignore
Response	15.14	0
Non-response	-0.68	0

Copyright © 2011, SAS Institute Inc., Cary, North Carolina, USA. ALL RIGHTS RESERVED.

16. Type the profit values into the corresponding cell of the profit weight matrix. (Do not forget to change the Ignore column to **0** for Level 0 and to add the negative sign in front of the Solicit column value for Level 0.)

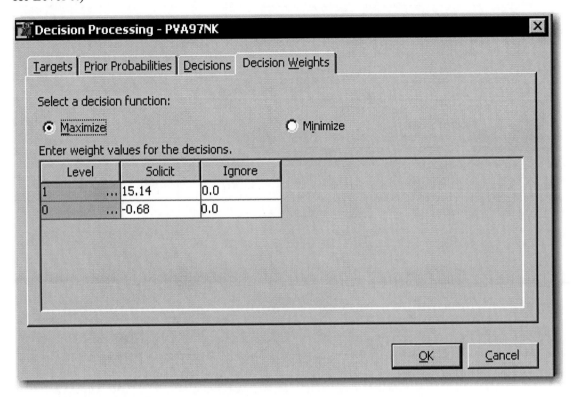

17. Select **OK** to close the Decision Processing - PVA97NK dialog box.

18. Change the Selection Statistic in the properties panel of the Model Comparison Node to **Average Profit/Loss**.

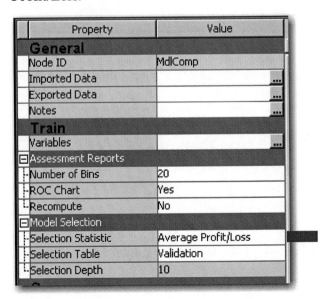

17. Run the Model Comparison node.

✐   It will take some time to rerun the analysis.

Copyright © 2011, SAS Institute Inc., Cary, North Carolina, USA. ALL RIGHTS RESERVED.

6.4 Profit Matrices

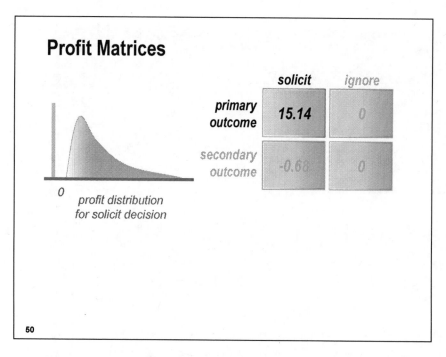

Statistical decision theory is an aid to making optimal decisions from predictive models. Using decision theory, each target outcome is matched to a particular decision or course of action. A *profit value* is assigned to both correct (and incorrect) outcome and decision combinations. The profit value can be random and vary between cases.

A vast simplification and common practice in prediction is to assume that the profit associated with each case, outcome, and decision is a constant. This is the default behavior of SAS Enterprise Miner.

  This simplifying assumption can lead to biased model assessment and incorrect prediction decisions.

For the demonstration, the overall donation average minus the solicitation cost is used as the (constant) profit associated with the primary outcome and the solicit decision.

Copyright © 2011, SAS Institute Inc., Cary, North Carolina, USA. ALL RIGHTS RESERVED.

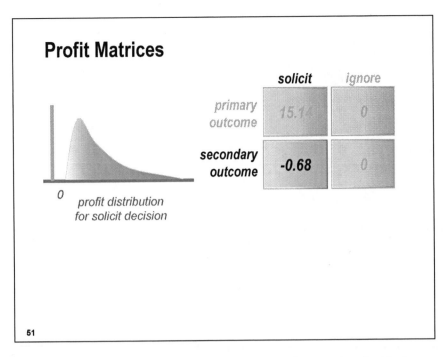

Similarly, the solicitation cost is taken as the profit associated with the secondary outcome and the solicit decision.

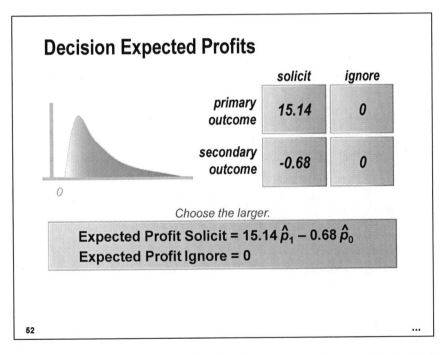

Making the reasonable assumption that there is no profit associated with the ignore decision, you can complete the profit matrix as shown above.

With the completed profit consequence matrix, you can calculate the expected profit associated with each decision. This is equal to the sum of the outcome/action profits multiplied by the outcome probabilities. The best decision for a case is the one that maximizes the expected profit for that case.

Copyright © 2011, SAS Institute Inc., Cary, North Carolina, USA. ALL RIGHTS RESERVED.

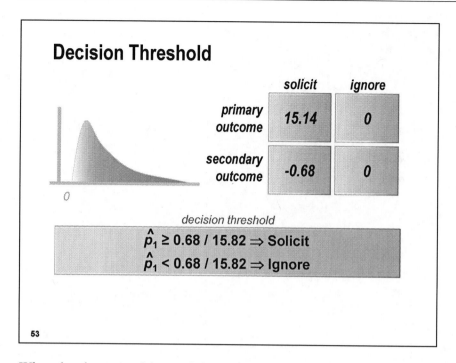

When the elements of the profit consequence matrix are constants, prediction decisions depend solely on the estimated probability of response and a constant decision threshold, as shown above.

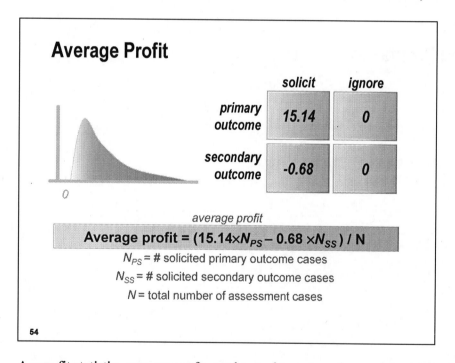

A new fit statistic, *average profit*, can be used to summarize model performance. For the profit matrix shown, average profit is computed by multiplying the number of cases by the corresponding profit in each outcome/decision combination, adding across all outcome/decision combinations, and dividing by the total number of cases in the assessment data.

Copyright © 2011, SAS Institute Inc., Cary, North Carolina, USA. ALL RIGHTS RESERVED.

Evaluating Model Profit

The consequences of incorporating a profit matrix in the analysis can be viewed in the Model Comparison node.

Follow these steps to evaluate a model with average profit:

1. Select **Results** in the Run Status dialog box. The Results - Node: Model Comparison window appears.

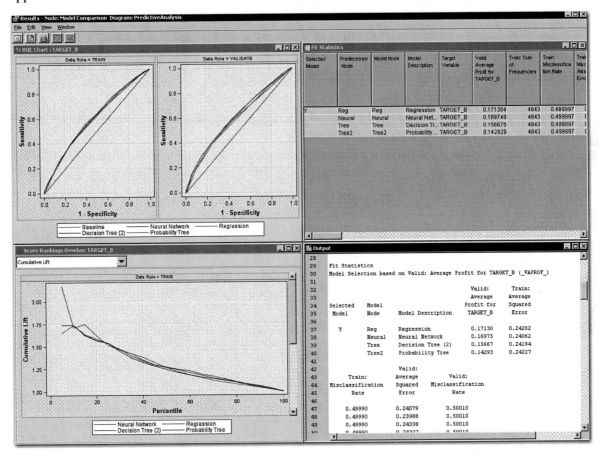

2. Maximize the Output window and go to line 29.

```
28
29    Fit Statistics
30    Model Selection based on Valid: Average Profit for TARGET_B (_VAPROF_)
31
32                                              Valid:          Train:
33                                             Average         Average
34    Selected    Model                       Profit for      Squared
35    Model       Node      Model Description   TARGET_B        Error
36
37       Y        Reg       Regression          0.17130        0.24202
38                Neural    Neural Network       0.16975        0.24062
39                Tree      Decision Tree (2)    0.15667        0.24194
40                Tree2     Probability Tree     0.14293        0.24227
41
```

With a profit matrix defined, model selection in the Model Assessment node is performed on validation profit. Based on this criterion, the selected model is the Regression Model. The Neural Network is a close second.

Copyright © 2011, SAS Institute Inc., Cary, North Carolina, USA. ALL RIGHTS RESERVED.

Viewing Additional Assessments

This demonstration shows several other assessments of possible interest.

1. Maximize the Score Rankings Overlay window.

2. Select **Select Chart: ⇨ Total Expected Profit**.

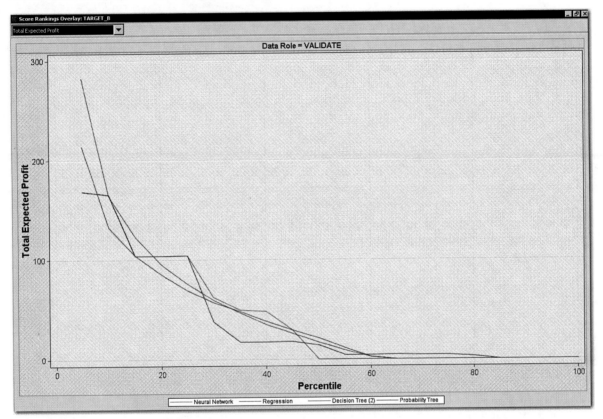

The Total Expected Profit plot shows the donation amount contributed within each demi-decile (5%) block of data. The result is that all models select approximately 60% of the cases (although cases in one model's 60% might not be in another model's 60%).

Copyright © 2011, SAS Institute Inc., Cary, North Carolina, USA. ALL RIGHTS RESERVED.

3.   Select **Select Chart:** ⇨ **Cumulative % Captured Response**.

4.   Double-click the **Data Role = VALIDATE** chart.

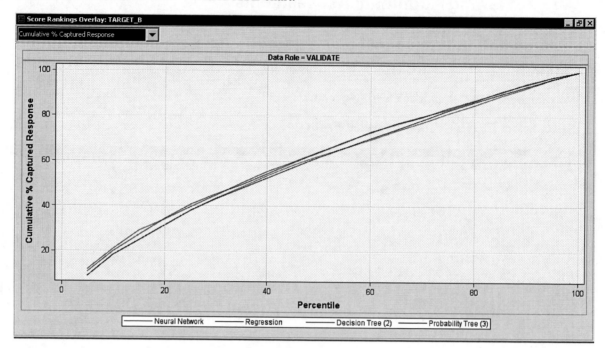

This plot shows sensitivity (also known as *Cumulative % Captured Response*) versus selection fraction (decile). By selecting 60% of the data, for example, you "capture" about 75% of the primary-outcome cases.

Copyright © 2011, SAS Institute Inc., Cary, North Carolina, USA. ALL RIGHTS RESERVED.

5. Select **Select Chart:⇨ Cumulative Total Expected Profit**.

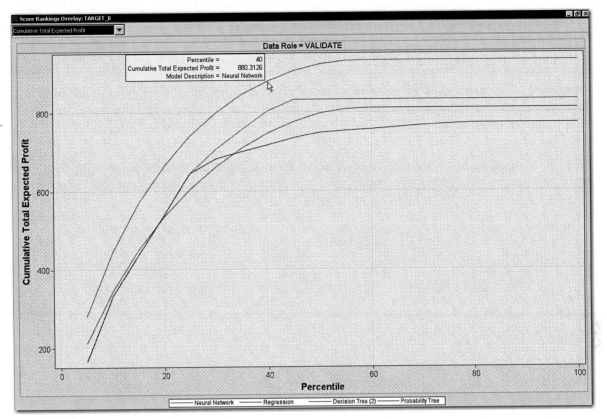

This chart shows that for the Neural Network model, at the 40% percentile of the validation data, the total expected profit is $880. This might seem a small total donation amount. Recall that the **Validation** data set represents a sample of 4,843 potential donors (from the partition node). This predictive model will be run against a **Scoring** data set with possibly hundreds of thousands of potential donors, yielding a much higher total donation amount than what is revealed in this chart.

6. Close the Results window.

Copyright © 2011, SAS Institute Inc., Cary, North Carolina, USA. ALL RIGHTS RESERVED.

Optimizing with Profit (Self-Study)

The models fit in the previous demonstrations were optimized to minimize average error. Because it is the most general optimization criterion, the best model selected by this criterion can rank and decide cases. If the ultimate goal of your model is to create prediction decisions, it might make sense to optimize on that criterion.

After you define a profit matrix, it is possible to optimize your model strictly on profit. Instead of seeking the model with the best prediction estimates, you find the model with best prediction decisions (those that maximize expected profit).

    The default model selection method in SAS Enterprise Miner is validation profit optimization, so these settings essentially restore the node defaults. Finding a meaningful profit matrix for most modeling scenarios, however, is difficult. Therefore, these notes recommend overriding the defaults and creating models with a general selection criterion such as validation average squared error.

Decision Tree Profit Optimization

One of the two tree models in the diagram is set up this way:

1. Select the original **Decision Tree** node.

2. Examine the Decision Tree node's Subtree property.

Subtree	
Method	Assessment
Number of Leaves	1
Assessment Measure	Decision
Assessment Fraction	0.25

The Decision Tree node is pruned using the default assessment measure, Decision. The goal of this tree is to make the best *decisions* rather than the best *estimates*.

3. Examine the Probability Tree node's Subtree property.

Subtree	
Method	Assessment
Number of Leaves	1
Assessment Measure	Average Square Error
Assessment Fraction	0.25

The Probability Tree node is pruned using average squared error. The goal of this tree is to provide the best *prediction estimates* rather than the best *decision*.

Copyright © 2011, SAS Institute Inc., Cary, North Carolina, USA. ALL RIGHTS RESERVED.

Regression Profit Optimization

Use the following settings to optimize a regression model using profit:

1. Select the **Regression** node.

2. Select **Selection Criterion** ⇨ **Validation Profit/Loss**.

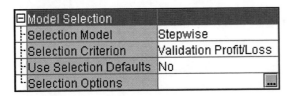

⊟ Model Selection	
Selection Model	Stepwise
Selection Criterion	Validation Profit/Loss
Use Selection Defaults	No
Selection Options	...

3. Repeat steps 1 and 2 for the Polynomial Regression node.

Neural Network Profit Optimization

1. Select the **Neural Network** node.

2. Select **Model Selection Criterion** ⇨ **Profit/Loss**.

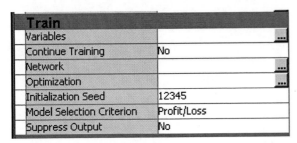

Train	
Variables	...
Continue Training	No
Network	...
Optimization	...
Initialization Seed	12345
Model Selection Criterion	Profit/Loss
Suppress Output	No

✎   The AutoNeural node does not support profit matrices.

The next step refits the models using profit optimization. Be aware that the demonstrations in Chapters 8 and 9 assume that the models are fit using average squared error optimization.

3. Run the Model Comparison node and view the results.

4. Maximize the Output window and go to line 29.

29	Fit Statistics				
30	Model Selection based on Valid: Average Profit for TARGET_B (_VAPROF_)				
31					
32				Valid:	Train:
33				Average	Average
34	Selected	Model		Profit for	Squared
35	Model	Node	Model Description	TARGET_B	Error
36					
37	Y	Neural	Neural Network	0.17328	0.23944
38		Reg	Regression	0.17283	0.24088
39		Tree	Decision Tree (2)	0.15667	0.24194
40		Tree2	Probability Tree (3)	0.14293	0.24227

The reported validation profits are now slightly higher, and the relative ordering of the models changed.

Copyright © 2011, SAS Institute Inc., Cary, North Carolina, USA. ALL RIGHTS RESERVED.

 **Exercises**

1. **Assessing Models**

   a. Connect all models in the ORGANICS diagram to a Model Comparison node.

   b. Run the Model Comparison node and view the results.

   Which model was selected? Based on what criteria? _____

   Which model has the best ROC curve? _____

   What is the corresponding ROC Index? _____

   c. Open the exported data from the Model Comparison node. Explore the **RANK** data set. What is the number of event cases for each model at a selection depth of 5%?

   _____

   Hint: Sort the **RANK** data set created by the model comparison node by increasing the percentile. Be sure to report on the validation data!

Copyright © 2011, SAS Institute Inc., Cary, North Carolina, USA. ALL RIGHTS RESERVED.

6.5 Chapter Summary

The Model Comparison node enables you to compare statistics and statistical graphics summarizing model performance. To make assessments applicable to the scoring population, you must account for differences in response proportions between the training, validation, and scoring data.

While you can choose to select a model based strictly on statistical measures, you can also consider profit as a measure of model performance. For each outcome, an appropriate decision must be defined. A profit matrix is constructed, characterizing the profit associated with each outcome and decision combination. The decision tools in SAS Enterprise Miner support only constant profit matrices.

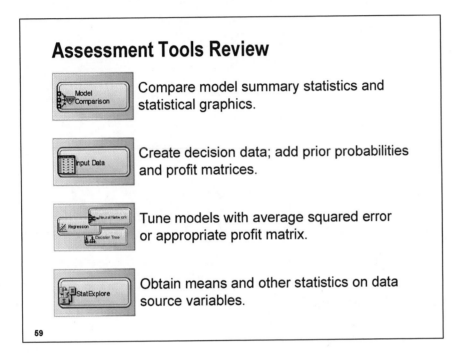

Assessment Tools Review

Compare model summary statistics and statistical graphics.

Create decision data; add prior probabilities and profit matrices.

Tune models with average squared error or appropriate profit matrix.

Obtain means and other statistics on data source variables.

59

Copyright © 2011, SAS Institute Inc., Cary, North Carolina, USA. ALL RIGHTS RESERVED.

6.6 Solutions

Solutions to Exercises

1. **Assessing Models**

    a. Connect all models in the ORGANICS diagram to a Model Comparison node.

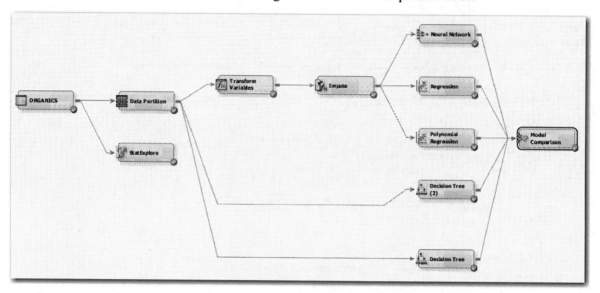

    b. Run the Model Comparison node and view the results.

    Which model was selected? Based on what criteria? **From the Results output window, the Valid: Misclassification Rate was used to select the Decision Tree model.**

				Train:		Valid:
			Valid:	Average	Train:	Average
Selected	Model		Misclassification	Squared	Misclassification	Squared
Model	Node	Model Description	Rate	Error	Rate	Error
Y	Tree	Decision Tree	0.18531	0.13286	0.18512	0.13277
	Neural	Neural Network	0.18585	0.13325	0.18332	0.13321
	Reg	Regression	0.18612	0.13955	0.18781	0.13820
	Tree2	Decision Tree (2)	0.18738	0.14001	0.18602	0.14020
	Reg2	Polynomial Regression	0.18828	0.13641	0.19024	0.13404

Fit Statistics
Model Selection based on Valid: Misclassification Rate (_VMISC_)

Copyright © 2011, SAS Institute Inc., Cary, North Carolina, USA. ALL RIGHTS RESERVED.

Which model has the best ROC curve? **The Decision Tree seems to have the best ROC curve.**

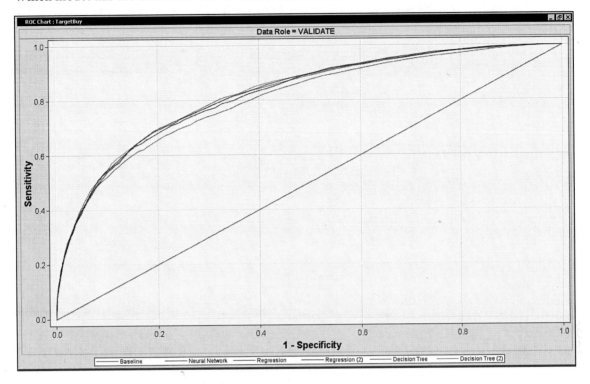

What is the corresponding ROC Index?

The ROC Index values are found in the Fit Statistics window.

(The Valid: ROC Index column was moved from its original location in the view below.)

Selected Model	Predecessor Node	Model Node	Model Description	Target Variable	Valid: Misclassification Rate	Valid: Roc Index	Train: Akaike's Information Criterion
Y	Tree	Tree	Decision Tree	TargetBuy	0.185312	0.824	.
	Neural	Neural	Neural Network	TargetBuy	0.185852	0.824	9577.636
	Reg	Reg	Regression	TargetBuy	0.186122	0.805	9758.609
	Tree2	Tree2	Decision Tree (2)	TargetBuy	0.187382	0.777	.
	Reg2	Reg2	Polynomial Regression	TargetBuy	0.188282	0.82	9529.938

Copyright © 2011, SAS Institute Inc., Cary, North Carolina, USA. ALL RIGHTS RESERVED.

The ROC Index can also be seen by selecting **View** ⇨ **Model** ⇨ **Statistics Comparison** in the Model Comparison Node Results window. Look for the Data Role: Valid and Statistics Label: Valid: ROC Index.

Statistics Comparison

Data Role	Target Variable	Fit Statistics	Statistics Label	Tree	Neural	Reg	Tree2	Reg2
Train	TargetBuy	_NW_	Train: Number of Estimate Weights		127	8		9
Train	TargetBuy	_RASE_	Train: Root Average Sum of Squares	0.364502	0.365037	0.373557	0.374183	0.369333
Train	TargetBuy	_RESPC_	Train: Cumulative Percent Response	78.56158	77.60791	76.50629	78.85806	76.4552
Train	TargetBuy	_RESP_	Train: Percent Response	70.1497	69.06475	67.9807	69.95565	68.46795
Train	TargetBuy	_RFPE_	Train: Root Final Prediction Error		0.369233	0.373826		0.369632
Train	TargetBuy	_RMSE_	Train: Root Mean Squared Error		0.367141	0.373692		0.369482
Train	TargetBuy	_SBC_	Train: Schwarz's Bayesian Criterion		10506.74	9817.136		9595.78
Train	TargetBuy	_SSE_	Train: Sum of Squared Errors	2952.712	2961.389	3101.251	3111.648	3031.498
Train	TargetBuy	_SUMW_	Train: Sum of Case Weights Times Freq		22224	22224		22224
Train	TargetBuy	_WRONG_	Train: Number of Wrong Classifications		2037			
Valid	TargetBuy	VKS	Valid: Kolmogorov-Smirnov Statistic	0.496	0.493	0.457	0.444	0.481
Valid	TargetBuy	_VASE_	Valid: Average Squared Error	0.132773	0.133209	0.138204	0.140196	0.134038
Valid	TargetBuy	_VAUR_	Valid: Roc Index	0.824	0.824	0.805	0.777	0.82
Valid	TargetBuy	_VAVERR_	Valid: Average Error Function		0.418894	0.43599		0.421824
Valid	TargetBuy	_VBINNED_KS_PROB_CUTOF_	Valid: Bin-Based Two-Way Kolmogorov-Smirnov ...	0.256	0.321	0.346	0.238	0.277
Valid	TargetBuy	_VCAPC_	Valid: Cumulative Percent Captured Response	31.27929	30.9593	31.23183	30.95235	31.28634
Valid	TargetBuy	_VCAP_	Valid: Percent Captured Response	14.15423	13.62645	13.81177	13.86612	13.98983
Valid	TargetBuy	_VDIV_	Valid: Divisor for VASE	22222	22222	22222	22222	22222
Valid	TargetBuy	_VERR_	Valid: Error Function		9308.673	9688.581		9373.784
Valid	TargetBuy	_VGAIN_	Valid: Gain	212.5397	209.3425	212.0655	209.273	212.6102
Valid	TargetBuy	_VGINI_	Valid: Gini Coefficient	0.648	0.648	0.61	0.555	0.64
Valid	TargetBuy	_VKS_BIN_	Valid: Bin-Based Two-Way Kolmogorov-Smirnov ...	0.49	0.489	0.454	0.439	0.48
Valid	TargetBuy	_VKS_PROB_CUTOFF_	Valid: Kolmogorov-Smirnov Probability Cutoff	0.28	0.28	0.3	0.22	0.26
Valid	TargetBuy	_VLIFTC_	Valid: Cumulative Lift	3.125397	3.093425	3.120655	3.09273	3.126102
Valid	TargetBuy	_VLIFT_	Valid: Lift	2.828554	2.723085	2.760119	2.770979	2.795701
Valid	TargetBuy	_VMAX_	Valid: Maximum Absolute Error	1	0.979105	0.994405	0.95288	0.986233
Valid	TargetBuy	_VMISC_	Valid: Misclassification Rate	0.185312	0.185852	0.186122	0.187382	0.188282
Valid	TargetBuy	_VMSE_	Valid: Mean Square Error		0.133209	0.139204		0.134038
Valid	TargetBuy	_VNOBS_	Valid: Sum of Frequencies	11111	11111	11111	11111	11111
Valid	TargetBuy	_VRASE_	Valid: Root Average Squared Error	0.36438	0.364978	0.371759	0.374428	0.366112
Valid	TargetBuy	_VRESPC_	Valid: Cumulative Percent Response	77.41061	76.61871	77.29317	76.60151	77.42806
Valid	TargetBuy	_VRESP_	Valid: Percent Response	70.05833	67.44604	68.36331	68.63229	69.2446
Valid	TargetBuy	_VRMSE_	Valid: Root Mean Square Error		0.364978	0.371759		0.366112
Valid	TargetBuy	_VSSE_	Valid: Sum of Square Errors	2950.479	2960.168	3071.178	3115.444	2978.59
Valid	TargetBuy	_VSUMW_	Valid: Sum of Case Weights Times Freq	22222	22222	22222	22222	22222
Valid	TargetBuy	_VWRONG_	Valid: Number of Wrong Classifications		2065			

c. Open the exported data from the Model Comparison node. Explore the **RANK** data set. What is the number of event cases for each model at a selection depth of 5%?

Open the Explorer for the EMRANK data set. Click on the Percentile column title to sort data in ascending order. You might need to click the column title twice. Notice that there are two rows for each of the five models: one for Train data and the other for Validate. The Number of Events column contains the answer to the question.

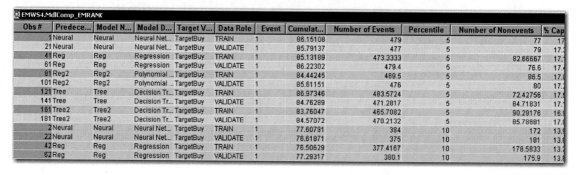

EMWS4.MdlComp_EMRANK

Obs #	Predece...	Model N...	Model D...	Target V...	Data Role	Event	Cumulat...	Number of Events	Percentile	Number of Nonevents	% Cap
1	Neural	Neural	Neural Net...	TargetBuy	TRAIN	1	86.15108	479	5	77	17
21	Neural	Neural	Neural Net...	TargetBuy	VALIDATE	1	85.79137	477	5	79	17.
41	Reg	Reg	Regression	TargetBuy	TRAIN	1	85.13189	473.3333	5	82.66667	17.
61	Reg	Reg	Regression	TargetBuy	VALIDATE	1	86.22302	479.4	5	76.6	17.
81	Reg2	Reg2	Polynomial ...	TargetBuy	TRAIN	1	84.44245	469.5	5	86.5	17.
101	Reg2	Reg2	Polynomial ...	TargetBuy	VALIDATE	1	85.61151	476	5	80	17.
121	Tree	Tree	Decision Tr...	TargetBuy	TRAIN	1	86.97346	483.5724	5	72.42756	17.
141	Tree	Tree	Decision Tr...	TargetBuy	VALIDATE	1	84.76289	471.2817	5	84.71831	17.
161	Tree2	Tree2	Decision Tr...	TargetBuy	TRAIN	1	83.76047	465.7082	5	90.29176	16.
181	Tree2	Tree2	Decision Tr...	TargetBuy	VALIDATE	1	84.57072	470.2132	5	85.78881	17.
2	Neural	Neural	Neural Net...	TargetBuy	TRAIN	1	77.60791	384	10	172	13.
22	Neural	Neural	Neural Net...	TargetBuy	VALIDATE	1	78.61871	375	10	181	13.
42	Reg	Reg	Regression	TargetBuy	TRAIN	1	76.50629	377.4167	10	178.5833	13.
62	Reg	Reg	Regression	TargetBuy	VALIDATE	1	77.29317	380.1	10	175.9	13.

Copyright © 2011, SAS Institute Inc., Cary, North Carolina, USA. ALL RIGHTS RESERVED.

Solutions to Student Activities (Polls/Quizzes)

6.01 Poll – Correct Answer

In practice, modelers often use several tools, sometimes both graphical and numerical, to choose a best model.

- ⬤ True
- ◯ False

36

Copyright © 2011, SAS Institute Inc., Cary, North Carolina, USA. ALL RIGHTS RESERVED.

Copyright © 2011, SAS Institute Inc., Cary, North Carolina, USA. ALL RIGHTS RESERVED.

Chapter 7 Model Implementation

Copyright © 2011, SAS Institute Inc., Cary, North Carolina, USA. ALL RIGHTS RESERVED.

Copyright © 2011, SAS Institute Inc., Cary, North Carolina, USA. ALL RIGHTS RESERVED.

7.1 Introduction

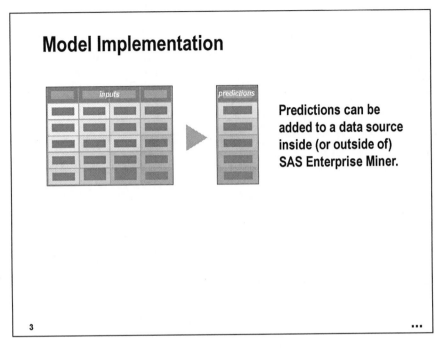

After you train and compare predictive models, one model is selected to represent the association between the inputs and the target. After it is selected, this model must be put to use. The contribution of SAS Enterprise Miner to model implementation is a scoring recipe capable of adding predictions to any data set structured in a manner similar to the training data.

SAS Enterprise Miner offers two options for model implementation.

- *Internally scored data sets* are created by combining the Score tool with a data set identified for scoring.

    🖎   A copy of the scored data set is stored on the SAS Foundation server assigned to your project. If the data set to be scored is very large, you should consider scoring the data outside the SAS Enterprise Miner environment and use the second deployment option.

- *Scoring code modules* are used to generate predicted target values in environments outside of SAS Enterprise Miner. SAS Enterprise Miner can create scoring code in the SAS, C, and Java programming languages. The SAS language code can be embedded directly into a SAS Foundation application to generate predictions. The C and Java language code must be compiled. The C code should compile with any C compiler that supports the ISO/IEC 9899 International Standard for Programming Languages -- C.

Copyright © 2011, SAS Institute Inc., Cary, North Carolina, USA. ALL RIGHTS RESERVED.

Discussion

At your place of business, how is model deployment handled? Do the model builders score new data with their own models or is this handled by another team? Is deployment typically handled by one group or department or across several?

4

Copyright © 2011, SAS Institute Inc., Cary, North Carolina, USA. ALL RIGHTS RESERVED.

7.2 Internally Scored Data Sets

To create an internally scored data set, you need to define a Score data source, integrate the Score data source and Score tool into your process flow diagram, and (optionally) relocate the scored data set to a library of your choice.

Copyright © 2011, SAS Institute Inc., Cary, North Carolina, USA. ALL RIGHTS RESERVED.

Creating a Score Data Source

Creating a score data source is similar to creating a modeling data source.

1. Right-click **Data Sources** in the Project panel and select **Create Data Source**. The Data Source Wizard appears.

2. Select the table **SCOREPVA97NK** in the **AAEM** library.

3. Select **Next** until you reach Data Source Wizard -- Step 7 of 8 Data Source Attributes.

4. Select **Score** as the role.

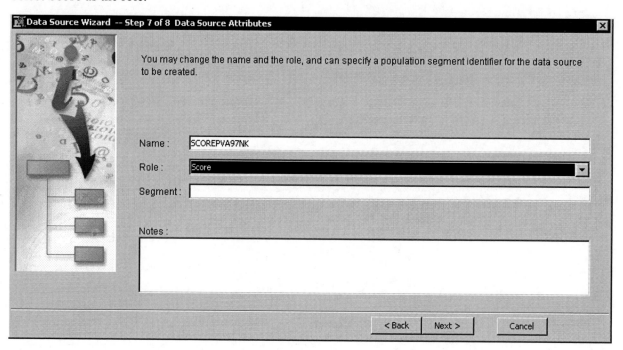

5. Select **Next** to move to step 8.

6. Select **Finish**. You now have a data source that is ready for scoring.

Copyright © 2011, SAS Institute Inc., Cary, North Carolina, USA. ALL RIGHTS RESERVED.

Scoring with the Score Tool

The Score tool attaches model predictions from a selected model to a score data set.

1. Select the **Assess** tab.

2. Drag a **Score** tool into the diagram workspace.

3. Connect the **Model Comparison** node to the **Score** node as shown.

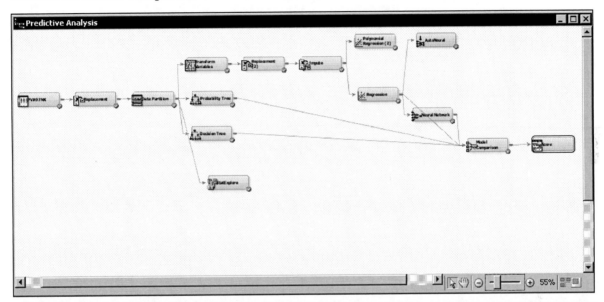

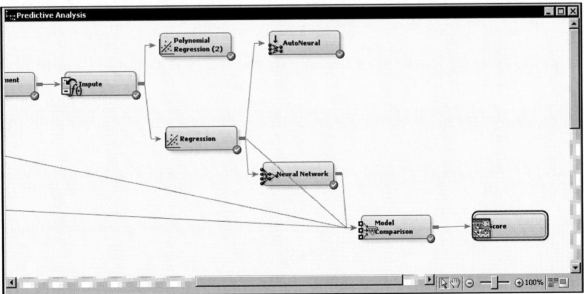

Copyright © 2011, SAS Institute Inc., Cary, North Carolina, USA. ALL RIGHTS RESERVED.

The Score node creates predictions using the model deemed best by the Model Comparison node (in this case, the Regression model).

✏   If you want to create predictions using a specific model, either delete the connection to the Model Comparison node of the models that you do not want to use, or connect the Score node directly to the desired model and continue as described below.

4. Drag the **SCOREPVA97NK** data source into the diagram workspace.

5. Connect the **SCOREPVA97NK** data source node to the **Score** node as shown.

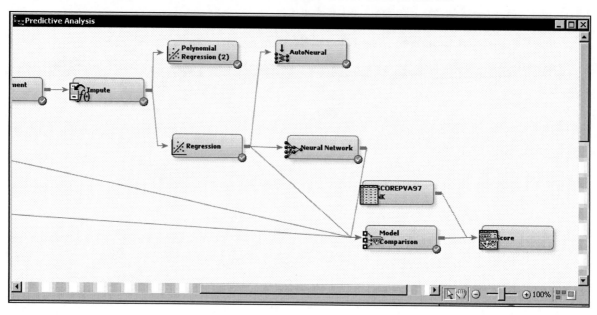

Copyright © 2011, SAS Institute Inc., Cary, North Carolina, USA. ALL RIGHTS RESERVED.

6. Run the Score node and view the results. The Results - Score window appears.

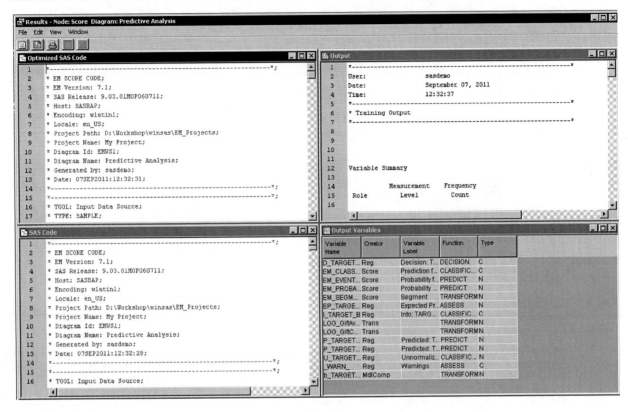

7. Maximize the Output window.

The item of greatest interest is a table of new variables added to the Score data set.

8. Go to line 43.

```
43    Score Output Variables
44
45    Variable Name          Function         Creator     Label
46
47    D_TARGET_B             DECISION         Reg         Decision: TARGET_B
48    EM_CLASSIFICATION      CLASSIFICATION   Score       Prediction for TARGET_B
49    EM_EVENTPROBABILITY    PREDICT          Score       Probability for level 1 of TARGET_B
50    EM_PROBABILITY         PREDICT          Score       Probability of Classification
51    EM_SEGMENT             TRANSFORM        Score       Segment
52    EP_TARGET_B            ASSESS           Reg         Expected Profit: TARGET_B
53    I_TARGET_B             CLASSIFICATION   Reg         Into: TARGET_B
54    LOG_GiftAvgAll         TRANSFORM        Trans
55    LOG_GiftCnt36          TRANSFORM        Trans
56    P_TARGET_B0            PREDICT          Reg         Predicted: TARGET_B=0
57    P_TARGET_B1            PREDICT          Reg         Predicted: TARGET_B=1
58    U_TARGET_B             CLASSIFICATION   Reg         Unnormalized Into: TARGET_B
59    _WARN_                 ASSESS           Reg         Warnings
60    b_TARGET_B             TRANSFORM        MdlComp
```

9. Close the Results window.

Copyright © 2011, SAS Institute Inc., Cary, North Carolina, USA. ALL RIGHTS RESERVED.

Exporting a Scored Table (Self-Study)

1. Select **Exported Data** ⇨ [...] from the Score node Properties panel.

Property	Value
General	
Node ID	Score
Imported Data	[...]
Exported Data	[...]
Notes	[...]
Train	
Variables	[...]
Type of Scored Data	View
Use Fixed Output Name	Yes
Hide Variables	No
Hide Selection	[...]

The Exported Data - Score dialog box appears.

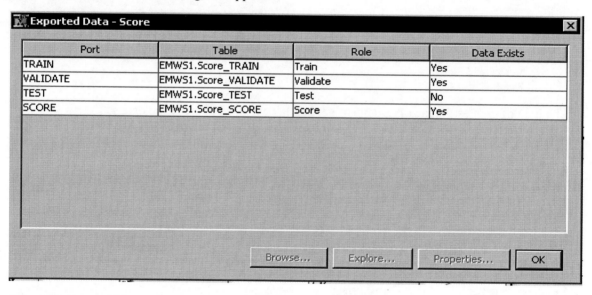

Port	Table	Role	Data Exists
TRAIN	EMWS1.Score_TRAIN	Train	Yes
VALIDATE	EMWS1.Score_VALIDATE	Validate	Yes
TEST	EMWS1.Score_TEST	Test	No
SCORE	EMWS1.Score_SCORE	Score	Yes

Browse...   Explore...   Properties...   OK

2. Select the **Score** table.

Copyright © 2011, SAS Institute Inc., Cary, North Carolina, USA. ALL RIGHTS RESERVED.

3. Select **Explore**. The Explore window appears with a 20,000-row sample of the
    EMWS1.Score_SCORE data set (the internal name in SAS Enterprise Miner for the scored
    SCOREPVA97NK data).

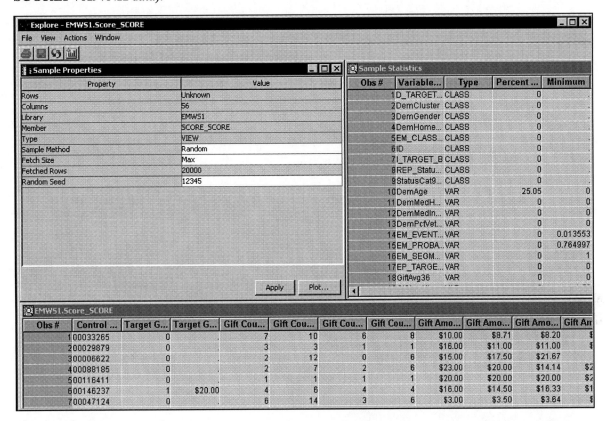

This scored table is situated on the SAS Foundation server in the current project directory. You might
want to place a copy of this table in another location. The easiest way to do this is with a SAS code
node.

4. Close the Explore window.

5. Select the **Utility** tab.

6. Drag a **SAS Code** node into the diagram workspace.

Copyright © 2011, SAS Institute Inc., Cary, North Carolina, USA. ALL RIGHTS RESERVED.

7. Connect the **Score** node to the **SAS Code** node as shown.

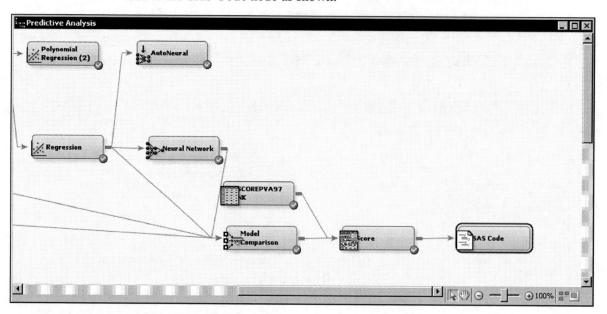

8. Select **Code Editor** ⇨ 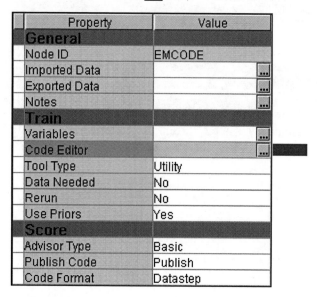 in the SAS Code node's Properties panel.

Property	Value
General	
Node ID	EMCODE
Imported Data	
Exported Data	
Notes	
Train	
Variables	
Code Editor	
Tool Type	Utility
Data Needed	No
Rerun	No
Use Priors	Yes
Score	
Advisor Type	Basic
Publish Code	Publish
Code Format	Datastep

Copyright © 2011, SAS Institute Inc., Cary, North Carolina, USA. ALL RIGHTS RESERVED.

The Training Code window appears.

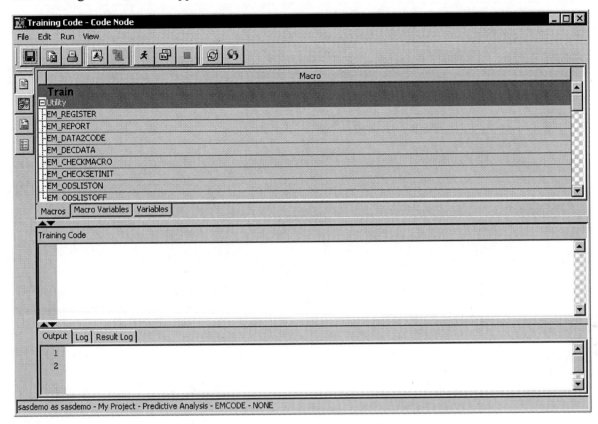

The Training Code window enables you to add new functionality to SAS Enterprise Miner by accessing the scripting language of SAS.

Copyright © 2011, SAS Institute Inc., Cary, North Carolina, USA. ALL RIGHTS RESERVED.

9. Type the following program in the Training Code window:

```
data AAEM.ExportedScoreData;
   set &EM_IMPORT_SCORE;
run;
```

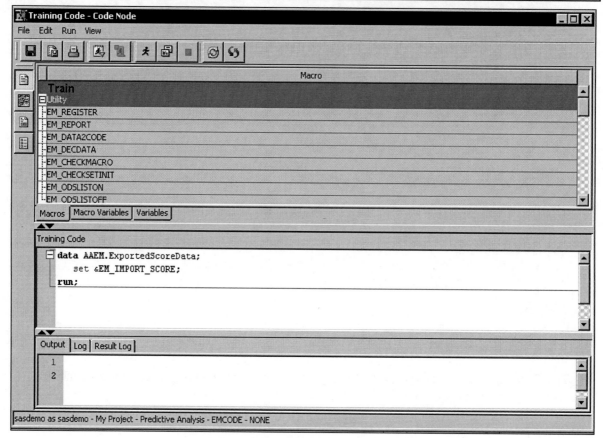

This program creates a new table named **ExportedScoreData** in the **AAEM** library.

10. Close the Training Code window and save the changes.

11. Run the SAS Code node. You do not need to view the results.

Copyright © 2011, SAS Institute Inc., Cary, North Carolina, USA. ALL RIGHTS RESERVED.

12. Select **View** ⇨ **Explorer** from the SAS Enterprise Miner menu bar. The Explorer window appears.

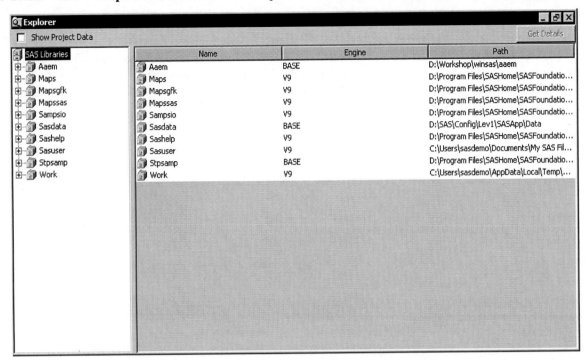

13. Select the **Aaem** library.

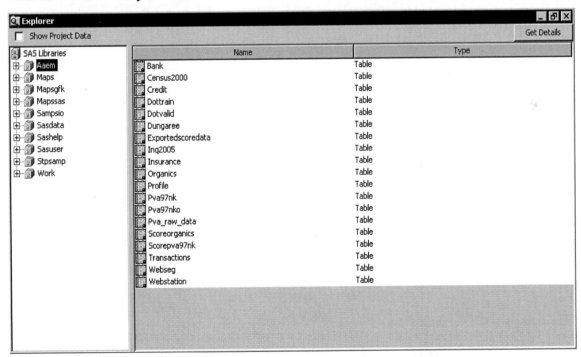

The **Aaem** library contains the **Exportedscoredata** table created by your SAS Code node. You can modify the SAS Code node to place the scored data in any library that is visible to the SAS Foundation server.

14. Close the Explorer window.

Copyright © 2011, SAS Institute Inc., Cary, North Carolina, USA. ALL RIGHTS RESERVED.

7.3 Score Code Modules

Model deployment usually occurs outside of SAS Enterprise Miner and sometimes even outside of SAS. To accommodate this need, SAS Enterprise Miner is designed to provide score code modules to create predictions from properly prepared tables. In addition to the prediction code, the score code modules include all the transformations that are found in your modeling process flow. You can save the code as a SAS, C, or Java program.

Copyright © 2011, SAS Institute Inc., Cary, North Carolina, USA. ALL RIGHTS RESERVED.

Creating a SAS Score Code Module

The SAS Score Code module is opened by default when you open the Score node.

1. Open the Score node Results window.

2. Maximize the SAS Code window.

The SAS Code window shows the SAS DATA step code that is necessary to append predictions from the selected model (in this case, the regression model) to a score data set. Each node in the process flow can contribute to the DATA step code. The following list describes some highlights of the generated SAS code:

- Go to line 21. This code removes the spurious zero from the median income input.

```
*------------------------------------------------------------*;
* TOOL: Extension Class;
* TYPE: MODIFY;
* NODE: Repl;
*------------------------------------------------------------*;
* ;
* Variable: DemMedIncome ;
* ;
Label REP_DemMedIncome='Replacement: Median Income Region';
REP_DemMedIncome =DemMedIncome ;
if DemMedIncome  ne .  and DemMedIncome <1  then REP_DemMedIncome  = .
```

- Go to line 45. This code takes the log transformation of selected inputs.

```
*------------------------------------------------------------*;
* TRANSFORM: GiftAvg36 , log(GiftAvg36 + 1);
*------------------------------------------------------------*;
label LOG_GiftAvg36 = 'Transformed: Gift Amount Average 36 Months';
if GiftAvg36 + 1 > 0 then LOG_GiftAvg36 = log(GiftAvg36 + 1);
else LOG_GiftAvg36 = .;
*------------------------------------------------------------*;
* TRANSFORM: GiftAvgAll , log(GiftAvgAll + 1);
*------------------------------------------------------------*;
label LOG_GiftAvgAll = 'Transformed: Gift Amount Average All Months';
if GiftAvgAll + 1 > 0 then LOG_GiftAvgAll = log(GiftAvgAll + 1);
else LOG_GiftAvgAll = .;
*------------------------------------------------------------*;
* TRANSFORM: GiftAvgCard36 , log(GiftAvgCard36 + 1);
*------------------------------------------------------------*;
label LOG_GiftAvgCard36 = 'Transformed: Gift Amount Average Card 36 Mon
if GiftAvgCard36 + 1 > 0 then LOG_GiftAvgCard36 = log(GiftAvgCard36 + 1
else LOG_GiftAvgCard36 = .;
     .
     .
     .
```

Copyright © 2011, SAS Institute Inc., Cary, North Carolina, USA. ALL RIGHTS RESERVED.

- Go to line 93. This code replaces the levels of the **StatusCat96NK** input.

```
*------------------------------------------------------------*;
* TOOL: Extension Class;
* TYPE: MODIFY;
* NODE: Repl2;
*------------------------------------------------------------*;

* ;
* Defining New Variables;
* ;
Length REP_StatusCat96NK $5;
Label REP_StatusCat96NK='Replacement: Status Category 96NK';
REP_StatusCat96NK= StatusCat96NK;

* ;
* Replace Specific Class Levels ;
* ;
length _UFormat200 $200;
drop    _UFORMAT200;
_UFORMAT200 = " ";
* ;
* Variable: StatusCat96NK;
* ;
_UFORMAT200 = strip(StatusCat96NK);
if _UFORMAT200 =   "A" then
REP_StatusCat96NK="A";
else
if _UFORMAT200 =   "S" then
REP_StatusCat96NK="A";
else
if _UFORMAT200 =   "F" then
REP_StatusCat96NK="N";
else
if _UFORMAT200 =   "N" then
REP_StatusCat96NK="N";
else
if _UFORMAT200 =   "E" then
REP_StatusCat96NK="L";
else
```

Copyright © 2011, SAS Institute Inc., Cary, North Carolina, USA. ALL RIGHTS RESERVED.

- Go to line 133. This code replaces missing values and creates missing value indicators.

```
*-------------------------------------------------------------*;
* TOOL: Imputation;
* TYPE: MODIFY;
* NODE: Impt;
*-------------------------------------------------------------*;
*;
*MEAN-MAX-MIN-MEDIAN-MIDRANGE AND ROBUST ESTIMATES;
*;
label IMP_DemAge = 'Imputed: Age';
IMP_DemAge = DemAge;
if DemAge = . then IMP_DemAge = 59.262912087912;
label IMP_LOG_GiftAvgCard36 = 'Imputed: Transformed: Gift Amount Averag
IMP_LOG_GiftAvgCard36 = LOG_GiftAvgCard36;
if LOG_GiftAvgCard36 = . then IMP_LOG_GiftAvgCard36 = 2.5855317177381;
label IMP_REP_DemMedIncome = 'Imputed: Replacement: Median Income Regio.
IMP_REP_DemMedIncome = REP_DemMedIncome;
if REP_DemMedIncome = . then IMP_REP_DemMedIncome = 53570.8504928806;
*;
*INDICATOR VARIABLES;
*;
label M_DemAge = "Imputation Indicator for DemAge";
if DemAge = . then M_DemAge = 1;
else M_DemAge= 0;
label M_LOG_GiftAvgCard36 = "Imputation Indicator for LOG_GiftAvgCard36
if LOG_GiftAvgCard36 = . then M_LOG_GiftAvgCard36 = 1;
else M_LOG_GiftAvgCard36= 0;
label M_REP_DemMedIncome = "Imputation Indicator for REP_DemMedIncome";
if REP_DemMedIncome = . then M_REP_DemMedIncome = 1;
else M_REP_DemMedIncome= 0;
```

Copyright © 2011, SAS Institute Inc., Cary, North Carolina, USA. ALL RIGHTS RESERVED.

- Go to line 162. This code comes from the Regression node. It is this code that actually adds the predictions to a Score data set.

```
*----------------------------------------------------------------*;
* TOOL: Regression;
* TYPE: MODEL;
* NODE: Reg;
*----------------------------------------------------------------*;
***************************************;
*** begin scoring code for regression;
***************************************;

length _WARN_ $4;
label _WARN_ = 'Warnings' ;

length I_TARGET_B $ 12;
label I_TARGET_B = 'Into: TARGET_B' ;
*** Target Values;
array REGDRF [2] $12 _temporary_ ('1' '0' );
label U_TARGET_B = 'Unnormalized Into: TARGET_B' ;
*** Unnormalized target values;
ARRAY REGDRU[2]  _TEMPORARY_ (1 0);

drop _DM_BAD;
_DM_BAD=0;

*** Check DemMedHomeValue for missing values ;
if missing( DemMedHomeValue ) then do;
  .
  .
  .
```

Copyright © 2011, SAS Institute Inc., Cary, North Carolina, USA. ALL RIGHTS RESERVED.

- Go to line 300. This block of code comes from the Model Comparison node. It adds demi-decile bin numbers to the scored output. For example, bin 1 corresponds to the top 5% of the data as scored by the Regression model, bin 2 corresponds to the next 5%, and so on.

```
*-----------------------------------------------------------*;
* TOOL: Model Compare Class;
* TYPE: ASSESS;
* NODE: MdlComp;
*-----------------------------------------------------------*;
if (P_TARGET_B1 ge 0.08433506126363) then do;
b_TARGET_B = 1;
end;
else
if (P_TARGET_B1 ge 0.07379667308709) then do;
b_TARGET_B = 2;
end;
else
if (P_TARGET_B1 ge 0.0675579857262) then do;
b_TARGET_B = 3;
end;
else
if (P_TARGET_B1 ge 0.06293120025423) then do;
b_TARGET_B = 4;
end;
else
     .
     .
     .
```

Copyright © 2011, SAS Institute Inc., Cary, North Carolina, USA. ALL RIGHTS RESERVED.

- Go to line 384. This block of code comes from the Score node. It adds the following standardized variables to the scored data set:

EM_CLASSIFICATION	Prediction for **TARGET_B**
EM_DECISION	Recommended Decision for **TARGET_B**
EM_EVENTPROBABILITY	Probability for Level 1 of **Target**
EM_PROBABILITY	Probability of Classification
EM_PROFIT	Expected Profit for **TARGET_B**
EM_SEGMENT	Segment

```
*------------------------------------------------------------*;
* TOOL: Score Node;
* TYPE: ASSESS;
* NODE: Score;
*------------------------------------------------------------*;
*------------------------------------------------------------*;
* Score: Creating Fixed Names;
*------------------------------------------------------------*;
LABEL EM_SEGMENT = 'Segment';
EM_SEGMENT = b_TARGET_B;
LABEL EM_EVENTPROBABILITY = 'Probability for level 1 of TARGET_B';
EM_EVENTPROBABILITY = P_TARGET_B1;
LABEL EM_PROBABILITY = 'Probability of Classification';
EM_PROBABILITY =
max(
P_TARGET_B1
,
.
.
.
```

✎   To use this code, you must embed it in a DATA step. The easiest way to do this is by saving it to a SAS code file and including it in your DATA step.

3. Select **File ⇨ Save As** to save this code to a location of your choice.

Copyright © 2011, SAS Institute Inc., Cary, North Carolina, USA. ALL RIGHTS RESERVED.

Creating Other Score Code Modules

To access scoring code for languages other than SAS, use the following procedure.

1. Select **View** ⇨ **Scoring** ⇨ **C Score Code**. The C Score Code window appears.

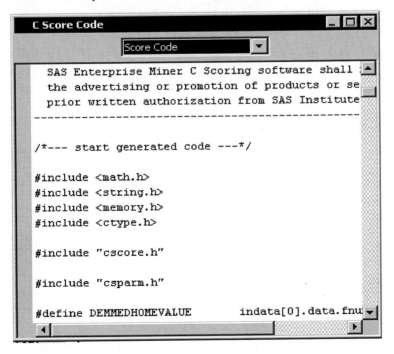

There are four parts to the C Score Code window. The actual C score code part is accessible from the menu at the top of the C Score Code window.

Copyright © 2011, SAS Institute Inc., Cary, North Carolina, USA. ALL RIGHTS RESERVED.

2.   Select **View** ⇨ **Scoring** ⇨ **Java Score Code**. The Java Score Code window appears.

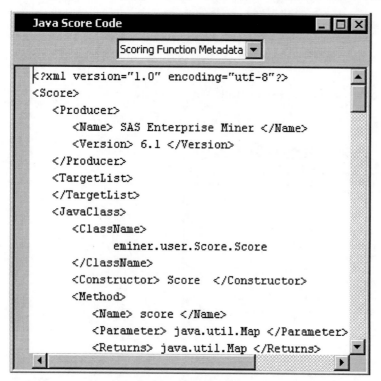

There are five parts to the Java Score Code window. The actual Java score code part is accessible from the menu at the top of the Java Score Code window.

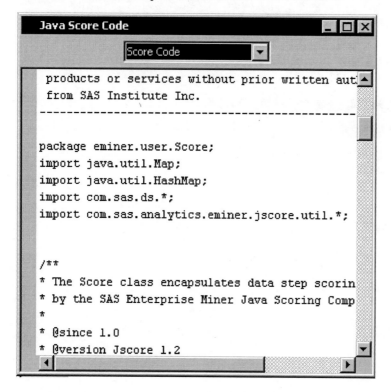

Copyright © 2011, SAS Institute Inc., Cary, North Carolina, USA. ALL RIGHTS RESERVED.

 **Exercises**

1. **Scoring Organics Data**

   a. Create a Score data source for the **ScoreOrganics** data.

   b. Score the **ScoreOrganics** data using the model selected with the Model Comparison node.

Copyright © 2011, SAS Institute Inc., Cary, North Carolina, USA. ALL RIGHTS RESERVED.

7.4 Chapter Summary

The Score node is used to score new data inside SAS Enterprise Miner and to create scoring modules for use outside SAS Enterprise Miner. The Score node adds predictions to any data source with a role of Score. This data source must have the same inputs as the training data. A scored data source is stored within the project directory. You can use a SAS Code tool to relocate it to another library.

The Score tool creates score code modules in the SAS, C, and Java languages. These score code modules can be saved and used outside of SAS Enterprise Miner.

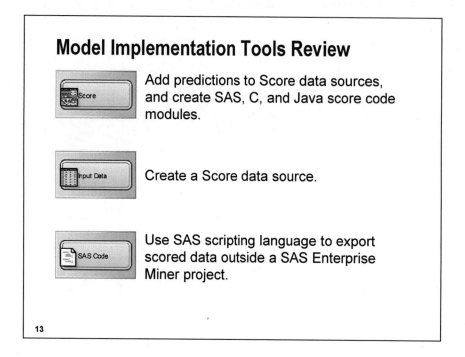

Model Implementation Tools Review

Score — Add predictions to Score data sources, and create SAS, C, and Java score code modules.

Input Data — Create a Score data source.

SAS Code — Use SAS scripting language to export scored data outside a SAS Enterprise Miner project.

13

Copyright © 2011, SAS Institute Inc., Cary, North Carolina, USA. ALL RIGHTS RESERVED.

7.5 Solutions to Exercises

1. **Scoring Organics Data**

   a. Create a Score data source for the **ScoreOrganics** data.

   1) Select **File** ⇨ **New** ⇨ **Data Source**.

   2) Proceed to step 2 of the Data Source Wizard by selecting **Next**.

   3) Select the **AAEM.SCOREORGANICS** data set.

   4) Proceed to step 7 of 8 of the Data Source Wizard.

   5) Select **Score** as the role.

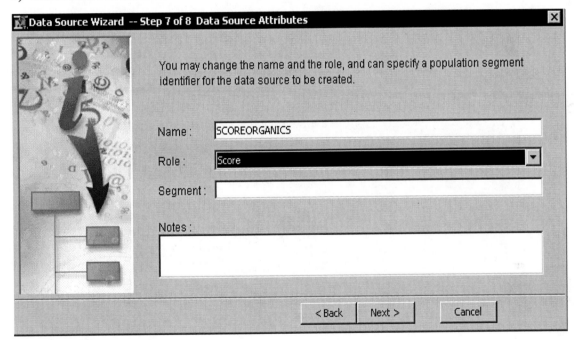

   6) Select **Next** ⇨ **Finish**.

Copyright © 2011, SAS Institute Inc., Cary, North Carolina, USA. ALL RIGHTS RESERVED.

b. Score the **ScoreOrganics** data using the model selected with the Model Comparison node.

.1) Connect a **Score** tool to the **Model Comparison** node.

2) Connect a **ScoreOrganics** data source to the **Score** node.

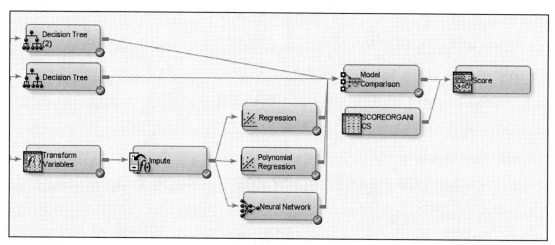

3) Run the Score node.

4) Browse the exported data from the Score node to confirm the scoring process.

	Unnormalized Into: TargetBuy	b_TargetBuy	Node	Probability for level 1 of TargetBuy	Probability of Classification	Prediction fo
1	0.0	13.0	48.0	0.1277330264672	0.87226697353279	0
2	0.0	7.0	28.0	0.23970037453183	0.76029962546816	0
3	0.0	8.0	54.0	0.20175438596491	0.79824561403508	0
4	1.0	1.0	39.0	0.93532338308457	0.93532338308457	1
5	0.0	18.0	57.0	0.0456333595594	0.95436664044059	0
6	0.0	15.0	52.0	0.05974842767295	0.94025157232704	0
7	1.0	3.0	37.0	0.53508771929824	0.53508771929824	1
8	0.0	18.0	57.0	0.0456333595594	0.95436664044059	0
9	0.0	13.0	48.0	0.1277330264672	0.87226697353279	0
10	0.0	8.0	54.0	0.20175438596491	0.79824561403508	0
11	0.0	11.0	43.0	0.15710382513661	0.84289617486338	0
12	0.0	18.0	57.0	0.0456333595594	0.95436664044059	0
13	0.0	18.0	57.0	0.0456333595594	0.95436664044059	0
14	0.0	18.0	57.0	0.0456333595594	0.95436664044059	0

EMWS2.Score_SCORE

A successfully scored data set features predicted probabilities and prediction decisions in the last three columns.

Copyright © 2011, SAS Institute Inc., Cary, North Carolina, USA. ALL RIGHTS RESERVED.

Chapter 8 Introduction to Pattern Discovery

Copyright © 2011, SAS Institute Inc., Cary, North Carolina, USA. ALL RIGHTS RESERVED.

Copyright © 2011, SAS Institute Inc., Cary, North Carolina, USA. ALL RIGHTS RESERVED.

8.1 Introduction

Pattern Discovery

The Essence of Data Mining?

"...the discovery of interesting, unexpected, or valuable structures in large data sets."

– David Hand

3   ...

There are a multitude of definitions for the field of data mining and knowledge discovery. Most center on the concept of pattern discovery. For example, David Hand, Professor of Statistics at Imperial College, London and a noted data mining authority, defines the field as "...*the discovery of interesting, unexpected, or valuable structures in large data sets.*" (Hand 2005) This is made possible by the ever-increasing data stores brought about by the era's information technology.

Copyright © 2011, SAS Institute Inc., Cary, North Carolina, USA. ALL RIGHTS RESERVED.

Pattern Discovery

The Essence of Data Mining?

"...the discovery of interesting, unexpected, or valuable structures in large data sets."

— David Hand

"If you've got terabytes of data, and you're relying on data mining to find interesting things in there for you, you've lost before you've even begun."

— Herb Edelstein

4

While Hand's pronouncement is grandly promising, experience has shown it to be overly optimistic. Herb Edelstein, President of Two Crows Corporation and an internationally recognized expert in data mining, data warehousing, and CRM, counters with the following (Beck (Editor) 1997):

> *"If you've got terabytes of data, and you're relying on data mining to find interesting things in there for you, you've lost before you've even begun. You really need people who understand what it is they are looking for – and what they can do with it once they find it."*

Many people think data mining (in particular, pattern discovery) means magically finding hidden nuggets of information without having to formulate the problem and without regard to the structure or content of the data. This is an unfortunate misconception.

Copyright © 2011, SAS Institute Inc., Cary, North Carolina, USA. ALL RIGHTS RESERVED.

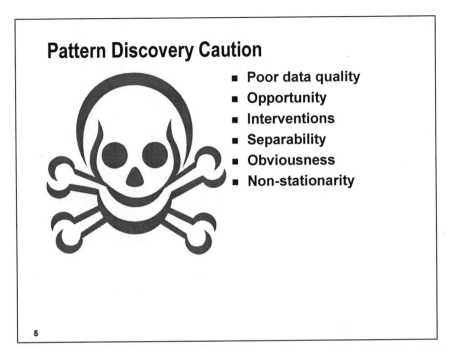

Pattern Discovery Caution

- Poor data quality
- Opportunity
- Interventions
- Separability
- Obviousness
- Non-stationarity

5

In his defense, David Hand is well aware of the limitations of pattern discovery and provides guidance on how these analyses can fail (Hand 2005). These failings often fall into one of six categories:

- **Poor data quality** assumes many guises: inaccuracies (measurement or recording errors), missing, incomplete or outdated values, and inconsistencies (changes of definition). Patterns found in false data are fantasies.

- **Opportunity** transforms the possible to the perceived. Hand refers to this as the problem of multiplicity, or the law of truly large numbers. Examples of this abound. Hand notes the odds of a person winning the lottery in the United States are extremely small and the odds of that person winning it twice are fantastically so. However, the odds of **someone in the United States** winning it twice (in a given year) are actually better than even. As another example, you can search the digits of *pi* for "prophetic" strings such as your birthday or significant dates in history and usually find them, given enough digits (**www.angio.net/pi/piquery**).

- **Intervention**, that is, taking action on the process that generates a set of data, can destroy or distort detected patterns. For example, fraud detection techniques lead to preventative measures, but the fraudulent behavior often evolves in response to this intervention.

- **Separability** of the interesting from the mundane is not always possible, given the information found in a data set. Despite the many safeguards in place, it is estimated that credit card companies lose $0.18 to $0.24 per $100 in online transactions (Rubinkam 2006).

- **Obviousness** in discovered patterns reduces the perceived utility of an analysis. Among the patterns discovered through automatic detection algorithms, you find that there is an almost equal number of married men as married women, and you learn that ovarian cancer occurs primarily in women and that check fraud occurs most often for customers with checking accounts.

- **Non-stationarity** occurs when the process that generates a data set changes of its own accord. In such circumstances, patterns detected from historic data can simply cease. As Eric Hoffer states, *"In times of change, learners inherit the Earth, while the learned find themselves beautifully equipped to deal with a world that no longer exists."*

Copyright © 2011, SAS Institute Inc., Cary, North Carolina, USA. ALL RIGHTS RESERVED.

Pattern Discovery Applications

 Data reduction

 Novelty detection

 Profiling

 Market basket analysis

 Sequence analysis

6   ...

Despite the potential pitfalls, there are many successful applications of pattern discovery:

- **Data reduction** is the most ubiquitous application, that is, exploiting patterns in data to create a more compact representation of the original. Though vastly broader in scope, data reduction includes analytic methods such as cluster analysis.

- **Novelty detection** methods seek unique or previously unobserved data patterns. The methods find application in business, science, and engineering. Business applications include fraud detection, warranty claims analysis, and general business process monitoring.

- **Profiling** is a by-product of reduction methods such as cluster analysis. The idea is to create rules that isolate clusters or segments, often based on demographic or behavioral measurements. A marketing analyst might develop profiles of a customer database to describe the consumers of a company's products.

- **Market basket analysis**, or *association rule discovery*, is used to analyze streams of transaction data (for example, market baskets) for **combinations** of items that occur (or do not occur) more (or less) commonly than expected. Retailers can use this as a way to identify interesting combinations of purchases or as predictors of customer segments.

- **Sequence analysis** is an extension of market basket analysis to include a time dimension to the analysis. In this way, transactions data is examined for **sequences** of items that occur (or do not occur) more (or less) commonly than expected. A Webmaster might use sequence analysis to identify patterns or problems of navigation through a Web site.

Copyright © 2011, SAS Institute Inc., Cary, North Carolina, USA. ALL RIGHTS RESERVED.

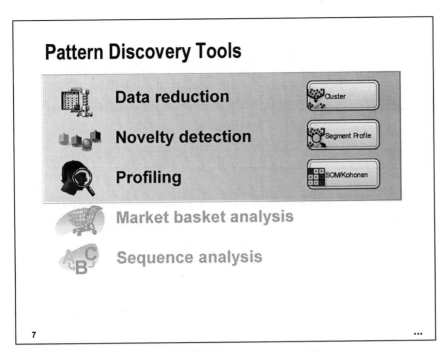

The first three pattern discovery applications are primarily served (in no particular order) by three tools in SAS Enterprise Miner: Cluster, SOM/Kohonen, and Segment Profile. The next section features a demonstration of the Cluster and Segment Profile tools.

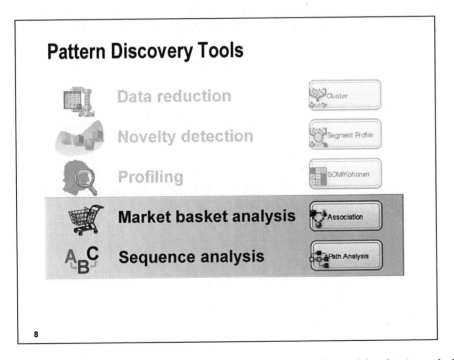

Market basket analysis and sequence analysis are performed by the Association tool. The Path Analysis tool can also be used to analyze sequence data. (An optional demonstration of the Association tool is presented at the end of this chapter.)

Copyright © 2011, SAS Institute Inc., Cary, North Carolina, USA. ALL RIGHTS RESERVED.

8.2 Cluster Analysis

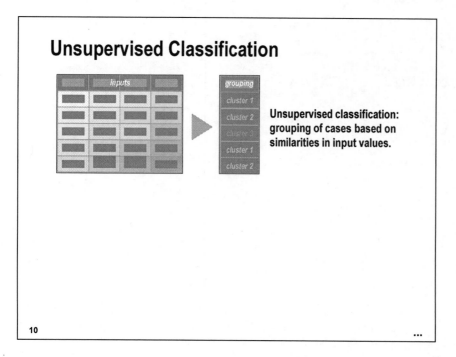

Unsupervised Classification

Unsupervised classification: grouping of cases based on similarities in input values.

10   ...

Unsupervised classification (also known as *clustering* and *segmenting*) attempts to group training data set cases based on similarities in **input** variables. It is a data reduction method because an entire training data set can be represented by a small number of clusters. The groupings are known as *clusters* or *segments*, and they can be applied to other data sets to classify new cases. It is distinguished from *supervised classification* (also known as *predictive modeling*), which is discussed in previous chapters.

The purpose of clustering is often description. For example, segmenting existing customers into groups and associating a distinct profile with each group might help future marketing strategies. However, there is no guarantee that the resulting clusters will be meaningful or useful.

Unsupervised classification is also useful as a step in predictive modeling. For example, customers can be clustered into homogenous groups based on sales of different items. Then a model can be built to predict the cluster membership based on more easily obtained input variables.

Copyright © 2011, SAS Institute Inc., Cary, North Carolina, USA. ALL RIGHTS RESERVED.

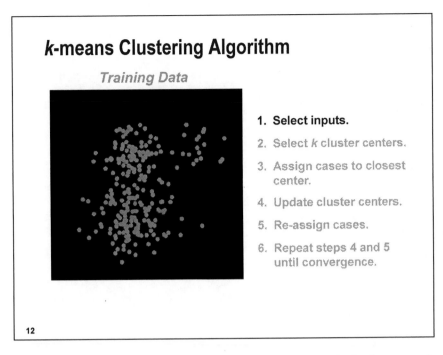

k-means Clustering Algorithm

Training Data

1. **Select inputs.**
2. Select *k* cluster centers.
3. Assign cases to closest center.
4. Update cluster centers.
5. Re-assign cases.
6. Repeat steps 4 and 5 until convergence.

12

One of the most commonly used methods for clustering is the *k-means algorithm*. It is a straightforward algorithm that scales well to large data sets and is, therefore, the primary tool for clustering in SAS Enterprise Miner.

While often overlooked as an important part of a clustering process, the first step in using the *k*-means algorithm is to choose a set of inputs. In general, you should seek inputs that have the following attributes:

- are meaningful to the analysis objective
- are relatively independent
- are limited in number
- have a measurement level of Interval
- have low kurtosis and skewness statistics (at least in the training data)

Choosing meaningful inputs is clearly important for interpretation and explanation of the generated clusters. Independence and limited input count make the resulting clusters more stable. (Small perturbations of training data usually do not result in large changes to the generated clusters.) An interval measurement level is recommended for *k*-means to produce non-trivial clusters. Low kurtosis and skewness statistics on the inputs avoid creating single-case outlier clusters.

Copyright © 2011, SAS Institute Inc., Cary, North Carolina, USA. ALL RIGHTS RESERVED.

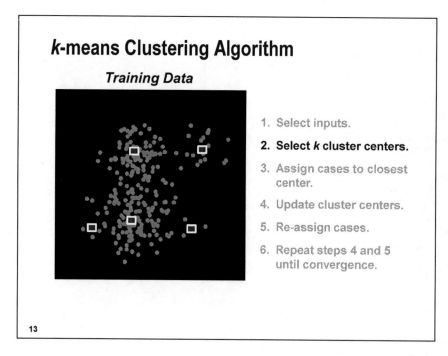

The next step in the k-means algorithm is to choose a value for k, the number of cluster centers. SAS Enterprise Miner features an automatic way to do this, assuming that the data has k distinct concentrations of cases. If this is not the case, you should choose k to be consistent with your analytic objectives.

With k selected, the k-means algorithm chooses cases to represent the initial *cluster centers* (also named *seeds*).

Copyright © 2011, SAS Institute Inc., Cary, North Carolina, USA. ALL RIGHTS RESERVED.

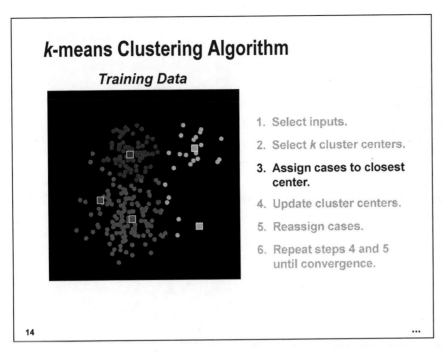

The Euclidean distance from each case in the training data to each cluster center is calculated. Cases are assigned to the closest cluster center.

   Because the distance metric is Euclidean, it is important for the inputs to have compatible measurement scales. Unexpected results can occur if one input's measurement scale differs greatly from the others.

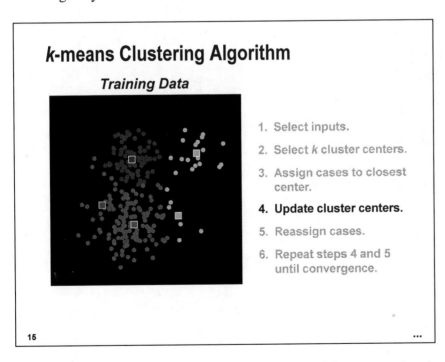

The cluster centers are updated to equal the average of the cases assigned to the cluster in the previous step.

Copyright © 2011, SAS Institute Inc., Cary, North Carolina, USA. ALL RIGHTS RESERVED.

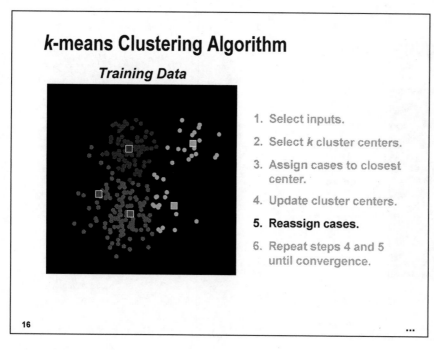

Cases are reassigned to the closest cluster center.

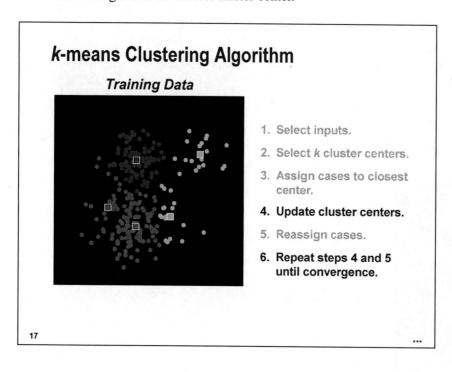

Copyright © 2011, SAS Institute Inc., Cary, North Carolina, USA. ALL RIGHTS RESERVED.

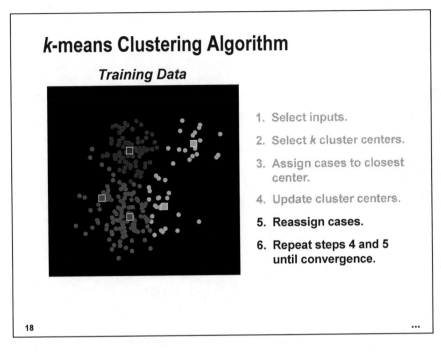

The update and reassign steps are repeated until the process converges.

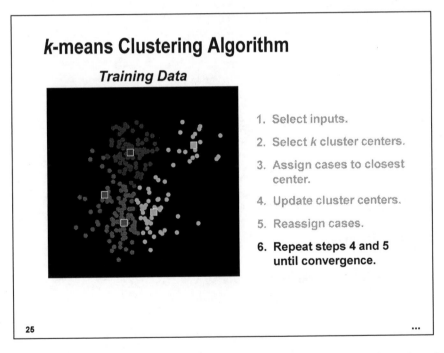

On convergence, final cluster assignments are made. Each case is assigned to a unique segment. The segment definitions can be stored and applied to new cases outside of the training data.

Copyright © 2011, SAS Institute Inc., Cary, North Carolina, USA. ALL RIGHTS RESERVED.

Segmentation Analysis

Training Data

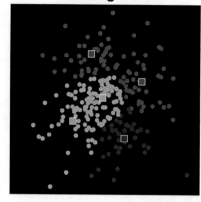

When no clusters exist, use the *k*-means algorithm to partition cases into contiguous groups.

27

While they are often used synonymously, a segmentation analysis is distinct from a traditional cluster analysis. A cluster analysis is geared toward identifying distinct concentrations of cases in a data set. When no distinct concentrations exist, the best you can do is a segmentation analysis – that is, algorithmically partitioning the input space into contiguous groups of cases.

8.01 Multiple Choice Poll

For a *k*-means clustering analysis, which of the following statements is true about input variables?

a. Input variables should be limited in number and be relatively independent.

b. Input variables should be of interval measurement level.

c. Input variables should have distributions that are somewhat symmetric.

d. Input variables should be meaningful to analysis objectives.

e. All of the above.

29

Copyright © 2011, SAS Institute Inc., Cary, North Carolina, USA. ALL RIGHTS RESERVED.

Demographic Segmentation Demonstration

Analysis goal:

Group geographic regions into segments based on:
income, **household size**, and **population density**.

Analysis plan:

- **Select and transform segmentation inputs.**
- **Select the number of segments to create.**
- **Create segments with the Cluster tool.**
- **Interpret the segments.**

31

The following demonstration illustrates the use of clustering tools. The goal of the analysis is to group people in the United States into distinct subsets based on urbanization, household size, and income factors. These factors are common to commercial lifestyle and life-stage segmentation products. (For examples, see **www.claritas.com** or **www.spectramarketing.com**.)

Copyright © 2011, SAS Institute Inc., Cary, North Carolina, USA. ALL RIGHTS RESERVED.

Segmenting Census Data

This demonstration introduces SAS Enterprise Miner tools and techniques for cluster and segmentation analysis. There are five parts:

- define the diagram and data source
- explore and filter the training data
- integrate the Cluster tool into the process flow and select the number of segments to create
- run a segmentation analysis
- use the Segment Profile tool to interpret the analysis results

Diagram Definition

Use the following steps to define the diagram for the segmentation analysis.

1. Right-click **Diagrams** in the Project panel and select **Create Diagram**. The Create New Diagram window appears and requests a diagram name.

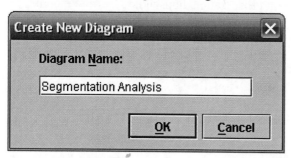

2. Type **Segmentation Analysis** in the **Diagram Name** field and select **OK**. SAS Enterprise Miner creates an analysis workspace window named Segmentation Analysis.

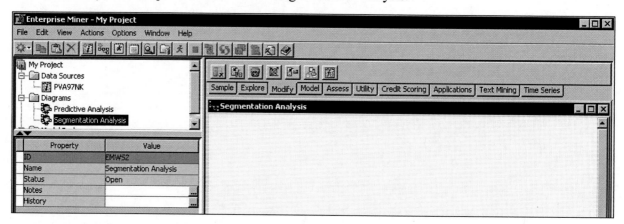

You use the Segmentation Analysis window to create process flow diagrams.

Copyright © 2011, SAS Institute Inc., Cary, North Carolina, USA. ALL RIGHTS RESERVED.

Data Source Definition

Follow these steps to create the segmentation analysis data source.

1. Right-click **Data Sources** in the Project panel and select **Create Data Source**. The Data Source Wizard appears.

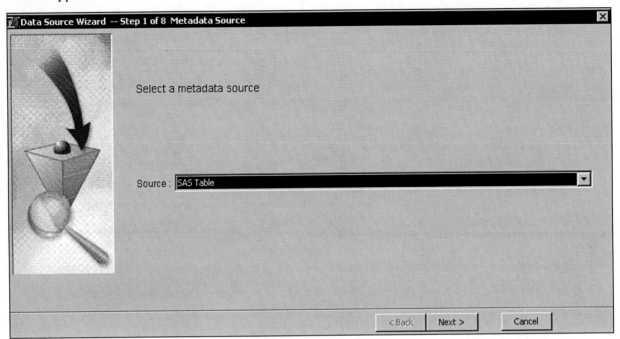

The Data Source Wizard guides you through a process to create a SAS Enterprise Miner data source.

2. Select **Next** to use a SAS table as the source for the metadata. (This is the usual choice.)

    In this step, select the SAS table that you want to make available to SAS Enterprise Miner. You can either type the library name and SAS table name as *libname.table-name* or select the SAS table from a list.

Copyright © 2011, SAS Institute Inc., Cary, North Carolina, USA. ALL RIGHTS RESERVED.

3. Select **Browse** to choose a SAS table from the libraries visible to the SAS Foundation server.

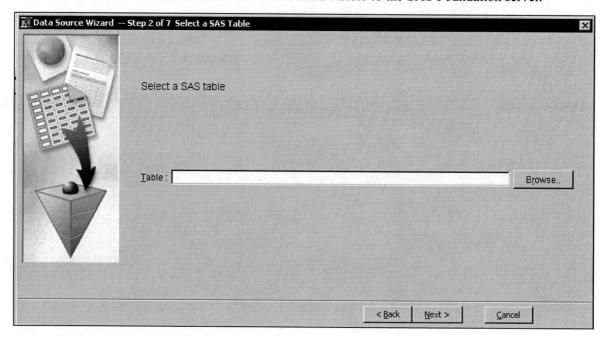

The Select a SAS Table dialog box appears.

One of the libraries listed is named AAEM, which is the library name defined in Chapter 2.

Select **Aaem** and the **Census2000** SAS table.

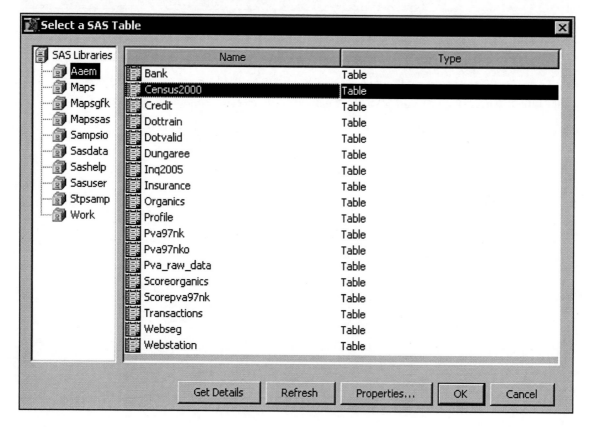

Copyright © 2011, SAS Institute Inc., Cary, North Carolina, USA. ALL RIGHTS RESERVED.

The **Census2000** data is a postal code-level summary of the entire 2000 United States Census. It features seven variables:

ID	postal code of the region
LOCX	region longitude
LOCY	region latitude
MEANHHSZ	average household size in the region
MEDHHINC	median household income in the region
REGDENS	region population density percentile (1=lowest density, 100=highest density)
REGPOP	number of people in the region

The data is suited for creation of life-stage, lifestyle segments using SAS Enterprise Miner's pattern discovery tools.

4. Select **OK**.

The Select a SAS Table dialog box closes and the selected table is entered in the **Table** field.

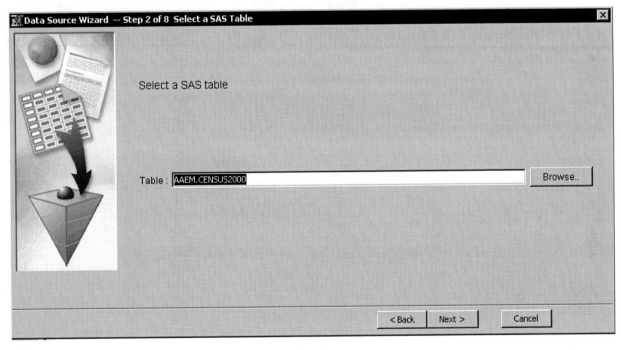

5. Select **Next** in two consecutive windows.

Copyright © 2011, SAS Institute Inc., Cary, North Carolina, USA. ALL RIGHTS RESERVED.

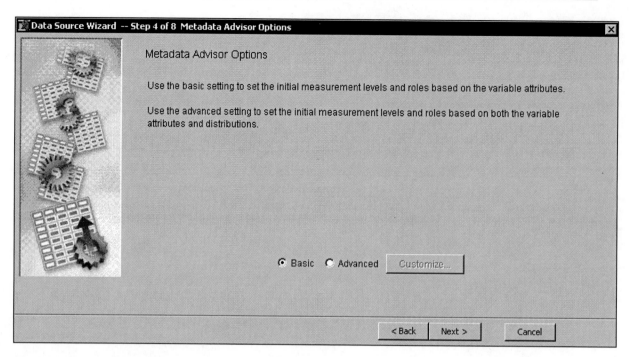

The Data Source Wizard starts the metadata definition process. SAS Enterprise Miner assigns initial values to the metadata based on characteristics of the selected SAS table. The Basic setting assigns initial values to the metadata based on variable attributes such as the variable name, data type, and assigned SAS format. The Advanced setting also includes information about the distribution of the variable to assign the initial metadata values.

Copyright © 2011, SAS Institute Inc., Cary, North Carolina, USA. ALL RIGHTS RESERVED.

6. Select **Next** to use the Basic setting.

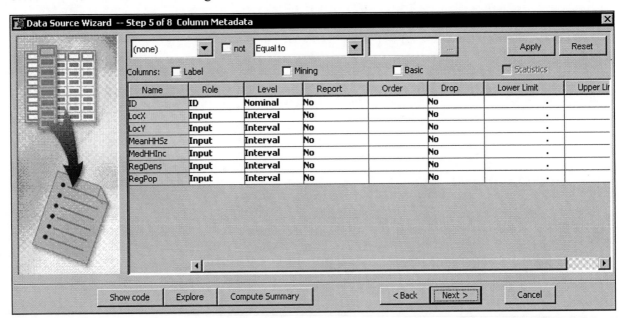

The Data Source Wizard enables you to specify the role and level for each variable in the selected SAS table. A default role is assigned based on the name of a variable. For example, the variable **ID** was given the role ID based on its name. When a variable does not have a name corresponding to one of the possible variable roles, it will, using the Basic setting, be given the default role of Input. An input variable is used for various types of analysis to describe a characteristic, measurement, or attribute of a record, or *case*, in a SAS table.

The metadata settings are correct for the upcoming analysis.

7. Select **Next** until you reach Step 7. This is the second-to-last step in the Data Source Wizard.

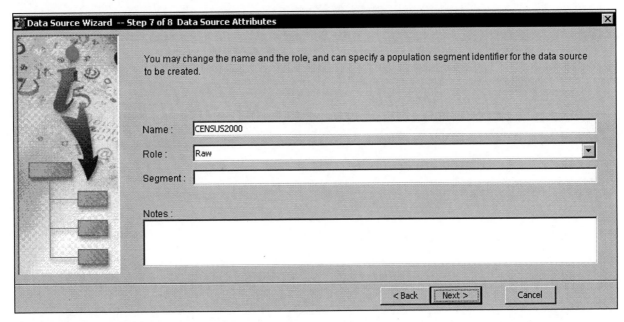

The Data Source Wizard enables you to set a role for the selected SAS table and provide descriptive comments about the data source definition.

Copyright © 2011, SAS Institute Inc., Cary, North Carolina, USA. ALL RIGHTS RESERVED.

For the impending analysis, a table role of Raw is acceptable.

8. Select **Finish** to complete the data source definition. The **CENSUS2000** table is added to the Data Sources entry in the Project panel.

Copyright © 2011, SAS Institute Inc., Cary, North Carolina, USA. ALL RIGHTS RESERVED.

Exploring and Filtering Analysis Data

A worthwhile next step in the process of defining a data source is to explore and validate its contents. By assaying the prepared data, you substantially reduce the chances of erroneous results in your analysis, and you can gain insights graphically into associations between variables.

Data Source Exploration

1. Right-click the **CENSUS2000** data source and select **Edit Variables** from the shortcut menu. The Variables - CENSUS2000 dialog box appears.

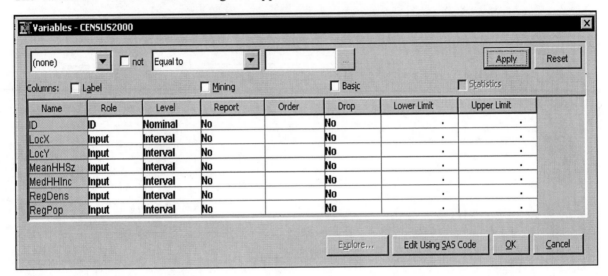

2. Examine histograms for the available variables.

3. Select all listed inputs by dragging the cursor across all of the input names or by holding down the CTRL key and typing A.

Copyright © 2011, SAS Institute Inc., Cary, North Carolina, USA. ALL RIGHTS RESERVED.

4. Select **Explore**. The Explore window appears, and this time displays histograms for all of the
    variables in the **CENSUS2000** data source.

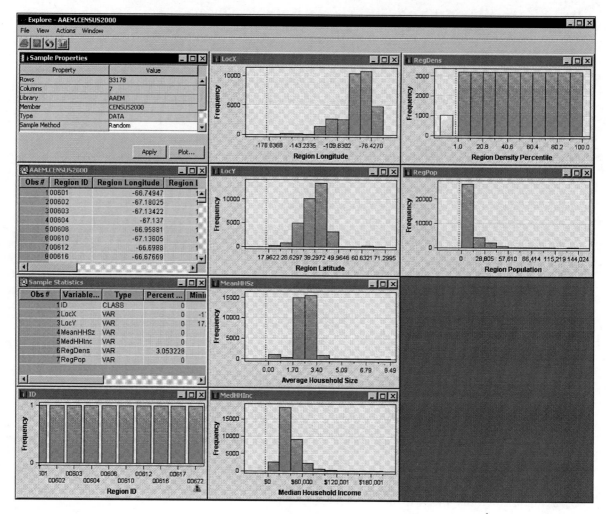

Copyright © 2011, SAS Institute Inc., Cary, North Carolina, USA. ALL RIGHTS RESERVED.

5. Maximize the **MeanHHSz** histogram by double-clicking its title bar. The histogram now fills the Explore window.

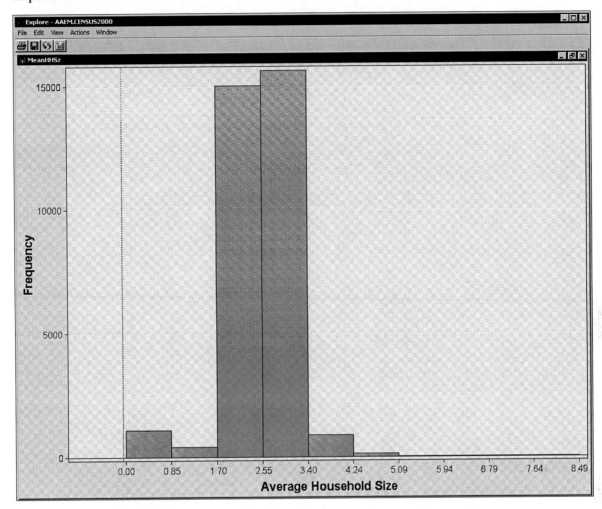

As before, increasing the number of histogram bins from the default of 10 increases your understanding of the data.

6. Right-click in the histogram window and select **Graph Properties** from the shortcut menu. The Properties - Histogram dialog box appears.

You can use the Properties - Histogram dialog box to change the appearance of the corresponding histogram. Type **100** in the **Number of X Bins** field and select **OK**.

Copyright © 2011, SAS Institute Inc., Cary, North Carolina, USA. ALL RIGHTS RESERVED.

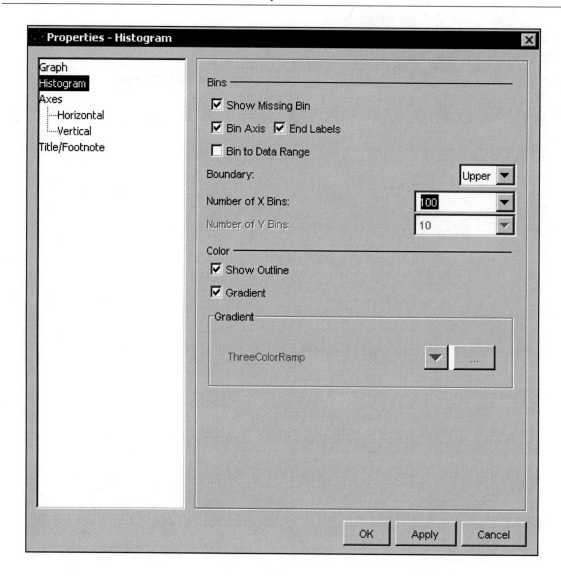

Copyright © 2011, SAS Institute Inc., Cary, North Carolina, USA. ALL RIGHTS RESERVED.

The histogram is updated to show 100 bins.

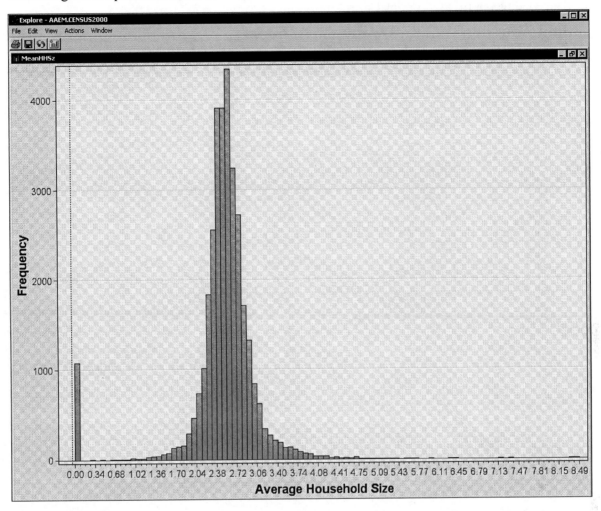

There is a curious spike in the histogram at (or near) zero. A zero household size does not make sense in the context of census data.

7. Select the bar near zero in the histogram.

Copyright © 2011, SAS Institute Inc., Cary, North Carolina, USA. ALL RIGHTS RESERVED.

8.   Restore the size of the window by double-clicking the title bar of the MeanHHSz window.
     The window returns to its original size.

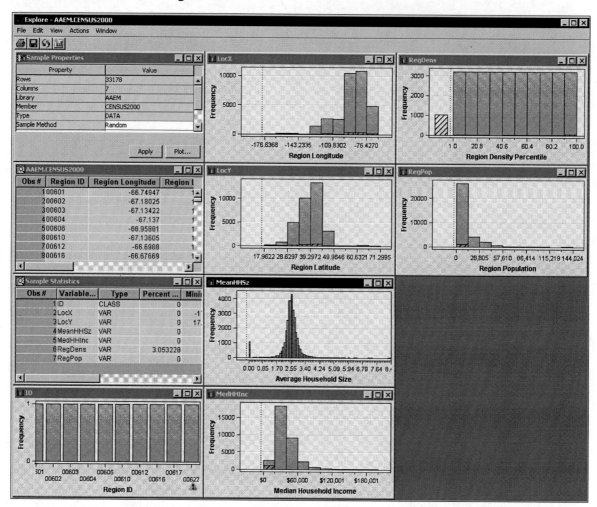

The zero average household size seems to be evenly distributed across the longitude, latitude, and
density percentile variables. It seems concentrated on low incomes and populations, and also makes
up the majority of the missing observations in the distribution of Region Density. It is worthwhile
to look at the individual records of the explore sample.

Copyright © 2011, SAS Institute Inc., Cary, North Carolina, USA. ALL RIGHTS RESERVED.

9. Maximize the **CENSUS2000** data table.

10. Scroll in the data table until you see the first selected row.

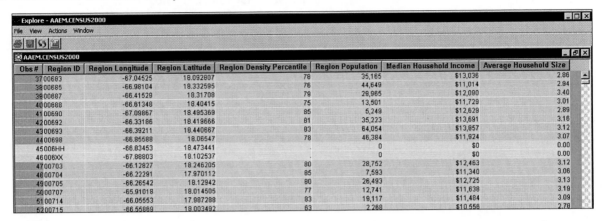

Records 45 and 46 (among others) have the zero Average Household Size characteristic. Other fields in these records also have unusual values.

11. Select the **Average Household Size** column heading twice to sort the table by ascending values in this field. Cases of interest are collected at the top of the data table.

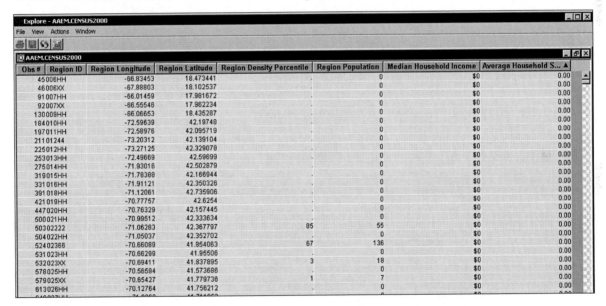

Most of the cases with zero Average Household Size have zero or missing on the remaining non-geographic attributes. There are some exceptions, but it could be argued that cases such as this are not of interest for analyzing household demographics. The next part of this demonstration shows how to remove cases such as this from the subsequent analyses.

12. Close the Explore and Variables windows.

Copyright © 2011, SAS Institute Inc., Cary, North Carolina, USA. ALL RIGHTS RESERVED.

Case Filtering

The SAS Enterprise Miner Filter tool enables you to remove unwanted records from an analysis. Use these steps to build a diagram to read a data source and to filter records.

1. Drag the **CENSUS2000** data source to the Segmentation Analysis workspace window.

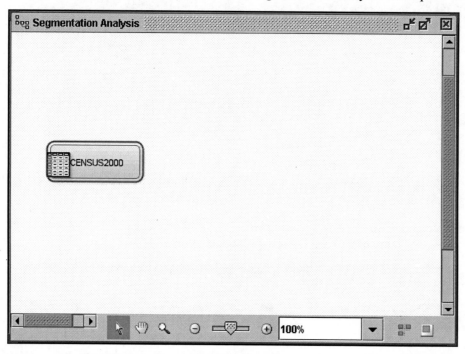

2. Select the **Sample** tab to access the Sample tool group.

3. Drag the **Filter** tool (fourth from the left) from the tools pallet into the Segmentation Analysis workspace window and connect it to the **CENSUS2000** data source.

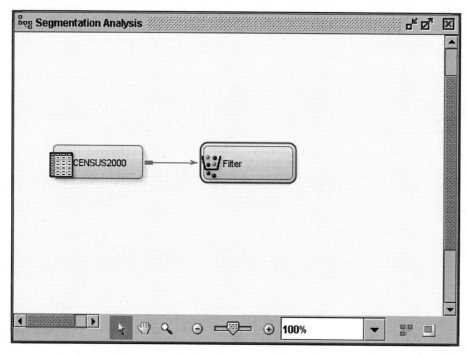

Copyright © 2011, SAS Institute Inc., Cary, North Carolina, USA. ALL RIGHTS RESERVED.

4. Select the **Filter** node and examine the Properties panel.

Property	Value
General	
Node ID	Filter
Imported Data	...
Exported Data	...
Notes	...
Train	
Export Table	Filtered
Tables to Filter	Training Data
Distribution Data Sets	Yes
⊟ Class Variables	
┈Class Variables	...
┈Default Filtering Method	Rare Values (Percentage)
┈Keep Missing Values	Yes
┈Normalized Values	Yes
┈Minimum Frequency Cutoff	1
┈Minimum Cutoff for Percentage	0.01
┈Maximum Number of Levels Cutoff	25
⊟ Interval Variables	
┈Interval Variables	...
┈Default Filtering Method	Standard Deviations from the Mean
┈Keep Missing Values	Yes
┈Tuning Parameters	...
Score	
Create score code	Yes
Update Measurement Level	No

Based on the values of the Properties panel, the node will, by default, filter cases in rare levels in any class input variable and cases exceeding three standard deviations from the mean on any interval input variable.

Because the **CENSUS2000** data source only contains interval inputs, only the Interval Variables criterion is considered.

5. Change the Default Filtering Method property to **User-Specified Limits**.

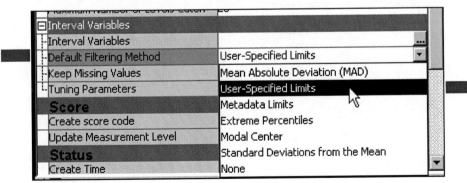

Copyright © 2011, SAS Institute Inc., Cary, North Carolina, USA. ALL RIGHTS RESERVED.

6. Select the Interval Variables ellipsis (**…**). The Interactive Interval Filter window appears.

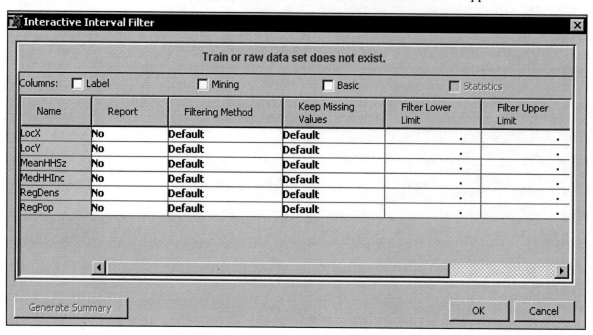

You are warned at the top of the dialog box that the Train or raw data set does not exist. This indicates that you are restricted from the interactive filtering elements of the node, which are available after a node is run. You can, nevertheless, enter filtering information.

7. Type **0.1** as the Filter Lower Limit value for the input variable **MeanHHSz**.

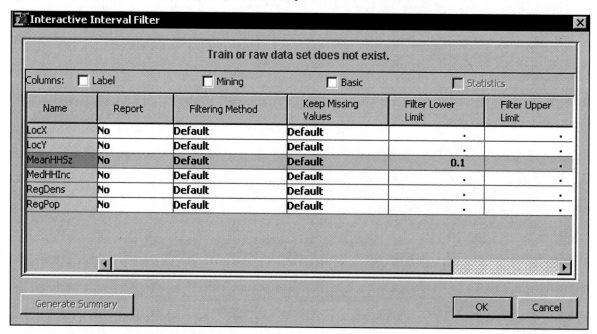

8. Select **OK** to close the Interactive Interval Filter dialog box. You are returned to the SAS Enterprise Miner interface window.

All cases with an average household size less than 0.1 will be filtered from subsequent analysis steps.

Copyright © 2011, SAS Institute Inc., Cary, North Carolina, USA. ALL RIGHTS RESERVED.

9. Run the Filter node and view the results. The Results window appears.

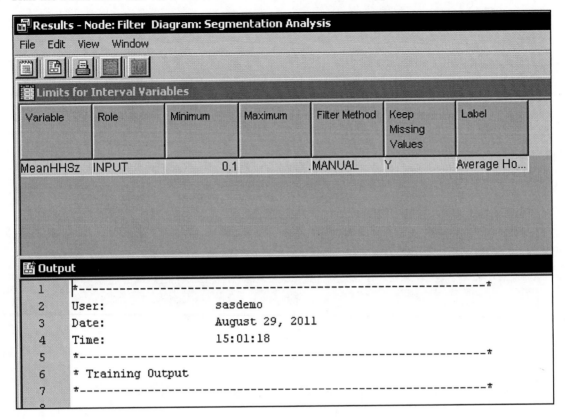

10. Go to line 38 in the Output window.

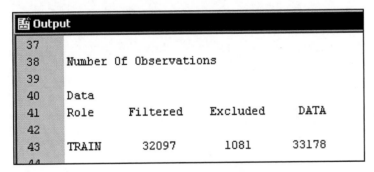

The Filter node removed 1081 cases with a household size of zero.

11. Close the Results window. The **CENSUS2000** data is ready for segmentation.

Copyright © 2011, SAS Institute Inc., Cary, North Carolina, USA. ALL RIGHTS RESERVED.

Setting Cluster Tool Options

The Cluster tool performs *k*-means cluster analyses, a widely used method for cluster and segmentation analysis. This demonstration shows you how to use the tool to segment the cases in the **CENSUS2000** data set.

1. Select the **Explore** tab.

2. Locate and drag a **Cluster** tool into the diagram workspace.

3. Connect the **Filter** node to the **Cluster** node.

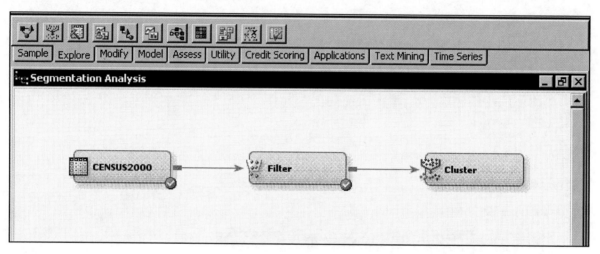

To create meaningful segments, you need to set the Cluster node to do the following:

*   ignore irrelevant inputs
*   standardize the inputs to have a similar range

4. Select the **Variables** property for the Cluster node. The Variables window appears.

Copyright © 2011, SAS Institute Inc., Cary, North Carolina, USA. ALL RIGHTS RESERVED.

5. Select **Use** ⇨ **No** for **LocX**, **LocY**, and **RegPop**.

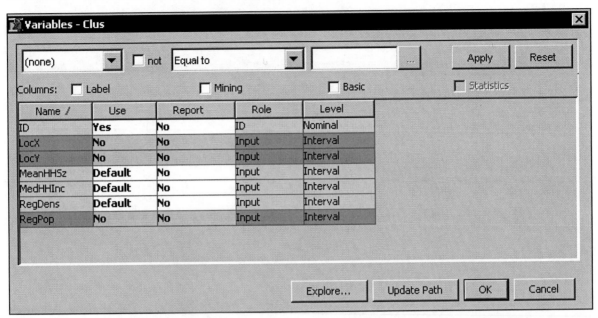

The Cluster node creates segments using the inputs **MedHHInc**, **MeanHHSz**, and **RegDens**.

Segments are created based on the (Euclidean) distance between each case in the space of selected inputs. If you want to use all the inputs to create clusters, these inputs should have similar measurement scales. Calculating distances using standardized distance measurements (subtracting the mean and dividing by the standard deviation of the input values) is one way to ensure this. You can standardize the input measurements using the Transform Variables node. However, it is easier to use the built-in property in the Cluster node.

Copyright © 2011, SAS Institute Inc., Cary, North Carolina, USA. ALL RIGHTS RESERVED.

6.   Select the inputs **MedHHInc**, **MeanHHSz**, and **RegDens** and select **Explore**. The Explore window appears.

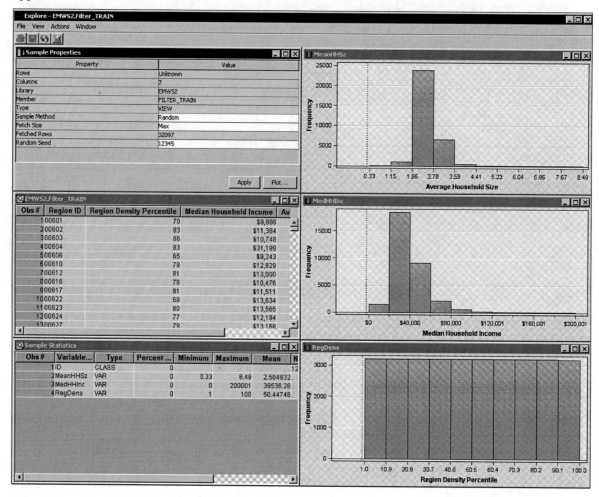

The inputs that are selected for use in the cluster are on three entirely different measurement scales. They need to be standardized if you want a meaningful clustering.

7.   Close the Explore window.

8.   Select **OK** to close the Variables window.

Copyright © 2011, SAS Institute Inc., Cary, North Carolina, USA. ALL RIGHTS RESERVED.

9. Note the default setting for Internal Standardization: **Internal Standardization ⇨ Standardization**. No change is required because standardization will be performed on input variables. Distances between points are calculated based on standardized measurements.

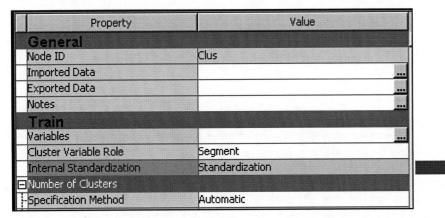

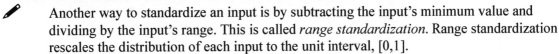

Another way to standardize an input is by subtracting the input's minimum value and dividing by the input's range. This is called *range standardization*. Range standardization rescales the distribution of each input to the unit interval, [0,1].

The Cluster node is ready to run.

Copyright © 2011, SAS Institute Inc., Cary, North Carolina, USA. ALL RIGHTS RESERVED.

Creating Clusters with the Cluster Tool

By default, the Cluster tool attempts to automatically determine the number of clusters in the data. A three-step process is used.

Step 1   A large number of cluster seeds are chosen (50 by default) and placed in the input space. Cases in the training data are assigned to the closest seed, and an initial clustering of the data is completed. The means of the input variables in each of these preliminary clusters are substituted for the original training data cases in the second step of the process.

Step 2   A hierarchical clustering algorithm (Ward's method) is used to sequentially consolidate the clusters that were formed in the first step. At each step of the consolidation, a statistic named the *cubic clustering criterion* (CCC) (Sarle 1983) is calculated. Then, the smallest number of clusters that meets both of the following criteria is selected:

- The number of clusters must be greater than or equal to the number that is specified as the minimum value in the Selection Criterion properties.

- The number of clusters must have cubic clustering criterion statistic values that are greater than the CCC threshold that is specified in the Selection Criterion properties.

Step 3   The number of clusters determined by the second step provides the value for k in a k-means clustering of the original training data cases.

Copyright © 2011, SAS Institute Inc., Cary, North Carolina, USA. ALL RIGHTS RESERVED.

1. Run the Cluster node and select **Results**. The Results - Cluster window appears.

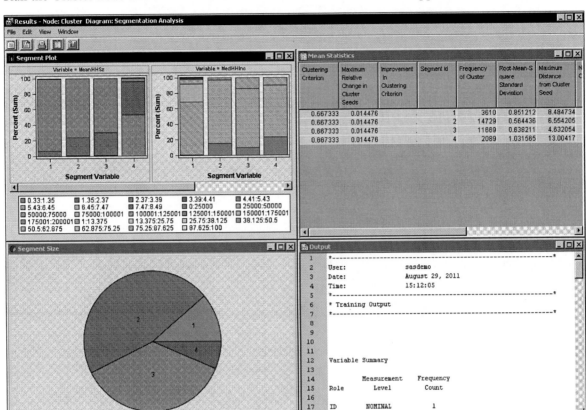

The Results - Cluster window contains four embedded windows.

- The Segment Plot window attempts to show the distribution of each input variable by cluster.
- The Mean Statistics window lists various descriptive statistics by cluster.
- The Segment Size window shows a pie chart describing the size of each cluster formed.
- The Output window shows the output of various SAS procedures run by the Cluster node.

Apparently, the Cluster node found four clusters in the **CENSUS2000** data. Because the number of clusters is based on the cubic clustering criterion, it might be interesting to examine the values of this statistic for various cluster counts.

Copyright © 2011, SAS Institute Inc., Cary, North Carolina, USA. ALL RIGHTS RESERVED.

2. Select **View** ⇨ **Summary Statistics** ⇨ **CCC Plot**. The CCC Plot window appears.

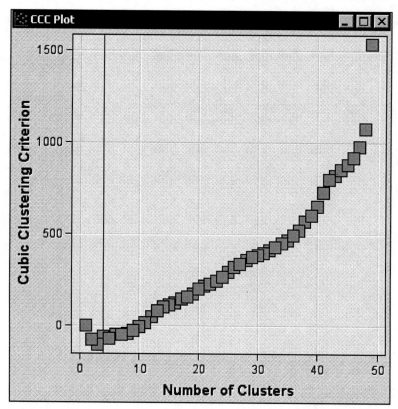

In theory, the number of clusters in a data set is revealed by the peak of the CCC versus Number of Clusters plot. However, when no distinct concentrations of data exist, the utility of the CCC statistic is somewhat suspect. SAS Enterprise Miner attempts to establish reasonable defaults for its analysis tools. The appropriateness of these defaults, however, strongly depends on the analysis objective and the nature of the data.

Copyright © 2011, SAS Institute Inc., Cary, North Carolina, USA. ALL RIGHTS RESERVED.

Specifying the Segment Count

You might want to increase the number of clusters created by the Cluster node. You can do this by changing the CCC cutoff property or by specifying the desired number of clusters.

1. In the Properties panel for the Cluster node, select **Specification Method** ⇨ **User Specify**.

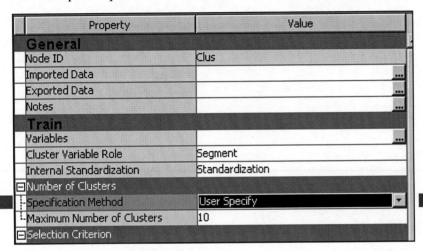

The User Specify setting creates a number of segments indicated by the Maximum Number of Clusters property (in this case, 10).

Copyright © 2011, SAS Institute Inc., Cary, North Carolina, USA. ALL RIGHTS RESERVED.

2. Run the Cluster node and select **Results**. The Results - Node: Cluster Diagram window appears, and
    shows a total of 10 generated segments.

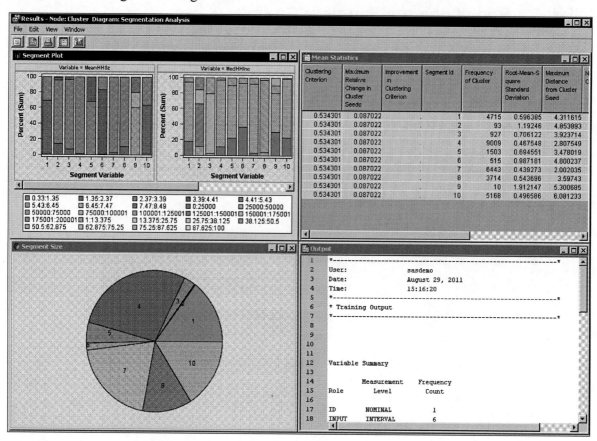

As seen in the Mean Statistics window, segment frequency counts vary from 10 cases to more than
9,000 cases.

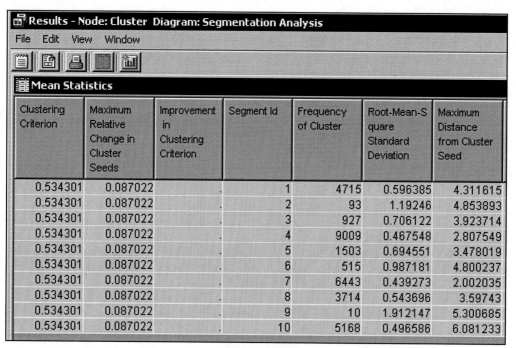

Clustering Criterion	Maximum Relative Change in Cluster Seeds	Improvement in Clustering Criterion	Segment Id	Frequency of Cluster	Root-Mean-Square Standard Deviation	Maximum Distance from Cluster Seed
0.534301	0.087022	.	1	4715	0.596385	4.311615
0.534301	0.087022	.	2	93	1.19246	4.853893
0.534301	0.087022	.	3	927	0.706122	3.923714
0.534301	0.087022	.	4	9009	0.467548	2.807549
0.534301	0.087022	.	5	1503	0.694551	3.478019
0.534301	0.087022	.	6	515	0.987181	4.800237
0.534301	0.087022	.	7	6443	0.439273	2.002035
0.534301	0.087022	.	8	3714	0.543696	3.59743
0.534301	0.087022	.	9	10	1.912147	5.300685
0.534301	0.087022		10	5168	0.496586	6.081233

Copyright © 2011, SAS Institute Inc., Cary, North Carolina, USA. ALL RIGHTS RESERVED.

Exploring Segments

While the Results window shows a variety of data summarizing the analysis, it is difficult to understand the composition of the generated clusters. If the number of cluster inputs is small, the Graph wizard can aid in interpreting the cluster analysis.

1. Close the Results - Cluster window.

2. Select **Exported Data** from the Properties panel for the Cluster node. The Exported Data - Cluster window appears.

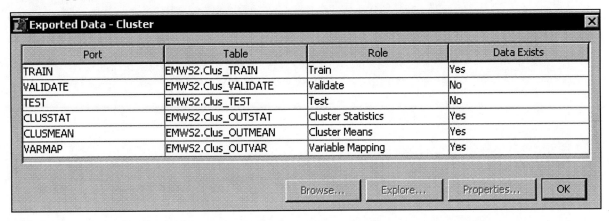

Port	Table	Role	Data Exists
TRAIN	EMWS2.Clus_TRAIN	Train	Yes
VALIDATE	EMWS2.Clus_VALIDATE	Validate	No
TEST	EMWS2.Clus_TEST	Test	No
CLUSSTAT	EMWS2.Clus_OUTSTAT	Cluster Statistics	Yes
CLUSMEAN	EMWS2.Clus_OUTMEAN	Cluster Means	Yes
VARMAP	EMWS2.Clus_OUTVAR	Variable Mapping	Yes

Browse...   Explore...   Properties...   OK

This window shows the data sets that are generated and exported by the Cluster node.

Copyright © 2011, SAS Institute Inc., Cary, North Carolina, USA. ALL RIGHTS RESERVED.

3. Select the **Train** data set and select **Explore**. The Explore window appears.

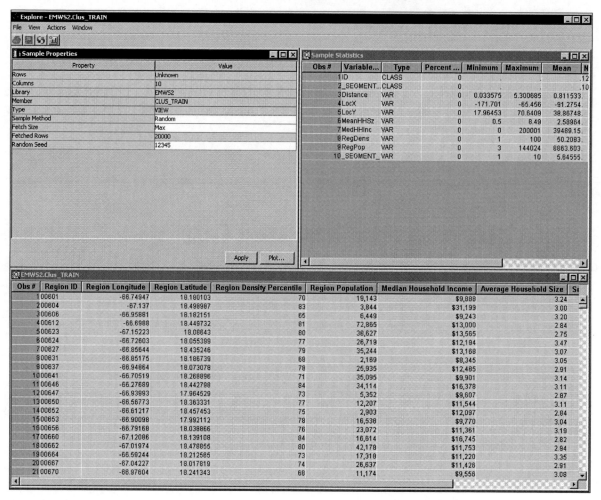

You can use the Graph wizard to generate plots of the **CENSUS2000** data.

Copyright © 2011, SAS Institute Inc., Cary, North Carolina, USA. ALL RIGHTS RESERVED.

4. Select **Actions** ⇨ **Plot**. The Select a Chart Type window appears. Select **Scatter** to create a scatter plot.

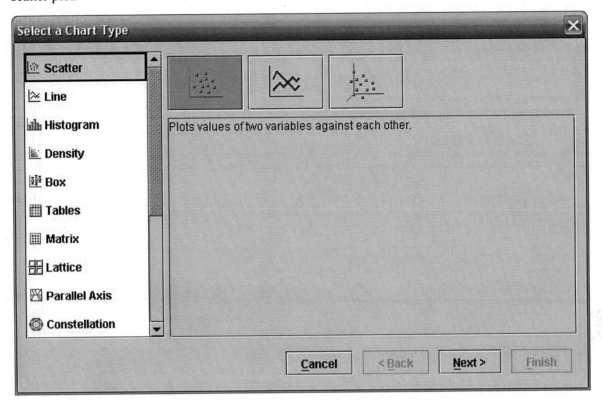

5. Select **Next**. The Graph wizard proceeds to the next step, Select Chart Roles.

Copyright © 2011, SAS Institute Inc., Cary, North Carolina, USA. ALL RIGHTS RESERVED.

6. Select roles of **X, Y,** for **LocX, LocY.** Select **Color** as the role for **_SEGMENT_.** And select **Tip** as the role for**MeanHHSz, MedHHInc,** and **RegDens..** Allow multiple role assignments by selecting the box at the bottom of the table.

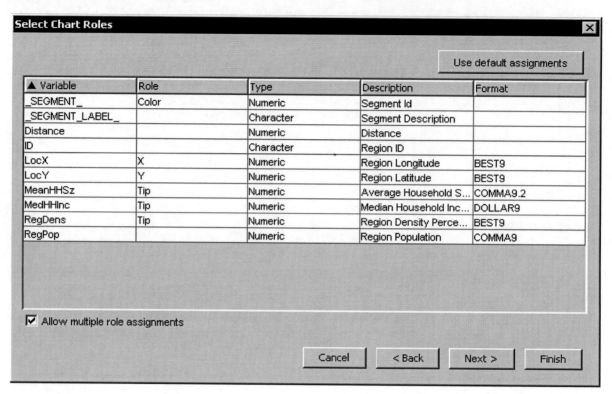

▲ Variable	Role	Type	Description	Format
SEGMENT	Color	Numeric	Segment Id	
_SEGMENT_LABEL_		Character	Segment Description	
Distance		Numeric	Distance	
ID		Character	Region ID	
LocX	X	Numeric	Region Longitude	BEST9
LocY	Y	Numeric	Region Latitude	BEST9
MeanHHSz	Tip	Numeric	Average Household S...	COMMA9.2
MedHHInc	Tip	Numeric	Median Household Inc...	DOLLAR9
RegDens	Tip	Numeric	Region Density Perce...	BEST9
RegPop		Numeric	Region Population	COMMA9

☑ Allow multiple role assignments

7. Select **Finish**.

Copyright © 2011, SAS Institute Inc., Cary, North Carolina, USA. ALL RIGHTS RESERVED.

The Explore window displays a plot of the **CENSUS2000** data.

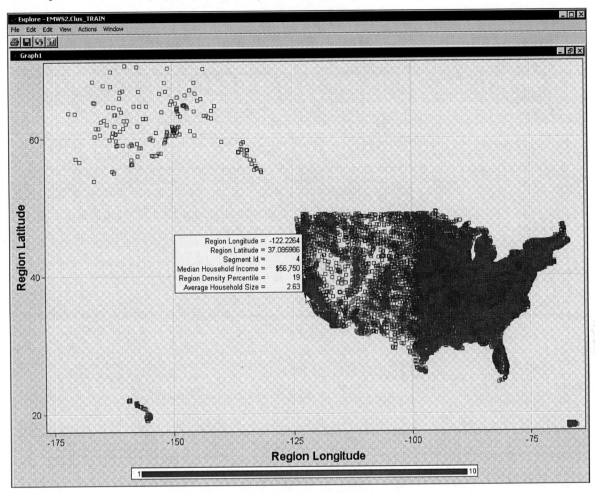

8. Display the tool tips by holding the cursor over a point in the plot.

Each square in the plot represents a unique postal code. The squares are color-coded by cluster segment.

Right-click in the plot to modify graph properties such as marker size and colors.

Copyright © 2011, SAS Institute Inc., Cary, North Carolina, USA. ALL RIGHTS RESERVED.

To further aid interpretability, add a distribution plot of the segment number.

1. Select **Action** ⇨ **Plot…**. The Select a Chart Type window appears.

2. Select **Bar**.

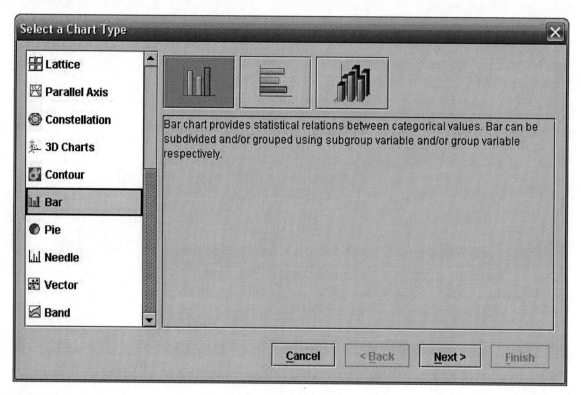

3. Select **Next**.

4. Select **Role** ⇨ **Category** for the variable **_SEGMENT_**.

Copyright © 2011, SAS Institute Inc., Cary, North Carolina, USA. ALL RIGHTS RESERVED.

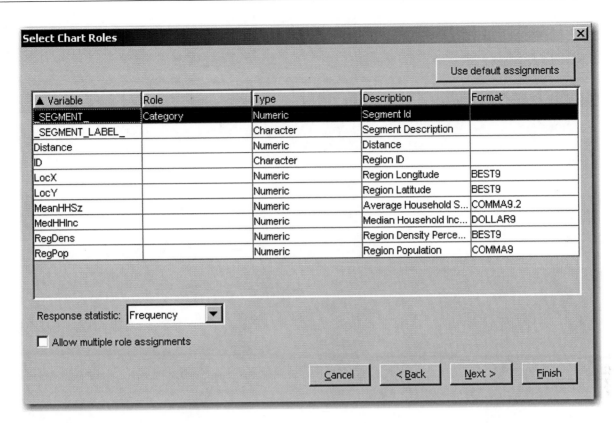

5. Select **Finish**.

Copyright © 2011, SAS Institute Inc., Cary, North Carolina, USA. ALL RIGHTS RESERVED.

A histogram of **_SEGMENT_** is displayed.

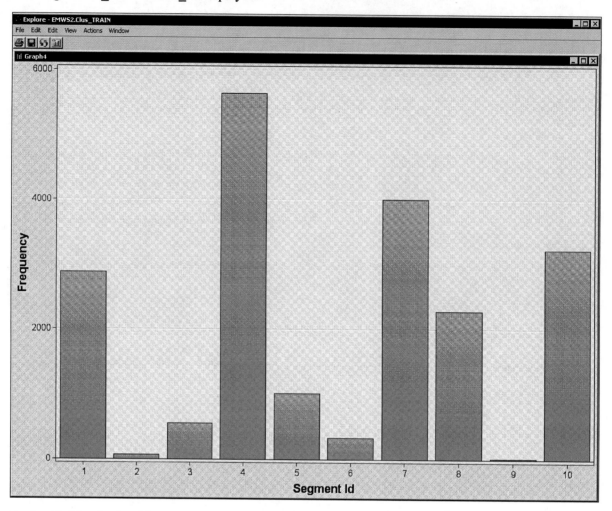

By itself, this plot is of limited use. However, when the plot is combined with the plot using latitude and longitude, you can easily interpret the generated segments in a two-dimensional plot of the USA.

Copyright © 2011, SAS Institute Inc., Cary, North Carolina, USA. ALL RIGHTS RESERVED.

6. Select **Window** ⇨ **Tile** to show both graphs after deleting the other tables from the Explore window. Drag the cursor over a segment of the plot of the USA and notice that the cluster segments in this area are highlighted in the histogram.

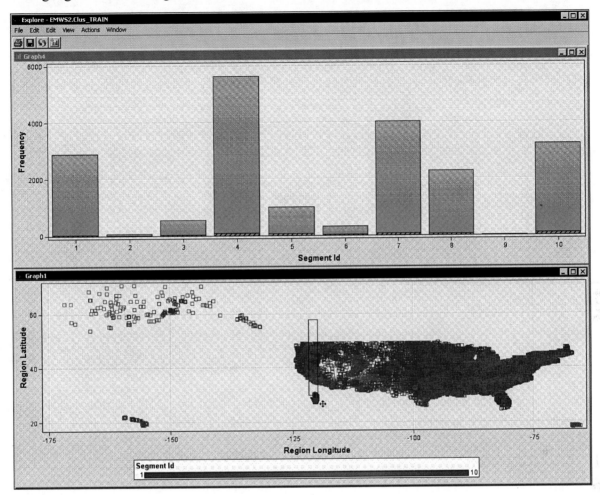

Copyright © 2011, SAS Institute Inc., Cary, North Carolina, USA. ALL RIGHTS RESERVED.

7. Move the box to the right and notice that the selected proportions in the histogram change as you move the box.

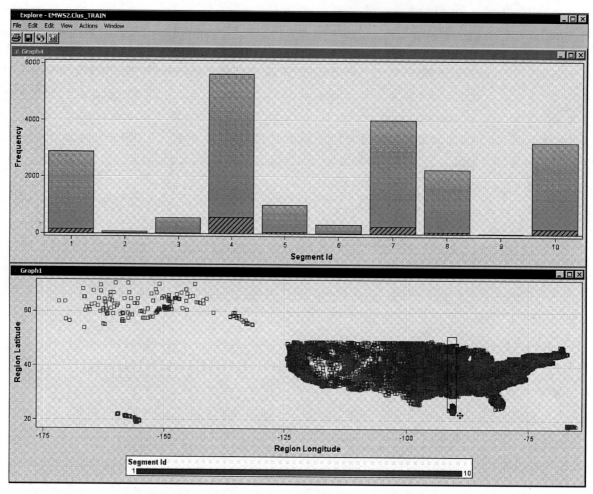

8. Experiment with creating other types of graphs with this data in the Explore window. For example, consider a three-dimensional scatter plot, using **MeanHHSz**, **MedHHInc**, and **RegDens** on each axis with the variable **_SEGMENT_** assigned the role Color.

9. Close the Explore, Exported Data, and Results windows.

Copyright © 2011, SAS Institute Inc., Cary, North Carolina, USA. ALL RIGHTS RESERVED.

Profiling Segments

You can gain a great deal of insight by creating plots as in the previous demonstration. Unfortunately, if more than three variables are used to generate the segments, the interpretation of such plots becomes difficult.

Fortunately, there is another useful tool in SAS Enterprise Miner for interpreting the composition of clusters: the Segment Profile tool. This tool enables you to compare the distribution of a variable in an individual segment to the distribution of the variable overall. As a bonus, the variables are sorted by how well they characterize the segment.

1. Drag a **Segment Profile** tool from the Assess tool palette into the diagram workspace.

2. Connect the **Cluster** node to the **Segment Profile** node.

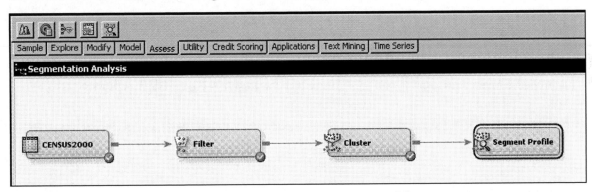

To best describe the segments, you should pick a reasonable subset of the available input variables.

3. Select the **Variables** property for the Segment Profile node.

4. Select **Use** ⇨ **No** for **ID**, **LocX**, **LocY**, and **RegPop**.

Copyright © 2011, SAS Institute Inc., Cary, North Carolina, USA. ALL RIGHTS RESERVED.

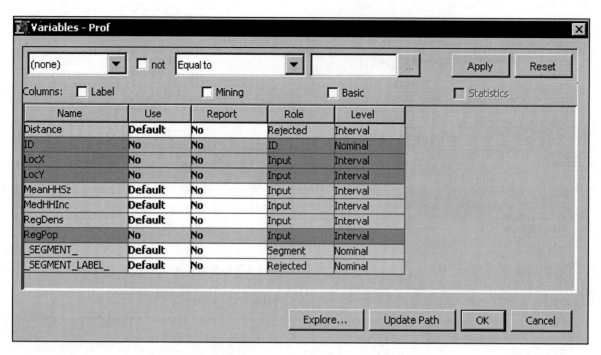

5. Select **OK** to close the Variables dialog box.

6. Run the Segment Profile node and select **Results**. The Results - Node: Segment Profile Diagram window appears.

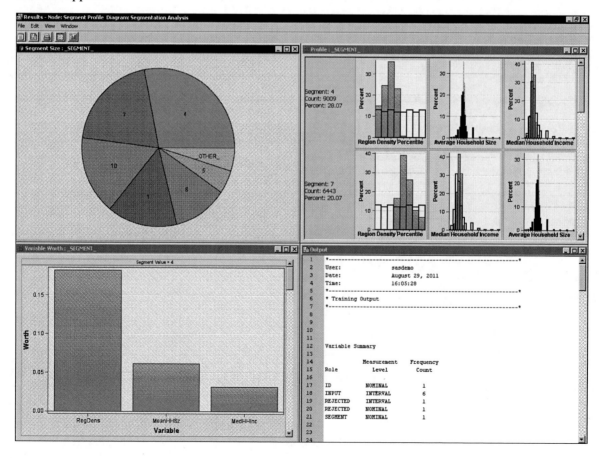

Copyright © 2011, SAS Institute Inc., Cary, North Carolina, USA. ALL RIGHTS RESERVED.

7. Maximize the Profile window.

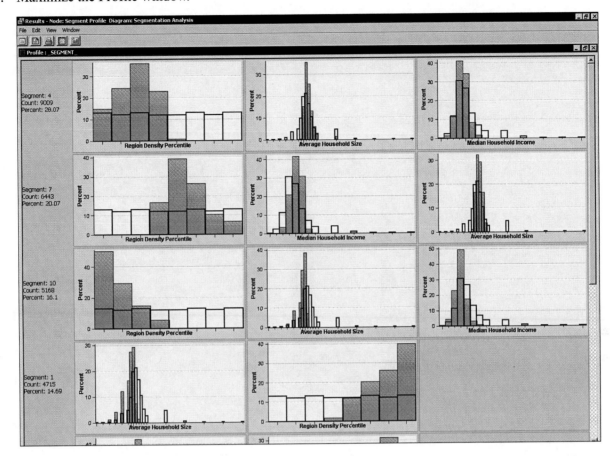

Features of each segment become apparent. For example, segment 4, when compared to the overall distributions, has a lower Region Density Percentile, more central Median Household Income, and slightly higher Average Household Size.

Copyright © 2011, SAS Institute Inc., Cary, North Carolina, USA. ALL RIGHTS RESERVED.

9. Maximize the Variable Worth: _SEGMENT_ window.

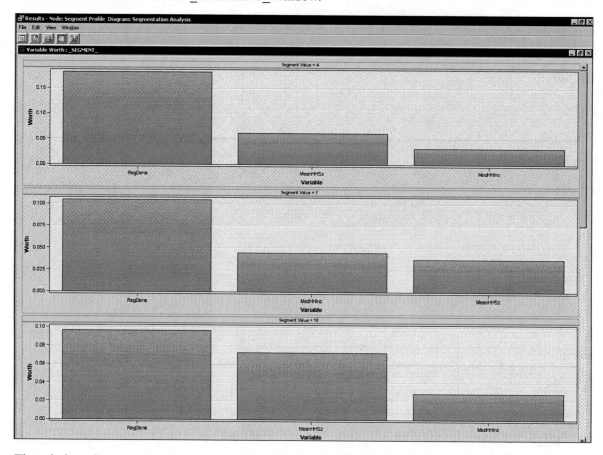

The window shows the relative worth of each variable in characterizing each segment. For example, segment 4 is largely characterized by the **RegDens** input, but the other two inputs also play a role.

Again, similar analyses can be used to describe the other segments. The advantage of the Segment Profile window (compared to direct viewing of the segmentation) is that the descriptions can be more than three-dimensional.

Copyright © 2011, SAS Institute Inc., Cary, North Carolina, USA. ALL RIGHTS RESERVED.

 **Exercises**

1. Conducting Cluster Analysis

The **DUNGAREE** data set gives the number of pairs of four different types of dungarees sold at stores over a specific time period. Each row represents an individual store. There are six columns in the data set. One column is the store identification number, and the remaining columns contain the number of pairs of each type of jeans sold.

Name	Model Role	Measurement Level	Description
STOREID	ID	Nominal	Identification number of the store
FASHION	Input	Interval	Number of pairs of fashion jeans sold at the store
LEISURE	Input	Interval	Number of pairs of leisure jeans sold at the store
STRETCH	Input	Interval	Number of pairs of stretch jeans sold at the store
ORIGINAL	Input	Interval	Number of pairs of original jeans sold at the store
SALESTOT	Rejected	Interval	Total number of pairs of jeans sold (the sum of **FASHION, LEISURE, STRETCH,** and **ORIGINAL**)

a. Create a new diagram in your project. Name the diagram **Jeans**.

b. Define the data set **DUNGAREE** as a data source.

c. Determine whether the model roles and measurement levels assigned to the variables are appropriate.

Examine the distribution of the variables.

- Are there any unusual data values? _____

- Are there missing values that should be replaced? _____

d. Assign the variable **STOREID** the model role ID and the variable **SALESTOT** the model role Rejected. Make sure that the remaining variables have the Input model role and the Interval measurement level. Why should the variable **SALESTOT** be rejected? _____

_____

e. Add an **Input Data Source** node to the diagram workspace and select the **DUNGAREE** data table as the data source.

Copyright © 2011, SAS Institute Inc., Cary, North Carolina, USA. ALL RIGHTS RESERVED.

f. Add a **Cluster** node to the diagram workspace and connect it to the **Input Data** node.

g. Select the **Cluster** node. Leave the default setting as **Internal Standardization** ⇨ **Standardization**. What would happen if inputs were not standardized? _____

_____

h. Run the diagram from the Cluster node and examine the results.
Does the number of clusters created seem reasonable? _____

i. Specify a maximum of six clusters and rerun the Cluster node. How does the number and quality of clusters compare to that obtained in part **h**? _____

_____

j. Use the Segment Profile node to summarize the nature of the clusters.

Copyright © 2011, SAS Institute Inc., Cary, North Carolina, USA. ALL RIGHTS RESERVED.

8.3 Market Basket Analysis (Self-Study)

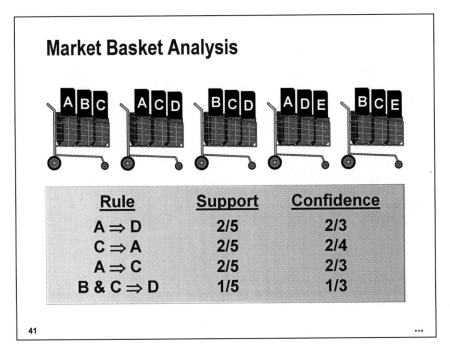

Market basket analysis (also known as *association rule discovery* or *affinity analysis*) is a popular data mining method. In the simplest situation, the data consists of two variables: a *transaction* and an *item*.

For each transaction, there is a list of items. Typically, a transaction is a single customer purchase, and the items are the things that were bought. An *association rule* is a statement of the form (item set A) $\Rightarrow$ (item set B).

The aim of the analysis is to determine the strength of all the association rules among a set of items.

The strength of the association is measured by the *support* and *confidence* of the rule. The support for the rule $A \Rightarrow B$ is the probability that the two item sets occur together. The support of the rule $A \Rightarrow B$ is estimated by the following:

$$\frac{transactions\ that\ contain\ every\ item\ in\ A\ and\ B}{all\ transactions}$$

Notice that support is symmetric. That is, the support of the rule $A \Rightarrow B$ is the same as the support of the rule $B \Rightarrow A$.

The confidence of an association rule $A \Rightarrow B$ is the conditional probability of a transaction containing item set B given that it contains item set A. The confidence is estimated by the following:

$$\frac{transactions\ that\ contain\ every\ item\ in\ A\ and\ B}{transactions\ that\ contain\ the\ items\ in\ A}$$

Copyright © 2011, SAS Institute Inc., Cary, North Carolina, USA. ALL RIGHTS RESERVED.

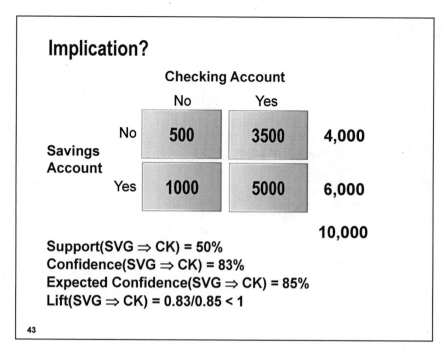

Implication?

Checking Account

		No	Yes	
Savings Account	No	500	3500	4,000
	Yes	1000	5000	6,000
				10,000

Support(SVG ⇒ CK) = 50%
Confidence(SVG ⇒ CK) = 83%
Expected Confidence(SVG ⇒ CK) = 85%
Lift(SVG ⇒ CK) = 0.83/0.85 < 1

43

The interpretation of the implication (⇒) in association rules is precarious. High confidence and support does not imply cause and effect. The rule is not necessarily interesting. The two items might not even be correlated. The term *confidence* is not related to the statistical usage; therefore, there is no repeated sampling interpretation.

Consider the association rule (saving account) ⇒ (checking account). This rule has 50% support (5,000/10,000) and 83% confidence (5,000/6,000). Based on these two measures, this might be considered a strong rule. On the contrary, those **without** a savings account are even more likely to have a checking account (87.5%). Saving and checking are, in fact, negatively correlated.

If the two accounts were independent, then knowing that a person has a saving account does not help in knowing whether that person has a checking account. The expected confidence if the two accounts were independent is 85% (8,500/10,000). This is higher than the confidence of SVG ⇒ CK.

The *lift* of the rule $A \Rightarrow B$ is the confidence of the rule divided by the expected confidence, assuming that the item sets are independent. The lift can be interpreted as a general measure of association between the two item sets. Values greater than 1 indicate positive correlation, values equal to 1 indicate zero correlation, and values less than 1 indicate negative correlation. Notice that lift is symmetric. That is, the lift of the rule $A \Rightarrow B$ is the same as the lift of the rule $B \Rightarrow A$.

Copyright © 2011, SAS Institute Inc., Cary, North Carolina, USA. ALL RIGHTS RESERVED.

Barbie Doll ⇒ Candy

1. Put them closer together in the store.
2. Put them far apart in the store.
3. Package candy bars with the dolls.
4. Package Barbie + candy + poorly selling item.
5. Raise the price on one, and lower it on the other.
6. Offer Barbie accessories for proofs of purchase.
7. Do not advertise candy and Barbie together.
8. Offer candies in the shape of a Barbie doll.

44

Forbes (Palmeri 1997) reported that a major retailer determined that customers who buy Barbie dolls have a 60% likelihood of buying one of three types of candy bars. The confidence of the rule Barbie ⇒ candy is 60%. The retailer was unsure what to do with this nugget. The online newsletter *Knowledge Discovery Nuggets* invited suggestions (Piatesky-Shapiro 1998).

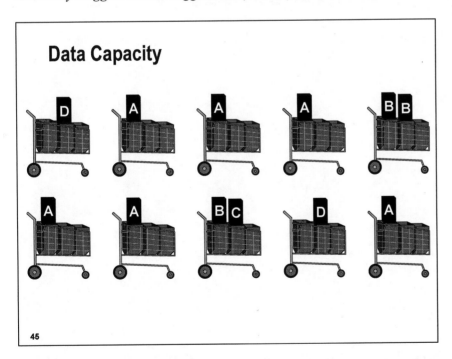

Data Capacity

45

In data mining, the data is not generated to meet the objectives of the analysis. It must be determined whether the data, as it exists, has the capacity to meet the objectives. For example, quantifying affinities among related items would be pointless if very few transactions involved multiple items. Therefore, it is important to do some initial examination of the data before attempting to do association analysis.

Copyright © 2011, SAS Institute Inc., Cary, North Carolina, USA. ALL RIGHTS RESERVED.

Association Tool Demonstration

Analysis goal:

Explore associations between retail banking services used by customers.

Analysis plan:
- **Create an association data source.**
- **Run an association analysis.**
- **Interpret the association rules.**
- **Run a sequence analysis.**
- **Interpret the sequence rules.**

46

A bank's Marketing Department is interested in examining associations between various retail banking services used by customers. Marketing would like to determine both typical and atypical service combinations as well as the order in which the services were first used.

These requirements suggest both a market basket analysis and a sequence analysis.

Copyright © 2011, SAS Institute Inc., Cary, North Carolina, USA. ALL RIGHTS RESERVED.

Market Basket Analysis

The **BANK** data set contains service information for nearly 8,000 customers. There are three variables in the data set, as shown in the table below.

Name	Model Role	Measurement Level	Description
ACCOUNT	ID	Nominal	Account Number
SERVICE	Target	Nominal	Type of Service
VISIT	Sequence	Ordinal	Order of Product Purchase

The **BANK** data set has over 32,000 rows. Each row of the data set represents a customer-service combination. Therefore, a single customer can have multiple rows in the data set, and each row represents one of the products he or she owns. The median number of products per customer is three.

The 13 products are represented in the data set using the following abbreviations:

ATM	automated teller machine debit card
AUTO	automobile installment loan
CCRD	credit card
CD	certificate of deposit
CKCRD	check/debit card
CKING	checking account
HMEQLC	home equity line of credit
IRA	individual retirement account
MMDA	money market deposit account
MTG	mortgage
PLOAN	personal/consumer installment loan
SVG	saving account
TRUST	personal trust account

Your first task is to create a new analysis diagram and data source for the **BANK** data set.

1. Create a new diagram named Associations Analysis to contain this analysis.

2. Select **Create Data Source** from the Data Sources project property.

3. Select the **BANK** table from the **AAEM** library.

Copyright © 2011, SAS Institute Inc., Cary, North Carolina, USA. ALL RIGHTS RESERVED.

4. In Step 5, assign roles to the table variables as shown below.

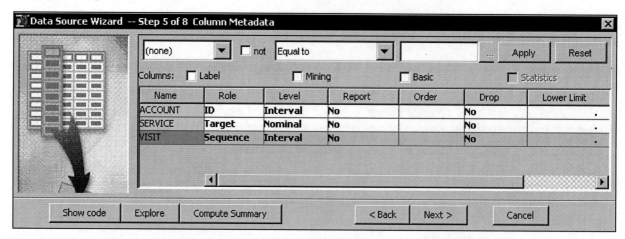

An association analysis requires exactly one target variable and at least one ID variable. Both should have a nominal measurement level; however, a level of Interval for the ID variable is sufficient. A sequence analysis also requires a sequence variable. It usually has an ordinal measurement scale; however, in SAS Enterprise Miner the sequence variable must be assigned the level Interval.

5. For an association analysis, the data source should have a role of Transaction.

    Select **Role** ⇨ **Transaction**.

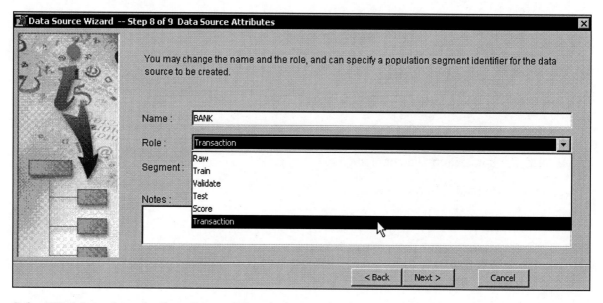

6. Select **Finish** to close the Data Source Wizard.

7. Drag a **BANK** data source into the diagram workspace.

8. Select the **Explore** tab and drag an **Association** tool into the diagram workspace.

Copyright © 2011, SAS Institute Inc., Cary, North Carolina, USA. ALL RIGHTS RESERVED.

9. Connect the **BANK** node to the **Association** node.

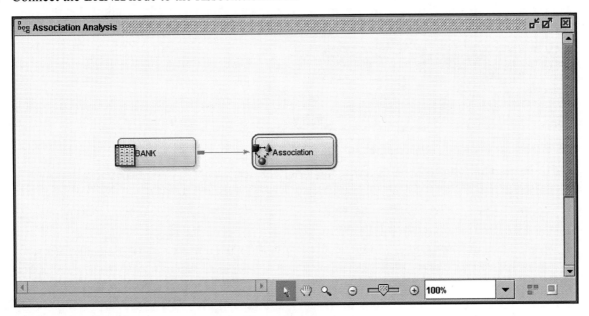

10. Select the **Association** node and examine its Properties panel.

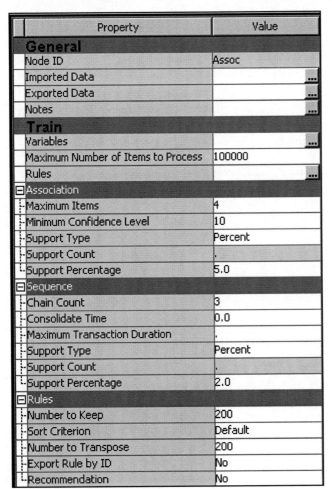

Property	Value
General	
Node ID	Assoc
Imported Data	...
Exported Data	...
Notes	...
Train	
Variables	...
Maximum Number of Items to Process	100000
Rules	...
⊟Association	
├Maximum Items	4
├Minimum Confidence Level	10
├Support Type	Percent
├Support Count	.
└Support Percentage	5.0
⊟Sequence	
├Chain Count	3
├Consolidate Time	0.0
├Maximum Transaction Duration	.
├Support Type	Percent
├Support Count	.
└Support Percentage	2.0
⊟Rules	
├Number to Keep	200
├Sort Criterion	Default
├Number to Transpose	200
├Export Rule by ID	No
└Recommendation	No

Copyright © 2011, SAS Institute Inc., Cary, North Carolina, USA. ALL RIGHTS RESERVED.

11. The Export Rule by ID property determines whether the **Rule-by-ID** data is exported from the node and if the **Rule Description** table will be available for display in the Results window. Set the value for Export Rule by ID to **Yes**.

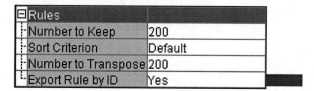

Other options in the Properties panel include the following:

- **Minimum Confidence Level** specifies the minimum confidence level to generate a rule. The default level is **10%**.

- **Support Type** specifies whether the analysis should use the support count or support percentage property. The default setting is **Percent**.

- **Support Count** specifies a minimum level of support to claim that items are associated (that is, they occur together in the database).

- **Support Percentage** specifies a minimum level of support to claim that items are associated (that is, they occur together in the database). The default frequency is 5%. The support percentage figure that you specify refers to the proportion of the largest single item frequency, and not the end support.

- **Maximum Items** determines the maximum size of the item set to be considered. For example, the default of four items indicates that a maximum of four items will be included in a single association rule.

   If you are interested in associations that involve fairly rare products, you should consider reducing the support count or percentage when you run the Association node. If you obtain too many rules to be practically useful, you should consider raising the minimum support count or percentage as one possible solution.

   Because you first want to perform a market basket analysis, you do not need the sequence variable.

12. Access the Variables dialog box for the Association node.

Copyright © 2011, SAS Institute Inc., Cary, North Carolina, USA. ALL RIGHTS RESERVED.

13. Select **Use** ⇨ **No** for the **VISIT** variable.

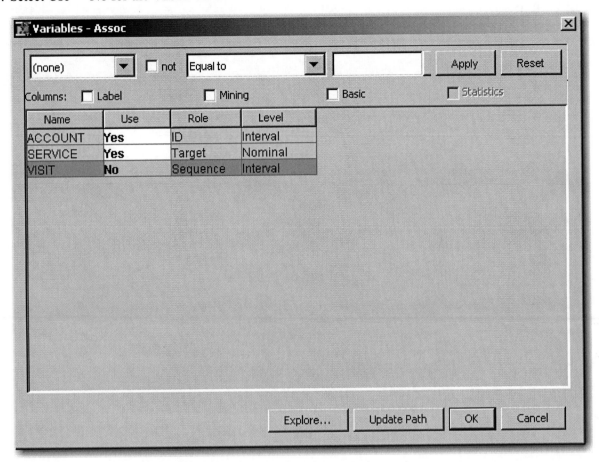

14. Select **OK** to close the Variables dialog box.

15. Run the diagram from the Association node and view the results.

Copyright © 2011, SAS Institute Inc., Cary, North Carolina, USA. ALL RIGHTS RESERVED.

The Results - Node: Association Diagram window appears with the Statistics Plot, Statistics Line Plot, Rule Matrix, and Output windows visible.

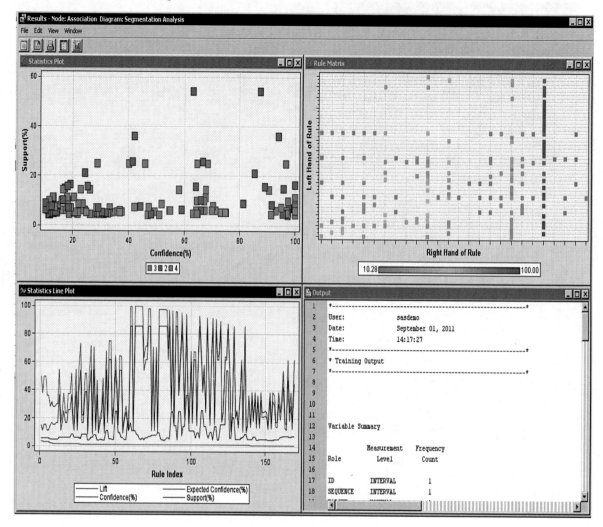

Copyright © 2011, SAS Institute Inc., Cary, North Carolina, USA. ALL RIGHTS RESERVED.

16. Maximize the Statistics Line Plot window.

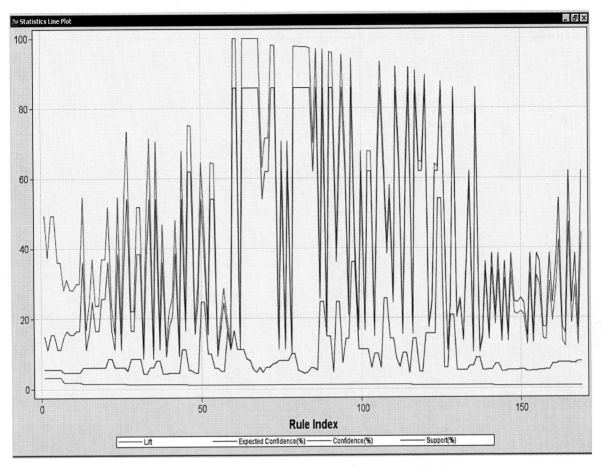

The statistics line plot graphs the lift, expected confidence, confidence, and support for each of the rules by rule index number.

Consider the rule A $\Rightarrow$ B. Recall the following:

- **Support** of A $\Rightarrow$ B is the probability that a customer has both A and B.
- **Confidence** of A $\Rightarrow$ B is the probability that a customer has B given that the customer has A.
- **Expected Confidence** of A $\Rightarrow$ B is the probability that a customer has B.
- **Lift** of A $\Rightarrow$ B is a measure of the strength of the association. If Lift=2 for the rule A=>B, then a customer having A is twice as likely to have B than a customer chosen at random. Lift is the confidence divided by the expected confidence.

Notice that the rules are ordered in descending order of lift.

Copyright © 2011, SAS Institute Inc., Cary, North Carolina, USA. ALL RIGHTS RESERVED.

17. To view the descriptions of the rules, select **View** ⇨ **Rules** ⇨ **Rule description**.

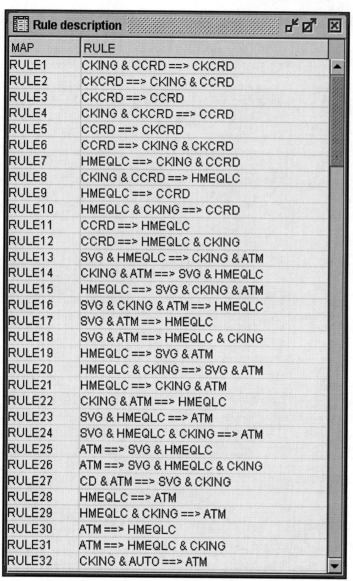

MAP	RULE
RULE1	CKING & CCRD ==> CKCRD
RULE2	CKCRD ==> CKING & CCRD
RULE3	CKCRD ==> CCRD
RULE4	CKING & CKCRD ==> CCRD
RULE5	CCRD ==> CKCRD
RULE6	CCRD ==> CKING & CKCRD
RULE7	HMEQLC ==> CKING & CCRD
RULE8	CKING & CCRD ==> HMEQLC
RULE9	HMEQLC ==> CCRD
RULE10	HMEQLC & CKING ==> CCRD
RULE11	CCRD ==> HMEQLC
RULE12	CCRD ==> HMEQLC & CKING
RULE13	SVG & HMEQLC ==> CKING & ATM
RULE14	CKING & ATM ==> SVG & HMEQLC
RULE15	HMEQLC ==> SVG & CKING & ATM
RULE16	SVG & CKING & ATM ==> HMEQLC
RULE17	SVG & ATM ==> HMEQLC
RULE18	SVG & ATM ==> HMEQLC & CKING
RULE19	HMEQLC ==> SVG & ATM
RULE20	HMEQLC & CKING ==> SVG & ATM
RULE21	HMEQLC ==> CKING & ATM
RULE22	CKING & ATM ==> HMEQLC
RULE23	SVG & HMEQLC ==> ATM
RULE24	SVG & HMEQLC & CKING ==> ATM
RULE25	ATM ==> SVG & HMEQLC
RULE26	ATM ==> SVG & HMEQLC & CKING
RULE27	CD & ATM ==> SVG & CKING
RULE28	HMEQLC ==> ATM
RULE29	HMEQLC & CKING ==> ATM
RULE30	ATM ==> HMEQLC
RULE31	ATM ==> HMEQLC & CKING
RULE32	CKING & AUTO ==> ATM

The highest lift rule is checking, and credit card implies check card. This is not surprising given that many check cards include credit card logos. Notice the symmetry in rules 1 and 2. This is not accidental because, as noted earlier, lift is symmetric.

Copyright © 2011, SAS Institute Inc., Cary, North Carolina, USA. ALL RIGHTS RESERVED.

18. (Optional) Examine the rule matrix.

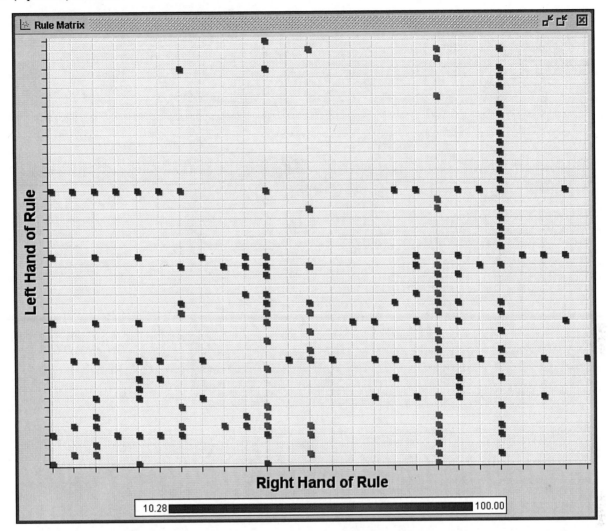

The rule matrix plots the rules based on the items on the left side of the rule and the items on the right side of the rule. The points are colored, based on the confidence of the rules. For example, the rules with the highest confidence are in the column in the picture above. Using the interactive feature of the graph, you discover that these rules all have checking on the right side of the rule.

Another way to explore the rules found in the analysis is by plotting the Rules table.

Copyright © 2011, SAS Institute Inc., Cary, North Carolina, USA. ALL RIGHTS RESERVED.

19. Select **View** ⇨ **Rules** ⇨ **Rules Table**. The Rules Table window appears.

Relations	Expected Confidence(%)	Confidence(%)	Support(%)	Lift
3	11.30	37.57	5.58	3.33
3	14.85	49.39	5.58	3.33
2	15.48	49.39	5.58	3.19
3	15.48	49.39	5.58	3.19
2	11.30	36.05	5.58	3.19
3	11.30	36.05	5.58	3.19
3	14.85	28.12	4.63	1.89
3	16.47	31.17	4.63	1.89
2	15.48	28.12	4.63	1.82
3	15.48	28.12	4.63	1.82
2	16.47	29.91	4.63	1.82
3	16.47	29.91	4.63	1.82
4	36.19	54.66	6.09	1.51
4	11.15	16.84	6.09	1.51
4	24.85	37.01	6.09	1.49
4	16.47	24.52	6.09	1.49
3	16.47	23.72	6.09	1.44
4	16.47	23.72	6.09	1.44

20. Select ▥ (the Plot Wizard icon).

21. Choose a Matrix graph for the type of chart, and select **Next >**.

Copyright © 2011, SAS Institute Inc., Cary, North Carolina, USA. ALL RIGHTS RESERVED.

22. Select the matrix variables: **Lift, Conf** and **Support** as shown below right. Select **Next** .

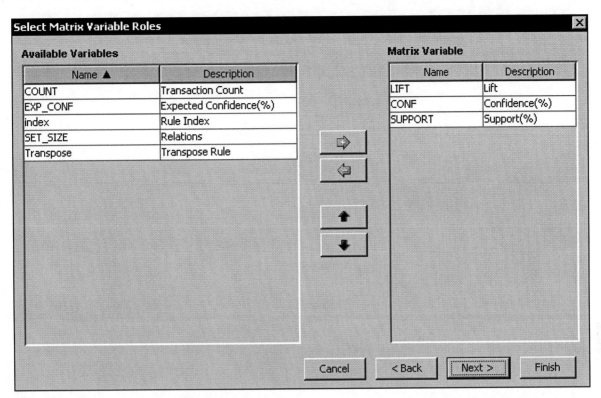

23. Select the **Group** role for **_RHAND** and the **Tip** role for **LIFT** and **RULE** to add these details to the tooltip action.

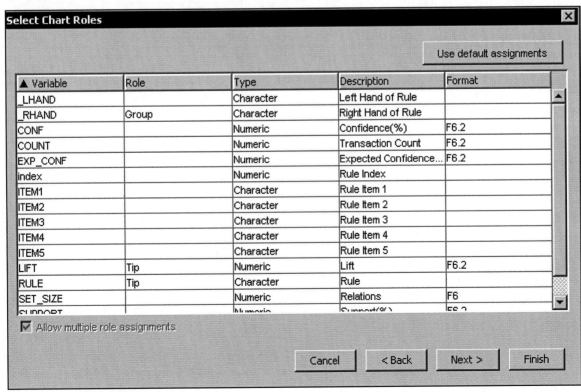

Copyright © 2011, SAS Institute Inc., Cary, North Carolina, USA. ALL RIGHTS RESERVED.

24. Select **Finish** to generate the plot.

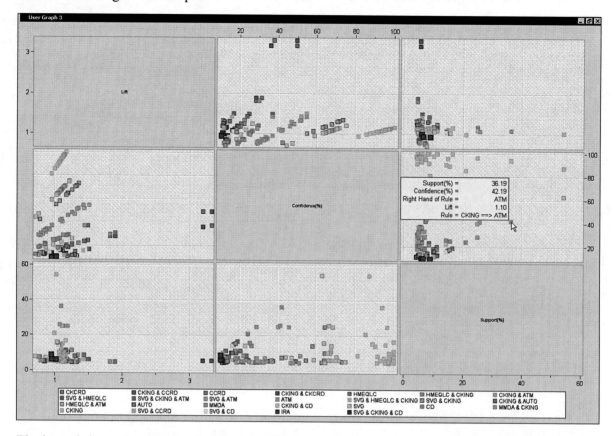

The legend shows the right hand of the rule. When you click a service or group of services in the legend, the points in the matrix graphs are highlighted. This plot enables you to explore the relationships among the various metrics in association analysis.

When you hover the cursor over a selected point in the plot, the tooltips show the details of the point, including the full rule.

Copyright © 2011, SAS Institute Inc., Cary, North Carolina, USA. ALL RIGHTS RESERVED.

25. Right-click in the graph and select **Data Options**. Select the **Where** tab. Specify **Expected Confidence(%)** as the column name and **Greater than** as the operator. Click the elipses next to **Value**. Set the slider to include values greater than 40, or type **40** for the value.

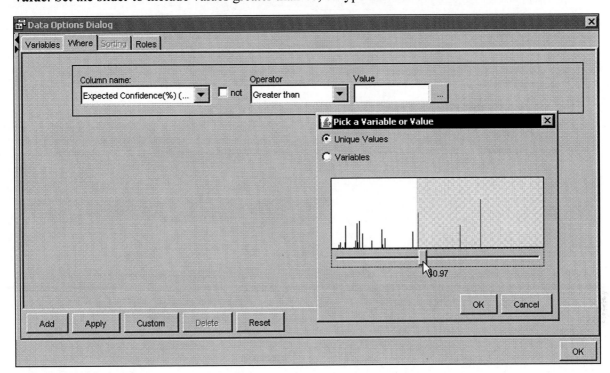

26. Select **OK** and **Apply**.

Copyright © 2011, SAS Institute Inc., Cary, North Carolina, USA. ALL RIGHTS RESERVED.

27. Select **OK** . The subset selected cases represent three different sets of services in the legend for the right hand of the rules.

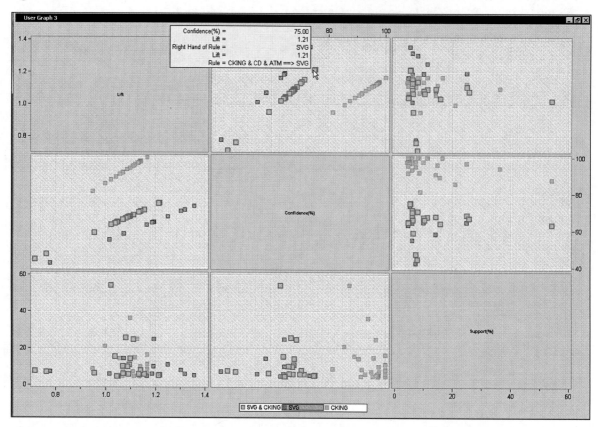

28. You can modify the look of the graph. Right-click the graph and select **Graph Properties**. Change the plot matrix diagonal type to **Histogram**.

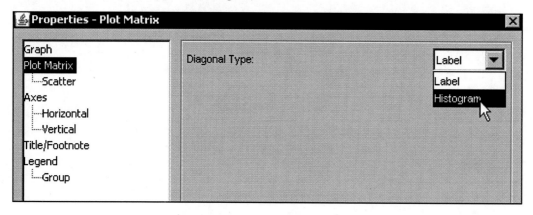

Copyright © 2011, SAS Institute Inc., Cary, North Carolina, USA. ALL RIGHTS RESERVED.

29. Label the legend by selecting **Legend** and selecting the check box in the Title are next to **Show (Right hand of Rule)**. Select **OK**.

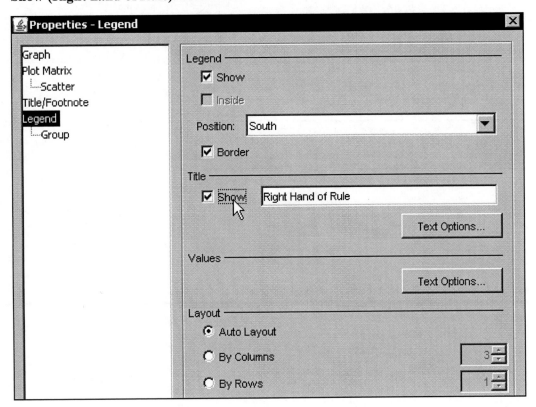

Copyright © 2011, SAS Institute Inc., Cary, North Carolina, USA. ALL RIGHTS RESERVED.

30. Click the **SVG** (Savings Account) category in the legend and notice that the histograms show the distribution of the selected rules in the diagonal.

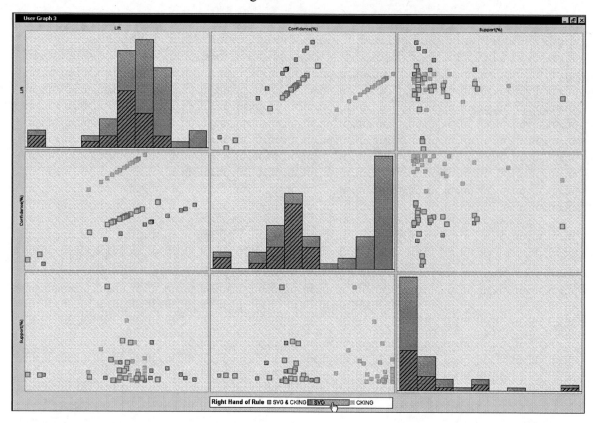

31. Close the Results window.

Copyright © 2011, SAS Institute Inc., Cary, North Carolina, USA. ALL RIGHTS RESERVED.

Sequence Analysis

In addition to the products owned by its customers, the bank is interested in examining the order in which the products are purchased. The sequence variable in the data set enables you to conduct a sequence analysis.

1. Add an **Association** node to the diagram workspace and connect it to the **BANK** node.

2. Rename the new node **Sequence Analysis**.

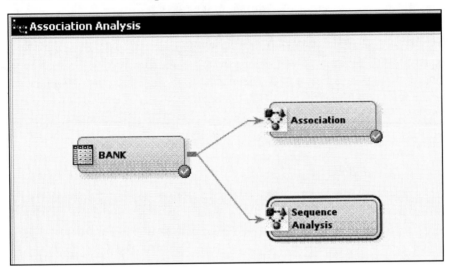

3. Set Export Rule by ID to **Yes**.

⊟Rules	
Number to Keep	200
Sort Criterion	Default
Number to Transpose	200
Export Rule by ID	Yes

4. Examine the Sequence panel in the Properties panel.

⊟Sequence	
Chain Count	3
Consolidate Time	0.0
Maximum Transaction Duration	.
Support Type	Percent
Support Count	.
Support Percentage	2.0

Copyright © 2011, SAS Institute Inc., Cary, North Carolina, USA. ALL RIGHTS RESERVED.

The options in the Sequence panel enable you to specify the following properties:

- **Chain Count** is the maximum number of items that can be included in a sequence. The default value is 3 and the maximum value is 10.

- **Consolidate Time** enables you to specify whether consecutive visits to a location or consecutive purchases over a given interval can be consolidated into a single visit for analysis purposes. For example, two products purchased less than a day apart might be considered to be a single transaction.

- **Maximum Transaction Duration** enables you to specify the maximum length of time for a series of transactions to be considered a sequence. For example, you might want to specify that the purchase of two products more than three months apart does not constitute a sequence.

- **Support Type** specifies whether the sequence analysis should use the Support Count or Support Percentage property. The default setting is **Percent**.

- **Support Count** specifies the minimum frequency required to include a sequence in the sequence analysis when the Sequence Support Type property is set to **Count**. If a sequence has a count less than the specified value, that sequence is excluded from the output.

- **Support Percentage** specifies the minimum level of support to include the sequence in the analysis when the Support Type property is set to **Percent**. If a sequence has a frequency that is less than the specified percentage of the total number of transactions, then that sequence is excluded from the output. The default percentage is 2%. Permissible values are real numbers between 0 and 100.

5. Run the diagram from the Sequence Analysis node and view the results.

6. Maximize the Statistics Line Plot window.

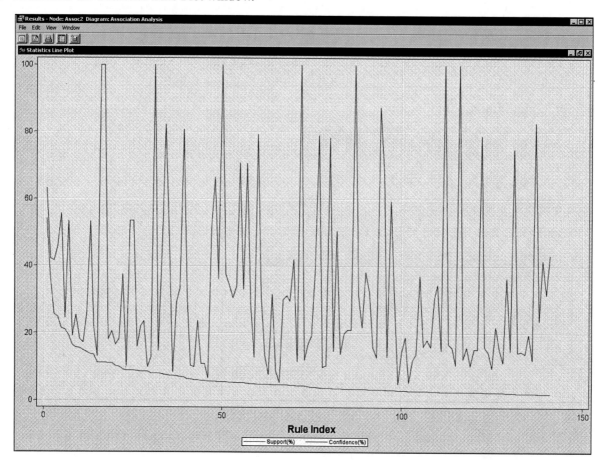

Copyright © 2011, SAS Institute Inc., Cary, North Carolina, USA. ALL RIGHTS RESERVED.

The statistics line plot graphs the confidence and support for each of the rules by rule index number.

The *percent support* is the transaction count divided by the total number of customers, which would be the maximum transaction count. The *percent confidence* is the transaction count divided by the transaction count for the left side of the sequence.

7. Select **View** ⇨ **Rules** ⇨ **Rule description** to view the descriptions of the rules.

map	Rule
RULE1	CKING ==> SVG
RULE2	CKING ==> ATM
RULE3	SVG ==> ATM
RULE4	CKING ==> SVG ==> ATM
RULE5	ATM ==> ATM
RULE6	CKING ==> CD
RULE7	CKING ==> ATM ==> ATM
RULE8	CKING ==> HMEQLC
RULE9	SVG ==> CD
RULE10	CKING ==> MMDA
RULE11	CKING ==> CCRD
RULE12	CKING ==> SVG ==> CD
RULE13	SVG ==> ATM ==> ATM
RULE14	SVG ==> SVG
RULE15	CKCRD ==> CKCRD
RULE16	CKING ==> CKCRD
RULE17	CKING ==> CKCRD ==> CKCRD
RULE18	SVG ==> HMEQLC
RULE19	CKING ==> SVG ==> HMEQLC

The confidence for many of the rules changes after the order of service acquisition is considered.

Copyright © 2011, SAS Institute Inc., Cary, North Carolina, USA. ALL RIGHTS RESERVED.

Exercises

2. Conducting an Association Analysis

A store is interested in determining the associations between items purchased from the Health and Beauty Aids Department and the Stationery Department. The store chose to conduct a market basket analysis of specific items purchased from these two departments. The **TRANSACTIONS** data set contains information about more than 400,000 transactions made over the past three months. The following products are represented in the data set:

1. bar soap

2. bows

3. candy bars

4. deodorant

5. greeting cards

6. magazines

7. markers

8. pain relievers

9. pencils

10. pens

11. perfume

12. photo processing

13. prescription medications

14. shampoo

15. toothbrushes

16. toothpaste

17. wrapping paper

Copyright © 2011, SAS Institute Inc., Cary, North Carolina, USA. ALL RIGHTS RESERVED.

There are four variables in the data set:

Name	Model Role	Measurement Level	Description
STORE	Rejected	Nominal	Identification number of the store
TRANSACTION	ID	Nominal	Transaction identification number
PRODUCT	Target	Nominal	Product purchased
QUANTITY	Rejected	Interval	Quantity of this product purchased

a. Create a new diagram. Name the diagram **Transactions**.

b. Create a new data source using the data set **AAEM.TRANSACTIONS**.

c. Assign the variables **STORE** and **QUANTITY** the model role Rejected. These variables will not be used in this analysis. Assign the ID model role to the variable **TRANSACTION** and the Target model role to the variable **PRODUCT**.

d. Add the node for the **TRANSACTIONS** data set and an Association node to the diagram.

e. Change the setting for Export Rule by ID to **Yes**.

f. Leave the remaining default settings for the Association node and run the analysis.

g. Examine the results of the association analysis.

What is the highest lift value for the resulting rules? _____

Which rule has this value? _____

Copyright © 2011, SAS Institute Inc., Cary, North Carolina, USA. ALL RIGHTS RESERVED.

8.4 Chapter Summary

Pattern discovery seems to embody the promise of data mining, but there are many ways for an analysis to fail. SAS Enterprise Miner provides tools to help with data reduction, novelty detection, profiling, market basket analysis, and sequence analysis.

Cluster and segmentation analyses are similar in intent but differ in execution. In cluster analysis, the goal is to identify distinct groupings of cases across a set of inputs. In segmentation analysis, the goal is to partition cases from a single cluster into contiguous groups.

SAS Enterprise Miner offers several tools for exploring the results of a cluster and segmentation analysis. For low dimension data, you can use capabilities provided by the Graph Wizard and the Explore window. For higher dimensional data, you can choose the Segment Profile tool to understand the generated partitions.

Market basket and sequence analyses are handled by the Association tool. This tool transforms transaction data sets into rules. The value of the generated rules is gauged by confidence, support, and lift. The Association tool features a variety of plots and tables to help you explore the analysis results.

Pattern Discovery Tools: Review

 Generate cluster models using automatic settings and segmentation models with user-defined settings.

 Compare within-segment distributions of selected inputs to overall distributions. This helps you understand segment definition.

 Conduct market basket and sequence analysis on transactions data. A data source must have one target, one ID, and (if desired) one sequence variable in the data source.

50

Copyright © 2011, SAS Institute Inc., Cary, North Carolina, USA. ALL RIGHTS RESERVED.

8.5 Solutions

Solutions to Exercises

1. **Conducting Cluster Analysis**

   a. Create a new diagram in your project.

      1) To open a diagram, select **File** ⇨ **New** ⇨ **Diagram**.

      2) Type the name of the new diagram, **Jeans**, and select **OK**.

   b. Define the data set **DUNGAREE** as a data source.

      1) Select **File** ⇨ **New** ⇨ **Data Source**.

      2) In the Data Source Wizard - Metadata Source window, make sure that **SAS Table** is selected as the source and select **Next**.

      3) To choose the desired data table, select **Browse**.

      4) Double-click on the **AAEM** library to see the data tables in the library.

      5) Select the **DUNGAREE** data set, and then select **OK**.

      6) Select **Next**.

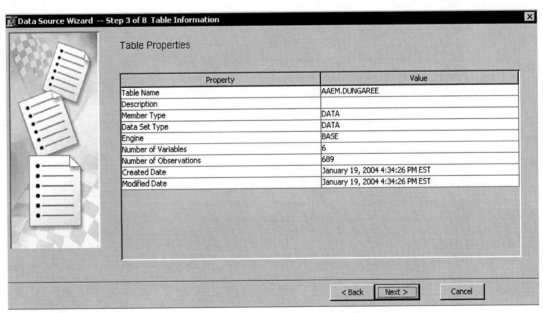

      7) Select **Next**.

      8) Select **Advanced** to use the Advanced Advisor, and then select **Next**.

Copyright © 2011, SAS Institute Inc., Cary, North Carolina, USA. ALL RIGHTS RESERVED.

c. Determine whether the model roles and measurement levels assigned to the variables are appropriate.

Examine the distribution of the variables.

1) Hold down the CTRL key and click to select the variables of interest.

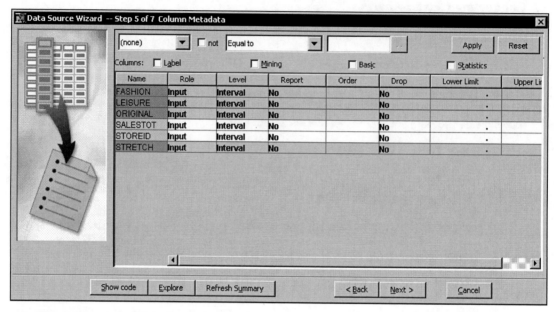

2) Select **Explore**.

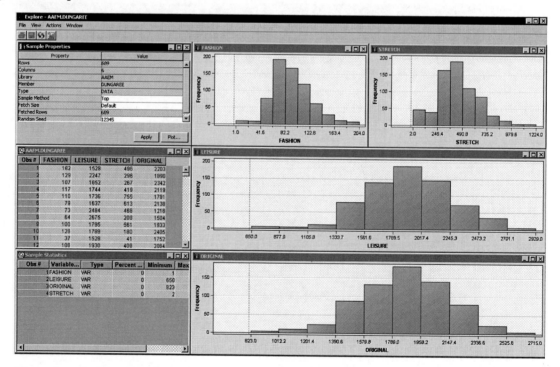

There do not appear to be any unusual or missing data values. Close the Explore window.

Copyright © 2011, SAS Institute Inc., Cary, North Carolina, USA. ALL RIGHTS RESERVED.

d. The variable **STOREID** should have the ID model role and the variable **SALESTOT** should have the Rejected model role.

The variable SALESTOT should be rejected because it is the sum of the other input variables in the data set. Therefore, it should not be considered as an independent input value.

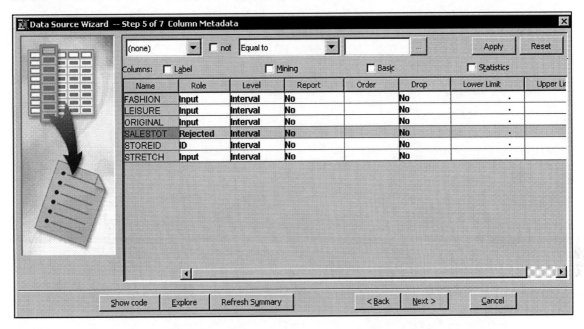

Select **Next** several times and then select **Finish** to complete the data source creation.

e. To add an Input Data node to the diagram workspace and select the **DUNGAREE** data table as the data source, drag the **DUNGAREE** data source onto the diagram workspace.

f. Add a **Cluster** node to the diagram workspace. The workspace should appear as shown.

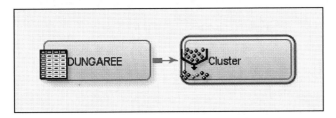

g. Select the **Cluster** node.

In the property sheet, note the default: **Internal Standardization ⇨ Standardization**.

If you do not standardize, the clustering will occur strictly on the inputs with the largest range (Original and Leisure).

Copyright © 2011, SAS Institute Inc., Cary, North Carolina, USA. ALL RIGHTS RESERVED.

h. Run the diagram from the Cluster node and examine the results.

1) Run the Cluster node and view the results.

2) To view the results, right-click the **Cluster** node and select **Results**.

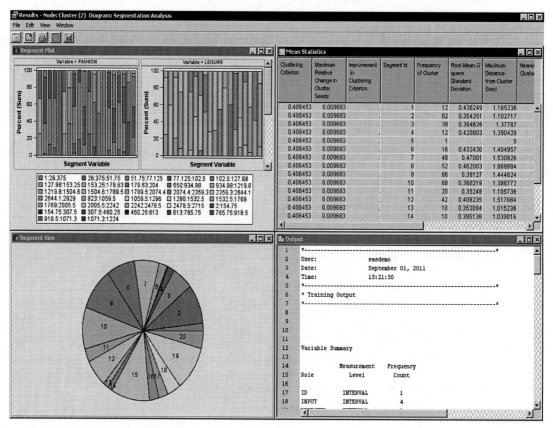

The Cluster node's **Automatic number of cluster specification** method seems to generate an excessive number of clusters.

i. Specify a maximum of six clusters.

1) Select **Specification Method** ⇨ **User Specify**.

2) Select **Maximum Number of Clusters** ⇨ **6**.

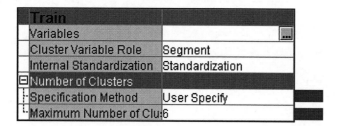

Copyright © 2011, SAS Institute Inc., Cary, North Carolina, USA. ALL RIGHTS RESERVED.

3) Run the Cluster node and view the results.

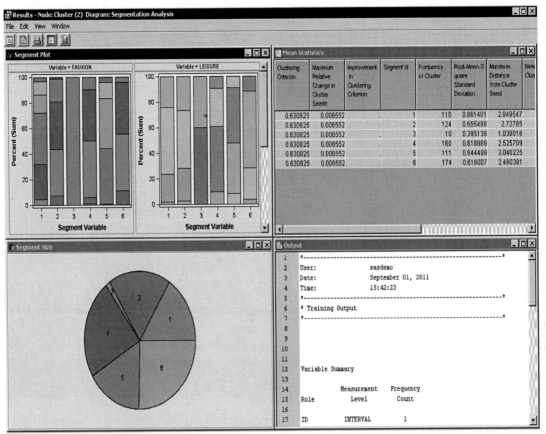

Apparently, all but one of the segments is well populated. There are more details about the segment composition in the next step.

j. Connect a **Segment Profile** node to the **Cluster** node.

1) Run the Segment Profile node and view the results.

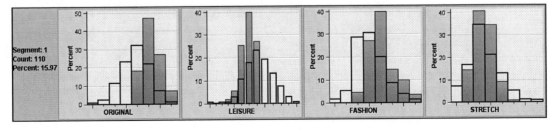

Segment 1 contains stores selling a higher-than-average number of original jeans.

Copyright © 2011, SAS Institute Inc., Cary, North Carolina, USA. ALL RIGHTS RESERVED.

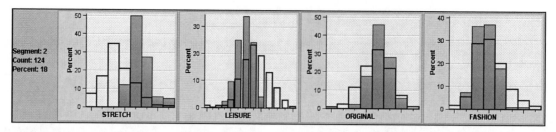

Segment 2 contains stores selling a higher-than-average number of stretch jeans.

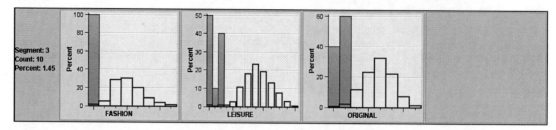

Segment 3 contains stores selling small numbers of all jean styles.

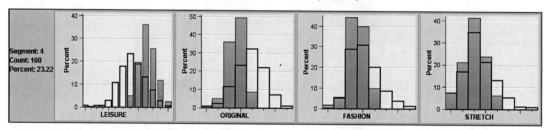

Segment 4 contains stores selling a higher-than-average number of leisure jeans.

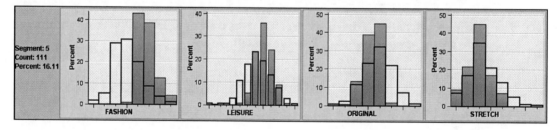

Segment 5 contains stores selling a higher-than-average number of fashion jeans.

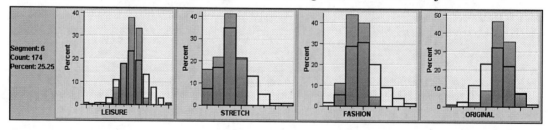

Segment 6 contains stores selling a higher-than-average number of original jeans, but lower-than-average number of stretch and fashion.

Copyright © 2011, SAS Institute Inc., Cary, North Carolina, USA. ALL RIGHTS RESERVED.

2. **Conducting an Association Analysis**

 a. Create the Transactions diagram.

   1) To open a new diagram in the project, select **File** ⇨ **New** ⇨ **Diagram**.

   2) Name the new diagram **Transactions** and select **OK**.

 b. Create a new data source using the data set **AAEM.TRANSACTIONS**.

   1) Right-click **Data Sources** in the project tree and select **Create Data Source**.

   2) In the Data Source Wizard - Metadata Source window, make sure that **SAS Table** is selected as the source and select **Next**.

   3) Select **Browse** to choose a data set.

   4) Double-click on the **AAEM** library and select the **TRANSACTIONS** data set.

   5) Select **OK**.

   6) Select **Next**.

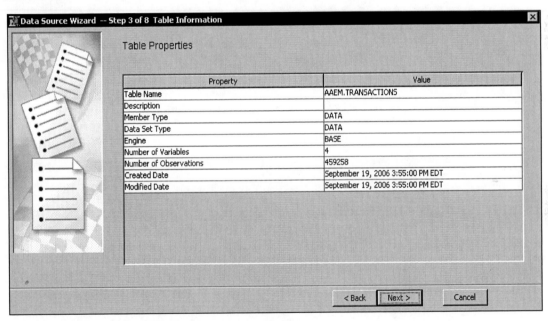

   7) Examine the data table properties, and then select **Next**.

   8) Select **Advanced** to use the Advanced Advisor, and then select **Next**.

Copyright © 2011, SAS Institute Inc., Cary, North Carolina, USA. ALL RIGHTS RESERVED.

c. Assign appropriate model roles to the variables.

1) Hold down the CTRL key and select the rows for the variables **STORE** and **QUANTITY**. In the Role column of one of these rows, select **Rejected**.

2) Select the **TRANSACTION** row and select **ID** as the role.

3) Select the **PRODUCT** row and select **Target** as the role.

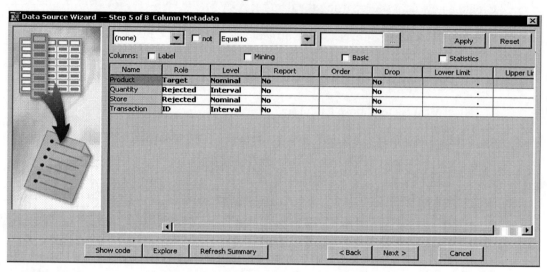

4) Select **Next**.

5) To skip decision processing, select **Next**. To skip creation of a sample, select **Next**.

6) Change the role to **Transaction**.

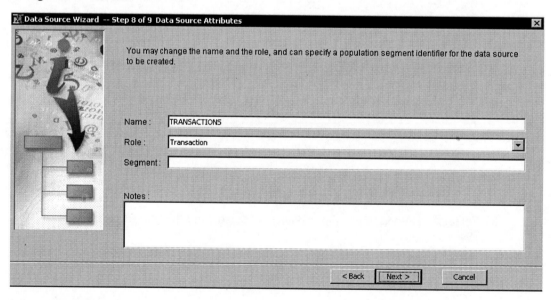

7) Select **Next** ⇨ **Finish**.

Copyright © 2011, SAS Institute Inc., Cary, North Carolina, USA. ALL RIGHTS RESERVED.

d. Add the node for the **TRANSACTIONS** data set and an **Association** node to the diagram. The workspace should appear as shown.

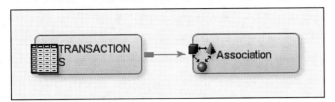

e. Change the setting for Export Rule by ID to **Yes**.

Property	Value
Train	
Variables	...
Maximum Number of Item	100000
Rules	...
⊟ Association	
Maximum Items	4
Minimum Confidence Lev	10
Support Type	Percent
Support Count	1
Support Percentage	5.0
⊟ Sequence	
Chain Count	3
Consolidate Time	0.0
Maximum Transaction Du	0.0
Support Type	Percent
Support Count	1
Support Percentage	2.0
⊟ Rules	
Number to Keep	200
Sort Criterion	Default
Number to Transpose	200
Export Rule by ID	Yes

Copyright © 2011, SAS Institute Inc., Cary, North Carolina, USA. ALL RIGHTS RESERVED.

f. Run the Association node and view the results.

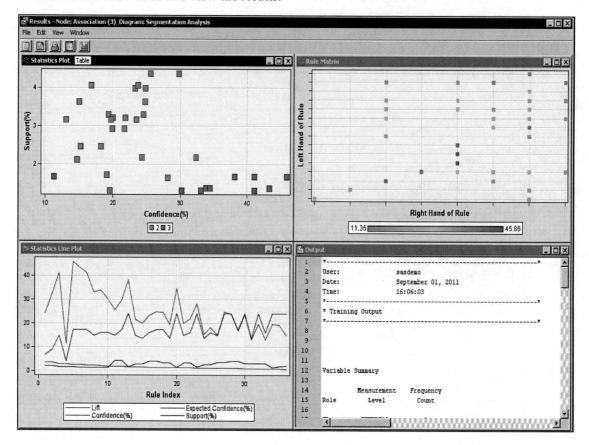

Copyright © 2011, SAS Institute Inc., Cary, North Carolina, USA. ALL RIGHTS RESERVED.

g. Examine the results of the association analysis.

Examine the Statistics Line plot.

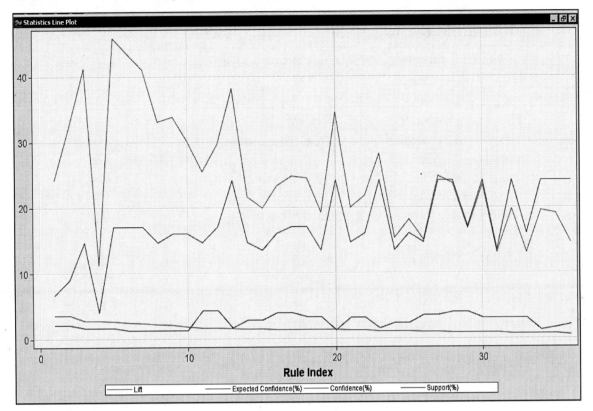

Rule 1 has the highest lift value, 3.60.

Looking at the output reveals that Rule 1 is the rule Perfume ⇨ Toothbrush.

Copyright © 2011, SAS Institute Inc., Cary, North Carolina, USA. ALL RIGHTS RESERVED.

Solutions to Student Activities (Polls/Quizzes)

8.01 Multiple Choice Poll – Correct Answer

For a *k*-means clustering analysis, which of the following statements is true about input variables?

a. Input variables should be limited in number and be relatively independent.

b. Input variables should be of interval measurement level.

c. Input variables should have distributions that are somewhat symmetric.

d. Input variables should be meaningful to analysis objectives.

e. All of the above.

30

Copyright © 2011, SAS Institute Inc., Cary, North Carolina, USA. ALL RIGHTS RESERVED.

Chapter 9 Special Topics

Copyright © 2011, SAS Institute Inc., Cary, North Carolina, USA. ALL RIGHTS RESERVED.

Copyright © 2011, SAS Institute Inc., Cary, North Carolina, USA. ALL RIGHTS RESERVED.

9.1 Introduction

This chapter contains a selection of optional special topics related to predictive modeling. Unlike other chapters, each section is independent of the preceding section. However, demonstrations in this chapter depend on the demonstrations found in Chapters 2 through 7.

Copyright © 2011, SAS Institute Inc., Cary, North Carolina, USA. ALL RIGHTS RESERVED.

9.2 Ensemble Models

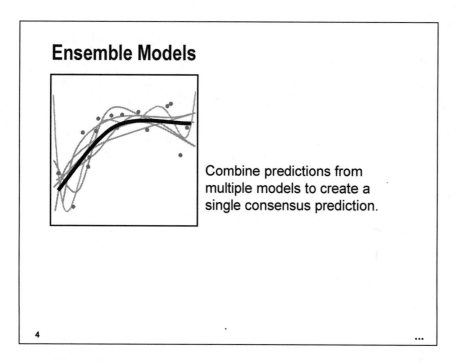

Ensemble Models

Combine predictions from multiple models to create a single consensus prediction.

4   ...

The Ensemble node creates a new model by combining the predictions from multiple models. For prediction estimates and rankings, this is usually done by averaging. When the predictions are decisions, this is done by voting. The commonly observed advantage of ensemble models is that the combined model is better than the individual models that compose it. It is important to note that the ensemble model can be more accurate than the individual models only if the individual models disagree with one another. You should always compare the model performance of the ensemble model with the individual models.

Copyright © 2011, SAS Institute Inc., Cary, North Carolina, USA. ALL RIGHTS RESERVED.

 **Creating Ensemble Models**

This demonstration continues from the Predictive Analysis diagram. This demonstration proceeds in two parts. First, a control point is added to the process flow to reduce clutter. Then, the Ensemble tool is introduced as potential prediction model.

Diagram Control Point

Follow these steps to add a control point to your analysis diagram:

1. Select the **Utility** tab.

2. Drag a **Control Point** tool into the diagram workspace.

3. Delete all connections to the Model Comparison node.

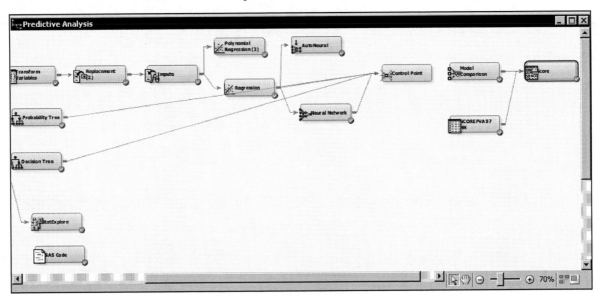

4. Connect model nodes of interest to the **Control Point** node. Connect the **Regression** node first, followed by the two trees, and then the neural network.

5. Connect the **Control Point** node to the **Model Comparison** node.

Copyright © 2011, SAS Institute Inc., Cary, North Carolina, USA. ALL RIGHTS RESERVED.

The completed process flow should appear as shown.

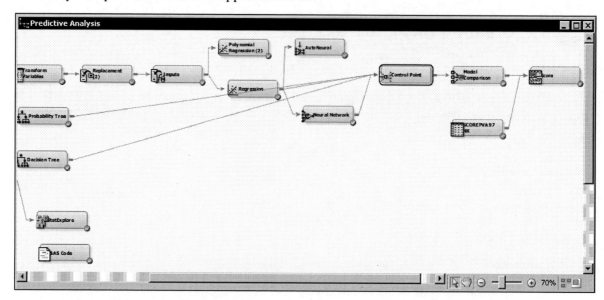

The Control Point node serves as a junction in the diagram. A single connection out of the Control Point node is equivalent to all the connections into the node.

6. Select the **Model** tab.

7. Drag an **Ensemble** tool into the diagram.

8. Connect the **Control Point** node to the **Ensemble** node.

9. Connect the **Ensemble** node to the **Model Comparison** node.

The completed process should appear as shown.

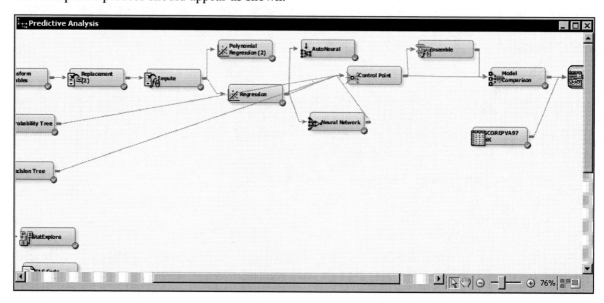

Copyright © 2011, SAS Institute Inc., Cary, North Carolina, USA. ALL RIGHTS RESERVED.

Ensemble Tool

The Ensemble node is not itself a model. It merely combines model predictions. For a categorical target variable, you can choose to combine models using the following functions:

- **Average** takes the average of the prediction estimates from the different models as the prediction from the Ensemble node. This is the default method.

- **Maximum** takes the maximum of the prediction estimates from the different models as the prediction from the Ensemble node.

- **Voting** uses one of two methods for prediction. The average method averages the prediction estimates from the models that decide the primary outcome and ignores any model that decides the secondary outcome. The proportion method ignores the prediction estimates and instead returns the proportion of models deciding the primary outcome.

Run the Model Comparison node and view the results. This enables you to see how the ensemble model compares to the individual models.

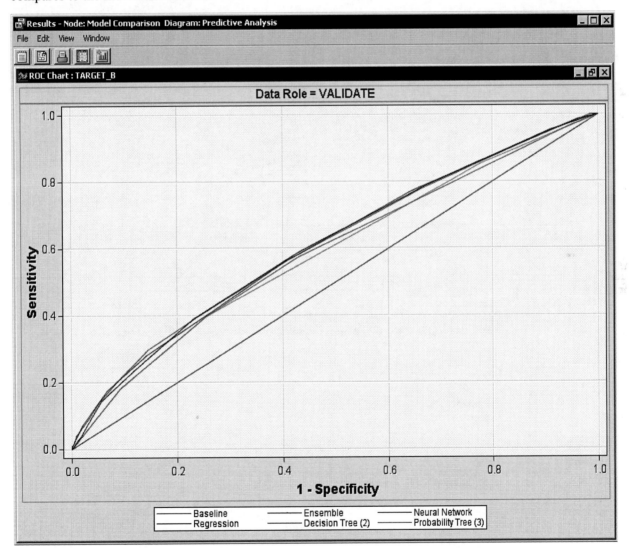

Copyright © 2011, SAS Institute Inc., Cary, North Carolina, USA. ALL RIGHTS RESERVED.

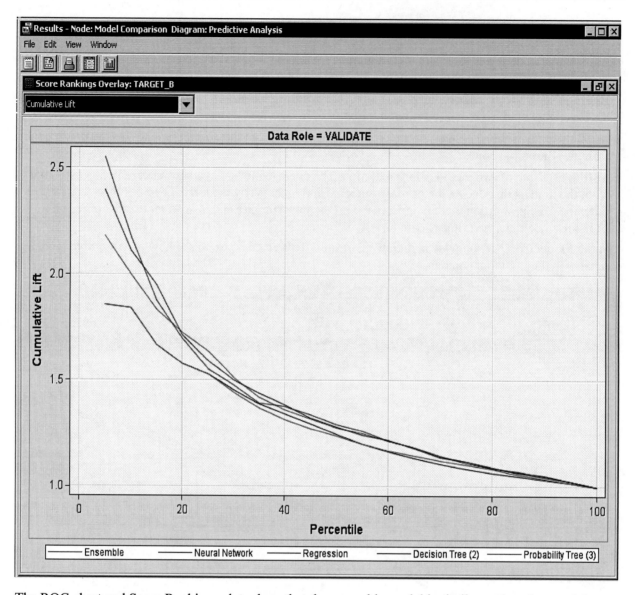

The ROC chart and Score Rankings plots show that the ensemble model is similar to the other models.

Copyright © 2011, SAS Institute Inc., Cary, North Carolina, USA. ALL RIGHTS RESERVED.

9.3 Variable Selection

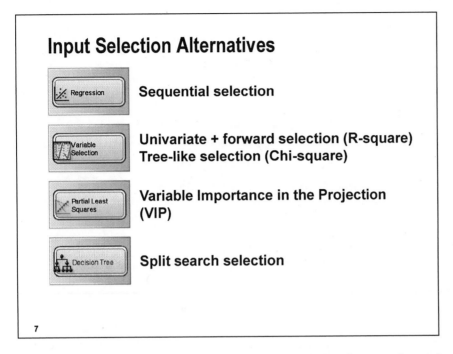

Removing redundant or irrelevant inputs from a training data set often reduces overfitting and improves prediction performance. Some prediction models (for example, neural networks) do not include methods for selecting inputs. For these models, input selection is done with a separate SAS Enterprise Miner tool.

Chapter 4 introduced sequential selection to find useful inputs for regression models. Later in Chapter 5, these inputs were used to compensate for the Neural Networks tool's lack of input selection capabilities. SAS Enterprise Miner features several additional methods to perform input selection for modeling tools inherently missing this capability. The following demonstrations illustrate the use of the Variable Selection, Partial Least Squares, and Decision Tree tools for selection of potentially useful inputs.

Copyright © 2011, SAS Institute Inc., Cary, North Carolina, USA. ALL RIGHTS RESERVED.

Using the Variable Selection Node

The Variable Selection tool provides a selection based on one of two criteria.

When you use the ***R-squared variable selection criterion***, a two-step process is followed:

1. SAS Enterprise Miner computes the squared correlation for each variable and then assigns the Rejected role to those variables that have a value less than the squared correlation criterion. (The default is 0.005.)

2. SAS Enterprise Miner evaluates the remaining (not rejected) variables using a forward stepwise R-squared regression. Variables that have a stepwise R-squared improvement less than the threshold criterion (default=0.0005) are assigned the Rejected role.

When you use the ***chi-squared selection criterion***, variable selection is performed using binary splits for maximizing the chi-squared value of a 2x2 frequency table. The rows of the 2x2 table are defined by the (binary) target variable. The columns of the table are formed by a partition of the training data using a selected input.

Several partitions are considered for each input. For an L-level class input (binary, ordinal, or nominal), partitions are formed by comparing each input level separately to the remaining L-1 input levels, creating a collection of L possible data partitions. The partition with the highest chi-squared value is chosen as the input's best partition. For interval inputs, partitions are formed by dividing the input range into (a maximum of) 50 equal-length bins and splitting the data into two subsets at 1 of the 49 bin boundaries. The partition with the highest chi-squared statistic is chosen as the interval input's best partition. The partition/variable combination with the highest chi-squared statistic is used to split the data, and the process is repeated within both subsets. The partitioning stops when no input has a chi-squared statistic in excess of a user-specified threshold. All variables not used in at least one partition are rejected.

The Variable Selection node's chi-squared approach is quite similar to a decision tree algorithm with its ability to detect nonlinear and nonadditive relationships between the inputs and the target. However, the method for handling categorical inputs makes it sensitive to spurious input/target correlations. Instead of the Variable Selection node's chi-squared setting, you might want to try the Decision Tree node, properly configured for input selection.

The following steps show how to use the Variable Selection tool with the R-squared setting.

1. Select the **Explore** tab.

2. Drag a **Variable Selection** tool into the diagram workspace.

Copyright © 2011, SAS Institute Inc., Cary, North Carolina, USA. ALL RIGHTS RESERVED.

3. Connect the **Impute** node to the **Variable Selection** node.

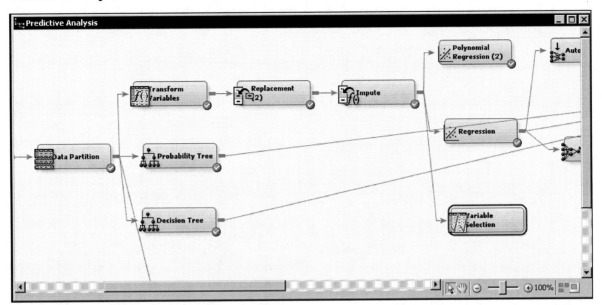

The default Target Model (input selection method) property is set to **Default**. With this default setting, if the target is binary and the total parameter count for a regression model exceeds 400, the chi-squared method is used. Otherwise, the R-squared method of variable selection is used.

4. Select **Target Model ⇨ R-Square**.

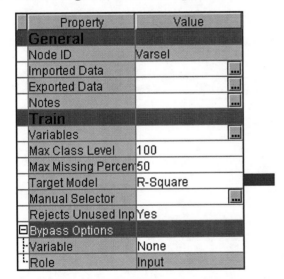

Property	Value
General	
Node ID	Varsel
Imported Data	
Exported Data	
Notes	
Train	
Variables	
Max Class Level	100
Max Missing Percen	50
Target Model	R-Square
Manual Selector	
Rejects Unused Inp	Yes
⊟ Bypass Options	
Variable	None
Role	Input

Recall that a two-step process is performed when you apply the R-squared variable selection criterion to a binary target. The Properties panel enables you to specify the maximum number of variables that can be selected, the cutoff minimum squared correlation measure for an individual variable to be selected, and the necessary R-squared improvement for a variable to remain as an input variable.

Copyright © 2011, SAS Institute Inc., Cary, North Carolina, USA. ALL RIGHTS RESERVED.

Additional available options include the following:

- **Use AOV16 Variables** – When selected, this option requests SAS Enterprise Miner to bin interval variables into 16 equally spaced groups (AOV16). The AOV16 variables are created to help identify nonlinear relationships with the target. Bins with zero observations are eliminated, which means that an AOV16 variable can have fewer than 16 bins.

- **Use Group Variables** – When set to **Yes**, this option enables the number of levels of a class variable to be reduced, based on the relationship of the levels to the target variable.

- **Use Interactions** – When this option is selected, SAS Enterprise Miner evaluates two-way interactions for categorical inputs.

5. Run the Variable Selection node and view the results. The Results window appears.

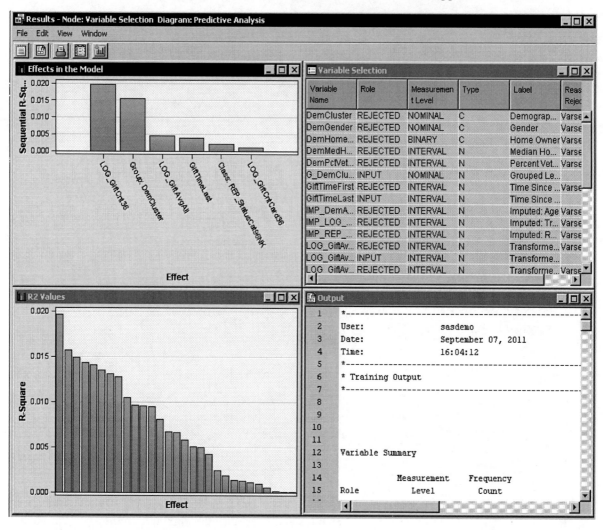

6. Maximize the Variable Selection window.

Copyright © 2011, SAS Institute Inc., Cary, North Carolina, USA. ALL RIGHTS RESERVED.

7. Select the **ROLE** column heading to sort the variables by their assigned roles.

8. Select the **Reasons for Rejection** column heading.

Variable Name	ROLE	LEVEL	TYPE	Variable Label	Reasons for Rejection ▲
G_DemClu...	INPUT	NOMINAL	N		
GiftTimeLast	INPUT	INTERVAL	N	Time Since ...	
LOG_GiftAv...	INPUT	INTERVAL	N	Transforme...	
LOG_GiftC...	INPUT	INTERVAL	N	Transforme...	
LOG_GiftC...	INPUT	INTERVAL	N	Transforme...	
REP_Statu...	INPUT	NOMINAL	C	Replace:St...	
DemGender	REJECTED	NOMINAL	C	Gender	Varsel:Sma...
DemHome...	REJECTED	BINARY	C	Home Owner	Varsel:Sma...
DemMedH...	REJECTED	INTERVAL	N	Median Ho...	Varsel:Sma...
DemPctVet...	REJECTED	INTERVAL	N	Percent Vet...	Varsel:Sma...
GiftTimeFirst	REJECTED	INTERVAL	N	Time Since ...	Varsel:Sma...
IMP_DemA...	REJECTED	INTERVAL	N	Imputed: Age	Varsel:Sma...
IMP_LOG_...	REJECTED	INTERVAL	N	Imputed: Tr...	Varsel:Sma...
IMP_REP_...	REJECTED	INTERVAL	N	Imputed: R...	Varsel:Sma...
LOG_GiftAv...	REJECTED	INTERVAL	N	Transforme...	Varsel:Sma...
LOG_GiftAv...	REJECTED	INTERVAL	N	Transforme...	Varsel:Sma...
LOG_GiftC...	REJECTED	INTERVAL	N	Transforme...	Varsel:Sma...
LOG_GiftC...	REJECTED	INTERVAL	N	Transforme...	Varsel:Sma...
M_DemAge	REJECTED	BINARY	N	Imputation I...	Varsel:Sma...
M_LOG_Gif...	REJECTED	BINARY	N	Imputation I...	Varsel:Sma...
M_REP_De...	REJECTED	BINARY	N	Imputation I...	Varsel:Sma...
PromCnt12	REJECTED	INTERVAL	N	Promotion ...	Varsel:Sma...
PromCnt36	REJECTED	INTERVAL	N	Promotion ...	Varsel:Sma...
PromCntAll	REJECTED	INTERVAL	N	Promotion ...	Varsel:Sma...
PromCntCa...	REJECTED	INTERVAL	N	Promotion ...	Varsel:Sma...
PromCntCa...	REJECTED	INTERVAL	N	Promotion ...	Varsel:Sma...
PromCntCa...	REJECTED	INTERVAL	N	Promotion ...	Varsel:Sma...
StatusCatSt...	REJECTED	BINARY	N	Status Cate...	Varsel:Sma...
DemCluster	REJECTED	NOMINAL	C	Demograp...	Varsel:Sma...

The Variable Selection node finds that most inputs have insufficient target correlation to justify keeping them. You can try these inputs in a subsequent model or adjust the R-squared settings to be less severe. Notice the input **G_DemCluster** is a grouping of the original **DemCluster** input.

 Binary targets generate notoriously low R-squared statistics. A more appropriate association measure might be the likelihood chi-squared statistic found in the Regression node.

Copyright © 2011, SAS Institute Inc., Cary, North Carolina, USA. ALL RIGHTS RESERVED.

Using Partial Least Squares for Input Selection

Partial least squares (PLS) regression can be thought of as a merging of multiple and principal components regression. In multiple regression, the goal is to find linear combinations of the inputs that account for as much (linear) variation in the target as possible. In principal component regression, the goal is to find linear combinations of the inputs that account for as much (linear) variation in the input space as possible, and then use these linear combinations (called *principal component vectors*) as the inputs to a multiple regression model. In PLS regression, the goal is to have linear combinations of the inputs (called *latent vectors*) that account for variation in **both** the inputs and the target. The technique can extract a small number of latent vectors from a set of correlated inputs that correlate with the target.

A useful feature of the PLS procedure is the inclusion of an input importance metric named *variable importance in the projection* (VIP). VIP quantifies the relative importance of the original input variables to the latent vectors. A sufficiently small VIP for an input (less than 0.8, by default) plus a small parameter estimate (less than 0.1, by default) permits removal of the input from the model.

The following steps demonstrate the use of the PLS tool for variable selection:

1. Select the **Model** tab.

2. Drag a **Partial Least Squares** tool into the diagram workspace.

3. Connect the **Impute** node to the **Partial Least Squares** node.

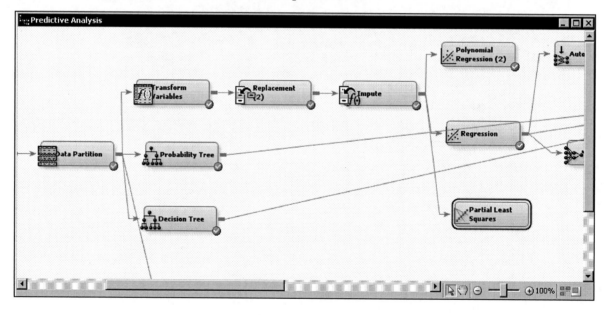

Copyright © 2011, SAS Institute Inc., Cary, North Carolina, USA. ALL RIGHTS RESERVED.

4. Select **Export Selected Variables** ⇨ **Yes**.

Train	
Variables	[...]
⊟ Modeling Techniques	
⊢ Regression Model	PLS
⊢ PLS Algorithm	NIPALS
⊢ Maximum Iteration	200
⊢ Epsilon	1.0E-12
⊟ Number of Factors	
⊢ Default	Yes
⊢ Number of Factors	15
⊟ Cross Validation	
⊢ CV Method	None
⊢ CV N Parameter	7
⊟ Random CV Options	
⊢ Number of Iterations	10
⊢ Default No. of Test Obs.	Yes
⊢ No. of Test Obs.	100
⊢ Default Random Seed	Yes
⊢ Random Seed	1234
Score	
⊟ Variable Selection	
⊢ Variable Selection Criterion	Both
⊢ Para. Est. Cutoff	0.1
⊢ VIP Cutoff	0.8
⊢ Export Selected Variables	Yes
⊢ Hide Rejected Variables	No

Copyright © 2011, SAS Institute Inc., Cary, North Carolina, USA. ALL RIGHTS RESERVED.

5. Run the Partial Least Squares node and view the results.

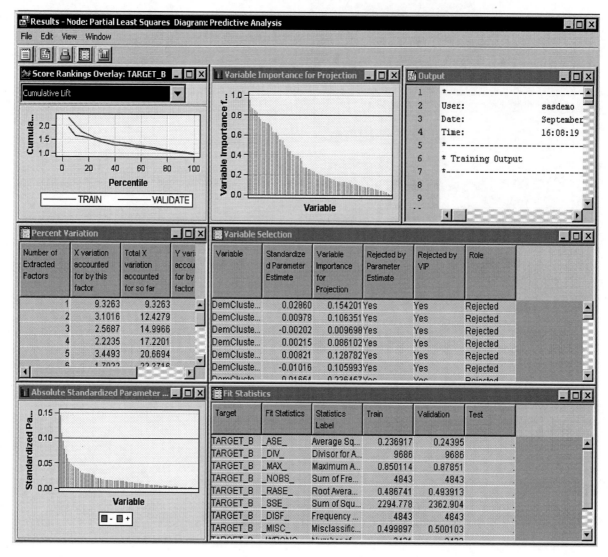

Copyright © 2011, SAS Institute Inc., Cary, North Carolina, USA. ALL RIGHTS RESERVED.

6. Maximize the Percent Variation window.

Percent Variation

Number of Extracted Factors	X variation accounted for by this factor	Total X variation accounted for so far	Y variation accounted for by this factor	Total Y variation accounted for so far
1	9.3263	9.3263	2.9889	2.9889
2	3.1016	12.4279	1.5930	4.5818
3	2.5687	14.9966	0.4026	4.9844
4	2.2235	17.2201	0.0909	5.0754
5	3.4493	20.6694	0.0223	5.0977
6	1.7022	22.3716	0.0290	5.1267
7	1.8648	24.2364	0.0134	5.1400
8	2.5094	26.7458	0.0113	5.1513
9	1.0899	27.8357	0.0238	5.1751
10	1.5489	29.3846	0.0096	5.1847
11	1.1964	30.5809	0.0086	5.1934
12	0.7255	31.3065	0.0158	5.2091
13	1.2303	32.5368	0.0087	5.2178
14	1.3137	33.8505	0.0065	5.2243
15	0.8789	34.7294	0.0089	5.2332

By default, the Partial Least Squares tool extracts 15 latent vectors or factors from the training data set. These factors account for 35% and 5.2% of the variation in the inputs and target, respectively.

Copyright © 2011, SAS Institute Inc., Cary, North Carolina, USA. ALL RIGHTS RESERVED.

7. Maximize the Variable Selection window.

8. Select the **Role** column heading to sort the table by variable role.

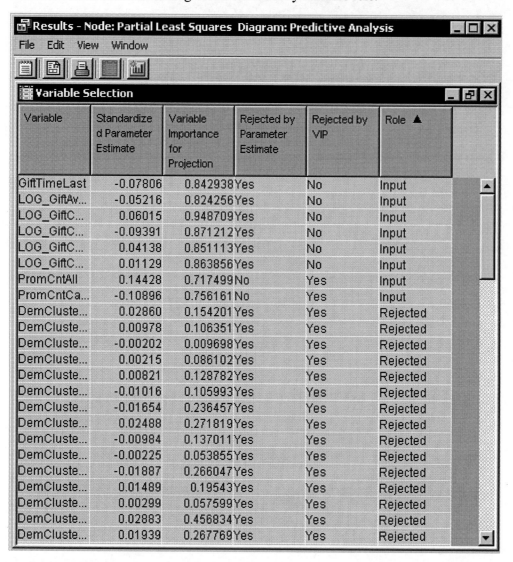

The majority of the selected inputs relate to donation count, promotion count, time since donation, and amount of donation.

Copyright © 2011, SAS Institute Inc., Cary, North Carolina, USA. ALL RIGHTS RESERVED.

Using the Decision Tree Node for Input Selection

Decision trees can be used to select inputs for flexible predictive models. They have an advantage over using a standard regression model or the Variable Selection tool's R-squared method if the inputs' relationships to the target are nonlinear or nonadditive.

1. Connect a **Decision Tree** node to the **Impute** node. Rename the Decision Tree node **Selection Tree**.

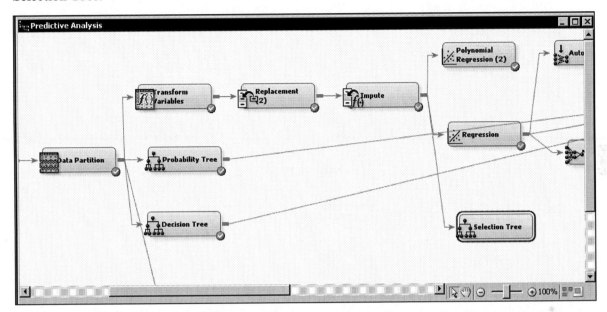

You can use the Tree node with default settings to select inputs. However, this tends to select too few inputs for a subsequent model. Two changes to the Tree defaults result in more inputs being selected. Generally, when you use trees to select inputs for flexible models, it is better to err on the side of too many inputs rather than too few. The model's complexity optimization method can usually compensate for the extra inputs.

✎   The following changes to the defaults act independently. You can experiment to discover which method generalizes best with your data.

Copyright © 2011, SAS Institute Inc., Cary, North Carolina, USA. ALL RIGHTS RESERVED.

2. Type **1** as the Number of Surrogate Rules value.

3. Select **Subtree** ⇨ **Method** ⇨ **Largest**.

Property	Value
⊟ Splitting Rule	
Interval Criterion	ProbF
Nominal Criterion	ProbChisq
Ordinal Criterion	Entropy
Significance Level	0.2
Missing Values	Use in search
Use Input Once	No
Maximum Branch	2
Maximum Depth	6
Minimum Categorical Size	5
⊟ Node	
Leaf Size	5
Number of Rules	5
Number of Surrogate Rules	1
Split Size	.
⊟ Split Search	
Use Decisions	No
Use Priors	No
Exhaustive	5000
Node Sample	20000
⊟ Subtree	
Method	Largest
Number of Leaves	1
Assessment Measure	Decision
Assessment Fraction	0.25
⊟ Cross Validation	

Changing the number of surrogates enables inclusion of surrogate splits in the variable selection process. By definition, surrogate inputs are typically correlated with the selected split input. While it is usually a bad practice to include redundant inputs in predictive models, many flexible models tolerate some degree of input redundancy. The advantage of including surrogates in the variable selection is to enable inclusion of inputs that do not appear in the tree explicitly but are still important predictors of the target.

Changing the Subtree method causes the tree algorithm to not prune the tree. As with adding surrogate splits to the variable selection process, it tends to add (possibly irrelevant) inputs to the selection list.

4. Run the Selection Tree node and view the results.

Copyright © 2011, SAS Institute Inc., Cary, North Carolina, USA. ALL RIGHTS RESERVED.

5. View lines 70 through 81 of the Output window. This is a list of the variables that appear in the Selection Tree, but it does not provide surrogate variables that do not appear in the tree.

Obs	NAME	LABEL	NRULES	NSURROGATES	IMPORTANCE	VIMPORTANCE	RATIO
1	LOG_GiftCnt36	Transformed: Gift Count 36 Months	1	0	1.00000	1.00000	1.00000
3	PromCnt12	Promotion Count 12 Months	2	1	0.66372	0.36177	0.54506
4	DemCluster	Demographic Cluster	3	2	0.65908	0.09777	0.14834
5	DemMedHomeValue	Median Home Value Region	2	1	0.64347	0.10861	0.16879
7	LOG_GiftAvgLast	Transformed: Gift Amount Last	1	0	0.52413	0.67188	1.28189
8	GiftTimeLast	Time Since Last Gift	1	0	0.48092	0.44530	0.92595
9	IMP_LOG_GiftAvgCard36	Imputed: Transformed: Gift Amount Average Card 36 Months	2	0	0.40002	0.32098	0.80240
10	LOG_GiftAvgAll	Transformed: Gift Amount Average All Months	1	0	0.39360	0.00000	0.00000
13	DemHomeOwner	Home Owner	1	0	0.30767	0.00000	0.00000
14	StatusCatStarAll	Status Category Star All Months	1	0	0.29456	0.06599	0.22403

6. To view a complete list of variables selected by the tree, including surrogate variables, select **View** ⇨ **Model** ⇨ **Variable Importance** from the Selection Tree results. Only variables with non-zero values for Importance are the variables selected by the Selection Tree. This list includes surrogate variables that do not appear in the tree.

Copyright © 2011, SAS Institute Inc., Cary, North Carolina, USA. ALL RIGHTS RESERVED.

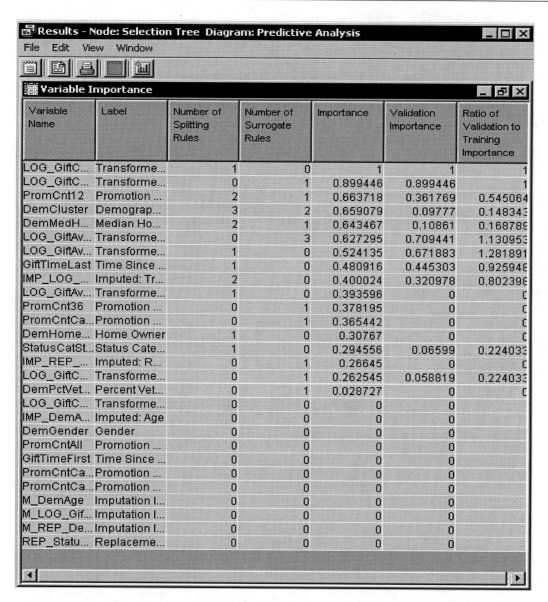

The Importance column quantifies approximately how much of the overall variability in the target each input explains. The values are normalized by the amount of variability explained by the input with the highest importance. The variable importance definition not only considers inputs selected as split variables, but it also accounts for surrogate inputs (if a positive number of surrogate rules are selected in the Properties panel). For example, the second most important input (**LOG_GiftCntCard36**) accounts for almost the same variability as the most important input (**LOG_GiftCnt36**) even though it does not explicitly appear in the tree.

Copyright © 2011, SAS Institute Inc., Cary, North Carolina, USA. ALL RIGHTS RESERVED.

9.4 Categorical Input Consolidation

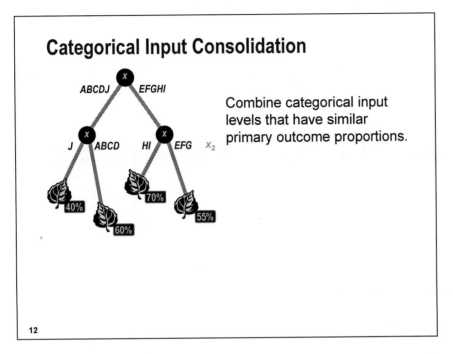

Categorical Input Consolidation

Combine categorical input levels that have similar primary outcome proportions.

Categorical inputs pose a major problem for parametric predictive models such as regressions and neural networks. Because each categorical level must be coded by an indicator variable, a single input can account for more model parameters than all other inputs combined.

Decision trees, on the other hand, thrive on categorical inputs. They can easily group the distinct levels of the categorical variable together and produce good predictions.

It is possible to use a decision tree to consolidate the levels of a categorical input. You simply build a decision tree using the categorical variable of interest as the sole modeling input. The split search algorithm then groups input levels with similar primary outcome proportions. The IDs for each leaf replace the original levels of the input.

Copyright © 2011, SAS Institute Inc., Cary, North Carolina, USA. ALL RIGHTS RESERVED.

Consolidating Categorical Inputs

Follow these steps to use a tree model to group categorical input levels and create useful inputs for regression and neural network models.

1. Connect a **Decision Tree** node to the **Impute** node, and rename the Decision Tree node **Consolidation Tree**.

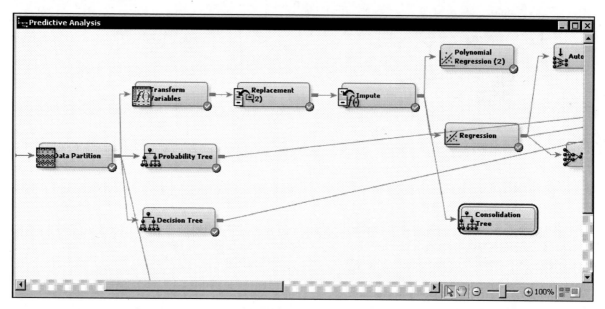

The Consolidation Tree node is used to group the levels of **DemCluster**, a categorical input with more than 50 levels.

You use a tree model to group these levels based on their associations with **TARGET_B**. From this grouping, a new modeling input is created. You can use this input in place of **DemCluster** in a regression or other model. In this way, the predictive prowess of **DemCluster** is incorporated into a model without the plethora of parameters needed to encode the original.

The grouping can be done autonomously by simply running the Decision Tree node, or interactively by using the node's interactive training features. You use the automatic method here.

Copyright © 2011, SAS Institute Inc., Cary, North Carolina, USA. ALL RIGHTS RESERVED.

2. Select **Variables** from the Consolidation Tree Properties panel.

3. Select **DemCluster** ⇨ **Explore**. The Explore window appears.

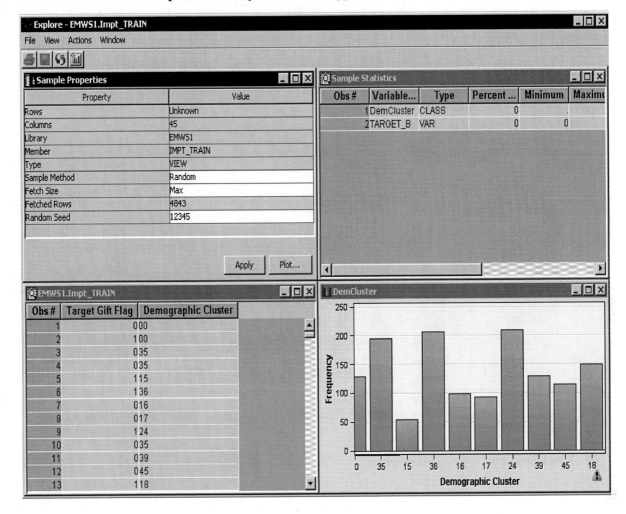

Copyright © 2011, SAS Institute Inc., Cary, North Carolina, USA. ALL RIGHTS RESERVED.

4. Maximize the **DemCluster** histogram.

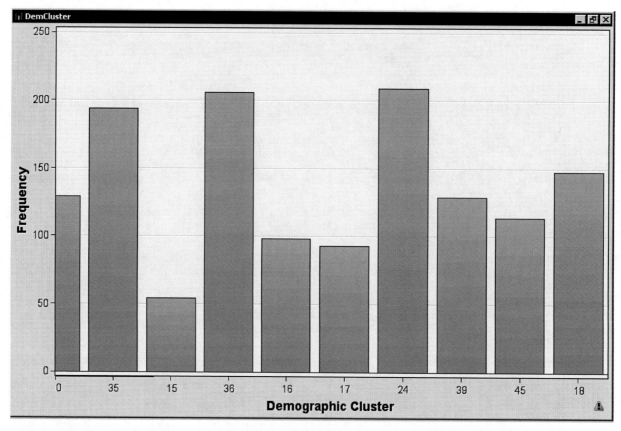

The **DemCluster** input has more than 50 levels, but you can see the distribution of only a few of these levels.

5. Click 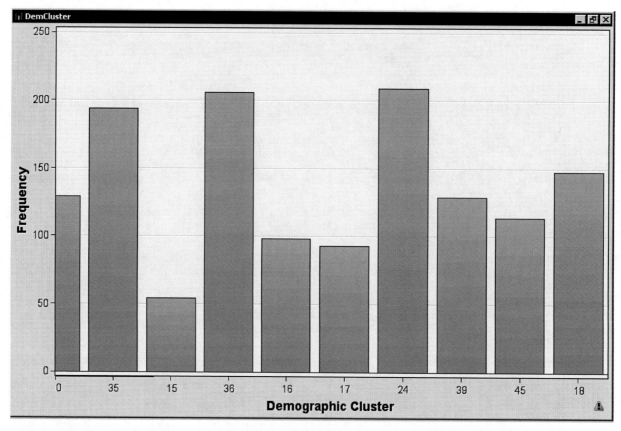 in the lower right corner of the DemCluster window.

Copyright © 2011, SAS Institute Inc., Cary, North Carolina, USA. ALL RIGHTS RESERVED.

The histogram expands to show the relative frequencies of each level of **DemCluster**.

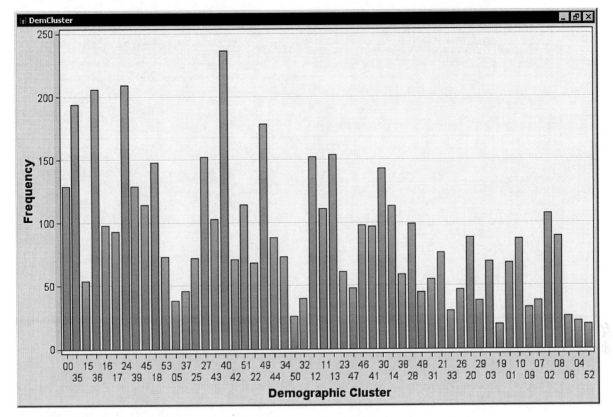

The histogram reveals input levels with low case counts. This can detrimentally affect the performance of most models.

6.   Close the Explore window.

Copyright © 2011, SAS Institute Inc., Cary, North Carolina, USA. ALL RIGHTS RESERVED.

7. Select **Use** ⇨ **No** for all variables in the Variables window.

8. Select **Use** ⇨ **Yes** for **DemCluster** and **TARGET_B**.

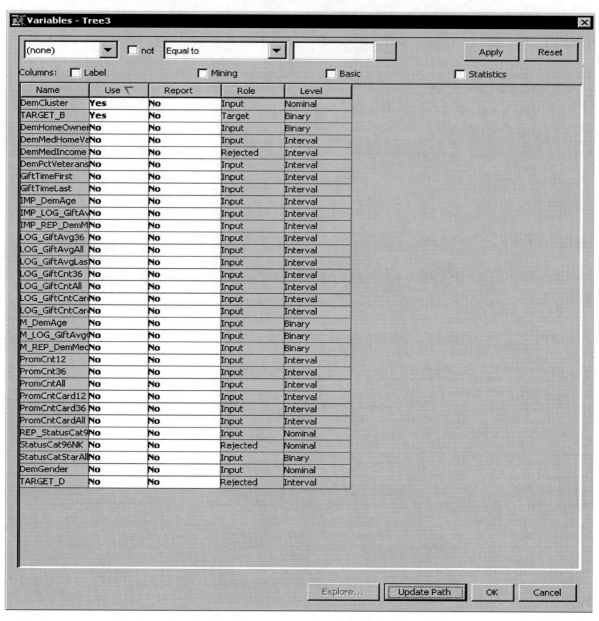

After sorting on the column **Use**, the Variables window should appear as shown.

9. Select **OK** to close the Variables window.

Copyright © 2011, SAS Institute Inc., Cary, North Carolina, USA. ALL RIGHTS RESERVED.

10. Make these changes in the Train property group.

   a. Select **Assessment Measure** ⇨ **Average Squared Error**. This optimizes the tree for prediction estimates.

   b. Select **Bonferroni Adjustment** ⇨ **No**.

   When you evaluate a potential split, the Decision Tree tool applies, by default, a Bonferroni adjustment to the splits logworth. The adjustment penalizes the logworth of potential **DemCluster** splits. The penalty is calculated as the log of the number of partitions of **DemCluster** levels split into two groups, or $log_{10}(2^{L-1} - 1)$. With 54 distinct levels, the penalty is quite large. It is also, in this case, quite unnecessary. The penalty avoids favoring inputs with many possible splits. Here you are building a tree with only one input. It is impossible to favor this input over others because there are no other inputs.

11. Make these changes in the Score property group.

   a. Select **Variable Selection** ⇨ **No**. This prevents the decision tree from rejecting inputs in subsequent nodes.

   b. Select **Leaf Role** ⇨ **Input**. This adds a new input (**_NODE_**) to the training data.

12. Now use the Interactive Tree tool to cluster **DemCluster** values into related groups.

   a. Select **Interactive** ⇨ **...** from the Decision Tree Properties panel.

Property	Value
Node ID	Tree4
Imported Data	...
Exported Data	...
Notes	...
Train	
Variables	...
Interactive	...
Use Frozen Tree	No
Use Multiple Targets	No

Copyright © 2011, SAS Institute Inc., Cary, North Carolina, USA. ALL RIGHTS RESERVED.

The SAS Enterprise Miner Tree Desktop Application opens.

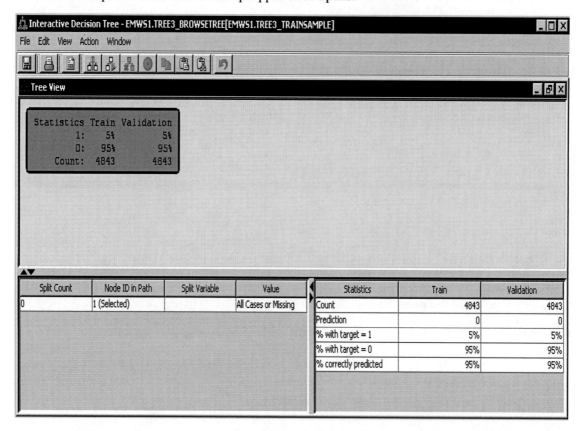

b.   Right-click the root node and select **Train Node** from the option menu.

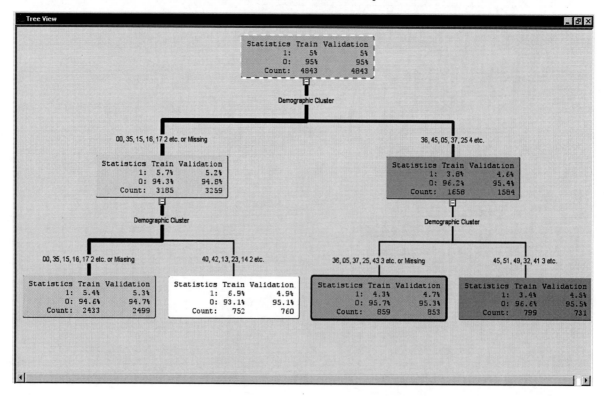

Copyright © 2011, SAS Institute Inc., Cary, North Carolina, USA. ALL RIGHTS RESERVED.

The levels of **DemCluster** are partitioned into four groups corresponding to the four leaves of the tree.

An input named **_NODE_** is added to the training data. You can use the Transform Variables tool to rename **_NODE_** to a more descriptive value. You can use the Replacement tool to change the level names.

Copyright © 2011, SAS Institute Inc., Cary, North Carolina, USA. ALL RIGHTS RESERVED.

9.5 Surrogate Models

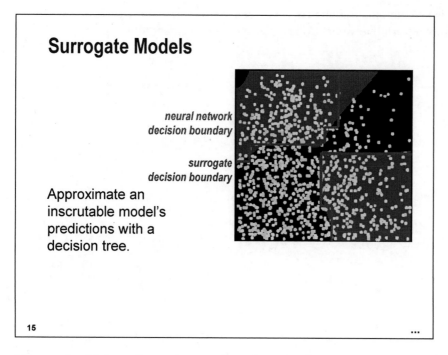

The usual criticism of neural networks and similar flexible models is the difficulty in understanding the predictions.

This criticism stems from the complex parameterizations found in the model. While it is true that little insight can be gained by analyzing the actual parameters of the model, much can be gained by analyzing the resulting prediction decisions.

A profit matrix or other mechanism for generating a decision threshold defines regions in the input space corresponding to the primary decision. The idea behind a surrogate model is building an easy-to-understand model that describes this region. In this way, characteristics used by the neural network to make the primary decision can be understood, even if the neural network model itself cannot be.

Copyright © 2011, SAS Institute Inc., Cary, North Carolina, USA. ALL RIGHTS RESERVED.

Describing Decision Segments with Surrogate Models

In this demonstration, a decision tree is used to isolate cases found solicitation-worthy by a neural network model. Using the decision tree, characteristics of solicit-decision donors can be understood even if the model making the decision is a mystery.

Setting Up the Diagram

You need to attach two nodes to the modeling node that you want to study.

1. Select the **Utilities** tab.

2. Drag a **Metadata** tool into the diagram workspace.

3. Connect the **Neural Network** node to the **Metadata** node.

4. Select the **Model** tab.

5. Drag a **Decision Tree** tool into the diagram workspace.

6. Connect the **Decision Tree** tool to the **Metadata** node.

7. Rename the Decision Tree node **Description Tree**.

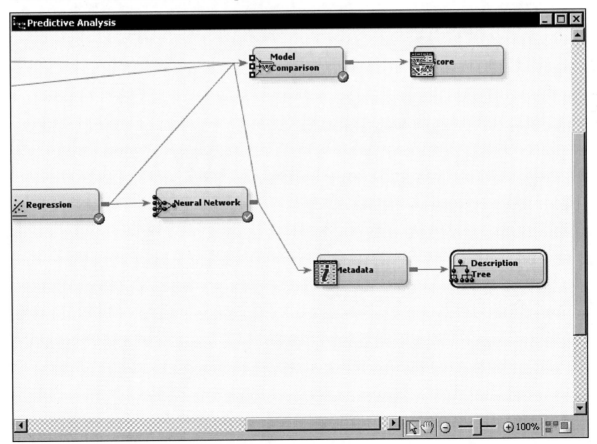

Copyright © 2011, SAS Institute Inc., Cary, North Carolina, USA. ALL RIGHTS RESERVED.

Changing the Metadata

You must change the focus of the analysis from **TARGET_B** to the variable describing the neural network decisions. SAS Enterprise Miner automatically creates this variable in the training and validation data sets exported from a modeling node. The variable's name is **D_*target***, where ***target*** is the name of the original target variable.

✎   **D_TARGET_B** is automatically created on the definition of decision data only.

The following steps change the target variable from **TARGET_B** to **D_TARGET_B**:

1. Scroll down to the Variables section in the Metadata node properties. Select **Train**. The Variables window appears.

2. Select **New Role** ⇨ **Target** for **D_TARGET_B**.

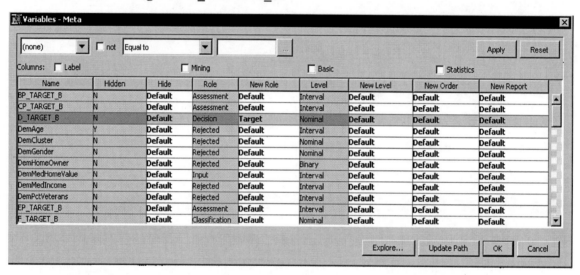

3. Select **New Role** ⇨ **Rejected** for **TARGET_B**.

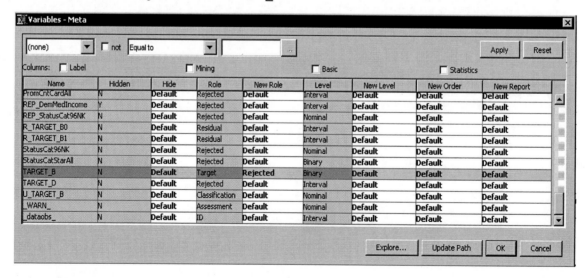

4. Select **OK** to close the Variables dialog box.

5. Run the Metadata node. Do not view the results.

Copyright © 2011, SAS Institute Inc., Cary, North Carolina, USA. ALL RIGHTS RESERVED.

Exploring the Description Tree

Follow these steps to explore the description tree.

1. Run the Description Tree node. View the results.

2. Select **View** ⇨ **Model** ⇨ **Subtree Assessment Plot** from the Description Tree results.

3. Change the basis of the plot to **Misclassification Rate**.

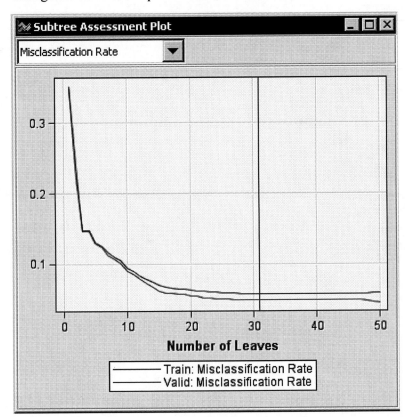

The Assessment plot shows the trade-off between tree complexity and agreement with the original neural network model. The autonomously fit description agrees with the neural network about 95% of the time, and as the tree becomes more complicated, the agreement with the neural network improves. You can scrutinize this tree for the input values resulting in a solicit decision, or you can simplify the description with some accuracy loss. Surprisingly, 85% of the decisions made by the neural network model can be summarized by a three-leaf tree.

The following steps generate the three-leaf description tree.

4. Close the Description Tree results window.

Copyright © 2011, SAS Institute Inc., Cary, North Carolina, USA. ALL RIGHTS RESERVED.

5. Under the Subtree properties of the description tree, change the Method setting to **N** and the Number of Leaves setting to **3**.

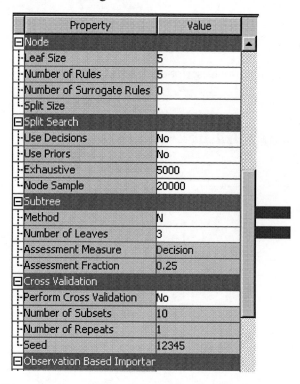

Property	Value
Node	
Leaf Size	5
Number of Rules	5
Number of Surrogate Rules	0
Split Size	.
Split Search	
Use Decisions	No
Use Priors	No
Exhaustive	5000
Node Sample	20000
Subtree	
Method	N
Number of Leaves	3
Assessment Measure	Decision
Assessment Fraction	0.25
Cross Validation	
Perform Cross Validation	No
Number of Subsets	10
Number of Repeats	1
Seed	12345
Observation Based Importar	

6. Run the Description Tree node and open the Results window.

Copyright © 2011, SAS Institute Inc., Cary, North Carolina, USA. ALL RIGHTS RESERVED.

7. Select **View** ⇨ **Model** ⇨ **Subtree Assessment Plot** from the Description Tree results.

8. Change the basis of the plot to **Misclassification Rate**.

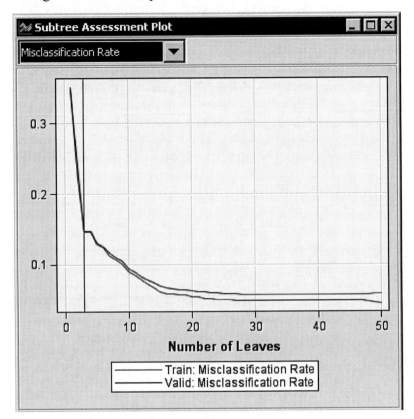

The accuracy dropped to 85%, but the tree has only two rules.

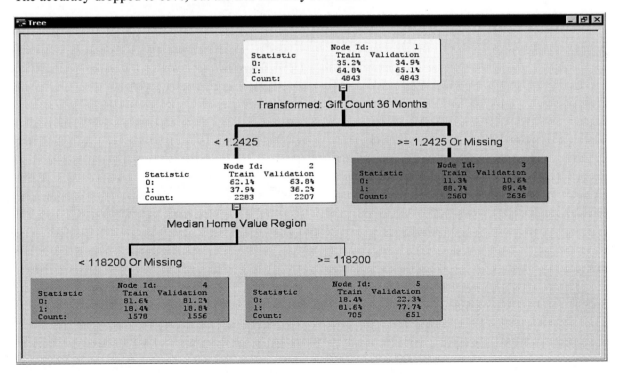

Copyright © 2011, SAS Institute Inc., Cary, North Carolina, USA. ALL RIGHTS RESERVED.

You can conclude from this tree that the neural network is soliciting donors who gave many times (relatively) in the past or donors who gave fewer times but live in more expensive neighborhoods.

You should experiment with accuracy versus tree size trade-offs (and other tree options) to achieve a description of the neural network model that is both understandable and accurate.

It should be noted that the inputs used to describe the tree are the same as the inputs used to build the neural network. You can also consider other inputs to describe the tree. For example, some of the monetary inputs were log-transformed. To improve understandability, you can substitute the original inputs for these without loss of model accuracy. You can also consider inputs that were *not* used to build the model to describe the decisions. For example, if a charity's Marketing Department was interested in soliciting new individuals similar to those selected by the neural network, but without a previous donation history, it could attempt to describe the donors using demographic inputs only.

 It should be noted that separate sampling distorts the results shown in this section. To accurately describe the solicit and ignore decisions, you must down-weight the primary cases and up-weight the secondary cases. This can be done by defining a frequency variable defined as shown.

```
if TARGET_B=1 then WEIGHT = 0.05/0.50;
else                WEIGHT = 0.95/0.50;
```

You can define this variable using a Transform Variables tool's Expression Builder. You then set the model role of this variable to **Frequency**.

Another approach is to build the model on the **Score** data set. Because the **Score** data set is not oversampled, you get accurate agreement percentages. This is possible because the description tree does not depend on the value of the target variables, only on the model predictions.

Copyright © 2011, SAS Institute Inc., Cary, North Carolina, USA. ALL RIGHTS RESERVED.

9.6 SAS Rapid Predictive Modeler

What Is SAS Rapid Predictive Modeler?

- A task for SAS Enterprise Guide 4.3 and the SAS Add-In for Microsoft Office 4.3 for Excel
- A way to construct useful predictive models quickly

18

SAS Rapid Predictive Modeler (referred to as RPM in the remainder of this section) is a task that runs in SAS Enterprise Guide 4.3 and the SAS Add-In for Microsoft Office 4.3 for Excel. It quickly executes prebuilt SAS Enterprise Miner 7.1 models.

In SAS Enterprise Guide 4.3 and the add-in for 4.3 for Excel, there are new data mining categories. This is where RPM is launched. The idea of RPM is to make predictive modeling more accessible to a business and build usable models quickly. Little to no statistical training is needed to run an RPM model. RPM does behind the scenes what statisticians/modelers do in person.

Copyright © 2011, SAS Institute Inc., Cary, North Carolina, USA. ALL RIGHTS RESERVED.

RPM Key Capabilities

- Prebuilt basic, intermediate, and advanced models
- "Load your data and go!"
- Presents customizable results as simple, easy-to-understand reports
- Allows models to be refined in SAS Enterprise Miner

19

Here are some key capabilities of RPM:

- Basic, intermediate, and advanced prebuilt models are available.

  Modeling methods are in a hierarchy in that intermediate models contain basic models and advanced models contain both intermediate and basic models. Basic models (8 nodes in SAS Enterprise Miner) use decision trees for variable selection and build forward selection regression models. Intermediate models (18 nodes in SAS Enterprise Miner) use several variable selection methods and several variable transformations, and build decision trees and regression models. Variable interactions are considered. The best performing model is chosen. Advanced models (32 nodes in SAS Enterprise Miner) include neural networks, advanced regression, and ensemble models. Again, the best performing model is chosen.

- "Load your data and go!" When all necessary steps in setting up the RPM task are complete, modeling is done automatically and results are presented.

- RPM presents results as simple, easy-to-understand reports, including a scorecard, lift/gains charts, and a list of key variables/variable importance. Results can be customized by selecting report options from a default list.

- RPM models can be customized, refined, and improved in SAS Enterprise Miner by an advanced modeler.

RPM is delivered with SAS Enterprise Miner 7.1and is free. The SAS Enterprise Guide 4.3 and SAS Add-In for Microsoft Office Excel clients are included in the SAS Enterprise Miner bundle at no charge. RPM can be server based or run from a personal work station.

Copyright © 2011, SAS Institute Inc., Cary, North Carolina, USA. ALL RIGHTS RESERVED.

Running a Basic RPM Model

This demonstration illustrates running a basic RPM model in SAS Enterprise Guide 4.3. It uses the **PVA97NK** data defined in Chapter 2. The demonstration requires no prior knowledge of SAS Enterprise Guide. A discussion of results is omitted from this demonstration. Interpretation of results is similar to the interpretation that is provided in previous chapters.

1. Open SAS Enterprise Guide 4.3 and select **New Project**. Connect as user **Sasdemo** with the password **Metadata0**. (For Excel, simply open the application.)

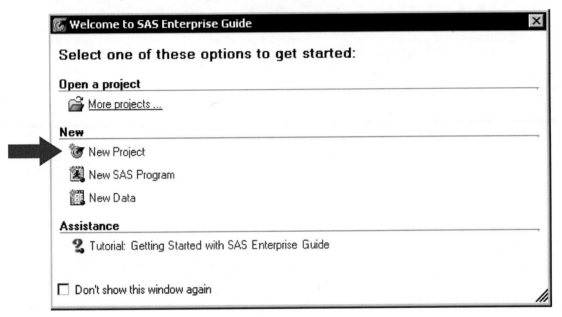

Copyright © 2011, SAS Institute Inc., Cary, North Carolina, USA. ALL RIGHTS RESERVED.

2. Select **Tasks** from the menu bar. Select **Data Mining** ⇨ **Rapid Predictive Modeler**. (In Excel, select the **SAS** tab first, and then select **Tasks** ⇨ **Data Mining** ⇨ **Rapid Predictive Modeler**.)

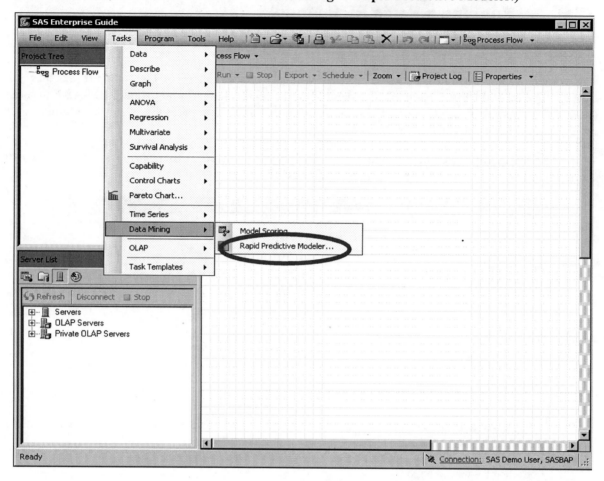

You can also open a data file first by selecting **File** ⇨ **Open** ⇨ **Data** and then invoking the RPM task.

Copyright © 2011, SAS Institute Inc., Cary, North Carolina, USA. ALL RIGHTS RESERVED.

3. A data selection window appears. Select the appropriate data table or browse to it. For the current demonstration, select the **Pva97nk** SAS data file located on the virtual machine at **D:\Workshop\winsas\aaem**. Select **Open**.

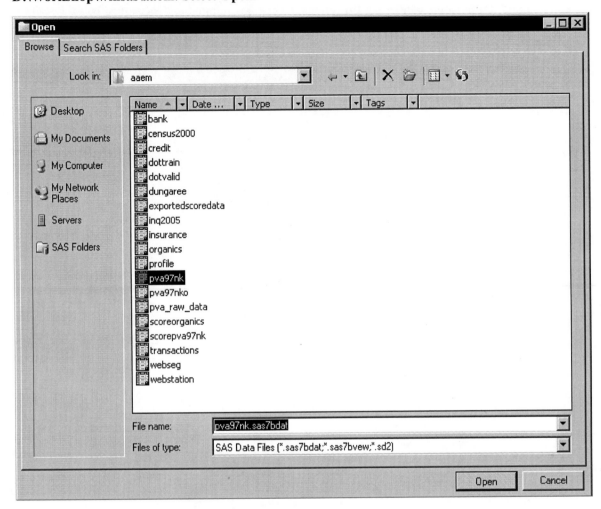

Copyright © 2011, SAS Institute Inc., Cary, North Carolina, USA. ALL RIGHTS RESERVED.

4. After data is loaded, the RPM task window appears. Define the modeling variables. To assign a particular variable to a certain role, highlight the variable from the Input Variable list and then select the arrow pointing right. Select the appropriate modeling role from the pop-up list. If variables are aptly named, for example containing **target** or **ID**, they are automatically assigned roles. Possible variable roles are Dependent, Frequency Count, ID, and Excluded. All other variables are considered as inputs.

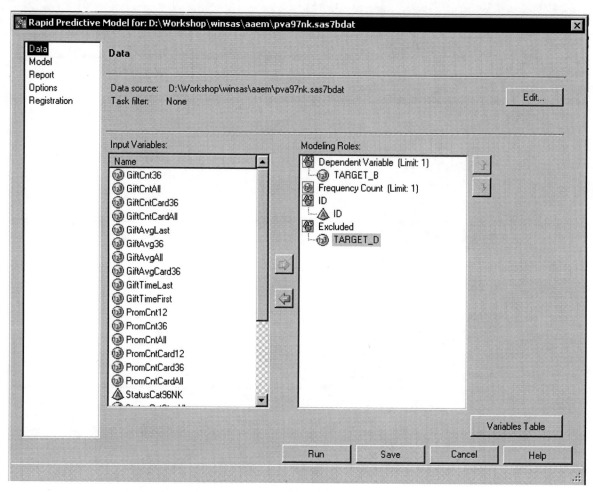

Be sure that your modeling roles match those shown above.

The dependent variable (or target) is the only required variable to run an RPM model. This is the variable that you want to predict. The dependent variable can be of class measurement (categorical) or of interval measurement (continuous). Different results are presented depending on the type of target measurement. This discussion considers only a binary target variable.

The Frequency Count variable is an optional variable used to provide different weights to rows of data (that is, to certain records or observations).

Copyright © 2011, SAS Institute Inc., Cary, North Carolina, USA. ALL RIGHTS RESERVED.

5. Select **Model** from the Menu of the RPM task window. Select **Basic** as the modeling method.

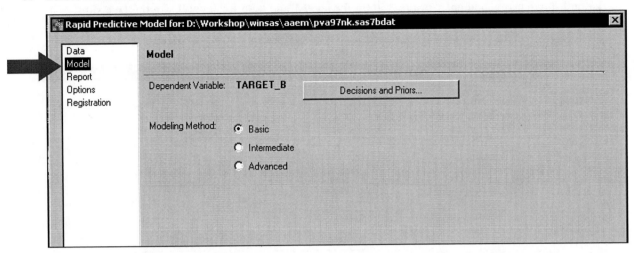

6. If necessary, when modeling a class target, select **Decisions and Priors** to define the target level, set prior probabilities, and set the decision function and matrix. Select **Decisions and Priors**, and the following window appears. Select **OK**.

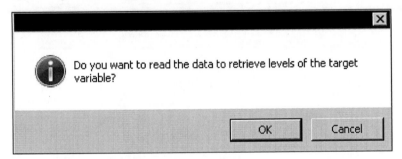

Copyright © 2011, SAS Institute Inc., Cary, North Carolina, USA. ALL RIGHTS RESERVED.

7. Verify that the **Event Level** field is set to 1. Set the **Prior probabilities** field to **User Defined** using the pull-down arrow and enter priors of 0.05 for level 1 and 0.95 for level 0. Set the **Decision function** field to **Maximum** and enter values 15.14, -0.68, 0, and 0 in the appropriate places of the profit matrix following what was done in Chapter 6. Select **OK** when complete.

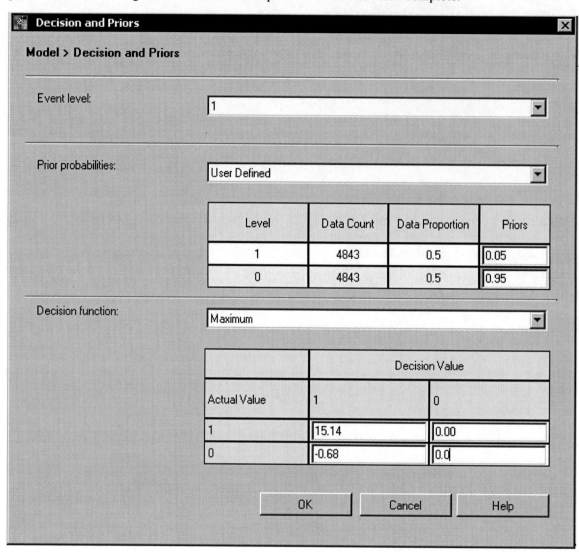

Copyright © 2011, SAS Institute Inc., Cary, North Carolina, USA. ALL RIGHTS RESERVED.

8. Select **Report** from the menu. Select the report options that you want. RPM Basic model results automatically include a model gains chart, a receiver operator characteristic (ROC) chart, a model scorecard, and other project information.

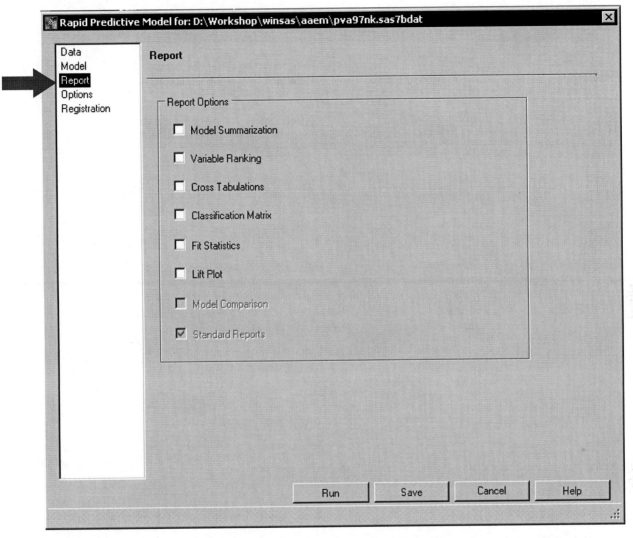

Model comparison reports are only possible when doing intermediate or advanced modeling.

Copyright © 2011, SAS Institute Inc., Cary, North Carolina, USA. ALL RIGHTS RESERVED.

9. Select **Options** from the menu. This window enables you to save the RPM model as a SAS Enterprise
    Miner project. Select the box next to **Save Enterprise Miner Project Data** and type **RPM** in the
    Project Name field if the name is not auto-filled. This folder location will be used in SAS Enterprise
    Miner later.

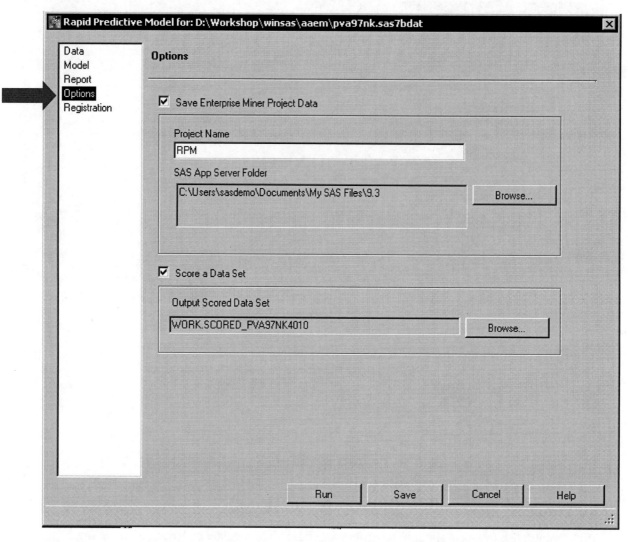

RPM models can be reviewed, fine-tuned, customized, and improved in SAS Enterprise Miner by
analytic experts after the models are run. The default location of the SAS Enterprise Miner project
that contains the RPM model is set upon installation of SAS Enterprise Guide, but it can be adjusted
by an administrator using SAS Management Console.

Copyright © 2011, SAS Institute Inc., Cary, North Carolina, USA. ALL RIGHTS RESERVED.

10. The RPM model is ready to be run. Return to the RPM Model menu and select **Run**. After the run is complete, the results are provided, starting with the Model Gains chart.

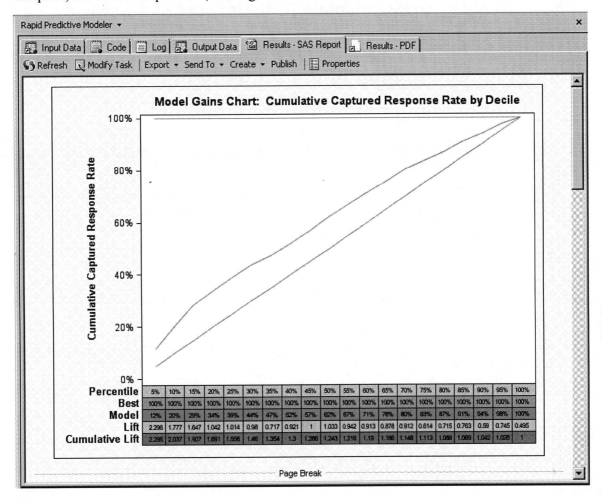

Copyright © 2011, SAS Institute Inc., Cary, North Carolina, USA. ALL RIGHTS RESERVED.

Running an Intermediate RPM Model (Self-Study)

This demonstration illustrates running an Intermediate RPM model in SAS Enterprise Guide 4.3.

1. Start the RPM model-building process as described above or select **Modify Task** if an RPM model has already been built and the project is still open.

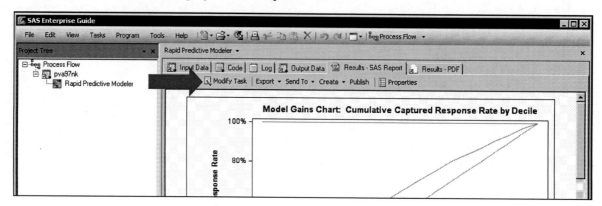

2. From the RPM task window, select **Model** from the menu in the left column. Select **Intermediate** as the modeling method.

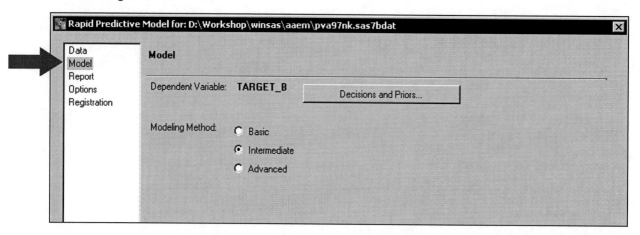

If you are modifying an existing task, you will be asked if you want to replace the existing results with the new ones. As stated above, for results such as a Model Comparison report, the appropriate report must be selected under the **Report** field from the RPM menu. Intermediate models take longer to run than basic models.

Although not covered here, running an Advanced model follows the same basic procedure as running an Intermediate model accept for selecting **Advanced** for the modeling method from the **Model** field in the RPM task window. The Advanced model setting takes longer to run than the intermediate models.

Copyright © 2011, SAS Institute Inc., Cary, North Carolina, USA. ALL RIGHTS RESERVED.

Opening an RPM Model in SAS Enterprise Miner

1. Open SAS Enterprise Miner and log on if prompted. Select **New Project**. In step 2 of 4, name the project **RPM** and set the location to be the same as the folder location provided in SAS Enterprise Guide. (See step 9 in the demonstration "Running a Basic RPM Model" above. Note that the location here matches the folder location given in SAS Enterprise Guide.)

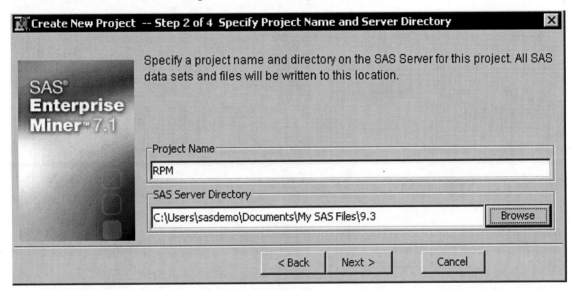

2. After clicking **Next**, a window appears. The window indicates that the selected project already exists and asks if you want to continue. Select **Yes**. Select **Next** ⇨ **Finish** to complete the creation of the project.

    Unless changed by a user, RPM always provides the same name, RPM, to a project. If an RPM model has already been created and is to be saved, one solution to create a second unique RPM model is to use Windows Explorer to navigate to the folder where the first project exists and rename this RPM project to something meaningful. Create another new project in SAS Enterprise Miner using this meaningful name given to the first project. Now a second RPM model can be run and the above steps can be used to open this new project, named RPM, in SAS Enterprise Miner.

Copyright © 2011, SAS Institute Inc., Cary, North Carolina, USA. ALL RIGHTS RESERVED.

The RPM project opens in SAS Enterprise Miner.

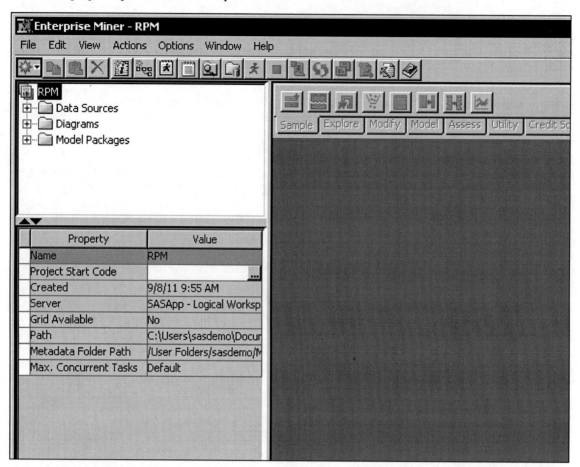

3. In the Project panel, expand the **Diagrams** folder by clicking the plus sign (+) next to it and then open the diagram **RPM1-TARGET_B** by double-clicking it. The RPM diagram work flow opens. (The flow below represents the result from a Basic RPM model.)

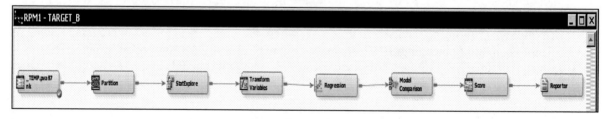

The analysis can now be customized or improved in SAS Enterprise Miner by an advanced analyst.

Copyright © 2011, SAS Institute Inc., Cary, North Carolina, USA. ALL RIGHTS RESERVED.

Registering an RPM Model

A developed RPM model can be registered in the SAS Metadata Repository from within the RPM task window in SAS Enterprise Guide. Registered models can be scored by other analysts using SAS Enterprise Guide or the SAS Add-In for Microsoft Office for Excel. Registered models can also be imported into other SAS Enterprise Miner sessions by other analysts to compare with existing models or review and refine the model. The model can even be imported into SAS Model Manager to manage with other modeling assets and monitor its performance for degradation over time. (SAS Model Manager is a separately licensed SAS product.)

An RPM model must be saved as a SAS Enterprise Miner project *and* the RPM task must have been run at least once, before the model can be registered.

RPM models built from a personal workstation cannot be registered with the SAS Metadata Repository.

1. After a model is developed in SAS Enterprise Guide (that is, the RPM task is run) and saved as an SAS Enterprise Miner project, select **Modify Task** ⇨ **Registration** from the menu in the left column of the RPM task window.

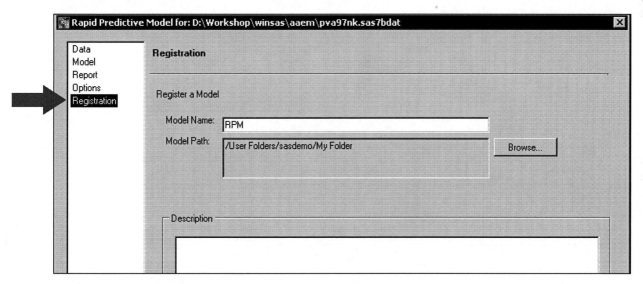

2. Select **Register**. A window appears that indicates a successful registration. The RPM model is now registered in the SAS Metadata Repository. Registration of the model can be verified for someone with administrative permissions using SAS Management Console.

Copyright © 2011, SAS Institute Inc., Cary, North Carolina, USA. ALL RIGHTS RESERVED.

Scoring in SAS Enterprise Guide with a Registered Model

1. Open the data set to be scored from within SAS Enterprise Guide. Select **File** ⇨ **Open** ⇨ **Data**. Select or browse to the data set to be scored. For the current demonstration, use **Scorepva97nk**. Now use the Model Scoring task. Select **Tasks** ⇨ **Data Mining** ⇨ **Model Scoring**. (In Excel, select the **SAS** tab first, and then select **Tasks** ⇨ **Data Mining** ⇨ **Model Scoring**.) It might take several moments for the Model Scoring window to appear.

2. Navigate through steps 1 through 6 of the Model Scoring task to verify the scoring data set. In step 1, verify that the correct data set to be scored has been selected. Select **Next**. In step 2, select the **RPM** model. Select **Browse**. Then navigate to My Folder and select the **RPM** model by highlighting it then selecting **OK**.

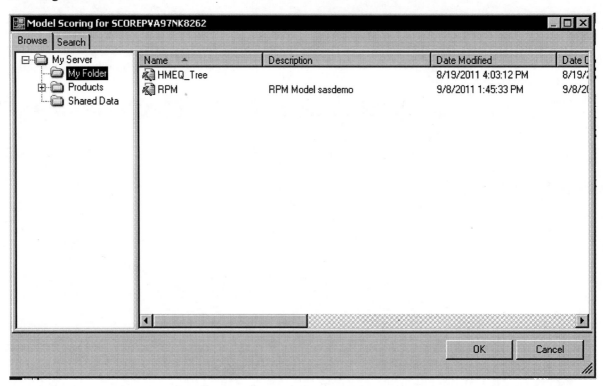

Copyright © 2011, SAS Institute Inc., Cary, North Carolina, USA. ALL RIGHTS RESERVED.

The Model Scoring task returns to step 2 of 6 showing that the RPM model has been selected for scoring.

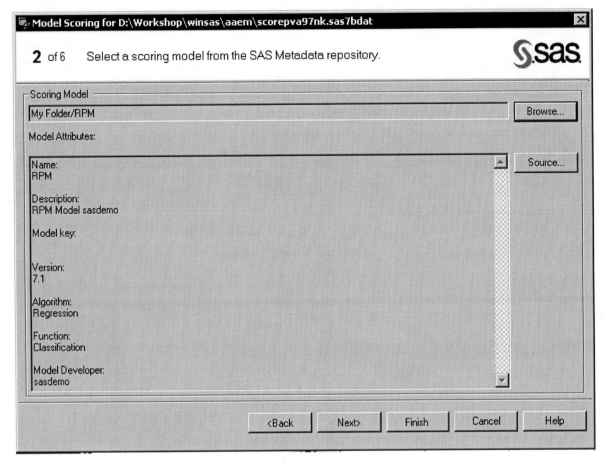

Copyright © 2011, SAS Institute Inc., Cary, North Carolina, USA. ALL RIGHTS RESERVED.

3. Select **Next**. In step 3 of 6, required model inputs must be mapped to the data variables. Model inputs and data variables that have the same name and type are mapped automatically.

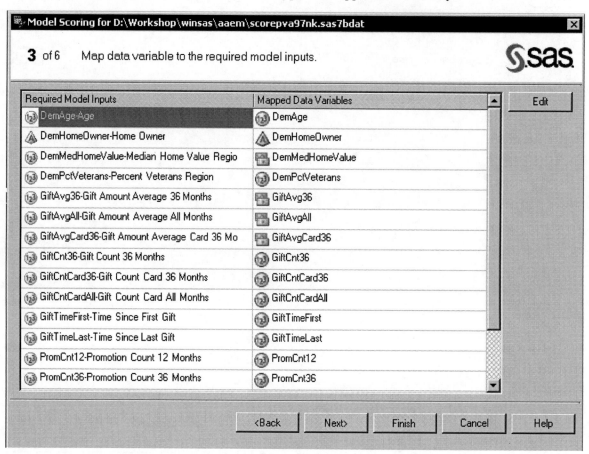

4. Select **Next**. When models are scored, several new variables are created (for example, a new variable that is the predicted probability of the event of interest).

Copyright © 2011, SAS Institute Inc., Cary, North Carolina, USA. ALL RIGHTS RESERVED.

5. In step 4 of 6, you can select which variables are included in the output after scoring. Variables that are listed under Selected Columns are reported in the output data set. To add or remove variables, highlight the variable or variables of interest and use the left or right arrows accordingly.

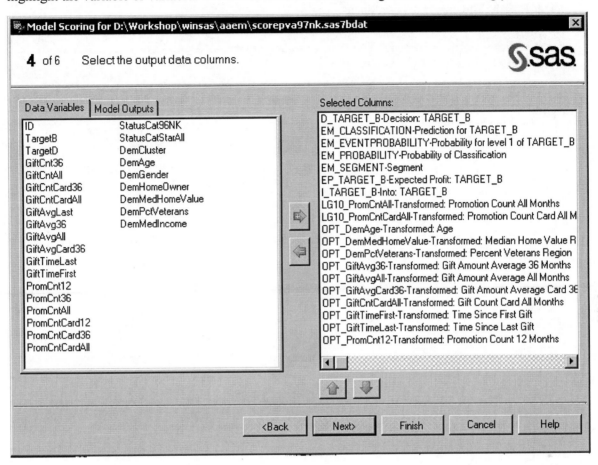

Copyright © 2011, SAS Institute Inc., Cary, North Carolina, USA. ALL RIGHTS RESERVED.

6. Select **Next**. Step 5 provides a summary of output data and provides an option to save the output as a SAS view instead of a table. (A SAS view contains descriptive information and instructions that build the data table.) Select **Next**. Step 6 is a confirmation of your selections in the Model Scoring task. Select **Finish**. The output data set opens.

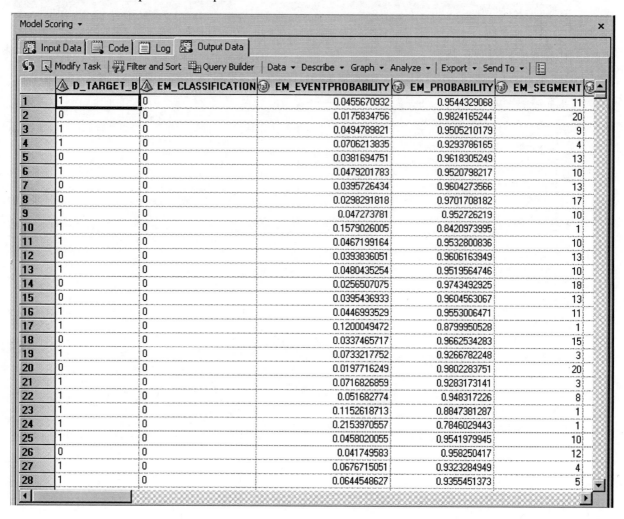

Model Scoring ▾   ✕

Input Data | Code | Log | Output Data

Modify Task | Filter and Sort | Query Builder | Data ▾ Describe ▾ Graph ▾ Analyze ▾ | Export ▾ Send To ▾ |

	D_TARGET_B	EM_CLASSIFICATION	EM_EVENTPROBABILITY	EM_PROBABILITY	EM_SEGMENT
1	1	0	0.0455670932	0.9544329068	11
2	0	0	0.0175834756	0.9824165244	20
3	1	0	0.0494789821	0.9505210179	9
4	1	0	0.0706213835	0.9293786165	4
5	0	0	0.0381694751	0.9618305249	13
6	1	0	0.0479201783	0.9520798217	10
7	0	0	0.0395726434	0.9604273566	13
8	0	0	0.0298291818	0.9701708182	17
9	1	0	0.047273781	0.952726219	10
10	1	0	0.1579026005	0.8420973995	1
11	1	0	0.0467199164	0.9532800836	10
12	0	0	0.0393836051	0.9606163949	13
13	1	0	0.0480435254	0.9519564746	10
14	0	0	0.0256507075	0.9743492925	18
15	0	0	0.0395436933	0.9604563067	13
16	1	0	0.0446993529	0.9553006471	11
17	1	0	0.1200049472	0.8799950528	1
18	0	0	0.0337465717	0.9662534283	15
19	1	0	0.0733217752	0.9266782248	3
20	0	0	0.0197716249	0.9802283751	20
21	1	0	0.0716826859	0.9283173141	3
22	1	0	0.051682774	0.948317226	8
23	1	0	0.1152618713	0.8847381287	1
24	1	0	0.2153970557	0.7846029443	1
25	1	0	0.0458020055	0.9541979945	10
26	0	0	0.041749583	0.958250417	12
27	1	0	0.0676715051	0.9323284949	4
28	1	0	0.0644548627	0.9355451373	5

Copyright © 2011, SAS Institute Inc., Cary, North Carolina, USA. ALL RIGHTS RESERVED.

Appendix A Case Studies

Copyright © 2011, SAS Institute Inc., Cary, North Carolina, USA. ALL RIGHTS RESERVED.

Copyright © 2011, SAS Institute Inc., Cary, North Carolina, USA. ALL RIGHTS RESERVED.

A.1 Banking Segmentation Case Study

Case Study Description

A consumer bank sought to segment its customers based on historic usage patterns. Segmentation was to be used for improving contact strategies in the Marketing Department.

A sample of 100,000 active consumer customers was selected. An *active consumer customer* was defined as an individual or household with at least one checking account and at least one transaction on the account during a three-month study period. All transactions during the three-month study period were recorded and classified into one of four activity categories:

- traditional banking methods (TBM)
- automatic teller machine (ATM)
- point of sale (POS)
- customer service (CSC)

A three-month activity profile for each customer was developed by combining historic activity averages with observed activity during the study period. Historically, for one CSC transaction, an average customer would conduct two POS transactions, three ATM transactions, and 10 TBM transactions. Each customer was assigned this initial profile at the beginning of the study period. The initial profile was updated by adding the total number of transactions in each activity category over the entire three-month study period.

The **PROFILE** data set contains all 100,000 three-month activity profiles. This case study describes the creation of customer activity segments based on the **PROFILE** data set.

  The diagram containing this analysis is stored as an XML file on the course data disk. You can open this file by right-clicking **Diagrams** and selecting **Import Diagram from XML** in SAS Enterprise Miner. All nodes in the opened file, except the data node, contain the property settings outlined in this case study. If you want to run the diagram, you need to re-create the case study data set using the metadata settings indicated below.

Case Study Data

Name	Model Role	Measurement Level	Description
ID	ID	Nominal	Customer ID
CNT_TBM	Input	Interval	Traditional bank method transaction count
CNT_ATM	Input	Interval	ATM transaction count
CNT_POS	Input	Interval	Point-of-sale transaction count
CNT_CSC	Input	Interval	Customer service transaction count
CNT_TOT	Input	Interval	Total transaction count

Copyright © 2011, SAS Institute Inc., Cary, North Carolina, USA. ALL RIGHTS RESERVED.

Accessing and Assaying the Data

A SAS Enterprise Miner data source was defined using the metadata settings indicated above. The StatExplore node was used to provide preliminary statistics on the input variables.

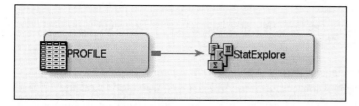

The Interval Variable Summary from the StatExplore node showed no missing values but did show a surprisingly large range on the transaction counts.

```
32    Interval Variable Summary Statistics
33    (maximum 500 observations printed)
34
35    Data Role=TRAIN
36
37                              Standard       Non
38    Variable   Role      Mean  Deviation  Missing   Missing   Minimum   Median   Maximum   Skewness
39
40    CNT_ATM    INPUT  19.49971   20.8561   100000        0         3       13       628    2.357293
41    CNT_CSC    INPUT   6.68411  12.12856   100000        0         1        2       607    6.236494
42    CNT_POS    INPUT   11.9233  20.73384   100000        0         2        2       345    3.343805
43    CNT_TBM    INPUT  68.13696  101.1542   100000        0        10       52     14934   53.05219
44    CNT_TOT    INPUT  106.2441  113.3704   100000        0        17       89     15225    39.2061
```

A plot of the input distributions showed highly skewed distributions for all inputs.

Copyright © 2011, SAS Institute Inc., Cary, North Carolina, USA. ALL RIGHTS RESERVED.

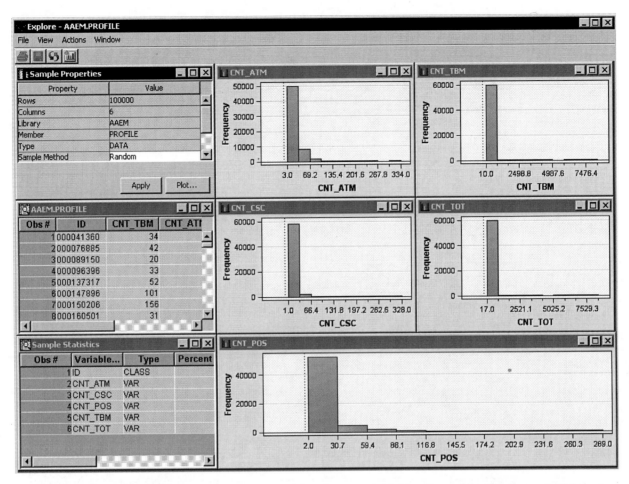

It would be difficult to develop meaningful segments from such highly skewed inputs. Instead of focusing on the transaction counts, it was decided to develop segments based on the relative proportions of transactions across the four categories. This required a transformation of the raw data.

A Transform Variables node was connected to the **PROFILE** node.

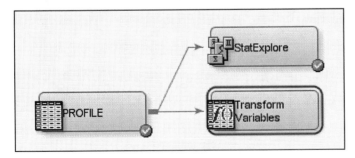

The Transform Variables node was used to create *category logit scores* for each transaction category.

$$category\ logit\ score = \log(transaction\ count_{\text{in category}}\ /\ transaction\ count_{\text{out of category}})$$

Copyright © 2011, SAS Institute Inc., Cary, North Carolina, USA. ALL RIGHTS RESERVED.

The transformations were created using these steps:

1. Select **Formulas** in the Transform Variable node's Properties panel. The Formulas window appears.

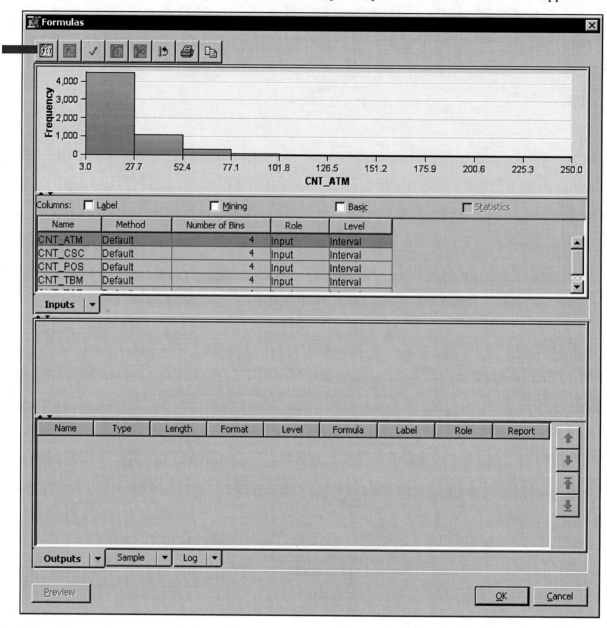

2. Select the Create icon as indicated above.

Copyright © 2011, SAS Institute Inc., Cary, North Carolina, USA. ALL RIGHTS RESERVED.

The Add Transformation dialog box appears.

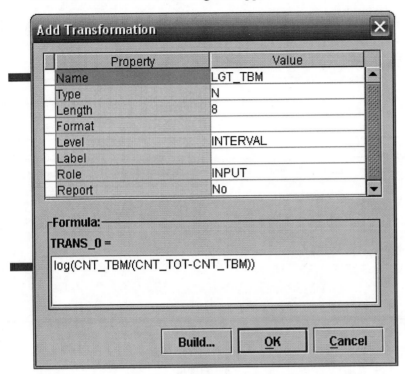

3. For each transaction category, type the name and formula as indicated.

4. Select **OK** to add the transformation. The Add Transformation dialog box closes and you return to the Formula Builder window.

Copyright © 2011, SAS Institute Inc., Cary, North Carolina, USA. ALL RIGHTS RESERVED.

5. Select **Preview** to see the distribution of the newly created input.

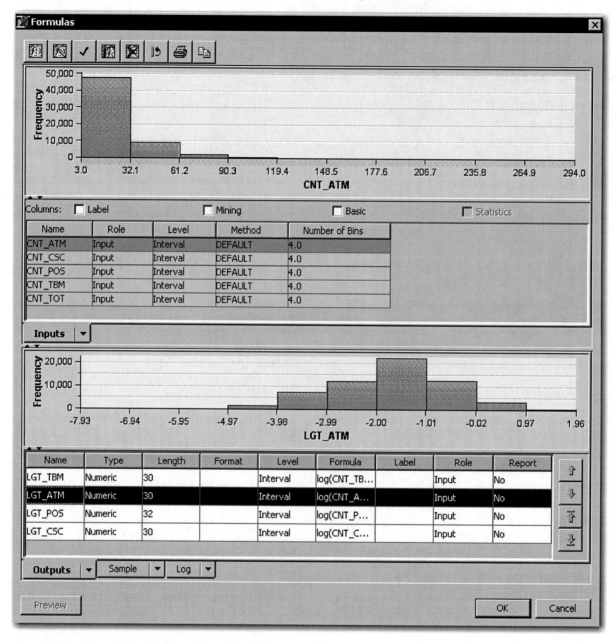

6. Repeat Steps 1-5 for the other three transaction categories.

7. Select **OK** to close the Formula Builder window.

8. Run the Transform Variables node.

Segmentation was to be based on the newly created category logit scores. Before proceeding, it was deemed reasonable to examine the joint distribution of the cases using these derived inputs. A scatter plot using any three of the four derived inputs would represent the joint distribution without significant loss of information.

Copyright © 2011, SAS Institute Inc., Cary, North Carolina, USA. ALL RIGHTS RESERVED.

A three-dimensional scatter plot was produced using the following steps:

1. Select **Exported Data** from the Properties panel of the Transform Variables node. The Exported Data window appears.

2. Select the **TRAIN** data and select **Explore**. The Explore window appears.

3. Select **Actions** ⇨ **Plot...** or click 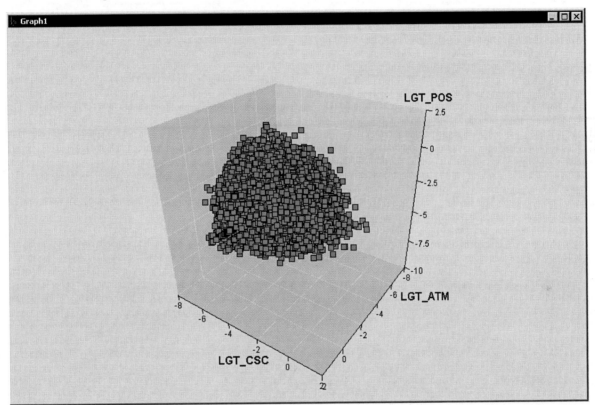 (the Plot Wizard icon). The Plot Wizard appears.

4. Select a three-dimensional scatter plot.

5. Select **Role** ⇨ **X, Y**, and **Z** for **LGT_ATM, LGT_CSC**, and **LGT_POS**, respectively.

6. Select **Finish** to generate the scatter plot.

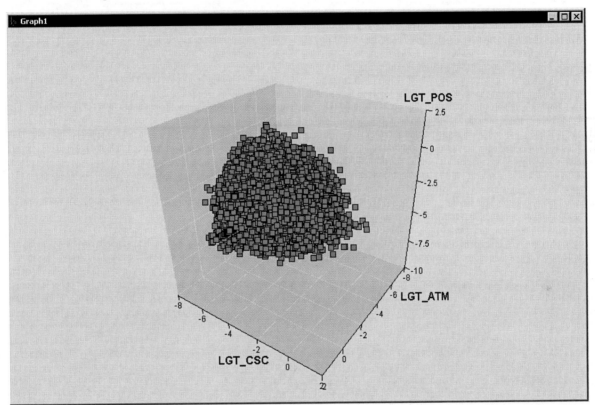

The scatter plot showed a single clump of cases, making this analysis a segmentation (rather than a clustering) of the customers. There were a few outlying cases with apparently low proportions on the three plotted inputs. Given that the proportions in the four original categories must sum to 1, it followed that these outlying cases must have a high proportion of transactions in the non-plotted category, TBM.

Copyright © 2011, SAS Institute Inc., Cary, North Carolina, USA. ALL RIGHTS RESERVED.

Creating Segments

Transactions segments were created using the Cluster node.

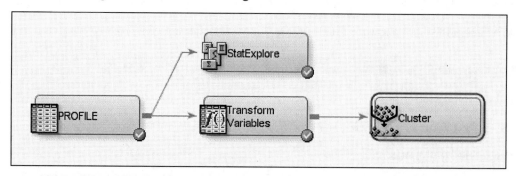

Two changes to the Cluster node default properties were made, as indicated below. Both were related to limiting the number of clusters created to 5.

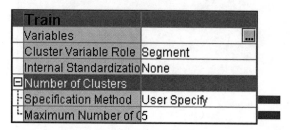

Train	
Variables	...
Cluster Variable Role	Segment
Internal Standardizatio	None
⊟ Number of Clusters	
┬ Specification Method	User Specify
└ Maximum Number of C	5

✎   Because the inputs were all on the same measurement scale (category logit score), it was decided to *not* standardize the inputs.

Only the four LGT inputs defined in the Transform Variables node were set to **Default** in the Cluster node.

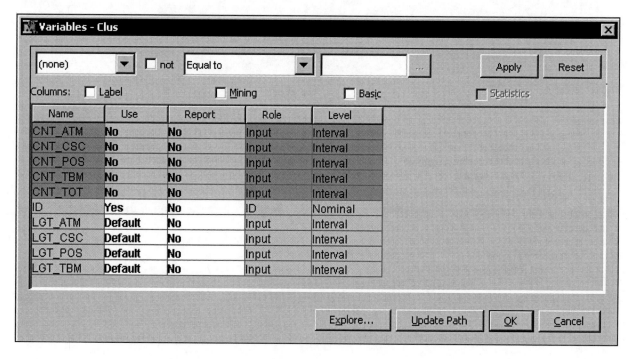

Running the Cluster node and viewing the Results window confirmed the creation of five nearly equally sized clusters.

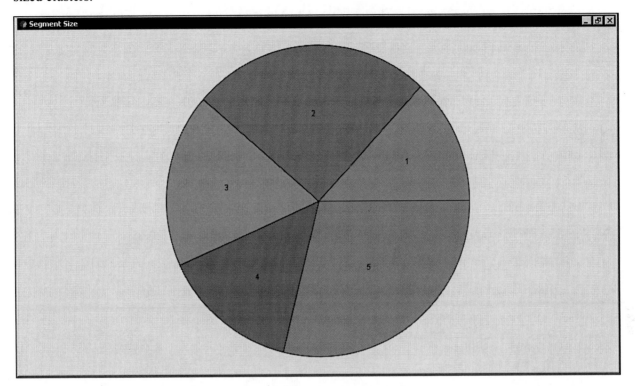

Additional cluster interpretations were made with the Segment Profile tool.

Copyright © 2011, SAS Institute Inc., Cary, North Carolina, USA. ALL RIGHTS RESERVED.

Interpreting Segments

A Segment Profile node attached to the Cluster node helped to interpret the contents of the generated segments.

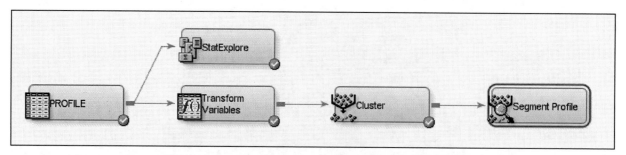

Only the **LGT** inputs were set to **Yes** in the Segment Profile node.

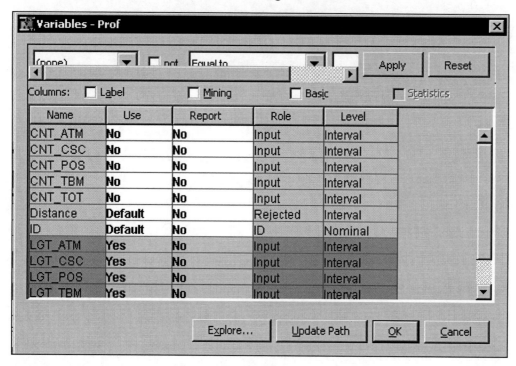

The following profiles were created for the generated segments:

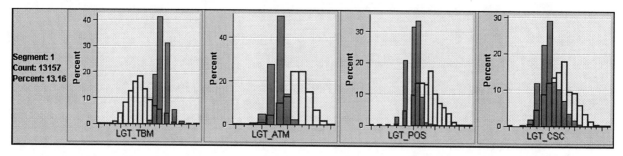

Segment 1 customers had a significantly higher than average use of traditional banking methods and lower than average use of all other transaction categories. This segment was labeled **Brick-and-Mortar**.

Copyright © 2011, SAS Institute Inc., Cary, North Carolina, USA. ALL RIGHTS RESERVED.

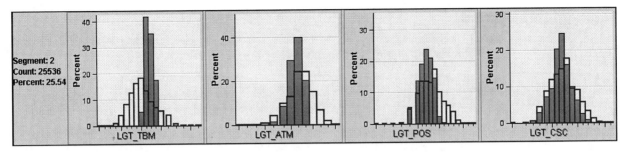

Segment 2 customers had a higher than average use of traditional banking methods but were close to the distribution centers on the other transaction categories. This segment was labeled **Transitionals** because they seem to be transitioning from brick-and-mortar to other usage patterns.

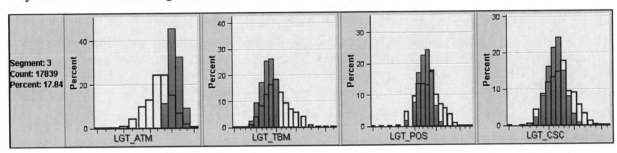

Segment 3 customers eschewed traditional banking methods in favor of ATMs. This segment was labeled **ATMs**.

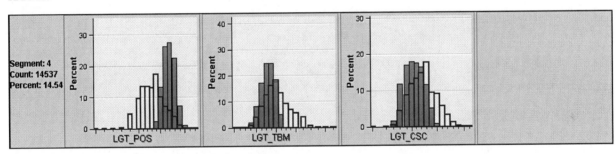

Segment 4 was characterized by a high prevalence of point-of-sale transactions and few traditional bank methods. This segment was labeled **Cashless**.

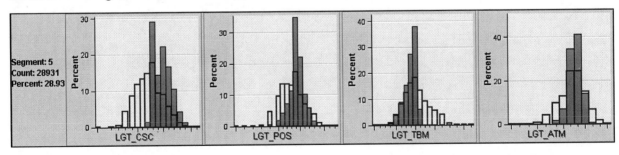

Segment 5 had a higher than average rate of customer service contacts and point-of-sale transactions. This segment was labeled **Service**.

Copyright © 2011, SAS Institute Inc., Cary, North Carolina, USA. ALL RIGHTS RESERVED.

Segment Deployment

Deployment of the transaction segmentation was facilitated by the Score node.

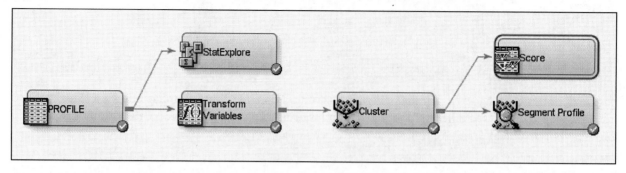

The Score node was attached to the Cluster node and run. The SAS Code window inside the Results window provided SAS code that was capable of transforming raw transaction counts to cluster assignments. The complete SAS scoring code is shown below.

Copyright © 2011, SAS Institute Inc., Cary, North Carolina, USA. ALL RIGHTS RESERVED.

```
*------------------------------------------------------------*;
* Formula Code;
*------------------------------------------------------------*;
LGT_TBM =log(CNT_TBM/(CNT_TOT-CNT_TBM)) ;
LGT_ATM =log(CNT_ATM/(CNT_TOT-CNT_ATM)) ;
LGT_POS =log(CNT_POS/(CNT_TOT - CNT_POS)) ;
LGT_CSC =log(CNT_CSC/(CNT_TOT-CNT_CSC)) ;
*------------------------------------------------------------*;
* TOOL: Clustering;
* TYPE: EXPLORE;
* NODE: Clus;
*------------------------------------------------------------*;
**********************************************;
*** Begin Scoring Code from PROC DMVQ ***;
**********************************************;


*** Begin Class Look-up, Standardization, Replacement ;
drop _dm_bad; _dm_bad = 0;

*** No transformation for LGT_ATM ;

*** No transformation for LGT_CSC ;

*** No transformation for LGT_POS ;

*** No transformation for LGT_TBM ;

*** End Class Look-up, Standardization, Replacement ;


*** Omitted Cases;
if _dm_bad then do;
   _SEGMENT_ = .; Distance = .;
   goto CLUSvlex ;
end; *** omitted;
```

```
* EM SCORE CODE;
* EM Version: 7.1;
* SAS Release: 9.03.01M0P060711;
* Host: SASBAP;
* Encoding: wlatin1;
* Locale: en_US;
* Project Path: D:\Workshop\winsas\EM_Projects;
* Project Name: apxa;
* Diagram Id: EMWS1;
* Diagram Name: case_study1;
* Generated by: sasdemo;
* Date: 09SEP2011:16:50:09;
*------------------------------------------------------------*;
*------------------------------------------------------------*;
```

Copyright © 2011, SAS Institute Inc., Cary, North Carolina, USA. ALL RIGHTS RESERVED.

```
* TOOL: Input Data Source;
* TYPE: SAMPLE;
* NODE: Ids2;
*-------------------------------------------------------------*;
*-------------------------------------------------------------*;
* TOOL: Transform;
* TYPE: MODIFY;
* NODE: Trans;
*-------------------------------------------------------------*;
LGT_ATM = log(CNT_ATM/(CNT_TOT-CNT_ATM));
LGT_CSC = log(CNT_CSC/(CNT_TOT-CNT_CSC));
LGT_POS = log(CNT_POS/(CNT_TOT - CNT_POS));
LGT_TBM = log(CNT_TBM/(CNT_TOT-CNT_TBM));
*-------------------------------------------------------------*;
* TOOL: Clustering;
* TYPE: EXPLORE;
* NODE: Clus;
*-------------------------------------------------------------*;
*******************************************;
*** Begin Scoring Code from PROC DMVQ ***;
*******************************************;
*** Begin Class Look-up, Standardization, Replacement ;
drop _dm_bad; _dm_bad = 0;

*** No transformation for LGT_ATM ;
*** No transformation for LGT_CSC ;
*** No transformation for LGT_POS ;
*** No transformation for LGT_TBM ;
*** End Class Look-up, Standardization, Replacement ;
*** Omitted Cases;
if _dm_bad then do;
   _SEGMENT_ = .; Distance = .;
   goto CLUSvlex ;
end; *** omitted;
*** Compute Distances and Cluster Membership;
label _SEGMENT_ = 'Segment Id' ;
label Distance = 'Distance' ;
array CLUSvads [5] _temporary_;
drop _vqclus _vqmvar _vqnvar;
_vqmvar = 0;
do _vqclus = 1 to 5; CLUSvads [_vqclus] = 0; end;
if not missing( LGT_ATM ) then do;
   CLUSvads [1] + ( LGT_ATM - -3.54995114884545 )**2;
   CLUSvads [2] + ( LGT_ATM - -2.2003888516185 )**2;
   CLUSvads [3] + ( LGT_ATM - -0.23695023328541 )**2;
   CLUSvads [4] + ( LGT_ATM - -1.47814712774378 )**2;
   CLUSvads [5] + ( LGT_ATM - -1.49704375204907 )**2;
end;
else _vqmvar + 1.31533540479169;
if not missing( LGT_CSC ) then do;
   CLUSvads [1] + ( LGT_CSC - -4.16334022538952 )**2;
```

Copyright © 2011, SAS Institute Inc., Cary, North Carolina, USA. ALL RIGHTS RESERVED.

```
      CLUSvads [2] + ( LGT_CSC - -3.38356120535047 )**2;
      CLUSvads [3] + ( LGT_CSC - -3.55519058753002 )**2;
      CLUSvads [4] + ( LGT_CSC - -3.96526745641347 )**2;
      CLUSvads [5] + ( LGT_CSC - -2.08727391873096 )**2;
end;
else _vqmvar + 1.20270093291078;
if not missing( LGT_POS ) then do;
      CLUSvads [1] + ( LGT_POS - -4.08779761080977 )**2;
      CLUSvads [2] + ( LGT_POS - -3.27644694006697 )**2;
      CLUSvads [3] + ( LGT_POS - -3.02915771770446 )**2;
      CLUSvads [4] + ( LGT_POS - -0.9841959454775 )**2;
      CLUSvads [5] + ( LGT_POS - -2.21538937073223 )**2;
end;
else _vqmvar + 1.3094245726273;
if not missing( LGT_TBM ) then do;
      CLUSvads [1] + ( LGT_TBM - 2.62509260779666 )**2;
      CLUSvads [2] + ( LGT_TBM - 1.40885156098965 )**2;
      CLUSvads [3] + ( LGT_TBM - -0.15878507901546 )**2;
      CLUSvads [4] + ( LGT_TBM - -0.11252803970828 )**2;
      CLUSvads [5] + ( LGT_TBM - 0.22075831354075 )**2;
end;
else _vqmvar + 1.17502484629096;
 _vqnvar = 5.00248575662075 - _vqmvar;
if _vqnvar <= 2.2748671456705E-12 then do;
    _SEGMENT_ = .; Distance = .;
end;
else do;
    _SEGMENT_ = 1; Distance = CLUSvads [1];
    _vqfzdst = Distance * 0.99999999999988; drop _vqfzdst;
    do _vqclus = 2 to 5;
       if CLUSvads [_vqclus] < _vqfzdst then do;
           _SEGMENT_ = _vqclus; Distance = CLUSvads [_vqclus];
           _vqfzdst = Distance * 0.99999999999988;
       end;
    end;
    Distance = sqrt(Distance * (5.00248575662075 / _vqnvar));
end;
CLUSvlex :;
*************************************;
*** End Scoring Code from PROC DMVQ ***;
*************************************;
*-----------------------------------------------------------*;
* Clus: Creating Segment Label;
*-----------------------------------------------------------*;
length _SEGMENT_LABEL_ $80;
label _SEGMENT_LABEL_ ='Segment Description';
if _SEGMENT_ = 1 then _SEGMENT_LABEL_ ="Cluster1";
else
if _SEGMENT_ = 2 then _SEGMENT_LABEL_ ="Cluster2";
else
if _SEGMENT_ = 3 then _SEGMENT_LABEL_ ="Cluster3";
```

Copyright © 2011, SAS Institute Inc., Cary, North Carolina, USA. ALL RIGHTS RESERVED.

```
else
if _SEGMENT_ = 4 then _SEGMENT_LABEL_="Cluster4";
else
if _SEGMENT_ = 5 then _SEGMENT_LABEL_="Cluster5";
*------------------------------------------------------------*;
* TOOL: Score Node;
* TYPE: ASSESS;
* NODE: Score;
*------------------------------------------------------------*;
*------------------------------------------------------------*;
* Score: Creating Fixed Names;
*------------------------------------------------------------*;
LABEL EM_SEGMENT = 'Segment Variable';
EM_SEGMENT = _SEGMENT_;
```

Copyright © 2011, SAS Institute Inc., Cary, North Carolina, USA. ALL RIGHTS RESERVED.

A.2 Web Site Usage Associations Case Study

Case Study Description

A radio station developed a Web site to broaden its audience appeal and its offerings. In addition to a simulcast of the station's primary broadcast, the Web site was designed to provide services to Web users, such as podcasts, news streams, music streams, archives, and live Web music performances. The station tracked usage of these services by URL. Analysts at the station wanted to see whether any unusual patterns existed in the combinations of services selected by its Web users.

The **WEBSTATION** data set contains services selected by more than 1.5 million unique Web users over a two-month period in 2006. For privacy reasons, the URLs are assigned anonymous ID numbers.

✎   The diagram containing this analysis is stored as an XML file on the course data disk. You can open this file by right-clicking **Diagrams ⇨ Import Diagram from XML** in SAS Enterprise Miner. All nodes in the opened file, except the data node, contain the property settings outlined in this case study. If you want to run the diagram, you need to re-create the case study data set using the metadata settings indicated below.

Case Study Data

Name	Model Role	Measurement Level	Description
ID	ID	Nominal	URL (with anonymous ID numbers)
TARGET	Target	Nominal	Web service selected

✎   The **WEBSTATION** data set should be assigned the role of **Transaction**. This role can be assigned either in the process of creating the data source or by changing the properties of the data source inside SAS Enterprise Miner.

Accessing and Assaying the Data

A SAS Enterprise Miner data source was defined for the **WEBSTATION** data set using the metadata settings indicated above. By right-clicking on the Data Source node in the diagram and selecting **Edit Variables**, the **TARGET** variable can be explored by highlighting the variable and then selecting **Explore**. (The following results are obtained by specifying **Random** and **Max** for the Sample Method and Fetch Size.)

The Sample Statistics window shows that there are over 128 unique URLs in the data set and 8 distinct services.

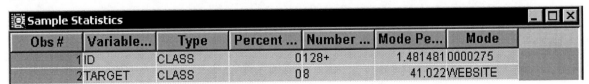

Obs #	Variable...	Type	Percent ...	Number ...	Mode Pe...	Mode
1	ID	CLASS		0 128+	1.4814	81 0000275
2	TARGET	CLASS		0 8	41.022	WEBSITE

Copyright © 2011, SAS Institute Inc., Cary, North Carolina, USA. ALL RIGHTS RESERVED.

A plot of target distribution (produced from the Explore window) identified the eight levels and displayed the relative frequency in a random sample of 100000 cases.

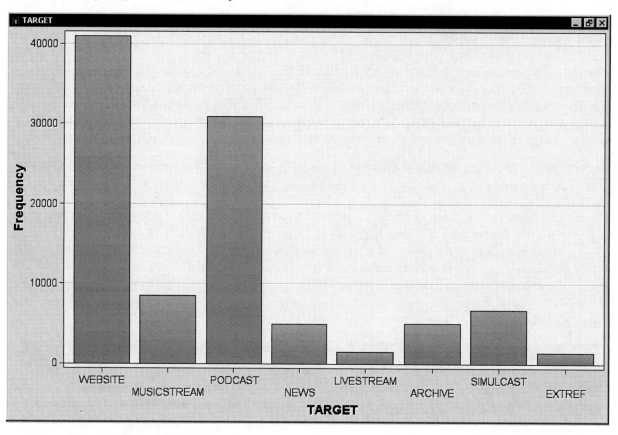

Generating Associations

An Association node was connected to the **WEBSTATION** node.

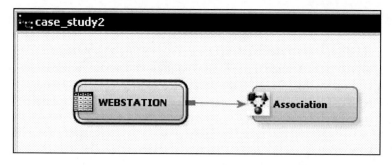

Copyright © 2011, SAS Institute Inc., Cary, North Carolina, USA. ALL RIGHTS RESERVED.

A preliminary run of the Association node yielded very few association rules. It was discovered that the default minimum Support Percentage setting was too large. (Many of the URLs selected only one service, diminishing the support of all association rules.) To obtain more association rules, the minimum Support Percentage setting was changed to **1.0**. In addition, the number of items to process was increased to **3000000** to account for the large training data set.

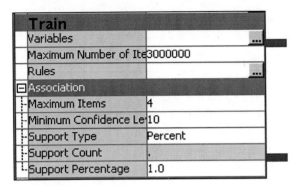

Using these changes, the analysis was rerun and yielded substantially more association rules.

The Rules Table was used to scrutinize the results.

Relations	Expected Confidence(%)	Confidence(%)	Support(%)	Lift	Transaction Count	Rule	Left Hand of Rule	Right Hand of Rule	Rule Item 1	Rule Item 2	Rule Item 3	Rule Item 4	Rule Item 5	Rule Index	Transpose Rule
3	7.32	98.32	1.69	13.42	26744	WEBSITE &...	WEBSITE &...	ARCHIVE	WEBSITE	EXTREF	=========...	ARCHIVE		1	1
3	1.71	23.02	1.69	13.42	26744	ARCHIVE =...	ARCHIVE	WEBSITE &...	ARCHIVE	=========...	WEBSITE	EXTREF		2	1
2	7.32	98.07	1.92	13.39	30419	EXTREF ==...	EXTREF	ARCHIVE	EXTREF	=========...	ARCHIVE			3	1
2	1.96	26.19	1.92	13.39	30419	ARCHIVE =...	ARCHIVE	EXTREF	ARCHIVE	=========...	EXTREF			4	1
3	1.96	23.90	1.69	12.22	26744	WEBSITE &...	WEBSITE &...	EXTREF	WEBSITE	ARCHIVE	=========...	EXTREF		6	1
3	7.05	86.22	1.69	12.22	26744	EXTREF ==...	EXTREF	WEBSITE &...	EXTREF	=========...	WEBSITE	ARCHIVE		5	1
4	1.78	16.05	0.66	9.03	10424	WEBSITE &...	WEBSITE &...	PODCAST...	WEBSITE	SIMULCAST	=========...	PODCAST	MUSICSTR...	7	1
4	4.10	36.97	0.66	9.03	10424	PODCAST...	PODCAST...	WEBSITE &...	PODCAST	MUSICSTR...	=========...	WEBSITE	SIMULCAST	8	1
4	1.58	12.29	0.66	7.80	10424	WEBSITE &...	WEBSITE &...	SIMULCAS...	WEBSITE	MUSICSTR...	=========...	SIMULCAST	PODCAST	9	1
4	5.35	41.71	0.66	7.80	10424	SIMULCAS...	SIMULCAS...	WEBSITE &...	SIMULCAST	PODCAST	=========...	WEBSITE	MUSICSTR...	10	1
3	9.47	64.45	0.90	6.81	14275	NEWS & M...	NEWS & M...	SIMULCAST	NEWS	MUSICSTR...	=========...	SIMULCAST		11	1
3	9.47	51.35	0.69	5.43	10944	WEBSITE &...	WEBSITE &...	SIMULCAST	WEBSITE	NEWS	=========...	SIMULCAST		12	1
4	9.47	44.86	0.66	4.74	10424	WEBSITE &...	WEBSITE &...	SIMULCAST	WEBSITE	PODCAST	MUSICSTR...	=========...	SIMULCAST	13	1
3	6.95	31.69	0.90	4.56	14275	SIMULCAS...	SIMULCAS...	NEWS	SIMULCAST	MUSICSTR...	=========...	NEWS		15	1
3	2.84	12.95	0.90	4.56	14275	NEWS ==>...	NEWS	SIMULCAS...	NEWS	=========...	SIMULCAST	MUSICSTR...		14	1
3	9.47	41.55	0.74	4.39	11714	PODCAST...	PODCAST...	SIMULCAST	PODCAST	MUSICSTR...	=========...	SIMULCAST		16	1
4	11.83	51.44	0.66	4.35	10424	WEBSITE &...	WEBSITE &...	MUSICSTR...	WEBSITE	SIMULCAST	PODCAST	=========...	MUSICSTR...	17	1
3	11.83	46.87	0.74	3.96	11714	SIMULCAS...	SIMULCAS...	MUSICSTR...	SIMULCAST	PODCAST	=========...	MUSICSTR...		18	1
3	11.83	44.61	0.60	3.77	9506.0	WEBSITE &...	WEBSITE &...	MUSICSTR...	WEBSITE	NEWS	=========...	MUSICSTR...		19	1
3	11.83	44.00	0.90	3.72	14275	SIMULCAS...	SIMULCAS...	MUSICSTR...	SIMULCAST	NEWS	=========...	MUSICSTR...		20	1
3	11.83	38.17	1.56	3.23	24794	WEBSITE &...	WEBSITE &...	MUSICSTR...	WEBSITE	SIMULCAST	=========...	MUSICSTR...		22	1
3	4.10	13.21	1.56	3.23	24794	MUSICSTR...	MUSICSTR...	WEBSITE &...	MUSICSTR...	=========...	WEBSITE	SIMULCAST		21	1
2	9.47	29.43	2.05	3.11	32444	NEWS ==>...	NEWS	SIMULCAST	NEWS	=========...	SIMULCAST			23	1
2	6.95	21.61	2.05	3.11	32444	SIMULCAS...	SIMULCAST	NEWS	SIMULCAST	=========...	NEWS			24	1
3	9.47	29.24	1.56	3.09	24794	WEBSITE &...	WEBSITE &...	SIMULCAST	WEBSITE	MUSICSTR...	=========...	SIMULCAST		25	1
3	5.35	16.51	1.56	3.09	24794	SIMULCAS...	SIMULCAS...	WEBSITE &...	SIMULCAST	=========...	WEBSITE	MUSICSTR...		26	1
2	11.83	30.01	2.84	2.54	45051	SIMULCAS...	SIMULCAST	MUSICSTR...	SIMULCAST	=========...	MUSICSTR...			27	1
2	9.47	24.01	2.84	2.54	45051	MUSICSTR...	MUSICSTR...	SIMULCAST	MUSICSTR...	=========...	SIMULCAST			28	1
3	7.32	18.30	0.75	2.50	11890	WEBSITE &...	WEBSITE &...	ARCHIVE	WEBSITE	SIMULCAST	=========...	ARCHIVE		30	1
3	4.10	10.24	0.75	2.50	11890	ARCHIVE =...	ARCHIVE	WEBSITE &...	ARCHIVE	=========...	WEBSITE	SIMULCAST		29	1
3	6.95	16.85	0.69	2.42	10944	WEBSITE &...	WEBSITE &...	NEWS	WEBSITE	SIMULCAST	=========...	NEWS		31	1
3	7.32	17.53	0.94	2.39	14861	WEBSITE &...	WEBSITE &...	ARCHIVE	WEBSITE	MUSICSTR...	=========...	ARCHIVE		32	1
3	5.35	12.79	0.94	2.39	14861	ARCHIVE =...	ARCHIVE	WEBSITE &...	ARCHIVE	=========...	WEBSITE	MUSICSTR...		33	1

The following were among the interesting findings from this analysis:

- Most external referrers to the Web site pointed to the programming archive (98% confidence).
- Selecting the simulcast service tripled the chances of selecting the news service.
- Users who streamed music, downloaded podcasts, used the news service, or listened to the simulcast were less likely to go to the Web site.

Copyright © 2011, SAS Institute Inc., Cary, North Carolina, USA. ALL RIGHTS RESERVED.

A.3 Credit Risk Case Study

A bank sought to use performance on an in-house subprime credit product to create an updated risk model. The risk model was to be combined with other factors to make future credit decisions.

A sample of applicants for the original credit product was selected. Credit bureau data describing these individuals (at the time of application) was recorded. The ultimate disposition of the loan was determined (paid off or bad debt). For loans rejected at the time of application, a disposition was inferred from credit bureau records on loans obtained in a similar time frame.

The credit scoring models pursued in this case study were required to conform to the standard industry practice of transparency and interpretability. This eliminated certain modeling tools from consideration (for example, neural networks) except for comparison purposes. If a neural network significantly outperformed a regression, for example, it could be interpreted as a sign of lack of fit for the regression. Measures could then be taken to improve the regression model.

    The diagram containing this analysis is stored as an XML file on the course data disk. You can open this file by right-clicking **Diagrams** ⇨ **Import Diagram from XML** in SAS Enterprise Miner. All nodes in the opened file, except the data node, contain the property settings outlined in this case study. If you want to run the diagram, you need to re-create the case study data set using the metadata settings indicated below.

Copyright © 2011, SAS Institute Inc., Cary, North Carolina, USA. ALL RIGHTS RESERVED.

Case Study Training Data

Name	Role	Level /	Label
TARGET	Target	Binary	
BanruptcyInd	Input	Binary	Bankruptcy Indicator
TLBadDerogCnt	Input	Interval	Number Bad Dept plus Public Derogatories
CollectCnt	Input	Interval	Number Collections
InqFinanceCnt24	Input	Interval	Number Finance Inquires 24 Months
InqCnt06	Input	Interval	Number Inquiries 6 Months
DerogCnt	Input	Interval	Number Public Derogatories
TLDel3060Cnt24	Input	Interval	Number Trade Lines 30 or 60 Days 24 Months
TL50UtilCnt	Input	Interval	Number Trade Lines 50 pct Utilized
TLDel60Cnt24	Input	Interval	Number Trade Lines 60 Days or Worse 24 Months
TLDel60CntAll	Input	Interval	Number Trade Lines 60 Days or Worse Ever
TL75UtilCnt	Input	Interval	Number Trade Lines 75 pct Utilized
TLDel90Cnt24	Input	Interval	Number Trade Lines 90+ 24 Months
TLBadCnt24	Input	Interval	Number Trade Lines Bad Debt 24 Months
TLDel60Cnt	Input	Interval	Number Trade Lines Currently 60 Days or Worse
TLSatCnt	Input	Interval	Number Trade Lines Currently Satisfactory
TLCnt12	Input	Interval	Number Trade Lines Opened 12 Months
TLCnt24	Input	Interval	Number Trade Lines Opened 24 Months
TLCnt03	Input	Interval	Number Trade Lines Opened 3 Months
TLSatPct	Input	Interval	Percent Satisfactory to Total Trade Lines
TLBalHCPct	Input	Interval	Percent Trade Line Balance to High Credit
TLOpenPct	Input	Interval	Percent Trade Lines Open
TLOpen24Pct	Input	Interval	Percent Trade Lines Open 24 Months
TLTimeFirst	Input	Interval	Time Since First Trade Line
InqTimeLast	Input	Interval	Time Since Last Inquiry
TLTimeLast	Input	Interval	Time Since Last Trade Line
TLSum	Input	Interval	Total Balance All Trade Lines
TLMaxSum	Input	Interval	Total High Credit All Trade Lines
TLCnt	Input	Interval	Total Open Trade Lines
ID	ID	Nominal	

Copyright © 2011, SAS Institute Inc., Cary, North Carolina, USA. ALL RIGHTS RESERVED.

Accessing and Assaying the Data

A SAS Enterprise Miner data source was defined for the **CREDIT** data set using the metadata settings indicated above. The Data source definition was expedited by customizing the Advanced Metadata Advisor in the Data Source Wizard as indicated.

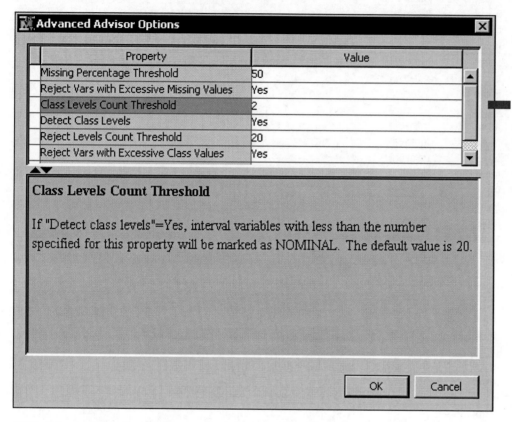

With this change, all metadata was set correctly by default.

Copyright © 2011, SAS Institute Inc., Cary, North Carolina, USA. ALL RIGHTS RESERVED.

Decision processing was selected in step 6 of the Data Source Wizard.

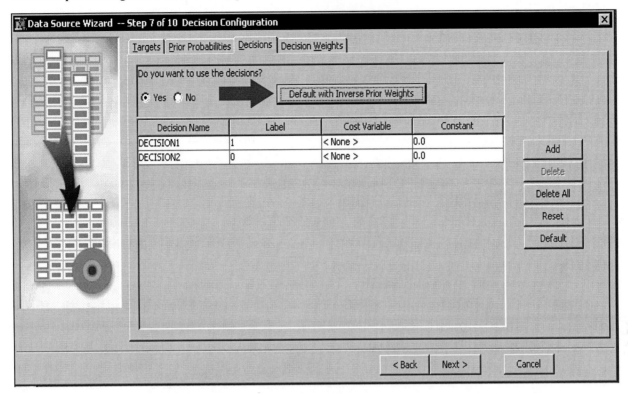

The Decisions option **Default with Inverse Prior Weights** was selected to provide the values in the Decision Weights tab.

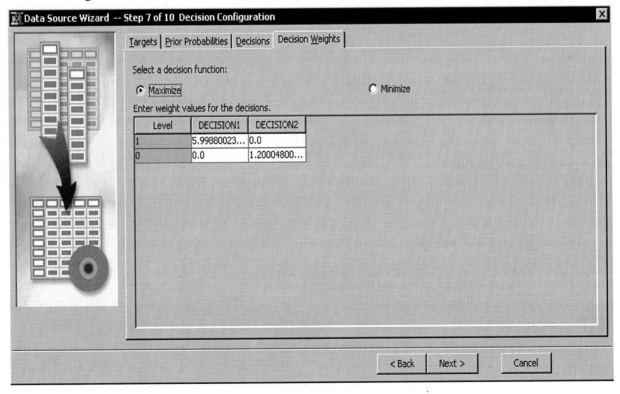

Copyright © 2011, SAS Institute Inc., Cary, North Carolina, USA. ALL RIGHTS RESERVED.

It can be shown that, theoretically, the so-called central decision rule optimizes model performance based on the KS statistic.

The StatExplore node was used to provide preliminary statistics on the target variable.

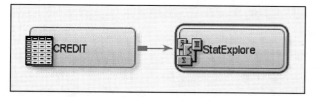

BanruptcyInd and **TARGET** were the only two class variables in the **CREDIT** data set.

```
Class Variable Summary Statistics
(maximum 500 observations printed)

Data Role=TRAIN
```

Data Role	Variable Name	Role	Number of Levels	Missing	Mode	Mode Percentage	Mode2	Mode2 Percentage
TRAIN	BanruptcyInd	INPUT	2	0	0	84.67	1	15.33
TRAIN	TARGET	TARGET	2	0	0	83.33	1	16.67

The Interval Variable Summary shows missing values on 11 of the 27 interval inputs.

```
Interval Variable Summary Statistics
(maximum 500 observations printed)

Data Role=TRAIN
```

Variable	Role	Mean	Standard Deviation	Non Missing	Missing	Minimum	Median	Maximum	Skewness	Kurtosis
CollectCnt	INPUT	0.857	2.161352	3000	0	0	0	50	7.556541	111.8365
DerogCnt	INPUT	1.43	2.731469	3000	0	0	0	51	5.045122	50.93801
InqCnt06	INPUT	3.108333	3.479171	3000	0	0	2	40	2.580016	12.82077
InqFinanceCnt24	INPUT	3.555	4.477536	3000	0	0	2	48	2.806893	13.05141
InqTimeLast	INPUT	3.108108	4.637831	2812	188	0	1	24	2.386563	5.626803
TL50UtilCnt	INPUT	4.077904	3.108076	2901	99	0	3	23	1.443077	3.350659
TL75UtilCnt	INPUT	3.121682	2.605435	2901	99	0	3	20	1.50789	3.686636
TLBadCnt24	INPUT	0.567	1.324423	3000	0	0	0	16	4.376858	28.58301
TLBadDerogCnt	INPUT	1.409	2.460434	3000	0	0	0	47	4.580204	48.24276
TLBalHCPct	INPUT	0.648178	0.266486	2959	41	0	0.6955	3.3613	-0.18073	4.015619
TLCnt	INPUT	7.879546	5.421595	2997	3	0	7	40	1.235579	2.195363
TLCnt03	INPUT	0.275	0.582084	3000	0	0	0	7	2.805575	12.66839
TLCnt12	INPUT	1.821333	1.925265	3000	0	0	1	15	1.623636	3.684793
TLCnt24	INPUT	3.882333	3.396714	3000	0	0	3	28	1.60771	4.379948
TLDel3060Cnt24	INPUT	0.726	1.163633	3000	0	0	0	8	1.381942	1.408509
TLDel60Cnt	INPUT	1.522	2.809653	3000	0	0	0	38	3.30846	17.76184
TLDel60Cnt24	INPUT	1.068333	1.806124	3000	0	0	0	20	3.080191	14.35044
TLDel60CntAll	INPUT	2.522	3.407255	3000	0	0	1	45	2.564126	12.70062
TLDel90Cnt24	INPUT	0.814667	1.609508	3000	0	0	0	19	3.623972	19.7006
TLMaxSum	INPUT	31205.9	29092.91	2960	40	0	24187	271036	2.061138	8.093434
TLOpen24Pct	INPUT	0.564219	0.480105	2997	3	0	0.5	6	2.779055	18.5329
TLOpenPct	INPUT	0.496168	0.206722	2997	3	0	0.5	1	0.379339	-0.01934
TLSatCnt	INPUT	13.51168	8.931769	2996	4	0	12	57	0.851193	0.690344
TLSatPct	INPUT	0.518331	0.234759	2996	4	0	0.5263	1	-0.12407	-0.48393
TLSum	INPUT	20151.1	19682.09	2960	40	0	15546	210612	2.276832	10.96413
TLTimeFirst	INPUT	170.1137	92.8137	3000	0	6	151	933	1.031307	2.860035
TLTimeLast	INPUT	11.87367	16.32141	3000	0	0	7	342	6.447907	80.31043

Copyright © 2011, SAS Institute Inc., Cary, North Carolina, USA. ALL RIGHTS RESERVED.

By creating plots using the Explore window, it was found that several of the interval inputs show somewhat skewed distributions. Transformation of the more severe cases was pursued in regression modeling.

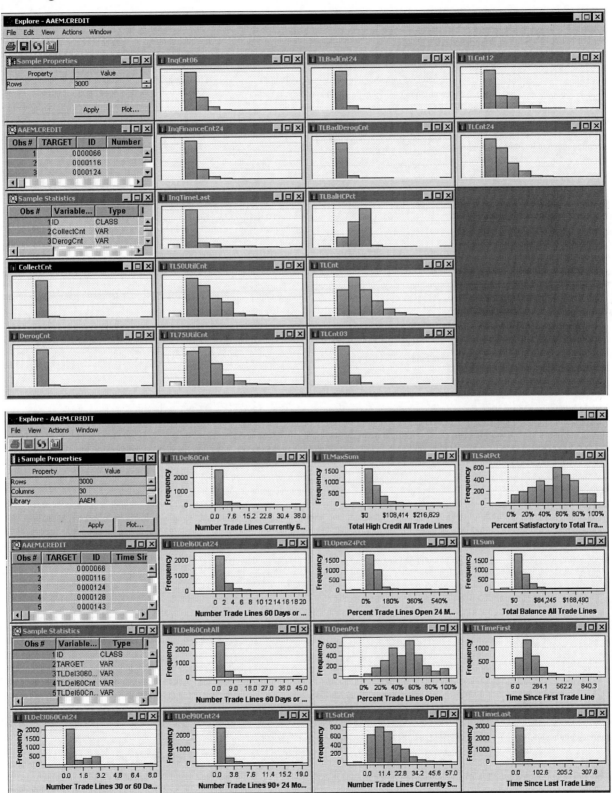

Copyright © 2011, SAS Institute Inc., Cary, North Carolina, USA. ALL RIGHTS RESERVED.

Creating Prediction Models: Simple Stepwise Regression

Because it was the most likely model to be selected for deployment, a regression model was considered first.

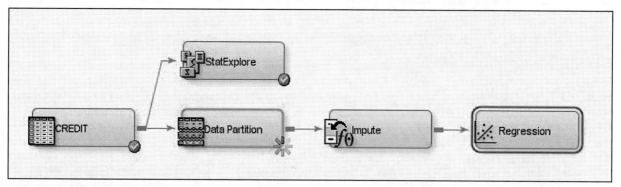

- In the Data Partition node, 50% of the data was chosen for training and 50% for validation.
- The Impute node replaced missing values for the interval inputs with the input mean (the default for interval valued input variables), and added unique imputation indicators for each input with missing values.
- The Regression node used the stepwise method for input variable selection, and validation profit for complexity optimization.

The selected model included seven inputs. See line 1197 of the Output window.

				Analysis of Maximum Likelihood Estimates			
Parameter Exp(Est)	DF	Estimate	Standard Error	Wald Chi-Square	Pr > ChiSq	Standardized Estimate	
Intercept 0.063	1	-2.7602	0.4089	45.57	<.0001		
IMP_TLBalHCPct 6.527	1	1.8759	0.3295	32.42	<.0001	0.2772	
IMP_TLSatPct 0.074	1	-2.6095	0.4515	33.40	<.0001	-0.3363	
InqFinanceCnt24 1.063	1	0.0610	0.0149	16.86	<.0001	0.1527	
TLDel3060Cnt24 1.399	1	0.3359	0.0623	29.11	<.0001	0.2108	
TLDel60Cnt24 1.119	1	0.1126	0.0408	7.62	0.0058	0.1102	
TLOpenPct 4.799	1	1.5684	0.4633	11.46	0.0007	0.1792	
TLTimeFirst 0.997	1	-0.00253	0.000923	7.50	0.0062	-0.1309	

The odds ratio estimates facilitated model interpretation. Increasing risk was associated with increasing values of **IMP_TLBalHCPct, InqFinanceCnt24, TLDel3060Cnt24, TLDel60Cnt,** and **TLOpenPct.** Increasing risk was associated with decreasing values of **IMP_TLSatPct** and **TLTimeFirst.**

Copyright © 2011, SAS Institute Inc., Cary, North Carolina, USA. ALL RIGHTS RESERVED.

```
                    Odds Ratio Estimates

                                      Point
                 Effect             Estimate

                 IMP_TLBalHCPct        6.527
                 IMP_TLSatPct          0.074
                 InqFinanceCnt24       1.063
                 TLDel3060Cnt24        1.399
                 TLDel60Cnt24          1.119
                 TLOpenPct             4.799
                 TLTimeFirst           0.997
```

The iteration plot (found by selecting **View** ⇨ **Model** ⇨ **Iteration Plot** in the Results window) can be set to show average profit versus iteration.

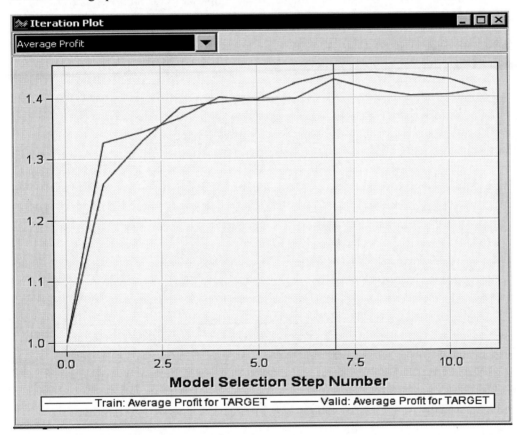

In theory, the average profit for a model using the defined profit matrix equals 1+KS statistic. Thus, the iteration plot (from the Regression node's Results window) showed how the profit (or, in turn, the KS statistic) varied with model complexity. From the plot, the maximum validation profit equaled 1.43, which implies that the maximum KS statistic equaled 0.43.

✎   The actual calculated value of KS (as found using the Model Comparison node) was found to differ slightly from this value (see below).

Copyright © 2011, SAS Institute Inc., Cary, North Carolina, USA. ALL RIGHTS RESERVED.

Creating Prediction Models: Neural Network

While it is not possible to deploy as the final prediction model, a neural network was used to investigate regression lack of fit.

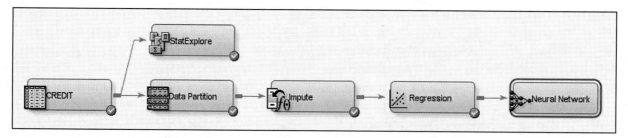

The default settings of the Neural Network node were used in combination with inputs selected by the Stepwise Regression node.

The iteration plot showed slightly higher validation average profit compared to the stepwise regression model.

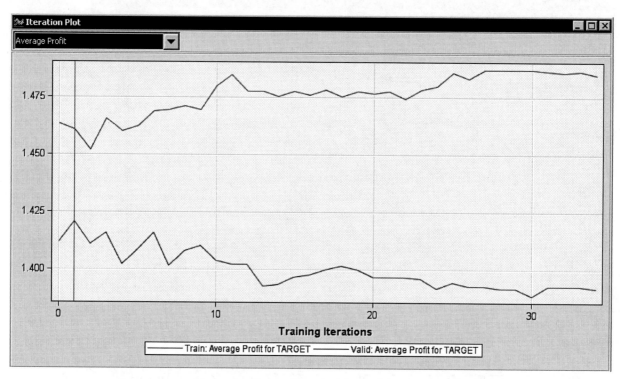

It was possible (although not likely) that transformations to the regression inputs could improve regression prediction.

Creating Prediction Models: Transformed Stepwise Regression

In assaying the data, it was noted that some of the inputs had rather skewed distributions. Such distributions create high leverage points that can distort an input's association with the target. The Transform Variables node was used to regularize the distributions of the model inputs before fitting the stepwise regression.

Copyright © 2011, SAS Institute Inc., Cary, North Carolina, USA. ALL RIGHTS RESERVED.

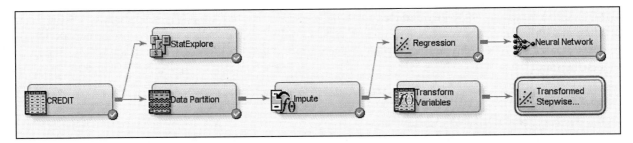

The Transform Variables node was set to maximize the normality of each interval input by selecting from one of several power and logarithmic transformations.

Property	Value
General	
Node ID	Trans
Imported Data	...
Exported Data	...
Notes	...
Train	
Variables	...
Formulas	...
Interactions	...
SAS Code	...
⊟ Default Methods	
├ Interval Inputs	Maximum Normal
├ Interval Targets	None
├ Class Inputs	None
└ Class Targets	None

The Transformed Stepwise Regression node performed stepwise selection from the transformed inputs. The selected model had many of the same inputs as the original stepwise regression model, but on a transformed (and difficult to interpret) scale.

	Odds Ratio Estimates	
1105		
1106		
1107		Point
1108	Effect	Estimate
1109		
1110	IMP_TLBalHCPct	4.237
1111	IMP_TLSatPct	0.090
1112	LOG_InqFinanceCnt24	9.648
1113	LOG_TLDel60Cnt24	9.478
1114	SQRT_IMP_TL75UtilCnt	5.684
1115	SQRT_TLDel3060Cnt24	4.708
1116	SQRT_TLTimeFirst	0.050

Copyright © 2011, SAS Institute Inc., Cary, North Carolina, USA. ALL RIGHTS RESERVED.

The transformations would be justified (despite the increased difficulty in model interpretation) if they resulted in significant improvement in model fit. Based on the profit calculation, the transformed stepwise regression model showed only marginal performance improvement compared to the original stepwise regression model.

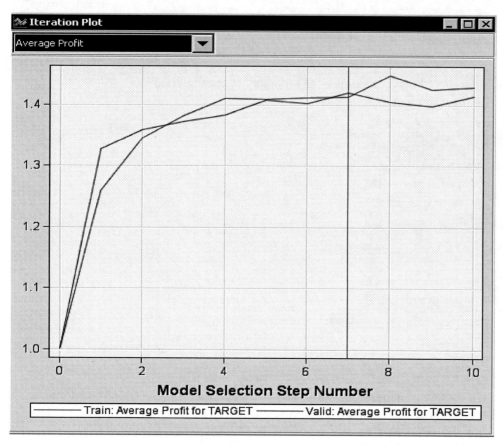

Creating Prediction Models: Discretized Stepwise Regression

Partitioning input variables into discrete ranges was another common risk-modeling method that was investigated.

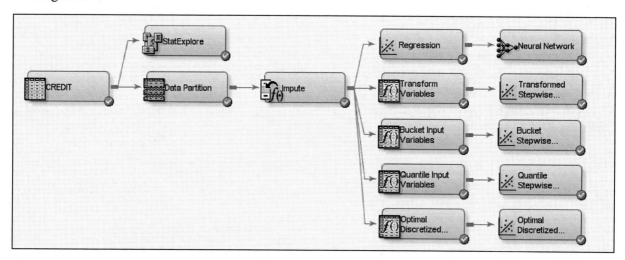

Copyright © 2011, SAS Institute Inc., Cary, North Carolina, USA. ALL RIGHTS RESERVED.

Three discretization approaches were investigated. The Bucket Input Variables node partitioned each interval input into four bins with equal *widths*. The Bin Input Variables node partitioned each interval input into four bins with equal *sizes*. The Optimal Discrete Input Variables node found optimal partitions for each input variable using decision tree methods.

Bucket Transformation

The relatively small size of the **CREDIT** data set resulted in problems for the bucket stepwise regression model. Many of the bins had a small number of observations, which resulted in quasi-complete separation problems for the regression model, as dramatically illustrated by the selected model's odds ratio report. Go to line 1059 of the Output window.

```
                           Odds Ratio Estimates


Point
          Effect
Estimate
          BIN_IMP_TL75UtilCnt 01:low -5 vs 04:15-high
999.000
          BIN_IMP_TL75UtilCnt 02:5-10 vs 04:15-high
999.000
          BIN_IMP_TL75UtilCnt 03:10-15 vs 04:15-high
999.000
          BIN_IMP_TLBalHCPct  01:low -0.840325 vs 04:2.520975-high
<0.001
          BIN_IMP_TLBalHCPct  02:0.840325-1.68065 vs 04:2.520975-high
<0.001
          BIN_IMP_TLBalHCPct  03:1.68065-2.520975 vs 04:2.520975-high
<0.001
          BIN_IMP_TLSatPct    01:low -0.25 vs 04:0.75-high
4.845
          BIN_IMP_TLSatPct    02:0.25-0.5 vs 04:0.75-high
1.819
          BIN_IMP_TLSatPct    03:0.5-0.75 vs 04:0.75-high
1.009
          BIN_InqFinanceCnt24 01:low -9.75 vs 04:29.25-high
0.173
          BIN_InqFinanceCnt24 02:9.75-19.5 vs 04:29.25-high
0.381
          BIN_InqFinanceCnt24 03:19.5-29.25 vs 04:29.25-high
0.640
          BIN_TLDel3060Cnt24  01:low -2 vs 04:6-high
999.000
          BIN_TLDel3060Cnt24  02:2-4 vs 04:6-high
999.000
          BIN_TLDel60CntAll   01:low -4.75 vs 04:14.25-high
0.171
```

Copyright © 2011, SAS Institute Inc., Cary, North Carolina, USA. ALL RIGHTS RESERVED.

```
         BIN_TLDel60CntAll     02:4.75-9.5 vs 04:14.25-high
0.138
         BIN_TLDel60CntAll     03:9.5-14.25 vs 04:14.25-high
0.166
         BIN_TLTimeFirst       01:low -198.75 vs 04:584.25-high
999.000
         BIN_TLTimeFirst       02:198.75-391.5 vs 04:584.25-high
999.000
         BIN_TLTimeFirst       03:391.5-584.25 vs 04:584.25-high
999.000
```

The iteration plot showed substantially worse performance compared to the other modeling efforts.

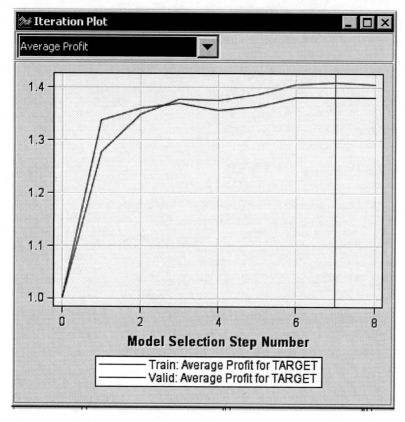

Bin (or Quantile) Transformation

Somewhat better results were seen with the binned stepwise regression model. By ensuring that each bin included a reasonable number of cases, more stable model parameter estimates could be made. See line 1249 of the Output window.

```
                        Odds Ratio Estimates


Point
            Effect
Estimate
```

Copyright © 2011, SAS Institute Inc., Cary, North Carolina, USA. ALL RIGHTS RESERVED.

	PCTL_IMP_TLBalHCPct	01:low -0.513 vs 04:0.8389-high
0.272		
	PCTL_IMP_TLBalHCPct	02:0.513-0.7041 vs 04:0.8389-high
0.452		
	PCTL_IMP_TLBalHCPct	03:0.7041-0.8389 vs 04:0.8389-high
0.630		
	PCTL_IMP_TLSatPct	01:low -0.3529 vs 04:0.6886-high
1.860		
	PCTL_IMP_TLSatPct	02:0.3529-0.5333 vs 04:0.6886-high
1.130		
	PCTL_IMP_TLSatPct	03:0.5333-0.6886 vs 04:0.6886-high
1.040		
	PCTL_InqFinanceCnt24	01:low -1 vs 04:5-high
0.599		
	PCTL_InqFinanceCnt24	02:1-2 vs 04:5-high
0.404		
	PCTL_InqFinanceCnt24	03:2-5 vs 04:5-high
0.807		
	PCTL_TLDel3060Cnt24	02:0-1 vs 03:1-high
0.453		
	PCTL_TLDel60Cnt24	02:0-1 vs 03:1-high
0.357		
	PCTL_TLTimeFirst	01:low -107 vs 04:230-high
1.688		
	PCTL_TLTimeFirst	02:107-152 vs 04:230-high
1.477		
	PCTL_TLTimeFirst	03:152-230 vs 04:230-high
0.837		

Copyright © 2011, SAS Institute Inc., Cary, North Carolina, USA. ALL RIGHTS RESERVED.

The improved model fit was also seen in the iteration plot, although the average profit of the selected model was still not as large as the original stepwise regression model.

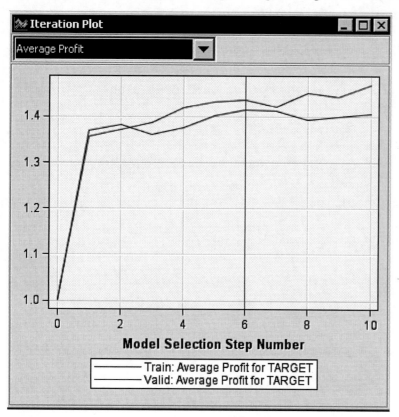

Optimal Transformation

A final attempt on discretization was made using the optimistically named Optimal Discrete transformation. The final 18 degree-of-freedom model included 10 separate inputs (more than any other model). Contents of the Output window starting at line 1698 are shown below.

```
                         Odds Ratio Estimates


Point
        Effect
Estimate
        BanruptcyInd         0 vs 1
2.267
        OPT_IMP_TL75UtilCnt 01:low -1.5 vs 03:8.5-high
0.270
        OPT_IMP_TL75UtilCnt 02:1.5-8.5, MISSING vs 03:8.5-high
0.409
        OPT_IMP_TLBalHCPct  01:low -0.6706, MISSING vs 04:1.0213-high
0.090
        OPT_IMP_TLBalHCPct  02:0.6706-0.86785 vs 04:1.0213-high
0.155
        OPT_IMP_TLBalHCPct  03:0.86785-1.0213 vs 04:1.0213-high
0.250
```

Copyright © 2011, SAS Institute Inc., Cary, North Carolina, USA. ALL RIGHTS RESERVED.

```
        OPT_IMP_TLSatPct     01:low -0.2094 vs 03:0.4655-high,
5.067
        OPT_IMP_TLSatPct     02:0.2094-0.4655 vs 03:0.4655-high,
1.970
        OPT_InqFinanceCnt24 01:low -2.5, MISSIN vs 03:7.5-high
0.353
        OPT_InqFinanceCnt24 02:2.5-7.5 vs 03:7.5-high
0.657
        OPT_TLDel3060Cnt24  01:low -1.5, MISSIN vs 02:1.5-high
0.499
        OPT_TLDel60Cnt       01:low -0.5, MISSIN vs 03:14.5-high
0.084
        OPT_TLDel60Cnt       02:0.5-14.5 vs 03:14.5-high
0.074
        OPT_TLDel60Cnt24     01:low -0.5, MISSIN vs 03:5.5-high
0.327
        OPT_TLDel60Cnt24     02:0.5-5.5 vs 03:5.5-high
0.882
        OPT_TLTimeFirst      01:low -154.5, MISSING vs 02:154.5-high
1.926
        TLOpenPct
3.337
```

The validation average profit was still slightly smaller than the original model. A substantial difference in profit between the training and validation data was also observed. Such a difference was suggestive of overfitting by the model.

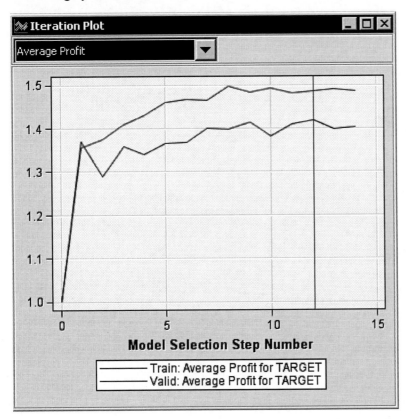

Copyright © 2011, SAS Institute Inc., Cary, North Carolina, USA. ALL RIGHTS RESERVED.

Assessing the Prediction Models

The collection of models was assessed using the Model Comparison node.

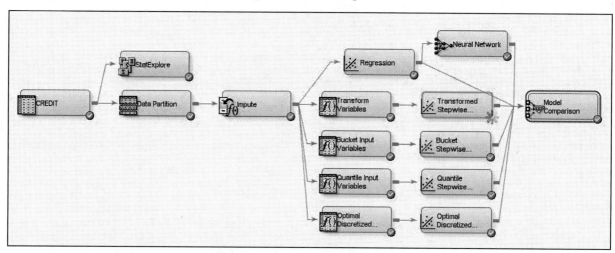

The ROC chart shows a jumble of models with no clear winner.

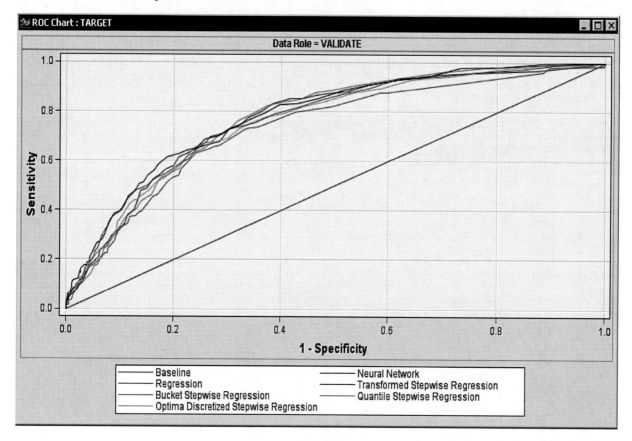

Copyright © 2011, SAS Institute Inc., Cary, North Carolina, USA. ALL RIGHTS RESERVED.

The Fit Statistics table from the Output window is shown below.

Data Role=Valid Statistics	Reg	Neural	Reg5	Reg2	Reg4	Reg3
Valid: Kolmogorov-Smirnov Statistic	0.43	0.46	0.42	0.44	0.45	0.39
Valid: Average Profit for TARGET	1.43	1.42	1.42	1.42	1.41	1.38
Valid: Average Squared Error	0.12	0.12	0.12	0.12	0.12	0.13
Valid: Roc Index	0.77	0.77	0.76	0.78	0.77	0.73
Valid: Average Error Function	0.38	0.39	0.40	0.38	0.39	0.43
Valid: Percent Capture Response	14.40	12.00	11.60	14.40	12.64	9.60
Valid: Divisor for VASE	3000.00	3000.00	3000.00	3000.00	3000.00	3000.00
Valid: Error Function	1152.26	1168.64	1186.46	1131.42	1158.23	1282.59
Valid: Gain	180.00	152.00	148.00	192.00	144.89	124.00
Valid: Gini Coefficient	0.54	0.54	0.53	0.56	0.54	0.47
Valid: Bin-Based Two-Way Kolmogorov-Smirnov Statistic	0.43	0.44	0.41	0.44	0.45	0.39
Valid: Lift	2.88	2.40	2.32	2.88	2.53	1.92
Valid: Maximum Absolute Error	0.97	0.99	1.00	0.98	0.99	1.00
Valid: Misclassification Rate	0.17	0.17	0.17	0.17	0.17	0.17
Valid: Mean Square Error	0.12	0.12	0.12	0.12	0.12	0.13
Valid: Sum of Frequencies	1500.00	1500.00	1500.00	1500.00	1500.00	1500.00
Valid: Total Profit for TARGET	2143.03	2131.02	2127.45	2127.44	2121.42	2072.25
Valid: Root Average Squared Error	0.35	0.35	0.35	0.34	0.35	0.36
Valid: Percent Response	48.00	40.00	38.67	48.00	42.13	32.00
Valid: Root Mean Square Error	0.35	0.35	0.35	0.34	0.35	0.36
Valid: Sum of Square Errors	359.70	367.22	371.58	352.69	366.76	381.44
Valid: Sum of Case Weights Times Freq	3000.00	3000.00	3000.00	3000.00	3000.00	3000.00

The best model, as measured by average profit, was the original regression. The neural network had the highest KS statistic. The log-transformed regression, Reg2, had the highest ROC-index.

If the purpose of a credit risk model is to order the cases, then Reg2, the transformed regression, had the highest rank decision statistic, the ROC index.

In short, the best model for deployment was as much a matter of taste as of statistical performance. The relatively small validation data set used to compare the models did not produce a clear winner.

In the end, the model selected for deployment was the original stepwise regression, because it offered consistently good performance across multiple assessment measures.

Copyright © 2011, SAS Institute Inc., Cary, North Carolina, USA. ALL RIGHTS RESERVED.

A.4 Enrollment Management Case Study

Case Study Description

In the fall of 2004, the administration of a large private university requested that the Office of Enrollment Management and the Office of Institutional Research work together to identify prospective students who would most likely enroll as new freshmen in the Fall 2005 semester. The administration stated several goals for this project:

- increase new freshman enrollment
- increase diversity
- increase SAT scores of entering students

Historically, inquiries numbered about 90,000+ students, and the university enrolled from 2400 to 2800 new freshmen each Fall semester.

   The diagram containing this analysis is stored as an XML file on the course data disk. You can open this file by right-clicking **Diagrams** ⇨ **Import Diagram from XML** in SAS Enterprise Miner. All nodes in the opened file, except the data node, contain the property settings outlined in this case study. If you want to run the diagram, you need to re-create the case study data set using the metadata settings indicated below.

Copyright © 2011, SAS Institute Inc., Cary, North Carolina, USA. ALL RIGHTS RESERVED.

Case Study Training Data

Name	Model Role	Measurement Level	Description
ACADEMIC_INTEREST_1	Rejected	Nominal	Primary academic interest code
ACADEMIC_INTEREST_2	Rejected	Nominal	Secondary academic interest code
CAMPUS_VISIT	Input	Nominal	Campus visit code
CONTACT_CODE1	Rejected	Nominal	First contact code
CONTACT_DATE1	Rejected	Nominal	First contact date
ETHNICITY	Rejected	Nominal	Ethnicity
ENROLL	Target	Binary	1=Enrolled F2004, 0=Not enrolled F2004
IRSCHOOL	Rejected	Nominal	High school code
INSTATE	Input	Binary	1=In state, 0=Out of state
LEVEL_YEAR	Rejected	Unary	Student academic level
REFERRAL_CNTCTS	Input	Ordinal	Referral contact count
SELF_INIT_CNTCTS	Input	Interval	Self initiated contact count
SOLICITED_CNTCTS	Input	Ordinal	Solicited contact count
TERRITORY	Input	Nominal	Recruitment area
TOTAL_CONTACTS	Input	Interval	Total contact count
TRAVEL_INIT_CNTCTS	Input	Ordinal	Travel initiated contact count
AVG_INCOME	Input	Interval	Commercial HH income estimate
DISTANCE	Input	Interval	Distance from university
HSCRAT	Input	Interval	5-year high school enrollment rate
INIT_SPAN	Input	Interval	Time from first contact to enrollment date
INT1RAT	Input	Interval	5-year primary interest code rate
INT2RAT	Input	Interval	5-year secondary interest code rate
INTEREST	Input	Ordinal	Number of indicated extracurricular interests
MAILQ	Input	Ordinal	Mail qualifying score (1=very interested)

(Continued on the next page.)

Copyright © 2011, SAS Institute Inc., Cary, North Carolina, USA. ALL RIGHTS RESERVED.

PREMIERE	Input	Binary	1=Attended campus recruitment event, 0=Did not
SATSCORE	Rejected	Interval	SAT (original) score
SEX	Rejected	Binary	Sex
STUEMAIL	Input	Binary	1=Have e-mail address, 0=Do not
TELECQ	Rejected	Ordinal	Telecounciling qualifying score (1=very interested)

The Office of Institutional Research assumed the task of building a predictive model, and the Office of Enrollment Management served as consultant to the project. The Office of Institutional Research built and maintained a data warehouse that contained information about enrollment for the past six years. It was decided that inquiries for Fall 2004 would be used to build the model to help shape the Fall 2005 freshman class. The data set **Inq2005** was built over a period of a several months in consultation with Enrollment Management. The data set included variables that could be classified as demographic, financial, number of correspondences, student interests, and campus visits. Many variables were created using historical data and trends. For example, high school code was replaced by the percentage of inquirers from that high school over the past five years who enrolled. The resulting data set included over 90,000 observations and over 50 variables. For this case study, the number of variables was reduced. The data set **Inq2005** is in the AAEM library, and the variables are described in the table above. Some of the variables were automatically rejected based on the number of missing values.

The nominal variables **ACADEMIC_INTEREST_1**, **ACADEMIC_INTEREST_2**, and **IRSCHOOL** were rejected because they were replaced by the interval variables **INT1RAT**, **INT2RAT**, and **HSCRAT**, respectively. For example, academic interest codes 1 and 2 were replaced by the percentage of inquirers over the past five years who indicated those interest codes and then enrolled. The variable **IRSCHOOL** is the high school code of the student, and it was replaced by the percentage of inquirers from that high school over the last five years who enrolled. The variables **ETHNICITY** and **SEX** were rejected because they cannot be used in admission decisions. Several variables count the various types of contacts the university has with the students.

Accessing and Assaying the Data

A SAS Enterprise Miner data source was defined using the metadata settings indicated above. The StatExplore node was used to provide preliminary statistics on the input variables.

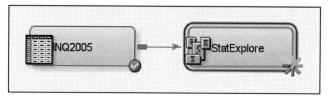

Copyright © 2011, SAS Institute Inc., Cary, North Carolina, USA. ALL RIGHTS RESERVED.

The following is extracted from the StatExplore node's Results window:

```
Class Variable Summary Statistics
(maximum 500 observations printed)

Data Role=TRAIN

                                       Number
Data                                     of                        Mode                Mode2
Role     Variable Name        Role     Levels   Missing   Mode   Percentage   Mode2   Percentage

TRAIN    CAMPUS_VISIT         INPUT       3        0        0      96.61        1        3.31
TRAIN    Instate              INPUT       2        0        Y      62.04        N       37.96
TRAIN    REFERRAL_CNTCTS      INPUT       6        0        0      96.46        1        3.21
TRAIN    SOLICITED_CNTCTS     INPUT       8        0        0      52.45        1       41.60
TRAIN    TERRITORY            INPUT      12        1        2      15.98        5       15.34
TRAIN    TRAVEL_INIT_CNTCTS   INPUT       7        0        0      67.00        1       29.90
TRAIN    interest             INPUT       4        0        0      95.01        1        4.62
TRAIN    mailq                INPUT       5        0        5      69.33        2       12.80
TRAIN    premiere             INPUT       2        0        0      97.11        1        2.89
TRAIN    stuemail             INPUT       2        0        0      51.01        1       48.99
TRAIN    Enroll               TARGET      2        0        0      96.86        1        3.14
```

The class input variables are listed first. Notice that most of the count variables have a high percent of 0s.

```
Distribution of Class Target and Segment Variables
(maximum 500 observations printed)

Data Role=TRAIN

Data      Variable                              Frequency
Role       Name      Role      Level      Count      Percent

TRAIN     Enroll     TARGET      0         88614      96.8650
TRAIN     Enroll     TARGET      1          2868       3.1350
```

Next is the target distribution. Only 3.1 % of the target values are 1s, making a 1 a rare event. Standard practice in this situation is to separately sample the 0s and 1s. The Sample tool, used below, enables you to create a stratified sample in SAS Enterprise Miner.

```
Interval Variable Summary Statistics
(maximum 500 observations printed)

Data Role=TRAIN

                               Standard      Non
Variable           Role   Mean   Deviation   Missing   Missing   Minimum   Median   Maximum   Skewness   Kurtosis

SELF_INIT_CNTCTS   INPUT  1.214119  1.666529   91482       0         0         1         56     2.916263   21.50072
TOTAL_CONTACTS     INPUT  2.166098  1.852537   91482       0         1         2         58     3.062389   19.60427
avg_income         INPUT  47315.33  20608.89   70553     20929      4940     42324    200001    1.258231    1.874903
distance           INPUT  380.4276  397.9788   72014     19468   0.417124  183.5467  4798.899  2.276541    9.369703
hscrat             INPUT  0.037652  0.057399   91482       0         0     0.033333      1      7.021978   93.31547
init_span          INPUT  19.68616  8.722109   91482       0       -216       19        228    0.758461   10.43657
intlrat            INPUT  0.037091  0.024026   91482       0         0     0.042105      1      3.496845   74.08503
int2rat            INPUT  0.042896  0.025244   91482       0         0     0.05667       1      3.215683   56.32374
```

Finally, interval variable summary statistics are presented. Notice that **avg_income** and **distance** have missing values.

Copyright © 2011, SAS Institute Inc., Cary, North Carolina, USA. ALL RIGHTS RESERVED.

The Explore window was used to study the distribution of the interval variables.

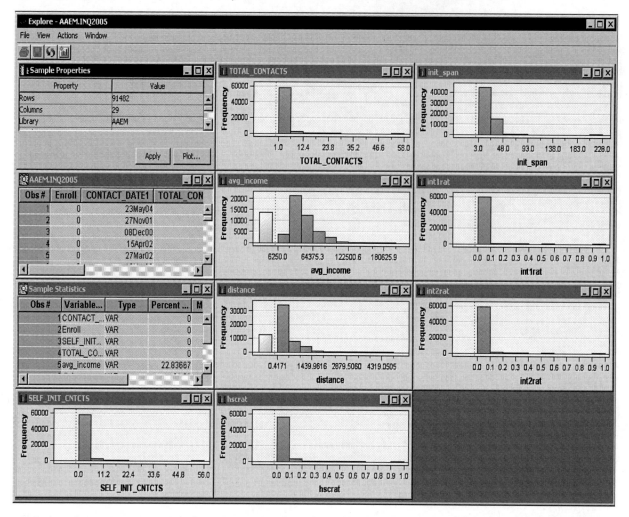

The apparent skewness of all inputs suggests that some transformations might be needed for regression models.

Copyright © 2011, SAS Institute Inc., Cary, North Carolina, USA. ALL RIGHTS RESERVED.

Creating a Training Sample

Cases from each target level were separately sampled. All cases with the primary outcome were selected. For each primary outcome case, seven secondary outcome cases were selected. This created a training sample with a 12.5% overall enrollment rate.

The Sample tool was used to create a training sample for subsequent modeling.

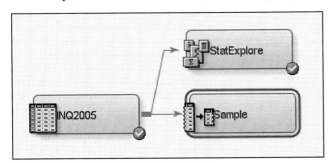

To create the sample as described, the following modifications were made to the Sample node's properties panel:

1. Type **100** as the Percentage value (in the Size property group).

2. Select **Criterion** ⇨ **Level Based** (in the Stratified property group).

3. Type **12.5** as the Sample Proportion value (in the Level Based Options property group).

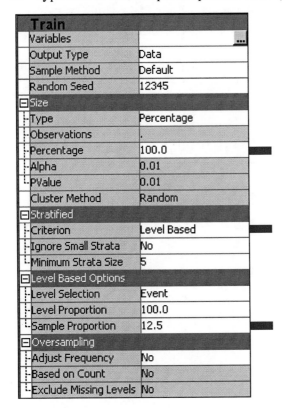

Copyright © 2011, SAS Institute Inc., Cary, North Carolina, USA. ALL RIGHTS RESERVED.

The Sample node Results window shows all primary outcome cases that are selected and a sufficient number of secondary outcome cases that are selected to achieve the 12.5% primary outcome proportion.

```
Summary Statistics for Class Targets
(maximum 500 observations printed)

Data=DATA

            Numeric    Formatted    Frequency
Variable     Value       Value        Count      Percent    Label

 Enroll        0           0          88614      96.8650
 Enroll        1           1           2868       3.1350


Data=SAMPLE

            Numeric    Formatted    Frequency
Variable     Value       Value        Count      Percent    Label

 Enroll        0           0          20076       87.5
 Enroll        1           1           2868        12.5
```

Configuring Decision Processing

The primary purpose of the predictions was decision optimization and, secondarily, ranking. An applicant was considered a good candidate if his or her probability of enrollment was higher than average.

Because of the Sample node, decision information consistent with the above objectives could not be entered in the data source node. To incorporate decision information, the Decisions tool was incorporated in the analysis.

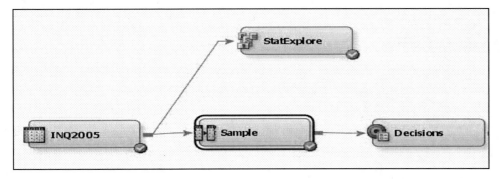

Copyright © 2011, SAS Institute Inc., Cary, North Carolina, USA. ALL RIGHTS RESERVED.

These steps were followed to configure the Decisions node:

1. In the Properties panel of the Decision node, set **Decisions** to Custom. Then select
    Custom Editor ⇨ 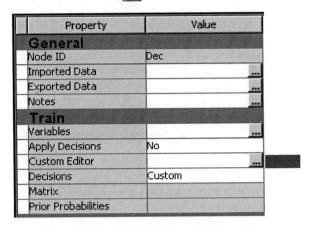.

After the analysis path is updated, the Decision window appears.

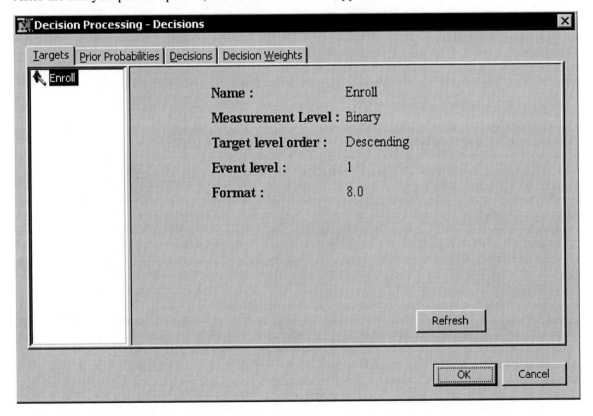

2. Select the **Decisions** tab.

Copyright © 2011, SAS Institute Inc., Cary, North Carolina, USA. ALL RIGHTS RESERVED.

3.   Select **Default with Inverse Prior Weights**.

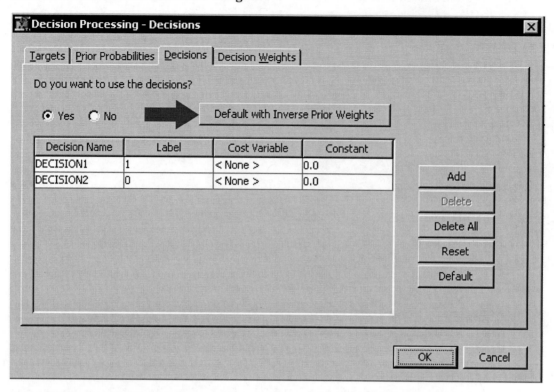

4.   Select the **Decision Weights** tab.

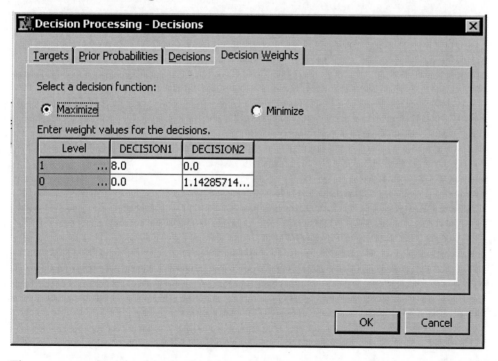

The nonzero values used in the decision matrix are the inverse of the prior probabilities (1/.125=8. and 1/0.875=1.142857). Such a decision matrix, sometimes referred to as the *central decision rule*, forces a primary decision when the estimated primary outcome probability for a case exceeds the primary outcome prior probability (0.125 in this case).

Copyright © 2011, SAS Institute Inc., Cary, North Carolina, USA. ALL RIGHTS RESERVED.

Creating Prediction Models (All Cases)

Two rounds of predictive modeling were performed. In the first round, all cases were considered for model building. From the Decision node, partitioning, imputation, modeling, and assessment were performed. The completed analysis appears as shown.

  If the Stepwise Regression model is not connected to the Model Comparison node, you might have to first delete the **connections** for the Instate Regression and Neural Network nodes to the Model Comparison node. Then connect the Stepwise Regression node, Neural Network node, and Regression nodes – in that order – to the Model Comparison node.

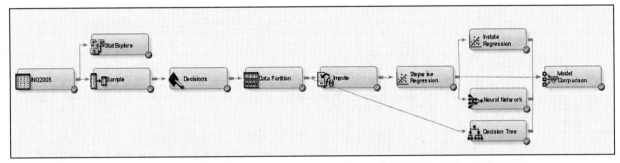

- The Data Partition node used 60% for training and 40% for validation.
- The Impute node used the Tree method for both class and interval variables. Unique missing indicator variables were also selected and used as inputs.
- The stepwise regression model was used as a variable selection method for the Neural Network and second Regression nodes.
- The Regression node labeled **Instate Regression** included the variables from the Stepwise Regression node and the variable **Instate**. It was felt that prospective students behave differently based on whether they are in state or out of state.

In this implementation of the case study, the Stepwise Regression node selected three inputs: high school, self-initiated contact count, and student e-mail indicator. The model output is shown below.

Analysis of Maximum Likelihood Estimates							
Parameter	DF	Estimate	Standard Error	Wald Chi-Square	Pr > ChiSq	Standardized Estimate	Exp(Est)
INTERCEPT	1	-12.1422	18.9832	0.41	0.5224		0.000
SELF_INIT_CNTCTS	1	0.6895	0.0203	1156.19	<.0001	0.8773	1.993
HSCRAT	1	16.4261	0.8108	410.46	<.0001	0.7506	999.000
STUEMAIL	0	1	-7.7776	18.9824	0.17	0.6820	0.000

Odds Ratio Estimates		
Effect		Point Estimate
SELF_INIT_CNTCTS		1.993
HSCRAT		999.000
STUEMAIL	0 VS 1	<0.001

The unusual odds ratio estimates for **HSCRAT** and **STUEMAIL** result from an extremely strong association in those inputs. For example, certain high schools had all applicants or no applicants enroll. Likewise, very few students enrolled who did not provide an e-mail address.

Copyright © 2011, SAS Institute Inc., Cary, North Carolina, USA. ALL RIGHTS RESERVED.

Adding the **INSTATE** input in the Instate Regression model changed the significance of inputs selected by the stepwise regression model. The input **STUEMAIL** is no longer statistically significant after including the **INSTATE** input.

```
                          Analysis of Maximum Likelihood Estimates

                                    Standard      Wald              Standardized
Parameter            DF   Estimate    Error    Chi-Square  Pr > ChiSq   Estimate   Exp(Est)
INTERCEPT             1   -12.0541   16.7449      0.52       0.4716                   0.000
INSTATE          N   1    -0.4145    0.0577      51.67       <.0001                   0.661
SELF_INIT_CNTCTS     1     0.6889    0.0196    1233.22       <.0001      0.8231       1.992
HSCRAT               1    16.2327    0.7553     461.95       <.0001      0.7142     999.000
STUEMAIL         0   1    -7.3528   16.7443      0.19       0.6606                   0.001


          Odds Ratio Estimates
                          Point
Effect                  Estimate
INSTATE          N VS Y    0.437
SELF_INIT_CNTCTS           1.992
HSCRAT                   999.000
STUEMAIL         0 VS 1   <0.001
```

A slight increase in validation profit (the criterion used to tune models) was found using the neural network model.

The tree provides insight into the strength of model fit. The Subtree Assessment plot shows the highest profit having 17 leaves. Most of the predictive performance, however, is provided by the initial splits.

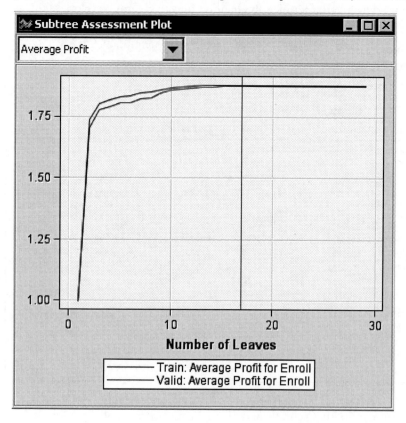

Copyright © 2011, SAS Institute Inc., Cary, North Carolina, USA. ALL RIGHTS RESERVED.

A simpler tree is scrutinized to aid in interpretation.

The tree model was rerun with properties changed as follows to produce a tree with three leaves: Method=**N**, Number of Leaves=**3**.

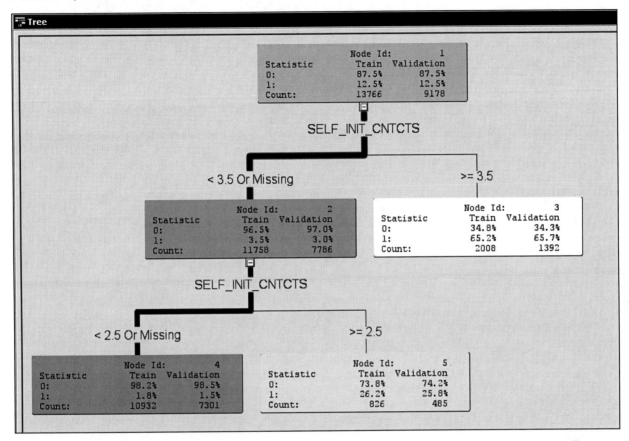

Students with three or fewer self-initiated contacts rarely enrolled (as seen in the left leaf of the first split). Enrollment was even rarer for students with two or fewer self-initiated contacts (as seen in the left leaf of the second split). Notice that the primary target percentage is rounded down. Also notice that most of the secondary target cases can be found in the lower left leaf.

✎   The decision tree results shown in the rest of this case study are generated by the original, 17-leaf tree.

Copyright © 2011, SAS Institute Inc., Cary, North Carolina, USA. ALL RIGHTS RESERVED.

Assessing the Prediction Models

Model performance was compared in the Model Comparison node.

 If the Stepwise Regression model does not appear in the ROC chart, it might not be connected to the Model Comparison node. You might have to first delete the *connections* for the Instate Regression and Neural Network nodes to the Model Comparison node. Connect the Stepwise Regression node, Neural Network node, and Regression nodes – in that order – to the Model Comparison node and re-run the Model Comparison node to make all models visible.

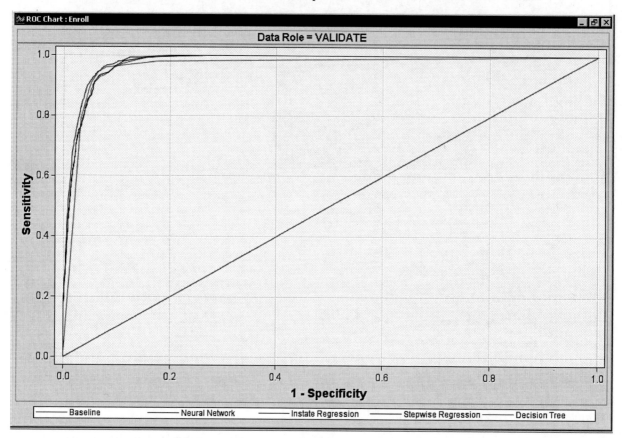

The validation ROC chart showed an extremely good performance for all models. The neural model seemed to have a slight edge over the other models. This was mirrored in the Fit Statistics table (abstracted below to show only the validation performance).

Copyright © 2011, SAS Institute Inc., Cary, North Carolina, USA. ALL RIGHTS RESERVED.

```
Data Role=Valid
```

Statistics	Neural	Tree	Reg	Reg2
Valid: Kolmogorov-Smirnov Statistic	0.89	0.88	0.87	0.86
Valid: Average Profit for Enroll	1.88	1.88	1.87	1.86
Valid: Average Squared Error	0.04	0.04	0.04	0.04
Valid: Roc Index	0.98	0.96	0.98	0.98
Valid: Average Error Function	0.11	.	0.14	0.14
Valid: Percent Capture Response	30.94	30.95	29.72	29.55
Valid: Divisor for VASE	18356.00	18356.00	18356.00	18356.00
Valid: Error Function	2097.03	.	2521.91	2486.75
Valid: Gain	576.37	519.90	552.83	552.83
Valid: Gini Coefficient	0.96	0.93	0.95	0.95
Valid: Bin-Based Two-Way Kolmogorov-Smirnov Statistic	0.88	0.87	0.86	0.86
Valid: Lift	6.19	6.19	5.94	5.91
Valid: Maximum Absolute Error	1.00	1.00	1.00	1.00
Valid: Misclassification Rate	0.05	0.05	0.06	0.06
Valid: Mean Square Error	0.04	.	0.04	0.04
Valid: Sum of Frequencies	9178.00	9178.00	9178.00	9178.00
Valid: Total Profit for Enroll	17285.71	17256.00	17122.29	17099.43
Valid: Root Average Squared Error	0.19	0.20	0.20	0.20
Valid: Percent Response	77.34	77.36	74.29	73.85
Valid: Root Mean Square Error	0.19	.	0.20	0.20
Valid: Sum of Square Errors	657.78	735.99	752.78	754.37
Valid: Sum of Case Weights Times Freq	18356.00	18356.00	18356.00	18356.00
Valid: Number of Wrong Classifications.	463.00	.	.	.

It should be noted that a ROC Index of 0.98 needed careful consideration because it suggested a near-perfect separation of the primary and secondary outcomes. The decision tree model provides some insight into this apparently outstanding model fit. Self-initiated contacts are critical to enrollment. Fewer than three self-initiated contacts almost guarantees non-enrollment.

Creating Prediction Models (Instate-Only Cases)

A second round of analysis was performed on instate-only cases. The analysis sample was reduced using the Filter node. The Filter node was attached to the Decisions node, as shown below.

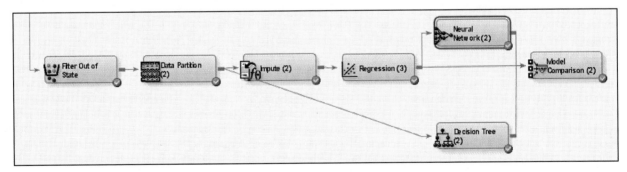

Copyright © 2011, SAS Institute Inc., Cary, North Carolina, USA. ALL RIGHTS RESERVED.

The following configuration steps were applied:

1. In the Filter Out of State node, select **Default Filtering Method** ⇨ **None** for both the class and interval variables.

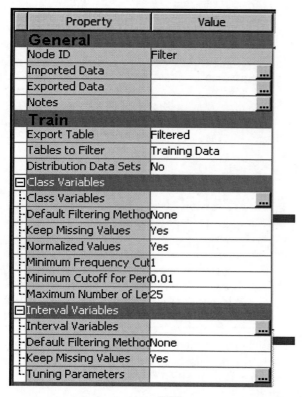

2. Select **Class Variables** ⇨ [...]. After the path is updated, the Interactive Class Filter window appears.

3. Select **Generate Summary** and then select **Yes** to generate summary statistics.

Copyright © 2011, SAS Institute Inc., Cary, North Carolina, USA. ALL RIGHTS RESERVED.

4. Select **Instate**. The Interactive Class Filter window is updated to show the distribution of the **Instate** input.

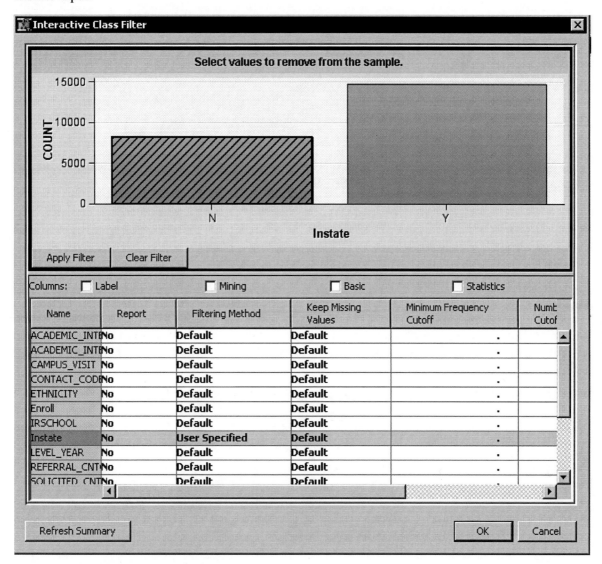

5. Select the **N** bar and select **Apply Filter**.

6. Select **OK** to close the Interactive Class Filter window.

7. Run the Filter node and view the results.

```
                       Excluded Class Values
                  (maximum 500 observations printed)
                                                            Keep
                                Train     Train      Filter   Missing
      Variable   Role   Level   Count     Percent  Label  Method   Values
      Instate    INPUT    N     8200     35.7392         MANUAL
```

All out-of-state cases were filtered from the analysis.

After filtering, an analysis similar to the above was conducted with stepwise regression, neural network, and decision tree models.

Copyright © 2011, SAS Institute Inc., Cary, North Carolina, USA. ALL RIGHTS RESERVED.

The partial diagram (after the Filter node) is shown below:

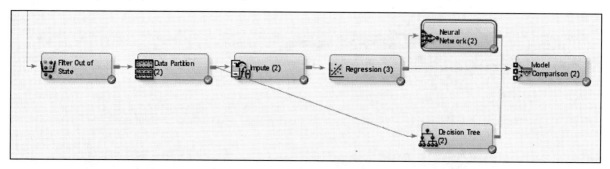

As for the models in this subset analysis, the **Instate** Stepwise Regression model selects two of the same inputs found in the first round of modeling, **SELF_INIT_CNTCTS** and **STUEMAIL**.

				Standard	Wald		Standardized	
Parameter		DF	Estimate	Error	Chi-Square	Pr > ChiSq	Estimate	Exp(Est)
Intercept		1	-10.1372	20.8246	0.24	0.6264		0.000
SELF_INIT_CNTCTS		1	0.7188	0.0210	1174.00	<.0001	0.9297	2.052
stuemail	0	1	-6.8602	20.8245	0.11	0.7418		0.001

Analysis of Maximum Likelihood Estimates

The **Instate** decision tree showed a structure similar to the decision tree model from the first round. The tree with the highest validation profit possessed 20 leaves. The best five-leaf tree, whose validation profit is 97% of the selected tree, is shown below.

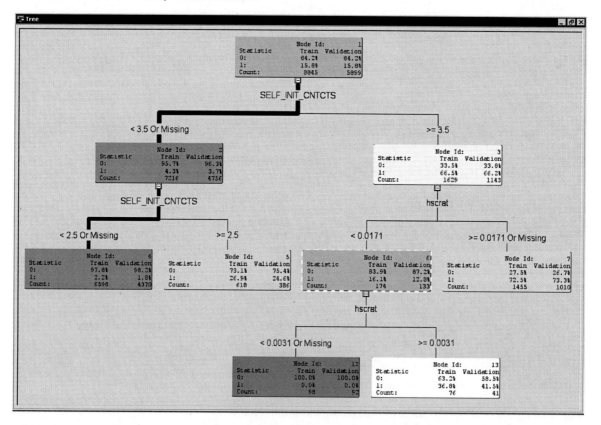

Again, much of the performance of the model is due to a low self-initiated contacts count.

Copyright © 2011, SAS Institute Inc., Cary, North Carolina, USA. ALL RIGHTS RESERVED.

Assessing Prediction Models (Instate-Only Cases)

As before, model performance was gauged in the Model Comparison node.

The ROC chart showed no clearly superior model, although all models had rather exceptional performance.

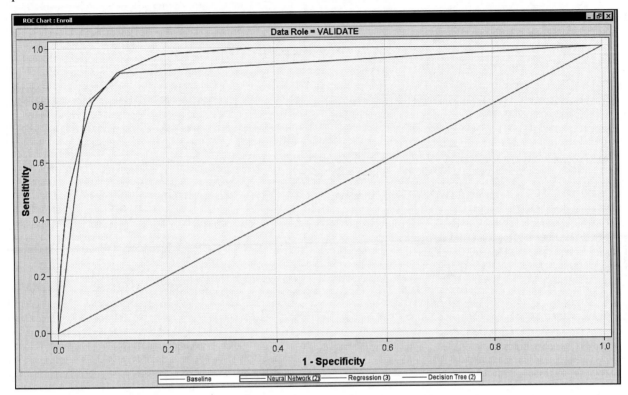

The Fit Statistics table of the Output window showed a slight edge over the tree model in misclassification rate. The validation ROC index and validation average profit favored the Stepwise Regression and Neural Network models. Again, it should be noted that these were unusually high model performance statistics.

Copyright © 2011, SAS Institute Inc., Cary, North Carolina, USA. ALL RIGHTS RESERVED.

```
Data Role=Valid

Statistics                                                         Neural2       Reg3      Tree2

Valid: Kolmogorov-Smirnov Statistic                                   0.80       0.80       0.80
Valid: Average Profit                                                 2.02       2.02       2.00
Valid: Average Squared Error                                          0.06       0.06       0.06
Valid: Roc Index                                                      0.96       0.96       0.92
Valid: Average Error Function                                         0.19       0.20       0.21
Valid: Bin-Based Two-Way Kolmogorov-Smirnov Probability Cutoff          .          .          .
Valid: Cumulative Percent Captured Response                          50.69      50.69      46.38
Valid: Percent Captured Response                                     23.41      23.41      23.19
Valid: Frequency of Classified Cases                              5899.00    5899.00    5899.00
Valid: Divisor for ASE                                           11798.00   11798.00   11798.00
Valid: Error Function                                             2194.05    2330.78    2462.62
Valid: Gain                                                         406.85     406.85     363.74
Valid: Gini Coefficient                                               0.91       0.91       0.84
Valid: Bin-Based Two-Way Kolmogorov-Smirnov Statistic                 0.00       0.00       0.00
Valid: Kolmogorov-Smirnov Probability Cutoff                          0.14       0.14       0.03
Valid: Cumulative Lift                                                5.07       5.07       4.64
Valid: Lift                                                           4.68       4.68       4.64
Valid: Maximum Absolute Error                                         0.97       1.00       0.98
Valid: Misclassification Rate                                         0.09       0.09       0.08
Valid: Sum of Frequencies                                         5899.00    5899.00    5899.00
Valid: Total Profit                                              11901.71   11901.71   11824.00
Valid: Root Average Squared Error                                     0.24       0.25       0.25
Valid: Cumulative Percent Response                                   80.08      80.08      73.27
Valid: Percent Response                                              73.97      73.97      73.27
Valid: Sum of Squared Errors                                       705.43     725.26     716.66
Valid: Number of Wrong Classifications                             510.00     527.00     462.00
```

Deploying the Prediction Model

The Score node facilitated deployment of the prediction model, as shown in the diagram's final form.

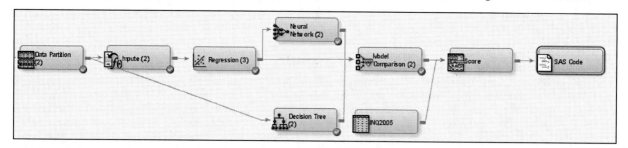

The best (instate) model was selected by the **Instate** Model Comparison node and passed on to the Score node. Another **INQ2005** data source was assigned a role of Score and attached to the Score node. Columns from the scored **INQ2005** were then passed into the Office of Enrollment Management's data management system by the final SAS Code node.

Copyright © 2011, SAS Institute Inc., Cary, North Carolina, USA. ALL RIGHTS RESERVED.

Appendix B Bibliography

Copyright © 2011, SAS Institute Inc., Cary, North Carolina, USA. ALL RIGHTS RESERVED.

Copyright © 2011, SAS Institute Inc., Cary, North Carolina, USA. ALL RIGHTS RESERVED.

B.1 References

Beck, A. 1997. "Herb Edelstein discusses the usefulness of data mining." *DS Star.* Vol. 1, N0. 2. Available www.tgc.com/dsstar/.

Bishop, C. M. 1995. *Neural Networks for Pattern Recognition.* New York: Oxford University Press.

Breiman, L. et al. 1984. *Classification and Regression Trees.* Belmont, CA: Wadsworth International Group.

Hand, D. J. 1997. *Construction and Assessment of Classification Rules.* New York: John Wiley & Sons, Inc.

Hand, D. J. 2005. "What you get is what you want? – Some dangers of black box data mining." *M2005 Conference Proceedings*, Cary, NC: SAS Institute Inc.

Hand, D. J. 2006. "Classifier technology and the illusion of progress." *Statistical Science* 21:1-14.

Hand, D. J. and W. E. Henley. 1997. "Statistical classification methods in consumer credit scoring: a review." *Journal of the Royal Statistical Society A* 160:523-541.

Hand, David, Heikki Mannila, and Padraic Smyth. 2001. *Principles of Data Mining.* Cambridge, Massachusetts: The MIT Press.

Harrell, F. E. 2006. *Regression Modeling Strategies.* New York: Springer-Verlag New York, Inc.

Hastie, Trevor, Robert Tibshirani, and Jerome Friedman. 2001. *The Elements of Statistical Learning: Data Mining, Inference, and Prediction.* New York: Springer-Verlag New York, Inc.

Hoaglin, D. C., F. Mosteller, and J. W. Tukey. 1983. *Understanding Robust and Exploratory Data Analysis.* New York: John Wiley & Sons, Inc.

Kass, G. V. 1980. "An exploratory technique for investigating large quantities of categorical data." *Applied Statistics* 29:119-127.

Mosteller, F. and J. W. Tukey. 1977. *Data Analysis and Regression.* Reading, MA: Addison-Wesley.

Piatesky-Shapiro, G. 1998. "What Wal-Mart might do with Barbie association rules." *Knowledge Discovery Nuggets*, 98:1. Available http://www.kdnuggets.com/.

Ripley, B. D. 1996. *Pattern Recognition and Neural Networks.* New York: Cambridge University Press.

Rubinkam, M. 2006. "Internet Merchants Fighting Costs of Credit Card Fraud," *AP Worldstream.* The Associated Press.

Rud, Olivia Parr. 2001. *Data Mining Cookbook: Modeling Data, Risk, and Customer Relationship Management.* New York: John Wiley & Sons, Inc.

Sarle, W. S. 1983. *Cubic Clustering Criterion.* SAS Technical Report A-108. Cary, NC: SAS Institute Inc.

Sarle, W. S. 1994a. "Neural Networks and Statistical Models," *Proceedings of the Nineteenth Annual SAS® Users Group International Conference.* Cary: NC, SAS Institute Inc., 1538-1550.

Sarle, W. S. 1994b. "Neural Network Implementation in SAS® Software," *Proceedings of the Nineteenth Annual SAS® Users Group International Conference.* Cary: NC, SAS Institute Inc., 1550-1573.

Copyright © 2011, SAS Institute Inc., Cary, North Carolina, USA. ALL RIGHTS RESERVED.

Sarle, W. S. 1995. "Stopped Training and Other Remedies for Overfitting." *Proceedings of the 27th Symposium on the Interface.*

SAS Institute Inc. 2002. *SAS® 9 Language: Reference, Volumes 1 and 2.* Cary, NC: SAS Institute Inc.

SAS Institute Inc. 2002. *SAS® 9 Procedures Guide.* Cary, NC: SAS Institute Inc.

SAS Institute Inc. 2002. *SAS/STAT® 9 User's Guide, Volumes 1,2, and 3.* Cary, NC: SAS Institute Inc.

Weiss, S. M. and C. A. Kulikowski. 1991. *Computer Systems That Learn: Classification and Prediction Methods from Statistics, Neural Nets, Machine Learning, and Expert Systems.* San Mateo, CA: Morgan Kaufmann.

Copyright © 2011, SAS Institute Inc., Cary, North Carolina, USA. ALL RIGHTS RESERVED.

Appendix C Index

Copyright © 2011, SAS Institute Inc., Cary, North Carolina, USA. ALL RIGHTS RESERVED.

Copyright © 2011, SAS Institute Inc., Cary, North Carolina, USA. ALL RIGHTS RESERVED.

Copyright © 2011, SAS Institute Inc., Cary, North Carolina, USA. ALL RIGHTS RESERVED.

Copyright © 2011, SAS Institute Inc., Cary, North Carolina, USA. ALL RIGHTS RESERVED.

Copyright © 2011, SAS Institute Inc., Cary, North Carolina, USA. ALL RIGHTS RESERVED.

Recommended SAS® Titles

Applied Analytics Using SAS® Enterprise Miner

ISBN	Title	Price (U.S. Dollars)
	SAS® Press	
978-1-59047-508-9	*CRM Segmentation and Clustering Using SAS® Enterprise Miner™*	$51.95
978-1-59047-567-6	*Decision Trees for Business Intelligence and Data Mining: Using SAS® Enterprise Miner™*	$49.95
978-1-59047-703-8	*Predictive Modeling with SAS® Enterprise Miner™: Practical Solutions for Business Applications*	$64.95
	SAS® Documentation	
978-1-59994-827-0	*Getting Started with SAS® Enterprise Miner™ 5.3*	$29.95
978-1-59994-321-3	*Getting Started with SAS® Enterprise Miner™ 6.1*	$9.95

Notes

- Prices are subject to change without notice.
- To order, please visit **support.sas.com/bookstore**.
- SAS documentation is also available to search, browse, or print **free** online at: **support.sas.com/documentation**.

Copyright © 2011, SAS Institute Inc., Cary, North Carolina, USA. ALL RIGHTS RESERVED.